GEOMETRICAL
AND PHYSICAL
OPTICS

GEOMETRICAL AND PHYSICAL OPTICS

by

R. S. LONGHURST

PH.D., A.R.C.S., D.I.C., F.Inst.P.

Senior Lecturer in Physics
Chelsea College of Science and Technology

SECOND EDITION

JOHN WILEY & SONS INC

NEW YORK, N.Y.

PUBLISHED THROUGHOUT THE WORLD
EXCEPT THE UNITED STATES OF AMERICA
BY LONGMANS, GREEN AND CO. LTD

First published 1957
Second edition 1967

Printed in Great Britain

PREFACE TO SECOND EDITION

IT is a pleasure to record my gratitude to many colleagues, including students, who have constructively criticized the first edition. I have made numerous alterations and additions in an attempt to make the text clearer and more up to date. A brief account of partial coherence is now included; the sections on interference and phase-contrast microscopy have been expanded; the sections on the Metre and on the speed of light have been brought up to date; and accounts are given of the important recent work on interference spectroscopy, on the production and use of diffraction gratings, and on image formation. Finally, I have expanded the list of books and reviews recommended for further reading.

I wish to thank my wife for her help in preparing the typescript, reading the proofs, and accepting the restricted social life that accompanied the preparation of this edition.

Chelsea College of Science and Technology   R. S. LONGHURST
March 1966

PREFACE TO FIRST EDITION

THIS book is intended primarily for students reading for an honours degree in physics, but it is hoped that it will be of use to those taking general or pass degrees and also to those who intend to specialize in optics at the post-graduate level. Thus, on the one hand I have tried to give a sufficiently detailed account of the subject to make the book useful to the more advanced student, and on the other hand I have borne in mind the fact that the mathematical equipment of some readers might be somewhat limited. For example, although an account is given of Kirchhoff's formulation of Huygens' principle, the chapters on diffraction and diffraction gratings are developed as far as possible along elementary lines. Most of the more mathematical parts of the book fall into separate sections and can be omitted by the less advanced student.

Since this is a students' textbook rather than a review, I have appended some suggestions for further reading instead of giving references to original papers. I feel this is the proper course since the undergraduate is always desperately short of time. The suggestions include more advanced books and some recent reviews; all are in English.

The book contains a number of photographs, but it has been necessary to group these together to form four plates. Since it is not possible to locate each photograph alongside the section that refers to it, I have thought it best to put the plates together near the front of the book, between pages 16 and 17.

It is a pleasure to record my gratitude to many friends for their help at various stages in the preparation of this book. In particular, I wish to thank Dr. L. J. Freeman, who read most of the original draft of the manuscript and with whom I have had many helpful discussions. I also wish to thank Dr. G. W. Series, who read and commented on the entire manuscript, Dr. H. H. Hopkins, who made numerous suggestions in connection with Chapters XIV–XVI, Dr. M. P. James, who read and commented on Chapters XVII and XVIII, and Dr. H. R. Paneth, who read and commented on Chapter XIX. I also wish to thank my wife for her help in preparing the typescript and reading the proofs.

I acknowledge with thanks permission to reproduce copyright material as follows:

The Director, N.P.L., the Council of the Royal Society, and the authors for Figs 9–13 and 9–14 from a paper by Sears and Barrell; the Oxford University Press for a quotation in Chapter IX from Tolansky's *Multiple Beam Interferometry of Surfaces and Films*; Constable and Co. Ltd. for Fig. 18–11 from Walsh's *Photometry*; Longmans, Green and Co. Ltd. for Fig. 5–25 from Watson's *Physics*; and Professor Partington for Figs 22–32 and 22–36 from *Advanced Treatise on Physical Chemistry*, Volume IV.

Chelsea Polytechnic
February 1957

R. S. LONGHURST

CONTENTS

CHAPTER I

INTRODUCTION AND ELEMENTARY THEORY

CHAPTER II

THE GENERAL GEOMETRICAL THEORY OF OPTICAL SYSTEMS

CHAPTER III

THE PARAXIAL THEORY OF OPTICAL INSTRUMENTS

CHAPTER IV

THE DETERMINATION OF THE PARAXIAL CONSTANTS
OF OPTICAL SYSTEMS

CHAPTER VII

INTERFERENCE OF TWO BEAMS. DIVISION OF WAVEFRONT

CHAPTER VIII

INTERFERENCE OF TWO BEAMS. DIVISION OF AMPLITUDE

CHAPTER IX

MULTIPLE BEAM INTERFEROMETRY

CHAPTER X

HUYGENS' PRINCIPLE AND
THE SCALAR THEORY OF DIFFRACTION

CHAPTER XI

FRAUNHOFER DIFFRACTION PATTERNS

CHAPTER XII

DIFFRACTION GRATINGS

CHAPTER XIII

FRESNEL DIFFRACTION PATTERNS

CHAPTER XIV

THE PHYSICAL THEORY OF IMAGE FORMATION IN OPTICAL INSTRUMENTS

CHAPTER XV

THE MONOCHROMATIC ABERRATIONS

CHAPTER XVI

THE OCCURRENCE AND CONTROL OF ABERRATIONS IN OPTICAL SYSTEMS

CHAPTER XVII

VISUAL OPTICS

CHAPTER XVIII

PHOTOMETRY

CHAPTER XIX

THE ELECTROMAGNETIC THEORY OF LIGHT

CHAPTER XXIII

OPTICAL ACTIVITY

CHAPTER XXIV

THE VELOCITY OF LIGHT

INTRODUCTION AND ELEMENTARY THEORY

1-1. Rays, Waves, and Particles

THE energy emitted by a source of light may be considered to be ejected as a stream of particles or *photons*, as a continuous stream of energy along a *ray*, or as a *wave motion*. The idea of discrete packets of energy is mainly of use when considering the origin of spectra, and the interaction of light with matter as in the photo-electric effect. It will be found that as far as the *propagation* of light is concerned it is convenient to suppose that a periodic wave motion is propagated from a source. It is then found that in certain cases the conception of streams of energy or rays provides a useful basis for calculating the approximate effect of the waves.

It is easily seen that the conception of energy streaming out from the source along the rays can be used to explain the rectilinear propagation of light and the formation of shadows. If, however, one attempts to isolate a ray by means of a series of small holes as in Fig. 1–1, it is found that the smaller the holes are made the less like a ray does the light behave. This phenomenon is readily explained in terms of the wave theory of light, and illustrates the fact that in some cases the ray conception breaks down.

Fig. 1–1. Attempt to isolate a ray.

1-2. Light as a Wave Motion—Progressive Waves

In order to consider energy to be transmitted as a wave motion, one usually requires a medium whose particles may oscillate. An oscillating particle then exerts a force on its neighbour, causing the latter to oscillate. In this way the motion is transmitted from one particle to the next and the energy is conveyed through the medium. Since light can be propagated in a vacuum the existence of an all-pervading medium was postulated. This was known as the *aether*, and was assumed to pervade all space and to provide the means whereby the light waves were propagated. For the present purpose it is quite unnecessary to assume anything about the nature of this medium. However, to explain certain properties of light it is necessary to assume that the actual "particle displacements" which occur as the disturbance passes a point in space are perpendicular to the direction of propagation, i.e. light waves are transverse waves. For example, in *plane polarized* light all the "particles" execute linear S.H.M. Later theory replaces the oscillating particles by an oscillatory electromagnetic field, but discussion of this is deferred to later chapters. At this stage it is convenient to think of oscillating particles. Let ϕ denote the transverse displacement of the particles set in motion by the passage of the wave. It is easy to see that any function of the type $\phi = f(ct - x)$ represents a disturbance moving in the positive x-direction with velocity c. For example, at time t_1, ϕ will have a certain value

1

at $x=x_1$, and at a later time t_2 it will have the same value at x_2 if $ct_1-x_1=ct_2-x_2$. Hence the disturbance travels a distance (x_2-x_1) in time (t_2-t_1) and the velocity is $(x_2-x_1)/(t_2-t_1)=c$. Similarly, $\phi=f(ct+x)$ represents a disturbance in the negative x-direction.

1–3. Simple Harmonic Waves

A point source in an isotropic medium will emit spherical waves and, assuming that the particles execute linear S.H.M., the above considerations indicate that one may write, for the expanding spherical waves,

$$\phi=\frac{a}{r}\sin k(ct-r),\qquad \ldots \ldots \quad (1\text{–}1)$$

where ϕ is the displacement of the particles distance r from the source at time t, and a is the amplitude at unit distance from the source. k is a constant. If, $\omega=kc$ one has

$$\phi=\frac{a}{r}\sin (\omega t-kr).\qquad \ldots \ldots \quad (1\text{–}2)$$

Since $\sin \theta$ is a periodic function of period 2π (i.e. $\sin (\theta\pm 2\pi)=\sin \theta$) it is seen, on putting $r=$constant, that at any particular point in space the particles execute S.H.M. of period $T=2\pi/\omega$ and of amplitude a/r. Now, for any progressive wave, the intensity is the rate of flow of energy across unit area perpendicular to the direction of propagation of the waves and, since the energy of a vibrating particle is proportional to the square of the amplitude, it will be seen that the intensity falls off as $1/r^2$. This gives the necessary agreement with the well established inverse square law for radiant energy, and is the reason for making the amplitude proportional to $1/r$. Equation (1–2) also shows that although all the particles oscillate with the same frequency, those at various distances from the source are at different stages in their oscillations. They are said to have different *phases*. The phase of any particle is given by the quantity $(\omega t-kr)$ so that at any instant the phase difference between particles at distances r and $r+d$ is kd. Since $\sin \theta$ has a period of 2π the particles will be in similar phases of their vibrations if $kd=2\pi$, i.e. if $d=\lambda$ where $\lambda=2\pi/k$. λ is called the *wavelength*. Now the particles whose distances from the source differ by λ have a phase difference of 2π, so that those whose distances differ by d have, by direct proportion, a phase difference $2\pi(d/\lambda)$. This is also evident if one puts $k=2\pi/\lambda$ so that $[\omega t-(2\pi/\lambda)r]$ specifies the phase. Referred to the phase of the source, the phase of a particle is then $(2\pi/\lambda)r$, and if one has particles at r and $r+d$ their phase difference is $(2\pi/\lambda)d$.

A continuous surface that is the locus of points where the particles are in phase is called a *wavefront*; any sphere centred on a point source is obviously a wavefront. Consider now the disturbance travelling outwards from the source. The quantity $k(ct-r)$ specifies the phase and the particle at r_2 at time t_2 will have the same phase as the particle at r_1 had at time t_1 if $ct_1-r_1=ct_2-r_2$. The particular phase may be said to have been propagated a distance (r_2-r_1) in time (t_2-t_1) and the velocity, $(r_2-r_1)/(t_2-t_1)=c$, may be referred to as the phase velocity. The wavefront associated with any particular phase may therefore be said to advance with velocity c, so that it advances a distance λ in time T. It is frequently convenient to look upon the advance of a wavefront as the advance of the initial disturbance from the source. Although this is usually done, it is fundamentally unsound since equation (1–1) implies a wave train of infinite extent.

The above discussion was concerned with a spherical wave. Another important type is the plane wave in which the wavefront is always a plane perpendicular to the direction of propagation. A simple harmonic plane wave travelling in the positive x-direction is represented by $\phi = a \sin k(ct-x)$. The phase is independent of y and z—it is constant over any plane perpendicular to the direction of propagation.

1–4. Refractive Index and Optical Path

It is found that the velocity of monochromatic light in a material medium is different from that in a vacuum. If the velocities are v and c respectively, the ratio c/v is called the *refractive index* and in this book is denoted by n. If f is the frequency of the vibrations, it follows from above that $f\lambda = c$. Now if light passes from one medium to another, the frequency of the separate oscillating particles remains unchanged, so that the wavelength alters; if λ and λ_m are the wavelengths in a vacuum and material medium respectively, $\lambda/\lambda_m = n$. From § 1–3 it follows that, referred to the source, the phase at a distance r from a source in a material medium is $(2\pi/\lambda_m)r$, which may be written $(2\pi/\lambda)rn$. If light reaches a point after passing through several different media, the phase at that point will be given by $(2\pi/\lambda)\Sigma rn$. A geometrical distance multiplied by the refractive index of the space in which it is measured is referred to as an *optical path*. It will be seen that in a given time a disturbance always traverses the same optical path. Frequently one is concerned with light which reaches a point or points after passing along different paths, and in this case it will be seen that the phase difference between the disturbances arriving by different routes is given by

$$\text{Phase difference} = (2\pi/\lambda)(\text{optical path difference}). \quad . \quad . \quad (1\text{–}3)$$

Sometimes several disturbances arrive at a point with different phases and are superposed. The way in which one calculates the total disturbance will be discussed in Chapter VI.

1–5. Huygens' Principle

It was stated above that the mechanism by which a disturbance can be propagated is that a vibrating particle exerts a force on its neighbour, causing it to vibrate. Thus every vibrating particle may be said to behave as a point source. According to *Huygens' Principle* it is supposed that every point on a wavefront acts as a point source in this way and becomes a source of so-called secondary wavelets. The subsequent disturbance is then found as a combination of all the secondary wavelets. This accounts at once for the failure of the principle of rectilinear propagation through small apertures, and explains why one fails to isolate a ray by using a succession of pinholes as in Fig. 1–1. When, for example, a plane wave impinges on a screen with a small hole, the element of wavefront at the hole acts as a point source, so that a spherical wave emerges on the far side of the screen (see Fig. 1–2). In practice most of the energy remains within a fairly small cone with the hole as apex.

Fig. 1–2. Passage of light through a small aperture.

In order to explain the approximately rectilinear propagation through large apertures and the formation of shadows, it is necessary to postulate that the secondary wavelets produce an appreciable effect on their forward envelope only. Consider a plane wave passing through a large aperture (see Fig. 1–3). When the wavefront lies in the plane of the aperture each point may be taken as a source. After a time t the secondary wavefronts have travelled a distance ct and the resultant disturbance is the forward envelope of the wavelets as shown. Subsequent positions of the wavefront may be found in a similar manner, and the result indicates that the disturbance passes through the aperture as a broad beam of light travelling in a direction perpendicular to the wavefront.

Fig. 1–3. Passage of a plane wave through a large aperture.

Fig. 1–4. Passage of a spherical wave through a large aperture.

The passage of a spherical wave through an aperture can be explained in an exactly similar manner, and, in this case also, the disturbance is propagated along the normals to the wavefront (see Fig. 1–4). It is obvious that the way in which light passes through a wide aperture can also be explained on the assumption that the light consists of streams of energy or rays. For isotropic media the rays in this interpretation of the phenomenon are always normal to the waves in the previous interpretation.

1–6. Reflection of a Plane Wave at a Plane Surface

In Fig. 1–5 let ABC be a plane wave incident on a reflecting surface XY. As each element of the wave reaches the surface, it can be regarded as a source of secondary wavelets. Some elements of the wave will, of course, reach the mirror before others, and in order to find the subsequent path of the wave, one must allow for the fact that some points on the mirror act as sources before others. In particular, A_1 acts as a source when C is at C_1, so that when C gets to C_2 the secondary wavelet from A_1 has expanded to a radius $A_1A_2 = C_1C_2$. Similarly,

B reaches B_2 before C reaches C_2, and the secondary wavelet from B_2 has a radius $B_2B_3=(C_1C_2-B_1B_2)$ when C reaches C_2. Treating all parts of the wave in this way and taking the envelope of these secondary wavelets, one obtains $A_2B_3C_2$ as the reflected position of the wave. The wave normals before and after reflection are in the same plane as, and equally inclined to, the normal to the mirror at the point of incidence, i.e. $I=I'$.

Fig. 1-5. Reflection of a plane wave at a plane surface.

Fig. 1-6. Refraction of a plane wave at a plane surface.

1-7. Refraction of a Plane Wave at a Plane Surface

In Fig. 1-6, suppose XY is a plane interface separating media whose refractive indices are n and n'. As before, one regards points A_1, B_2, C_2, as secondary sources. In this case the disturbance passes into the second medium where the velocity of light is different. The ratio of the velocities is given by $(v/v')=(n'/n)$. Consequently, while the disturbance travels from C_1 to C_2, the secondary wavelet from A_1 expands to a radius $A_1A_2=C_1C_2(v'/v)=C_1C_2(n/n')$. Similarly, when C is at C_2 the secondary wavelet from B_2 has a radius $B_2B_3=(C_1C_2-B_1B_2)(n/n')$. The envelope $A_2B_3C_2$ consequently gives the refracted position of the wave.

From the figure,
$$\frac{\sin I}{\sin I'} = \frac{C_1C_2/A_1C_2}{A_1A_2/A_1C_2} = \frac{v}{v'} = \frac{n'}{n},$$

i.e.
$$n \sin I = n' \sin I'. \quad \ldots \ldots \quad (1\text{-}4)$$

This relates the directions of the wave normals before and after refraction. As before, the two wave normals and the normal to the refracting surface lie in the same plane. These laws of refraction were first given by Snell. It will be seen that the larger is the angle of incidence I the greater is the deviation produced by refraction.

The reflection and refraction of plane and spherical waves at spherical surfaces may be treated in the same way.

1-8. Rays of Light

In the case of reflection and refraction one again has the energy propagated along the wave normals. Consequently, if the rays are defined to be wave normals, one can say that the light behaves as a stream of energy travelling along the rays which are directed outwards from the source and obey the classical laws of reflection and refraction given above. This is very convenient in practice since the laws governing the ray paths are so simple. However, there are cases when the assumption that the energy travels along rays leads to erroneous results. One example has already been discussed: the passage of light through a small hole. Another example of the failure of the ray conception is the case of a converging spherical wave. Here all the rays pass through the centre of curvature of the spherical wavefront, indicating an infinite energy density at that point. The simple wave theory as discussed above also fails to explain what happens in this case. On the other hand, there is no doubt that there is a concentration of energy near the focus of the wave, so that the rays do give some idea of where the energy goes. Newton thought of the rays as the paths along which particles travelled from the source, but to explain refraction he found it necessary to assume that the particles travelled more rapidly in material media than in a vacuum, which is contrary to the facts (see Chapter XXIV). The best procedure is to regard the rays merely as wave normals, where the rays obey the classical laws of reflection and refraction. The shape of the wavefront at any time can then be found as the surface that cuts the rays orthogonally.

In the above discussion it has been assumed that the media are isotropic. In anisotropic media the energy is not propagated in the direction of the wave normals—even when one is far removed from a focus or a screen. The rays are then taken to be the lines of energy flow and are not wave normals.

1-9. Fermat's Principle

The laws governing the behaviour of the rays can be summarized in one fundamental law known as *Fermat's principle*. This states that the *ray path along which a disturbance travels from one point to another is such that the time taken is at a stationary value*. If c is the velocity of light in a vacuum, the velocity in a

Fig. 1-7. Snell's law and Fermat's principle.

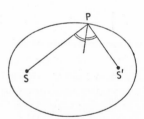

Fig. 1-8. Focal property of an ellipse.

medium of refractive index n is, by definition, c/n; in this medium the time taken for a disturbance to travel a distance l is nl/c. If the light passes through a number of media, the total time taken is $(1/c)\Sigma nl$ (or $(1/c)\int ndl$ if the refractive index varies continuously). Now Σnl is the total optical path, so that Fermat's principle states that the path of a ray is such that the *optical path* is at a stationary value. This principle is obviously in agreement with the fact that the rays are straight lines in a homogeneous isotropic medium. It is found that it also agrees with the classical laws of reflection and refraction. Consider, for example, refraction at a plane surface separating media whose refractive indices are n and

n' (see Fig. 1–7). Of the possible routes from A to B that give a straight path in each medium, it is easily proved that the path APB given by Snell's law is also the route that gives a stationary optical path length. Thus let Q be a point on the refracting surface close to P. The optical path difference [APB]−[AQB] is nPQ sin I−n'PQ sin I'. (It is usual to employ square brackets to denote optical path lengths.) Now, from Snell's law, n sin I−n' sin I'=0, so that the optical path difference is zero. That is, [APB] is at a stationary value when Snell's law is obeyed. Reflection at a plane surface can be dealt with in a similar manner.

The fact that the optical path is sometimes a maximum and sometimes a minimum can be demonstrated by using a well known property of ellipses. In Fig. 1–8, if S and S′ are the foci of an ellipse, it can be shown that SP+PS′ remains constant as P moves round the circumference, and SP and S′P make

(a)   (b)

Fig. 1–9. Fermat's principle. (a) Ray path a minimum. (b) Ray path a maximum.

equal angles with the normal at P. Referring now to Fig. 1–9(a) or (b), the ray path along which light travels from A to B via the mirror is, according to the classical law of reflection, that for which the angles of incidence and reflection are equal. The point of incidence P must be the point where the mirror touches an ellipse whose foci are A and B since AP and PB are then equally inclined to the normal. Also, it has been seen that (AP+BP)=(AQ+QB) if Q is another point on the ellipse. It follows that (AR+RB) is greater than (AP+PB) in (a), and less than (AP+PB) in (b), so that the ray path gives a minimum optical path in (a) but a maximum optical path in (b).

1–10. Image Formation by an Optical System

Consider the case of a single convex lens forming a real image (see Fig. 1–10). It can be shown that, within certain limits, points A and B exist such that the

Fig. 1–10. Image formation by a lens.

optical path from A to B is the same by any of the possible routes through the lens. Consequently, all the rays from A that enter the lens will intersect at B so that, corresponding to point sources on the left-hand side of the lens, there are concentrations of energy on the right-hand side. Since all the rays from A through the lens pass through B, the latter point is located if one can find where any *two* rays intersect. This is the interpretation of image formation in terms of rays but, as remarked earlier, one must ultimately treat this ray picture as an approximation since the energy does not flow exactly along the rays.

In terms of waves one may say that all the disturbances from A arrive in phase at B, i.e. a spherical wave from the point source A emerges from the lens as a spherical wave converging to B. A study of the ray paths is, however, of considerable importance in discussing the formation of images by optical systems, and, if necessary, the shapes of the wavefronts can be deduced from knowledge of the ray paths.

1–11. Refraction at a Spherical Surface—Notation

The reader is warned that, in places, the notation in this book appears at first sight to be rather cumbersome. It is certainly not the easiest convention to

Fig. 1–11. Refraction at a spherical surface.

describe, but it has the merit of completely universal applicability; when fully understood, its advantages become obvious. It is unfortunate that some of the conventions which may be employed very conveniently in elementary optics become almost unusable in the more advanced stages and are quite different from those employed in industry and commerce.

In Fig. 1–11, a ray directed towards B is refracted so as to pass through B' where B and B' lie on the axis of the refracting surface AP, centre C, and radius r, separating media whose refractive indices are n and n'. The ray intersection distances l and l', and the radius r, are measured from A, the pole of the surface. i and i' are the angles of incidence and refraction; u and u' are the angles between the ray and the optical axis before and after refraction; y is the height of the point of incidence, P, above the axis; and α is the angle subtended at C by the arc AP. For an object or image of finite size perpendicular to the axis, the object and image heights measured from the axis are h and h'. These symbols are also used to denote the distance off-axis of extra-axial point objects or images.

In Fig. 1–11 the undashed symbols refer to the ray before refraction (i.e. to the object) and the dashed symbols refer to the ray after refraction (i.e. to the image), but this is not universally the case. When a ray strikes a refracting surface it is deviated, but the undeviated continuation of the incident ray is referred to as a virtual ray in the second medium. Similarly, the refracted ray, produced backwards, is a virtual ray in the first medium. Thus any ray can be said to exist on both sides of the surface, being real on one side and virtual on the other. This concept is now extended and one says that the refracting surface divides space into two parts which are known as the *left-* and *right-hand spaces*.

One thinks of both spaces extending to infinity in both directions, the former being real on the left-hand side of the surface and virtual on the right-hand side, whilst the reverse is true of the right-hand space. One now says that *symbols associated with quantities or positions in the left-hand space are undashed and those in the right-hand space are dashed.* If the light travels from left to right, the incident ray is real on the left-hand side and is therefore in the left-hand space. The refracted ray is real on the right-hand side and is in the right-hand space. Similarly, if the light travels from right to left the incident ray is in the right-hand space and the refracted ray is in the left-hand space. It will be seen that the convention can be stated in the following alternative form. If the light travels from left to right, the undashed symbols refer to the ray before refraction (i.e. to the object) and the dashed to the ray after refraction (i.e. to the image). On

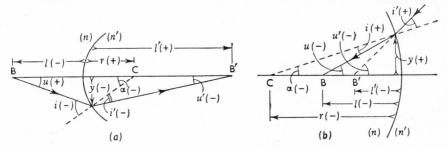

Fig. 1–12. Refraction at a spherical surface.

the other hand, if the light travels from right to left, the dashed quantities refer to the object and the undashed to the image. (Note that although it has not yet been proved that B′ is actually the image of B, this will be deduced shortly and, in the meantime, it is convenient to speak of object and image.) Usually the light will be taken as travelling from left to right so that the dashed quantities refer to the image, but it is frequently convenient to discuss an instrument with the light travelling, first one way, and then the other.

The sign convention for distances is the same as that used in co-ordinate geometry. Consequently, l and l' (measured from the pole of the surface) are positive if measured to the right, and y, h, and h' (measured from the axis) are positive if measured upwards.

The sign convention for angles is now chosen in such a way that it is possible to draw a diagram in which r, l, l', y, h, h', α, u, u', i, and i', are positive. One can then recall the notation and sign convention by remembering this diagram. Fig. 1–11 is an *all-positive* diagram.

To determine the sign of u or u', rotate about B or B′ through the angle concerned from the ray to the axis. A clockwise rotation defines a negative angle, and an anti-clockwise rotation a positive angle. The sign of α is similarly defined by a rotation from radius to axis. The sign of i or i' is determined by rotating about the point of incidence through the angle from ray to radius, when a clockwise rotation now defines a positive angle and an anti-clockwise rotation indicates a negative angle (see Fig. 1–12). The angles u, u', i, i', and α, are always acute.

2*

This notation and sign convention has the advantage that if the direction of the light is reversed (i.e. object and image interchanged), the same symbols represent the same quantities and positions without change of sign, and the same equations apply.

1-12. Method of Deriving Formulae

When it is necessary to derive from first principles a formula relating to some phenomenon, the procedure is to draw a diagram illustrating any special case, treat all the distances and angles as positive, and, from the geometry of the diagram, deduce an equation relating the quantities in which one is interested. When the final equation is obtained, it is necessary to change the sign in front of all the quantities that are negative in the figure. The result is the algebraic equation which can be applied to any possible case. It is never necessary to consider the signs of quantities that appear during the derivation but are absent from the final equation.

1-13. Refraction at a Spherical Surface

The simplest procedure is to deduce the relation between l and l' from the all-positive diagram but, to illustrate the method, Fig. 1–12(a) will be used.

It is assumed that the rays are at all times close to the optical axis and never inclined to it at large angles. That is to say, y is always small and the angles may be equated to their sines or tangents. In addition, the sagitta in the refracting surface may be neglected. Snell's law then becomes $ni=n'i'$.

Now, from Fig. 1–12(a),

$$i=\alpha+u \quad \text{and} \quad i'=\alpha-u'$$

and, writing the angles as their tangents, one has

$$n\left(\frac{y}{r}+\frac{y}{l}\right)=n'\left(\frac{y}{r}-\frac{y}{l'}\right)$$

or

$$\frac{n'}{l'}+\frac{n}{l}=\frac{n'-n}{r}.$$

In the figure, however, l is negative so that, inserting a negative sign in front of l, the algebraic equation becomes

$$\frac{n'}{l'}-\frac{n}{l}=\frac{n'-n}{r}.$$

Note also that u', i, i', and α, are negative so that, algebraically, $\alpha=u+i=u'+i'$. If $l=f$ when $l'=\infty$, and $l'=f'$ when $l=\infty$, f and f' are called the *first and second focal lengths*. In addition, it is frequently convenient to put $(n'/f')=-(n/f)=F$, where F is called the *power*. Consequently, one has

$$\frac{n'}{l'}-\frac{n}{l}=\frac{n'}{f'}=-\frac{n}{f}=\frac{n'-n}{r}=F. \quad \ldots \ldots (1\text{--}5)$$

Alternatively, one may write

$$\frac{f'}{l'}+\frac{f}{l}=1. \quad \ldots \ldots \ldots (1\text{--}6)$$

1–14. The Paraxial Region

In the above discussion it was assumed that the height of incidence, y, is small so that all the rays are close to the optical axis. Such rays are known as *paraxial rays*, and one speaks of the region immediately surrounding the axis as the *paraxial region*. That is to say, within the paraxial region the angles u, u', α, i, and i', may be equated to their sines or tangents. It will be observed that equation (1–5), relating l and l', does not involve y. Consequently, within the paraxial region, any ray directed through B before refraction will pass through B' after refraction. Therefore B' is the image of B, and may be located by considering any one ray. It is easy to see that within the paraxial region the image of a small but finite object perpendicular to the axis is itself perpendicular to the axis. For example, in Fig. 1–13, suppose the axial point B is imaged at B' by

Fig. 1–13. Imagery in the paraxial region.

the spherical refracting surface centred at C. For a spherical surface any line through the centre may be taken as the optical axis since there is nothing to distinguish one from another. Take a new axis DCD' where DC=BC and D'C=B'C. Then it is obvious that, for the new axis, D' is the axial image of D. If BD and B'D' are small, they may be assumed to be perpendicular to the original axis, the latter being the image of the former. It will be seen that for different object sizes the image sizes are in direct proportion. In addition, since there is symmetry about the axis BCB', a plane object perpendicular to the axis at B will give a geometrically similar image perpendicular to the axis at B'.

It is a common practice to use small letters to denote paraxial quantities and capital letters to denote quantities associated with rays incident at finite distances from the axis. Consequently, a ray lying outside the paraxial region will be inclined to the axis at an angle U (or U') and will intersect the axis at a distance L (or L') from the pole of the surface, the height of incidence being Y, and the angle of incidence I.

It is assumed that the reader is familiar with the simple properties of mirrors and lenses, especially the graphical constructions that can be used to locate the image. Nevertheless, in order to familiarize the student with the notation, the following paragraphs are included.

1–15. Thin Lens in Air

If one refracting surface is followed by another so that the separation between them may be neglected, one has a thin lens. The image formed by the first surface becomes the object for the second and one may write $l_2 = l_1'$. If one assumes that the thin lens is of refractive index n and is in air, one has

$$n_1 = n_2' = 1,$$
$$n_1' = n_2 = n.$$

Double application of equation (1–5) now gives

$$\frac{n}{l_1'} - \frac{1}{l_1} = \frac{n-1}{r_1}$$

and

$$\frac{1}{l_2'} - \frac{n}{l_1'} = \frac{1-n}{r_2}.$$

Now l_1 and l_2' are the object and image distances from the thin lens, and it is convenient to write them simply as l and l' respectively. Adding the last two equations, one then obtains

$$\frac{1}{l'} - \frac{1}{l} = (n-1)\left[\frac{1}{r_1} - \frac{1}{r_2}\right]$$

and again one writes

$$l = f \quad \text{if} \quad l' = \infty,$$
$$l' = f' \quad \text{if} \quad l = \infty,$$

so that

$$\frac{1}{l'} - \frac{1}{l} = \frac{1}{f'} = -\frac{1}{f} = F = (n-1)\left[\frac{1}{r_1} - \frac{1}{r_2}\right]. \quad \cdot \; \cdot \; \cdot \quad (1\text{–}7)$$

Thus the power of a thin lens is the algebraic sum of the powers of the separate surfaces. Since the reciprocals of the radii of curvature of refracting surfaces often appear, it is convenient to put $1/r = R$, where R is the curvature of a surface.

Fig. 1–14. The two focal lengths of a lens.

It will be seen that the second focal length of a converging lens is positive (and the first negative), whilst for a diverging lens the reverse is true (see Fig. 1–14). The two focal lengths of a thin lens in air are, of course, numerically equal. Frequently one refers simply to "the focal length" of a lens; it will be assumed that this always refers to the second focal length so that the focal length of a converging lens is positive, whilst for a diverging lens it is negative. The powers of these two lenses will be seen to be positive and negative respectively, which is in agreement with the convention adopted in ophthalmic optics. The power of a thin lens is often expressed in dioptres where the power in dioptres is the reciprocal of the focal length in metres. Thus a lens of focal length $+25$ cm. is a converging lens whose power is $+4$ dioptres.

1–16. Smallest Separation of Object and Real Image

In Fig. 1–15(a) the converging lens L forms a real image h' of the object h. It will now be shown that the smallest possible separation of h and h' is $4f'$.

One has

$$\frac{1}{l'} - \frac{1}{l} = \frac{1}{f'}. \quad \cdot \; \cdot \; \cdot \; \cdot \; \cdot \; \cdot \; \cdot \quad (1\text{–}8)$$

If the image is real, h and h' must lie on opposite sides of the lens as shown. That is, l is negative, and the separation of object and image is $l'-l$.

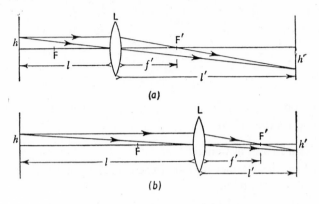

(a)

(b)

Fig. 1–15. Formation of a real image.

(1–8) gives
$$l'-l=-\frac{ll'}{f'}. \qquad \cdots \cdots \qquad (1\text{–}9)$$

At a maximum or a minimum $d(l'-l)/dl=0$. Using (1–9), this gives

$$-\frac{1}{f'}\left(l'+l\frac{dl'}{dl}\right)=0$$

or
$$\frac{dl'}{dl}=-\frac{l'}{l}. \qquad \cdots \cdots \cdots \qquad (1\text{–}10)$$

But
$$\frac{d(l'-l)}{dl}=\frac{dl'}{dl}-1,$$

therefore at a max. or min.
$$\frac{dl'}{dl}=1.$$

Hence, from (1–10),
$$l'=-l.$$

Now, either l or l' (but not both) may be infinite. Therefore this condition corresponds to a *minimum* separation.

Putting $l'=-l$ in (1–8), one obtains

$$l'=2f',$$

$$\therefore \quad (l'-l)=4f'.$$

This shows that the object and image have their smallest separation when the lens is midway between them. For larger separations there are two possible positions of the lens. From the symmetry of the problem it is obvious that the object distance for one position is numerically equal to the image distance for the other; one has $l_2=-l_1'$ and $l_2'=-l_1$ (see Fig. 1–15). Now, it can be assumed that a ray which passes through the centre of a thin lens is undeviated. If h_1' and h_2' are the image sizes for the two positions of the lens one has

$$\frac{h_1'}{h} = \frac{l_1'}{l_1} \quad \text{and} \quad \frac{h_2'}{h} = \frac{l_2'}{l_2} = \frac{l_1}{l_1'},$$

$$\therefore \frac{h_1'}{h} \cdot \frac{h_2'}{h} = 1$$

or $$h = \sqrt{(h_1' h_2')}. \quad \ldots \ldots \ldots \quad (1\text{--}11)$$

Sometimes this result provides a method of measuring the size of an inaccessible object h (see §7–4).

1–17. Two Thin Lenses in Contact

Two thin lenses in contact may be treated in the same way as two surfaces combined to form a thin lens.

One has, if the lenses are in air,

$$\frac{1}{l_1'} - \frac{1}{l_1} = \frac{1}{f_1'}$$

and $$\frac{1}{l_2'} - \frac{1}{l_2} = \frac{1}{f_2'}.$$

Putting $l_1' = l_2$, $l_1 = l$, $l_2' = l'$, as before, and adding the above equations, one obtains

$$\frac{1}{l'} - \frac{1}{l} = \frac{1}{f_1'} + \frac{1}{f_2'} = \frac{1}{f'} = -\frac{1}{f}, \quad \ldots \ldots \quad (1\text{--}12)$$

where f and f' have their usual meanings.

Thus the power of the combination is the sum of the powers of the separate lenses.

1–18. Refraction of a Wave at a Spherical Surface

It is interesting to deduce the equation relating l' to l for a single refracting surface by a consideration of the progress of the wavefront.

In Fig. 1–16 QAP is a refracting surface, centre C, radius r, separating media

Fig. 1–16. Refraction of a spherical wave at a spherical surface.

whose refractive indices are n and n'. Let QXP represent the position that a spherical wavefront would have in the absence of the refracting surface, and QX'P the position it does in fact have at the same instant. The centre of the wave QXP is the virtual object point B. Similarly, B' is the real image point. Drop the perpendicular PO and put $PO=y$, $OX=x_1$, $OX'=x_2$, $OA=x_3$. $n(x_3-x_1)$ is the optical distance which the axial disturbance would travel during the time in which it actually travels $n'(x_3-x_2)$. Now a disturbance always travels the same optical distance in the same time (§ 1–4),

$$\therefore\ n(x_3-x_1)=n'(x_3-x_2).$$

If y is small, the geometry of the figure gives

$$x_1=\frac{y^2}{2l},\qquad x_2=\frac{y^2}{2l'},\qquad x_3=\frac{y^2}{2r},$$

$$\therefore\ n\left(\frac{y^2}{2r}-\frac{y^2}{2l}\right)=n'\left(\frac{y^2}{2r}-\frac{y^2}{2l'}\right),$$

$$\therefore\ \frac{n'}{l'}-\frac{n}{l}=\frac{n'-n}{r},$$

which is the result obtained by the ray method using Snell's law.

1–19. Reflection at a Spherical Surface

In the case of reflection one may have a real object and a real image on the same side of the mirror. Consequently, one has both object and image distances real on the same side, i.e. both are measured in the same space. This, at first sight, is an embarrassment to the present notation since it would indicate either that both object and image distances are denoted by l or that both are l'. It is soon found, however, that there is no cause for alarm since the equation relating l and l' is such that it makes no difference which is which. One can, if one so desires, distinguish between object and image distances by using the alternative statement of the convention. That is to say, l denotes the object distance if the light travels from left to right initially. From Fig. 1–17,

Fig. 1–17. Reflection at a spherical surface.

$$i=\alpha-u=\frac{y}{r}-\frac{y}{l},$$

$$i'=u'-\alpha=\frac{y}{l'}-\frac{y}{r}.$$

For reflection $i=i'$ and one has

$$\frac{y}{r}-\frac{y}{l}=\frac{y}{l'}-\frac{y}{r}$$

or

$$\frac{1}{l'}+\frac{1}{l}=\frac{2}{r}=\frac{1}{f'}.\qquad\ldots\ldots\ (1\text{–}13)$$

This is the true algebraic equation since all the quantities are negative and changing all the signs leaves the equation unchanged.

It is seen at once that it makes no difference which symbol—l or l'—one uses to denote the object or image.

Another important point also emerges. In Fig. 1–17 i is negative and i' is positive so that the law of reflection, written algebraically, becomes $i = -i'$. This follows as a special case of Snell's law of refraction on putting $n' = -n$. In fact, if one puts $n' = -n$ in the equation governing refraction at a spherical surface, the equation for reflection emerges at once. One has

$$\frac{n'}{l'} - \frac{n}{l} = \frac{n'-n}{r}$$

and, putting $n' = -n$, one obtains immediately

$$\frac{1}{l'} + \frac{1}{l} = \frac{2}{r}.$$

One finds that this is always the case and any equation associated with refraction may be converted into the equation governing the corresponding phenomenon in reflection by putting $n' = -n$. This is very useful since it means that it is never necessary to discuss reflecting surfaces explicitly.

From the original definition of refractive index it is seen that a negative index implies a negative velocity. That is to say, negative distance is traversed in positive time. Now in co-ordinate geometry a negative distance is simply a distance measured from right to left, so that putting $n' = -n$ indicates that the direction of the light is reversed. One can, in fact, consistently use negative refractive indices if the light travels from right to left, but there is no advantage in doing so.

(*a*) Fringes obtained with a Fresnel Biprism.

(*b*) Newton's rings by reflection. (Similar in appearance to the fringes of equal inclination obtained by reflection with a plane parallel plate or with a Michelson interferometer.)

(*c*) Newton's rings by transmission. (Similar in appearance to the fringes of equal inclination obtained by transmission with a plane parallel plate.)

(*d*) Multiple beam fringes of equal inclination viewed by reflection. (Similar in appearance to multiple beam Newton's rings by reflection.)

(*e*) Multiple beam fringes of equal inclination by transmission (Fabry-Perot fringes). (Similar in appearance to multiple beam Newton's rings by transmission.)

(*f*) Wedge fringes by reflection with unsilvered surfaces.

(*g*) Multiple beam Fizeau fringes between an optical flat and an aluminized mica sheet.

PLATE I. INTERFERENCE FRINGES

(a) Point source and rectangular aperture. The orientation of the aperture is shown by the white rectangle.

(b) Slit source and slit aperture of same width as rectangular aperture.

(c) Slit source and single narrow slit aperture.

(d) Slit source and two narrow slit apertures.

(e) Slit source and three narrow slit apertures.

(f) Slit source and four narrow slit apertures.

(g) Slit source and five narrow slit apertures.

(h) Slit source and six narrow slit apertures.

In (c)–(h) inclusive the centre of the pattern was over-exposed and the outer maxima intensified during processing.

PLATE II. FRAUNHOFER DIFFRACTION PATTERNS

(a) Point source and circular obstacle.

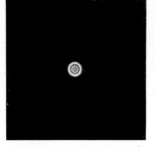

(b) Point source and small circular aperture.

(c) Point source and large circular aperture.

(d) Slit source and very narrow slit aperture.

(e) Slit source and slightly wider slit aperture.

(f) Slit source and very wide slit aperture.

(g) Slit source and straight edge.

(h) Slit source and thin wire.

(i) Slit source and two narrow slit apertures.

In (d)–(i) inclusive the positions of the geometrical shadows of the diffracting screens are indicated at the bottom of the patterns.

PLATE III. FRESNEL DIFFRACTION PATTERNS

(a) Photomicrograph with un-obstructed objective.

(b) Photomicrograph of same object, using reduced objective aperture.

(c) Airy disc (centre greatl[y] over-exposed).

(d) Photomicrograph of sheet of mica—ordinary illumination.

(e) Same sheet of mica with phase contrast.

(f) Image of a point source with about $\frac{1}{2}$ wavelength of coma.

(g) Mica sheet with dark-ground illumination.

(h) Image of point source with about 5 wavelengths of coma.

(i) Focal line with about 1 wavelength of astigmatism.

(j) Focal line with about $2\frac{1}{2}$ wavelengths of astigmatism.

(k) Disc of least confusion with about $2\frac{1}{2}$ wavelengths of astigmatism.

(l) Disc of least confusion with about $6\frac{1}{2}$ wavelengths of astigmatism.

PLATE IV. IMAGES IN OPTICAL INSTRUMENTS

THE GENERAL GEOMETRICAL THEORY
OF OPTICAL SYSTEMS

In terms of geometrical (ray) optics, it was shown in Chapter I that, within the paraxial region, a single spherical refracting (or reflecting) surface forms a point image of a point object. Moreover, if one has a small line object perpendicular to the axis, the image is also linear and perpendicular to the axis, and it was shown that for any plane object perpendicular to the axis a geometrically similar plane image is formed perpendicular to the axis. There is said to be a *collinear* relationship between objects and images in the left- and right-hand spaces; the image is said to be *conjugate* to the object, and a refracted ray is conjugate to the incident ray. Now the image, as formed by one surface, can be the object for a second surface and so on. Consequently, for a system of spherical refracting surfaces, there is a collinear transformation from the object space to the final image space. It is found that the general features of such image formation are the same for all optical systems. It is also found that these features can be deduced without referring to laws of optics such as the laws of refraction. That is, it is not necessary to discuss the way in which the rays traverse the system—one need discuss only their orientation in the final image space. All that is necessary is the assumption that any plane object perpendicular to the axis gives a geometrically similar image perpendicular to the axis. Actually Maxwell showed that it is sufficient to assume that this occurs for *two* pairs of conjugate planes, since it can then be shown that it must occur for all positions of the object and image planes.

In this chapter the general geometrical properties of such a "perfect" image-forming system will be discussed. In particular, it will be shown that if one combines two systems for which certain reference planes are known, the properties of the combination can be found. Now, since within the paraxial region a simple refracting surface gives geometrically perfect imagery, it is possible to deduce the paraxial properties of the combinations of surfaces forming thin and thick lenses and lens systems.

In the first fourteen sections the discussion is of a general nature and the conjugate points, lines, and planes, are not necessarily optical objects and images. Nevertheless one has its application to optics in view and it is often convenient to speak of "rays entering the system" instead of referring vaguely to "lines in the left-hand space", etc.

2–1. Principal Planes and Focal Planes

As mentioned above, the initial assumption is that by means of some unspecified mechanism plane objects perpendicular to an axis in one space give geometrically similar plane images perpendicular to an axis in another space. For simplicity it will be assumed that the axis is common to the two spaces—it is referred to as the axis of the system. Since there is geometrical similarity between plane objects and images perpendicular to the axis, there is a certain magnification associated with each pair of conjugate planes. This *transverse magnification* is denoted by m. The planes for which $m = +1$ are called the *principal planes* (or *unit planes*). These planes intersect the axis in the principal points P and P' (see Fig. 2–1). If H and H' are conjugate points in the principal planes, H'P' = HP, by definition. The plane in the left-hand space that is perpendicular to the axis and is conjugate to a similar plane at infinity in the right-hand space is called the *first focal plane*. Similarly, the *second focal plane* is the plane in the right-hand space that is conjugate to the plane at infinity in the left-hand space. The first and second focal planes intersect the axis at the points F and F', which are called the *first* and *second principal foci*. The distances PF and P'F' are called the *first* and *second focal lengths* of the system, and are denoted by f and f'.

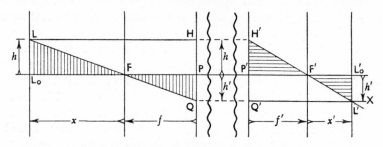

Fig. 2–1. Image formation by a perfect system.

It is convenient to write $f'/f = -n'/n$ where, for the purposes of the general theory, n and n' can be regarded simply as constants associated with the left- and right-hand spaces respectively. Actually they become identified with the refractive indices of these spaces when the theory is applied to an optical system. In general the ratio n'/n is more important than the absolute values n and n'.

Consider a line LH, parallel to the axis, which intersects the first principal plane at H. If HL is produced to the left, it intersects the axis at infinity, and F' is conjugate to this point of intersection. Also H' is conjugate to H, so that the line that is conjugate to LH passes through H' and F'. Thus, if the incident ray is parallel to the axis, the emergent ray passes through the appropriate principal focus, and vice versa.

If the paths of the rays LH and H'F' are known, one can quickly determine the point of intersection, H', and so find the second principal plane. This simple fact is of considerable practical importance. Obviously the position of the first principal plane may be determined in a similar manner.

2–2. Location of Objects and Images

Suppose it is necessary to determine the plane that is conjugate to the given plane L_0L (Fig. 2–1). As pointed out above, H'F' is conjugate to LH. Produce LF to Q. Q' is conjugate to Q where P'Q' = PQ. The line conjugate to LFQ must, therefore, pass through Q'. In addition, the emergent ray Q'X must be parallel to the axis since the incident ray passes through F. Since L lies on both LH and LFQ it follows that L' must lie on H'F' and Q'X, so that L' is the point of intersection of H'F' and Q'X. One may say that $L_0'L'$ is the image of L_0L.

Put $\qquad FL_0=x, \quad F'L'_0=x', \quad L_0L=h, \quad L_0'L'=h'.$

One has, also, $\qquad\qquad\qquad P'Q'=PQ=h'$

and $\qquad\qquad\qquad\qquad P'H'=PH=h.$

The triangles LL_0F, QPF (shaded vertically) are similar. Hence

$$\frac{h'}{h}=\frac{f}{x}.$$

Also, the triangles $L'L_0'F'$, $H'P'F'$ (shaded horizontally) are similar. Hence

$$\frac{h'}{h}=\frac{x'}{f'}.$$

In the figure x, f, and h', are negative so that, algebraically, one has

$$\frac{h'}{h}=-\frac{x'}{f'}=-\frac{f}{x}. \quad \cdot \quad \cdot \quad \cdot \quad \cdot \quad \cdot \quad \cdot \quad \cdot \quad (2\text{–}1)$$

Hence $\qquad\qquad\qquad xx'=ff'. \quad . \quad . \quad . \quad . \quad . \quad . \quad . \quad (2\text{–}2)$

This is known as Newton's equation.

2–3. Location of Conjugate Ray. General Case

Suppose that the principal and focal planes of a system are given, and that it is necessary to determine the path of the ray conjugate to the ray AB, incident

Fig. 2–2. Location of a conjugate ray.

in the left-hand space (see Fig. 2–2). Produce AB to intersect the first principal plane in H. Then the conjugate ray must emerge through H', where P'H'=PH. Draw FQ parallel to ABH, and let it intersect the first principal plane in Q. Then Q'R' must be conjugate to FQ, where P'Q'=PQ and Q'R' is parallel to the axis. Now ABH and FQ intersect at infinity, and the point which is conjugate to this point of intersection must lie in the second focal plane. It follows that if any two incident rays are parallel, their emergent rays intersect in the appropriate focal plane. In this case, the emergent rays which are conjugate to ABH and FQ intersect at R' in the second focal plane. This determines the path of the ray H'R' which is conjugate to AB.

2-4. Transverse and Angular Magnifications. The Helmholtz Equation

In Fig. 2-3 L_0L and $L_0'L'$ are conjugate elements with heights h and h', as shown. If a ray through L_0 at angle u emerges through L_0' at angle u', it is convenient to refer to $\tan u'/\tan u$ as the *angular magnification* for the conjugate planes L_0Y, $L_0'Y'$. Helmholtz's equation relates this to the transverse linear magnification h'/h associated with the same pair of conjugate planes.

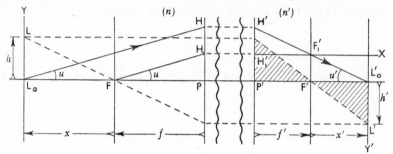

Fig. 2-3. Angular and lateral magnification.

From the similarity of the shaded triangles, it has already been shown that, algebraically,

$$\frac{h'}{h} = \frac{-x'}{f'} \quad \cdot \quad \cdots \cdots \cdots \quad (2\text{-}3)$$

The ray FH_1, which is parallel to L_0H, emerges along $H_1'F_1'X$, which is parallel to the axis, and intersects $H'L_0'$ at F_1' in the second focal plane.

In the figure, $PH_1 = f \tan u$

and $P'H_1' = F'F_1' = x' \tan u'$.

Since $PH_1 = P'H_1'$, and f and u are negative in the figure, one has, algebraically,

$$f \tan u = x' \tan u', \quad \cdots \cdots \quad (2\text{-}4)$$

$$\therefore \; \frac{\tan u'}{\tan u} = \frac{f}{x'} \cdot \quad \cdots \cdots \cdots \quad (2\text{-}5)$$

From equations (2-3) and (2-5),

$$\left(\frac{h'}{h}\right)\left(\frac{\tan u'}{\tan u}\right) = -\frac{f}{f'} = +\frac{n}{n'} \quad \cdots \quad (2\text{-}6)$$

which relates the angular and transverse linear magnifications for a pair of conjugate planes. This is usually written in the form

$$nh \tan u = n'h' \tan u' \quad \cdots \cdots \quad (2\text{-}7)$$

and is known as Helmholtz's equation. For small angles one has

$$nhu = n'h'u'. \quad \cdots \cdots \cdots \quad (2\text{-}8)$$

It will be seen that $H = nh \tan u = n'h' \tan u'$ is an invariant for the system (and, incidentally, for a series of systems).

Now an optical system forms the image of an off-axis object point by means of the cone of rays that enters the entrance pupil from the point (see Fig. 2–4). The semi-angle of this cone is a "generalized u" and the constant H may be regarded as a constant charac-terizing both the aperture (u) and the distance off-axis (h). As one increases the aperture and field the aberrations increase, and in discussing the aberrations it is found that H is a convenient measure of u and h.

Fig. 2–4. Cone of light entering a lens system.

2–5. The Nodal Points

If N and N′ are two conjugate axial points such that a ray through N′ is conjugate to a parallel ray through N, then N and N′ are called the *nodal points*. Thus for rays passing through the nodal points one has $u'=u$. The planes perpendicular to the axis at N and N′ are known as the *nodal planes*. For imagery in these planes it follows from equation (2–6) that

$$\frac{h'}{h} = \frac{-f}{f'}. \quad \ldots \ldots \ldots \quad (2\text{–}9)$$

The position of the second nodal point follows at once from equation (2–4) on putting $u=u'$. One obtains

$$x'_{N'}=f.$$

Similarly,
$$x_N =f'. \quad \ldots \ldots \ldots \quad (2\text{–}10)$$

The principal points, principal foci, and nodal points, are sometimes referred to as the *cardinal* points of the system. The six cardinal points for a typical case are illustrated in Fig. 2–5.

Fig. 2–5. Location of the nodal points.

If the refractive indices in the left- and right-hand spaces are equal, equations (2–10) show that the nodal and principal planes coincide. This fact also follows from (2–6) since, on putting $n=n'$, one has $h'/h=1$ when $u'=u$. That is, the nodal planes become the planes of unit magnification which, by definition, are the principal planes. The positions of the nodal planes can be deduced very quickly from first principles. In Fig. 2–5 take a point A in the first focal plane. Then the ray AN emerges along N'C' parallel to AN. The ray AB parallel to the axis emerges along B'F'. Also, since AN and AB intersect in the first focal plane, N'C' and B'F' are parallel. Thus, in the shaded right-angled triangles AFN, B'P'F', AF=B'P', and the angles at N and F' are equal. The triangles are therefore congruent and FN=P'F'=f'. Similarly, it may be shown that F'N'=PF=f.

2–6. Longitudinal or Axial Magnification

Consider conjugate points on the axis which are specified by their distances, x and x', from the focal planes. One has $xx'=ff'$. For small movements along the axis dx' will be conjugate to dx where $xdx'+x'dx=0$.

$$\therefore \quad \frac{dx'}{dx} = -\frac{x'}{x}.$$

From equations (2–1)
$$\frac{h'}{h} = -\frac{f}{x} = -\frac{x'}{f'},$$

whence
$$\frac{x'}{x} = \left(\frac{h'}{h}\right)^2 \cdot \frac{f'}{f}$$

so that
$$\frac{dx'}{dx} = -m^2 \cdot \frac{f'}{f} = +m^2 \cdot \frac{n'}{n}. \quad \cdots \cdots \quad (2\text{–}11)$$

This expression gives the magnification for small objects and images along the axis. It follows that while conjugate figures in planes perpendicular to the axis are geometrically similar, conjugate three-dimensional figures are not similar since the transverse and longitudinal magnifications are different.

2–7. Reference of Conjugate Distances to Principal Planes

It was seen to be convenient, theoretically, to specify the positions of conjugate planes by their distances, x and x', from the appropriate focal planes. If

Fig. 2–6. Reference to principal planes.

this is done, the relation between the conjugate distances is very simple (equation 2–2). It is frequently more convenient in practice to measure the conjugate distances from the principal planes. In this case they are denoted by l and l'. The conjugate planes may also be specified by their distances, z and z', from the nodal planes, or their distances, l_R and l'_R, from any other pair of conjugate planes. First, the conjugate distances will be referred to the principal planes. In Fig. 2–6 B and B′ are any pair of conjugate planes. From the figure one has

$$l'=f'+x'$$

and
$$l=f+x.$$

These are also the algebraic equations, so that the values $x'=l'-f'$, and $x=l-f$, may be substituted into Newton's equation.

One has
$$(l'-f')(l-f)=ff'$$

or
$$ll'-l'f-lf'=0$$

or
$$\frac{f}{l}+\frac{f'}{l'}=1. \qquad \cdots \cdots \quad (2\text{–}12)$$

Alternatively, since $nf'=-n'f$,

$$\frac{n'}{l'}-\frac{n}{l}=\frac{n'}{f'}=-\frac{n}{f}=F \text{ (say)}, \quad \cdots \cdots \quad (2\text{–}13)$$

where F is called the *power* of the system. If the indices of the initial and final spaces are equal, $n'=n$ and (2–13) reduces to

$$\frac{1}{l'}-\frac{1}{l}=\frac{1}{f'}. \qquad \cdots \cdots \cdots \quad (2\text{–}14)$$

2–8. Reference to Nodal Planes

From Fig. 2–7 it follows that
$$z=x+f'$$
and
$$z'=x'+f.$$

But x, z, and f, are negative so that, algebraically,

$$z=x-f',$$
$$z'=x'-f.$$

Fig. 2–7. Reference to nodal planes.

Then, from Newton's equation,

$$(z+f')(z'+f)=ff'$$

whence
$$\frac{f'}{z}+\frac{f}{z'}=-1. \qquad \cdots \cdots \cdots \quad (2\text{–}15)$$

Hence, putting $nf'=-n'f$, one has

$$\frac{n}{z'}-\frac{n'}{z}=\frac{n'}{f'}=-\frac{n}{f}=F \qquad \cdots \cdots \quad (2\text{–}16)$$

which reduces, as it should, to equation (2-14) when one puts $n=n'$, the condition that the nodal planes should coincide with the principal planes.

It is obvious, from Fig. 2-7, that the transverse magnification for the planes B and B′ is given by $m=z'/z$ which becomes $m=l'/l$ if $n'=n$.

2-9. Reference to Any Pair of Conjugate Planes

In Fig. 2-8, let R and R′ be the pair of conjugate planes chosen as reference planes. Let B and B′ be any other pair of conjugate planes. Let m_R and m be

Fig. 2-8. Reference to a pair of conjugate planes.

the transverse magnifications associated with the pairs of planes RR′ and BB′ respectively.

Applying the Helmholtz equation (2-6) *to the planes* R, R′,

$$n \tan \omega = n' m_R \tan \omega'.$$

From the figure, $h = l_R \tan \omega = -l_R \tan \omega$ algebraically,

$$h' = l'_R \tan \omega' = -l'_R \tan \omega' \text{ algebraically,}$$

whence $\dfrac{nh}{l_R} = n' m_R \dfrac{h'}{l'_R}$ algebraically

or, since $\dfrac{h'}{h} = m$,

$$\frac{l'_R}{l_R} = \frac{n'}{n} m_R m. \quad \ldots \ldots \quad (2\text{-}17)$$

2-10. Helmholtz Equation—Infinite Conjugate

For a finite image, $h \to \infty$ and $u \to 0$ as $l \to \infty$. $nh \tan u$ then becomes indeterminate. Suppose the object plane is at infinity to the left. Then the second focal plane is the image plane. Consider a ray in the left-hand space parallel to the axis at height y (see Fig. 2-9). This converges at an angle u' in the right-hand space to pass through F′. Consider also a ray inclined at an angle ω to the axis. This and the parallel ray through F may be considered as having come from an off-axis object point at infinity which is specified by the angle ω which it subtends at the system. On emerging from the system, these two rays intersect in the second focal plane. Thus h' is determined, since the ray incident through F emerges parallel to the axis.

It follows immediately from the figure that

$$y = f' \tan u' \quad \ldots \ldots \quad (2\text{-}18)$$

and $$h' = f \tan \omega \quad \ldots \ldots \quad (2\text{-}19)$$

and these are also the algebraic equations. Equation (2–19) is important since it shows where, in the second focal plane, one will find the image of an extra-axial point at infinity; it gives the size of the image in terms of the angular size of the object.

From (2–18) and (2–19), it follows that

$$n'h' \tan u' = n'f \tan \omega . \frac{y}{f'} = -ny \tan \omega.$$

Fig. 2-9. Helmholtz equation with infinite conjugate.

Therefore if the first conjugate is infinite one may write the Helmholtz equation in the form

$$H = -ny \tan \omega = n'h' \tan u'. \quad \ldots \quad (2\text{–}20)$$

For telescopic systems both conjugates can be infinite and one has

$$H = -ny \tan \omega = -n'y' \tan \omega'. \quad \ldots \quad (2\text{–}21)$$

2–11. Telescopic Systems

The discussions so far have assumed that the cardinal points lie at finite distances from the system. In what is known as a *telescopic* system the principal foci are at infinity and the focal lengths f, f' are infinite. In this case one cannot specify the positions of conjugate planes by means of their distances from the cardinal points but only by means of their distances from another pair of conjugate planes. It should be noted here that not all the systems colloquially referred to as telescopes are true telescopic systems. For example, a "telescope" adjusted for observation of a relatively near object is not truly telescopic. It should be noted also that, although one usually thinks of a truly telescopic system as being used to form an image of an object at infinity, such a system also images near objects.

In Fig. 2–10, suppose AB is a ray entering a telescopic system from an axial object point at infinity so that AB is parallel to the axis. In general, the emergent ray must pass through the second principal focus. If the second focal plane is at infinity, the ray CD which is conjugate to AB must also be parallel to the axis although it is not usually at the same height as AB. CD may, in fact, be below the axis. Consider the object L_0L of height h; the image of L_0 must be on the axis and the image of L must be on the line CD. Consequently, the image height

h' will be independent of the location of the object. Thus the magnification, $m = h'/h$, is the same for all pairs of conjugate planes L_0L, L'_0L'. This magnification may be referred to as the magnification of the telescope. The Helmholtz equation (2–6) gives

$$\frac{h'}{h} = -\frac{f}{f'}\frac{\tan u}{\tan u'}.$$

If f and f' each tend to infinity while the ratio f'/f remains constant (and equal to $-n'/n$), then the ratio $\tan u'/\tan u$ is also constant for all object and image positions. If $n'=n$ it is the reciprocal of the transverse linear magnification. There are no cardinal planes that can be used as reference planes and one must specify the object and image positions by their distances from a convenient pair of conjugate planes chosen as reference planes. As before, let l_R and l'_R be the

Fig. 2–10. Telescopic system.

distances of object and image from the reference planes. Since, for a telescopic system, the magnification is the same for all pairs of conjugate planes, one can put $m_R = m$ in equation (2–17). Consequently, for a telescopic system one has

$$\frac{l'_R}{l_R} = \left(\frac{n'}{n}\right) m^2. \qquad \ldots \ldots \quad (2\text{–}22)$$

This equation also follows from equation (2–11) since, in the present case, m is constant and one may take finite increments along the axis in place of dx and dx'.

2–12. The Combination of Two Systems

In general terms, suppose a transformation from one space to another is effected by a system. The geometry of the transformation can be evolved if the cardinal points of the system are known. It may happen that a second system now effects a transformation from the second to a third space. It is obvious that one can look upon the two systems as being equivalent to a single system which effects a transformation from the first to the third space. In terms of optics the image formed by one optical system becomes the object for a second system and the two systems act as one—forming the final image from the original object. The problem now is to find the cardinal points of this combined system, given the cardinal points of the two separate systems and the position of the second system relative to the first.

It will be assumed that there is a common axis of symmetry. In this case the separation of the two systems is specified by the separation of their "adjacent" principal foci, $F_1'F_2=g$, or by the separation of their "adjacent" principal planes, $P_1'P_2=d$. The sign convention for g is that g is positive when measured to the right from F_1' to F_2. Similarly, d is positive when measured to the right from P_1' to P_2.

From Fig. 2–11, $d=f_1'+g+f_2$, but f_2 is negative; one has, algebraically,

$$d=f_1'+g-f_2. \qquad \cdots \cdots \cdots \quad (2\text{–}23)$$

Consider a ray in the first space parallel to the axis and at height y. The conjugate ray in the second space is AF_1' which is determined at once since it must emerge from the point A, at height y, and pass through F_1'. Let this ray

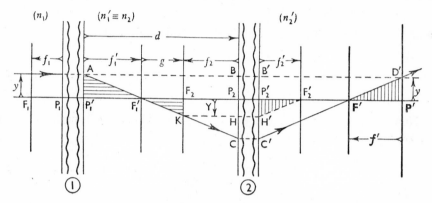

Fig. 2–11. Combination of two systems.

intersect the first focal plane and the first principal plane of the second system in K and C respectively. It follows at once that the conjugate ray in the third space must pass through C'. To find the direction of the final ray, consider a line KH parallel to the axis. This is obviously conjugate to $H'F_2'$. The ray C'D' conjugate to $AF_1'KC$ is now located since it must be parallel to $H'F_2'$. The second principal plane P'D' of the complete system is determined by the point D', where the ray C'D' in the third space intersects the path of the initial ray parallel to the axis. The second principal focus F' of the complete system is also determined; it is the point where the final ray C'D' intersects the axis. The second focal length of the combination is $f'=P'F'$ which, in the figure, is negative. It follows that the complete system as illustrated in Fig. 2–11 is a diverging system; it is interesting to note that it represents the system of the compound microscope (see §3–7).

In the figure the large triangle ABC and the smaller triangles $AP_1'F_1'$, KF_2F_1' (shaded horizontally) are similar. It follows that

$$\frac{y}{Y}=\frac{f_1'}{g} \qquad \cdots \cdots \cdots \quad (2\text{–}24)$$

and

$$\frac{BC}{Y}=\frac{d}{g}. \qquad \cdots \cdots \cdots \quad (2\text{–}25)$$

Also, the large triangle B′C′D′, and the smaller triangles $P_2'H'F_2'$, P′D′F′ (shaded vertically) are similar.

$$\therefore \quad \frac{y}{Y} = \frac{f'}{f_2'} \qquad \cdots \cdots \cdots \quad (2\text{--}26)$$

and

$$\frac{B'C'}{Y} = \frac{B'D'}{f_2'}. \qquad \cdots \cdots \cdots \quad (2\text{--}27)$$

From (2–24) and (2–26)

$$\frac{f_1'}{g} = \frac{f'}{f_2'}, \qquad \cdots \cdots \cdots \quad (2\text{--}28)$$

and from (2–25) and (2–27), since B′C′=BC and B′D′=$P_2'P'$,

$$\frac{d}{g} = \frac{P_2'P'}{f_2'}. \qquad \cdots \cdots \cdots \quad (2\text{--}29)$$

Now, in the figure, f_1', f_2', g, d, and $P_2'P'$, are positive but f' is negative. Thus (2–28) and (2–29) give, algebraically,

$$f' = -\frac{f_1'f_2'}{g} \qquad \cdots \cdots \cdots \quad (2\text{--}30)$$

and

$$P_2'P' = \frac{f_2'd}{g} = -\frac{df'}{f_1'}. \qquad \cdots \cdots \cdots \quad (2\text{--}31)$$

Similarly it may be shown that

$$f = \frac{f_1 f_2}{g} \qquad \cdots \cdots \cdots \quad (2\text{--}32)$$

and

$$P_1 P = \frac{f_1 d}{g} = \frac{df}{f_2}. \qquad \cdots \cdots \cdots \quad (2\text{--}33)$$

(P and F are not shown in the figure.)

Using equations (2–30) to (2–33) it is possible to find the cardinal points of the combined system in terms of the constants of the constituent parts. The combination is equivalent to a single system whose cardinal points are P, P′, F, and F′, and the quantities f and f' are usually referred to as the *equivalent focal lengths* (E.F.L.s). In terms of optics: if a thin lens of the same E.F.L. as a complete optical system is placed at the first principal plane, the imagery produced is identical to that of the system except for a bodily lateral shift of magnitude PP′. The thin lens is known as the *equivalent lens*. (See §2–17 and Fig. 2–16.)

One special case is worthy of recognition at once: if $g=0$, f, f', P_1P, and $P_2'P'$, are infinite, i.e. the system is telescopic.

2–13. Use of Powers and Reduced Distances

The powers F, F_1, and F_2, of the combination and the separate systems are respectively given by

$$\left.\begin{aligned} F &= -\frac{n_1}{f} = \frac{n_2'}{f'}, \\ F_1 &= -\frac{n_1}{f_1} = \frac{n_1'}{f_1'}, \\ F_2 &= -\frac{n_1'}{f_2} = \frac{n_2'}{f_2'}. \end{aligned}\right\} \qquad \cdots \cdots \quad (2\text{--}34)$$

Any distance divided by the refractive index of the space in which it is measured is called a *reduced distance*, and is denoted by the use of a "bar". For example, the reduced separation is $\bar{d} = d/n_1'$. A *reduced angle*, on the other hand, is the product of an angle and the appropriate refractive index: $n'u' = \bar{u}'$. Using this notation one has, from (2–31),

$$P_2'P' = -\frac{n_2'\bar{d}F_1}{F}, \qquad \cdots \cdots \quad (2\text{--}35)$$

and similarly, from (2–33),

$$P_1P = \frac{n_1\bar{d}F_2}{F}. \qquad \cdots \cdots \quad (2\text{--}36)$$

Also, from (2–30) and (2–23),

$$\frac{n_2'}{F} = -\frac{\dfrac{n_1'}{F_1}\cdot\dfrac{n_2'}{F_2}}{d - \dfrac{n_1'}{F_2} - \dfrac{n_1'}{F_1}} = -\frac{n_2'}{F_1 F_2 \dfrac{d}{n_1'} - F_1 - F_2}$$

or

$$F = F_1 + F_2 - \bar{d}F_1 F_2. \qquad \cdots \cdots \quad (2\text{--}37)$$

Examination candidates should note that (2–35), (2–36), and (2–37) are the most generally useful equations for solving problems involving two systems. Sometimes it is useful to have expressions for P_1F and $P_2'F'$. In Fig. 2–11 one has

$$P_2'F' = P_2'P' - P'F'$$

or, since $P'F'$ is negative, one has, algebraically,

$$P_2'F' = P_2'P' + f'$$

$$= f' - \frac{df'}{f_1'} = f'(1 - d/f_1'), \qquad \cdots \cdots \quad (2\text{--}38)$$

or

$$P_2'F' = \frac{n_2'(1 - \bar{d}F_1)}{F}. \qquad \cdots \cdots \quad (2\text{--}39)$$

Similarly

$$P_1F = -\frac{n_1(1 - \bar{d}F_2)}{F}. \qquad \cdots \cdots \quad (2\text{--}40)$$

P_1F and $P_2'F'$ are sometimes called the *front and back focal lengths* respectively (F.F.L. and B.F.L.). $-n_1/P_1F$ $[=F/(1-dF_2)]$, and $n_2'/P_2'F'$ $[=F/(1-dF_1)]$, are known as the *front and back vertex powers.*

It should be noted that the proof given in §2–12 breaks down if one of the systems has zero power (infinite focal length). g and either f_2 and f_2' or f_1 and f_1' are then infinite and equations (2–30) and (2–32) become indeterminate. However, the proof is valid as this condition is approached, and equations (2–35) to (2–40) inclusive are still applicable in the limiting case. The alternative proof given in §2–23 does not break down and gives the same results.

2–14. Two Systems in Air

For two optical systems in air one has $n_1=n_1'=n_2'=1$ and the general equation (2–37) becomes

$$\frac{1}{f'}=\frac{1}{f_1'}+\frac{1}{f_2'}-\frac{d}{f_1'f_2'}, \qquad \dots \dots \quad (2\text{–}41)$$

i.e.

$$f'=\frac{f_1'f_2'}{f_1'+f_2'-d}.$$

The positions of the principal planes are given by

$$\left.\begin{aligned} P_1P&=\frac{df_1'}{f_1'+f_2'-d} \\[2mm] P_2'P'&=-\frac{df_2'}{f_1'+f_2'-d}, \end{aligned}\right\} \qquad \dots \dots \quad (2\text{–}42)$$

and

and the front and back focal lengths are

$$\left.\begin{aligned} P_1F&=-\frac{f_1'(f_2'-d)}{f_1'+f_2'-d} \\[2mm] P_2'F'&=\frac{f_2'(f_1'-d)}{f_1'+f_2'-d}. \end{aligned}\right\} \qquad \dots \dots \quad (2\text{–}43)$$

and

2–15. Paraxial Refraction at a Spherical Surface

At the beginning of this chapter it was pointed out that within the paraxial region there is a collinear relationship between the object and image spaces of a spherical refracting surface. Thus, within the paraxial region, such a surface is an image-forming system of the type which has been under discussion above. Now it was shown in Chapter I that, if one specifies the positions of the conjugate planes by their distances l and l' from the pole of the surface, one has

$$\frac{n'}{l'}-\frac{n}{l}=\frac{n'-n}{r}=-\frac{n}{f}=\frac{n'}{f'} \qquad \dots \dots \quad (2\text{–}44)$$

with the usual notation, where f and f' are the values of l and l' when l' and l respectively are infinite. If one compares this equation with equation (2–13), where l and l' were measured from the principal points, it will be seen that a single refracting surface is a system whose principal points coincide with the pole of the surface. The paraxial approximation is such that the sagitta in the refracting surface is negligible, and in this sense one may say that the principal *planes* coincide with the refracting *surface*. The constants n and n' in the general theory can now definitely be identified with the refractive indices of the media separated by the refracting surface. The focal lengths and the power of a single surface are given by

$$f=-\frac{nr}{n'-n}, \qquad f'=\frac{n'r}{n'-n}, \qquad F=\frac{n'-n}{r}. \qquad \text{. . (2–45)}$$

A ray through the centre of curvature of the surface will be incident normally at the surface and will therefore pass through undeviated. By definition, therefore, both the nodal points of a single refracting surface coincide with the centre of curvature. Happily, this result also follows analytically. The second nodal point, for example, is distance l' from the pole of the surface where, as always, $l'=f'+x'$. Thus, for this point one has

$$l'=\frac{n'r}{n'-n}-\frac{nr}{n'-n}=r.$$

The cardinal points of a single refracting surface are shown in Fig. 2–12, for $n=1$ and $n'=1\cdot5$.

Fig. 2–12. Cardinal points of a single spherical refracting surface.

In the first fourteen sections of this chapter a number of results have been deduced for a system giving geometrically perfect imagery. Within the paraxial region these results can now be applied to a single spherical refracting surface. For example, the equations giving the cardinal points of a combination of systems can now be applied to find the cardinal points of combinations of refracting surfaces. The most important applications are to the combination of two surfaces to form a thin lens or a thick lens, and to the combination of two separated thin lenses. Before considering these applications, the paraxial form of the Helmholtz equation will be deduced from first principles for a refracting surface. This serves as further evidence that the results deduced in the general analysis do, in fact, apply to the paraxial region of an optical system.

Fig. 2–13. Helmholtz equation for a single surface.

In Fig. 2–13 the small object BC, of height h, is imaged at B′C′ by the refracting surface AH separating media whose refractive indices are n and n'. The ray from B at angle u is incident at height y and is refracted to B′ at angle u'. The ray CA is refracted along AC′ and the angles of incidence and refraction are as indicated. The paraxial form of Snell's law of refraction gives

$$ni=n'i'$$

or, from the figure, $\qquad n(h/l)=n'(h'/l'),$

$$\therefore \; \frac{nh}{n'h'}=\frac{l}{l'}. \qquad \cdots \cdots \quad (2\text{--}46)$$

Again from the figure one has

$$y=lu=l'u',$$

$$\therefore \; \frac{l}{l'}=\frac{u'}{u}. \qquad \cdots \cdots \quad (2\text{--}47)$$

From (2–46) and (2–47) one has, at once,

$$nhu=n'h'u'$$

which is the paraxial form of the Helmholtz equation.

2–16. The Thin Lens

When two refracting surfaces are combined to form a lens the positions of the cardinal points of the lens are given by the general equations of §§2–12 and 2–13. If the lens is thin, the separation of the surfaces, i.e. of the adjacent principal points, is negligible. Thus one puts $d=0$. Equation (2–37) then shows that the power of the lens is the sum of the powers of the separate surfaces. One has

$$F=F_1+F_2=\frac{n_1'-n_1}{r_1}+\frac{n_2'-n_1'}{r_2}. \qquad \cdots \cdots \quad (2\text{--}48)$$

Equations (2–35) and (2–36) show that the principal planes of the lens coincide with the lens itself. The relation between the conjugate distances l and l' is given by the usual equation

$$\frac{n'}{l'}-\frac{n}{l}=F, \qquad \cdots \cdots \quad (2\text{--}49)$$

where F is given by (2–48) and n and n' are now the refractive indices of the initial and final media.

The case of a thin lens in air follows if one puts $n_1=n_2'=1$ and $n_1'=n$, the refractive index of the material of the lens. One has

$$F=\frac{n-1}{r_1}+\frac{1-n}{r_2},$$

i.e. $\qquad \dfrac{1}{l'}-\dfrac{1}{l}=(n-1)\left(\dfrac{1}{r_1}-\dfrac{1}{r_2}\right). \qquad \cdots \cdots \quad (2\text{--}50)$

The principal planes again coincide with the lens, and since the initial and final media are the same the nodal planes also coincide with the lens (see §2-5).

It is convenient to point out here that the physical positions of the principal foci of a system have no special significance in the spaces to which they do not belong. For example, for a diverging lens the principal foci are virtual. The second principal focus is, as always, in the right-hand space; here it is virtual and lies on the left-hand side of the lens. A real object placed at this point lies in the *left*-hand space and its image is not at infinity; it lies between the object and the lens (see Fig. 2-14). Similarly, a virtual object at a

Fig. 2-14. Principal foci of lenses.

principal focus of a convex lens is in a space different from that of the focus and, again, the image is not at infinity (Fig. 2-14).

2-17. The Thick Lens

Consider the thick lens consisting of the combination of surfaces whose radii are r_1 and r_2 and whose poles A and B are distance d apart. Equations (2-35), (2-36), and (2-37), give the power and the positions of the principal planes. One has

$$\left. \begin{aligned} AP &= \frac{n_1 d F_2}{n_1' F} \\ BP' &= -\frac{n_2' d F_1}{n_1' F}, \end{aligned} \right\} \quad \cdots \cdots \quad (2\text{-}51)$$

and

where

$$F_1 = \frac{n_1' - n_1}{r_1}$$

and

$$F_2 = \frac{n_2' - n_1'}{r_2}$$

and

$$F = \frac{n_1' - n_1}{r_1} + \frac{n_2' - n_1'}{r_2} - \frac{d(n_1' - n_1)(n_2' - n_1')}{n_1' r_1 r_2}. \quad \cdots \quad (2\text{-}52)$$

For a thick lens of index n, thickness d, in air one has $F_1 = (n-1)/r_1$, $F_2 = (1-n)/r_2$, and the expression for F reduces to

$$F = (n-1)\left(\frac{1}{r_1} - \frac{1}{r_2}\right) + \frac{d(n-1)^2}{n r_1 r_2} \quad \cdots \cdots \quad (2\text{-}53)$$

$$= \frac{n(n-1)(r_2 - r_1) + d(n-1)^2}{n r_1 r_2}. \quad \cdots \cdots \quad (2\text{-}54)$$

In equation (2-53) the first term is the power of the thin lens that has the same radii of curvature. If one imagines the surfaces of this thin lens being pulled apart the power is modified by the amount given by the second term.

The positions of the principal points of a thick lens in air follow at once from equations (2–51). One has

$$AP = \frac{dF_2}{nF}$$

and

$$BP' = -\frac{dF_1}{nF},$$

. . . . (2–55)

whence

$$AP = -\frac{dr_1}{n(r_2-r_1)+d(n-1)},$$

$$BP' = -\frac{dr_2}{n(r_2-r_1)+d(n-1)}.$$

. . . . (2–56)

Frequently $n(r_2-r_1)$ is considerably larger than $d(n-1)$ and the latter can be neglected in comparison with the former. Thus, for a moderately thick lens, one has

$$AP = -\frac{dr_1}{n(r_2-r_1)},$$

$$BP' = -\frac{dr_2}{n(r_2-r_1)}.$$

. . . . (2–57)

Since the initial and final media are the same, the nodal and principal planes coincide (Fig. 2–15). For a biconvex or biconcave lens r_1 and r_2 have opposite

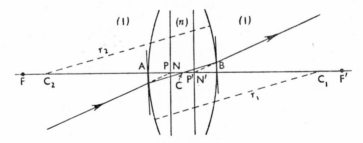

Fig. 2–15. Thick lens.

signs, and for many meniscus lenses the radii will be widely different. The result is that $|r_2-r_1|$ is often fairly large and (2–57) sufficiently accurate.

If one has a ray that is directed towards the first nodal point, it emerges from the direction of N′ and the incident and emergent rays are parallel. Consequently, the tangents to the surfaces at the points of incidence and emergence must be parallel, and it may be said that the ray passes through the lens as though through a plane-parallel plate. The axial point C, through which such a ray passes in the middle space, is known as the *optical centre*. Since it must remain in the paraxial region, the ray must, in fact, make a small angle with the optical axis. The tangents to the surfaces at the points of incidence and emergence are therefore almost normal to the axis. Now the points P and P′ are the images of C as formed by the first and second refracting surfaces respectively, and since the lens behaves as a parallel-sided plate for the ray illustrated, it follows that $AC=nAP$ and $BC=nBP'$.

$$\therefore \quad \frac{AC}{BC}=\frac{AP}{BP'}=\frac{r_1}{r_2}. \qquad \cdots \cdots \quad (2\text{–}58)$$

It will be seen that, in general, the optical centre is not the physical centre of the lens. In fact, C is at the pole of the curved surface if the lens is plano, and lies outside the lens if the latter is meniscus.

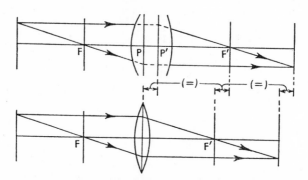

Fig. 2–16. Imagery by a thick lens.

The general paraxial image-forming properties of a thick lens or lens system are completely determined by the positions of the cardinal planes. If these are known one can, for example, find the image of any object without making a detailed study of the passage of the image-forming rays through the system. That is, it is not necessary to consider the refractions of the rays at the various surfaces. The geometrical construction for finding the image is as given in §2–2 and is the same as the simple method used for a thin lens. This is illustrated by Fig. 2–16 which shows the construction for a thick lens and the equivalent thin lens. The figure confirms the statement, made in §2–12, that the latter gives the same image except for a displacement PP'.

2–18. The Spherical Lens

Consider the case of a lens consisting simply of a sphere of index n in air. It is at once obvious that the nodal and principal points must coincide with the centre. This also follows from the equations given above. (Note that, since r_2 is negative, one has $d=r_1-r_2$ or, since $r_2=-r_1$, $d=2r_1$.) The power of the lens follows from equation (2–54). One has

$$F=\frac{-n(n-1)2r+2r(n-1)^2}{-nr^2}$$

$$=\frac{2(n-1)}{nr}$$

or
$$\text{E.F.L.}=\frac{nr}{2(n-1)}. \qquad \cdots \cdots \quad (2\text{–}59)$$

2–19. Examples of Principal Planes of a Thick Lens in Air

Fig. 2–17 illustrates the positions of the principal planes of a *moderately* thick lens in air. If the lens is equiconvex or equiconcave and is not very thick, one may put $F_1=F_2\stackrel{.}{=}F/2$. Taking $n=1\cdot5$ one has, from equations (2–55), $AP=-BP'=d/3$. For a plano-convex or plano-concave lens where $r_2=\infty$, $F_2=0$ and equations (2–55) give $AP=0$ and $BP'=-2d/3$. For meniscus lenses

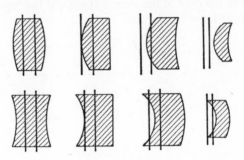

Fig. 2–17. Principal planes of thick lenses.

the principal planes move outside the lens as indicated in the figure. It can easily be shown from equations (2–57) that if $n=1\cdot5$ the second principal plane reaches the first surface when $r_2=3r_1$. In the figure $|F|$ is approximately the same for all the lenses. It should be noted that in order to apply the approximate equations (2–57) to a steep meniscus lens, the lens must be relatively thin.

2–20. Two Separated Thin Lenses in Air

Suppose one has two thin lenses A and B whose focal lengths are f_1' and f_2' respectively, the lenses being separated by a distance d. The results of §2–14 will apply so that one has

i.e.

$$\left.\begin{aligned}\frac{1}{f'}&=\frac{1}{f_1'}+\frac{1}{f_2'}-\frac{d}{f_1'f_2'},\\[2mm]f'&=\text{E.F.L.}=\frac{f_1'f_2'}{f_1'+f_2'-d}.\end{aligned}\right\}\quad\ldots\ldots\;(2\text{–}60)$$

$$\left.\begin{aligned}AP&=\frac{df_1'}{f_1'+f_2'-d},\\[2mm]BP'&=-\frac{df_2'}{f_1'+f_2'-d},\end{aligned}\right\}\quad\ldots\ldots\;(2\text{–}61)$$

with corresponding equations for the front and back focal lengths. Since the system is in air, the nodal points coincide with the principal points.

It should be noted that for two convex lenses a short distance apart, the cardinal planes have positions that are similar to those for a biconvex thick lens except that in the present case the principal planes are "crossed". That is to say, P' actually lies to the left of P [see Fig. 2–18(a)].

(a) $d = 0\cdot5 f_2'$

(b) $d = f_2'$

(c) $d = 1\cdot5 f_2'$ (Huygens Eyepiece)

(d) $d = 2 f_2'$

(e) $d = 3 f_2'$ (Astronomical Telescope)

(Cardinal points at infinity)

(f) $d = 5 f_2'$ (Compound Microscope)

(g) $d = -0\cdot5 f_2'$

(h) $d = -f_2'$ (Galilean Telescope)

(Cardinal points at infinity)

(i) $d = -1\cdot5 f_2'$ (Telephoto Lens)

Fig. 2-18. Cardinal points of a system of two separated thin lenses. In (a)–(f) $f_1' = 2 f_2'$, and in (g)–(i) $f_1' = -2 f_2'$.

Fig. 2–18 shows the positions of the cardinal points for a number of combinations of separated thin lenses. In each case $|f_1'|=2|f_2'|$. (c) represents the

Huygen's eyepiece, (e) the astronomical telescope, (f) the compound microscope, (h) the Galilean telescope, and (i) the telephoto lens. Each of these is discussed further in Chapter III.

In addition to the cardinal points, one shonld mention the *Bravais* points. These are self-conjugate points; their existence for a system of two separated thin lenses is illustrated by Fig. 2–19. It can be shown that for a system consisting of two separated thin lenses, Bravais points exist if $d^2>4f_1'f_2'$.'

Fig. 2–19. Bravais points.

This condition is always satisfied if one lens is converging and the other diverging because this makes $f_1'f_2'$ negative.

2–21. The Deviation Method for Tracing Paraxial Rays

Figs 2–20(a) and (b) illustrate the passage of a paraxial ray through a complete optical system and through a simple refracting surface respectively; the discussion applies equally well to either.

Fig. 2–20. Deviation of a ray.

One has

$$\frac{n'}{l'}-\frac{n}{l}=F,$$

$$\therefore \quad \frac{n'y}{l'}-\frac{ny}{l}=Fy,$$

$$\therefore \quad n'u'-nu=Fy. \quad \cdot \quad \cdot \quad \cdot \quad \cdot \quad \cdot \quad \cdot \quad (2\text{–}62)$$

If u and y are known, the path of the incident ray is specified completely. Using (2–62) it is then possible to find the path of the emergent ray. For a system in air $(n'=n=1)$, Fy is simply the deviation of the ray $(\because \delta=u'-u$ algebraically), and it will be seen that the angle of deviation of a paraxial ray is independent of its initial direction. The most useful application of (2–62) is the tracing of a paraxial ray through a system of refracting surfaces. The path of the incident ray is specified by u_1 and y_1 and (2–62) gives the path after refraction at the first surface. In order to apply the equation to the second surface it is necessary to find y_2, the height of incidence. It will be seen, from Fig. 2–21, that

$$y_2 = y_1 - d_1' u_1'. \quad . \quad . \quad (2\text{–}63)$$

Remembering that $u_2 \equiv u_1'$, one can now apply (2–62) to the second refraction. By repeated alternate application of (2–62) and (2–63) one can

Fig. 2–21. Incidence heights at adjacent surfaces.

find the path of the ray through any number of refracting surfaces (or through any number of complete systems).

2–22. Location of Cardinal Points of Complicated Systems

For any optical system, it has been shown (§2–1) that if one has a ray entering parallel to the axis, the emergent ray passes through the appropriate principal focus, and the initial and final rays (produced if necessary) intersect in the corresponding principal plane. For complicated systems this provides the

Fig. 2–22. Cardinal points of complicated systems.

easiest method of calculating the positions of the cardinal planes. Suppose one has a system of k refracting surfaces. Starting with $u_1 = 0$, and using any convenient value of y_1 (usually $y_1 = 1$) one can use (2–62) and (2–63) to find the path of the ray through the system. These equations are applied alternately until y_k and u_k' are found. Then, from Fig. 2–22, one has

$$P_k'P' = -\frac{y_1 - y_k}{u_k'} \quad . \quad . \quad . \quad . \quad . \quad (2\text{–}64)$$

and

$$f' = \frac{y_1}{u_k'} \quad . \quad . \quad . \quad . \quad . \quad . \quad (2\text{–}65)$$

so that the positions of P' and F' can be found. In order to find P and F for the complete system it is necessary to trace the path of a ray entering parallel to the axis from the right. If the indices of the initial and final media are different, the nodal planes can be found from the relations $x_{N'}' = f$, $x_N = f'$.

The above equations, which apply to a number of complete systems as well as to a number of refracting surfaces, provide an alternative method of deriving the equations governing the combination of two optical systems.

2-23. Application of the Deviation Method to Two Systems

Before discussing the general problem, one special case should be noted: the combination of two thin lenses in contact in air. Since the lenses are thin and in contact, only one incidence height (y) is involved. Obviously the total deviation is Fy, and is the sum of the deviations F_1y and F_2y, F being the power of the combination and F_1 and F_2 the powers of the separate lenses. Thus one has, at once, the result $F=F_1+F_2$.

Fig. 2-23. Combination of two systems.

Figs 2–23(a) and (b) illustrate the combination of two complete systems and two refracting surfaces respectively. Again the discussion applies equally well to either. If the incident ray is parallel to the axis one has $u_1=0$.

Equation (2–62) gives

$$n_1'u_1'=F_1y_1. \qquad \ldots \ldots \ldots \quad (2\text{–}66)$$

For the second surface one has, since $n_2u_2\equiv n_1'u_1'$,

$$n_2'u_2'-n_1'u_1'=F_2y_2. \qquad \ldots \ldots \ldots \quad (2\text{–}67)$$

On adding these equations one has

$$n_2'u_2'=F_1y_1+F_2y_2. \qquad \ldots \ldots \ldots \quad (2\text{–}68)$$

Now the incident ray is parallel to the axis. Hence the incidence height in the first principal plane of the combination must be y_1 and one has, for the complete system,

$$n_2'u_2'=Fy_1. \qquad \ldots \ldots \ldots \quad (2\text{–}69)$$

(2–68) and (2–69) give

$$Fy_1=F_1y_1+F_2y_2. \qquad \ldots \ldots \ldots \quad (2\text{–}70)$$

Now from the figure

$$y_2=y_1-du_1', \quad \text{algebraically,}$$

or, using (2–66),

$$y_2=y_1-\frac{dF_1y_1}{n_1'}. \qquad \ldots \ldots \ldots \quad (2\text{–}71)$$

Therefore, from (2–70),

$$Fy_1 = F_1y_1 + F_2y_1 - \frac{F_2 dF_1 y_1}{n_1'}$$

or
$$F = F_1 + F_2 - dF_1F_2. \quad \ldots \ldots \quad (2\text{–}72)$$

The figure also gives

$$P_2'P' = -\frac{y_1 - y_2}{u_2'}, \quad \text{algebraically.}$$

Substituting from (2–71) for $y_1 - y_2$, and from (2–69) for u_2', one has

$$P_2'P' = -\frac{n_2' dF_1}{F}. \quad \ldots \ldots \quad (2\text{–}73)$$

Similarly, by tracing a ray incident parallel to the axis from the right, it can be shown that

$$P_1P = \frac{n_1 dF_2}{F}. \quad \ldots \ldots \quad (2\text{–}74)$$

Equations (2–72), (2–73), and (2–74), are identical to those derived in §2–12 but the present proof does not break down when F_1 or F_2 is zero.

3^*

THE PARAXIAL THEORY OF OPTICAL INSTRUMENTS

IN this chapter an account is given of the paraxial theory* of the chief optical instruments such as the camera lens, the telescope, and the microscope. The object of the discussion is to show the principle of each instrument; a more detailed account of the lenses employed is given in Chapter XVI, after the monochromatic aberrations have been discussed. Chromatic aberration and the achromatic combination of lenses are included in this chapter, however, because this subject forms part of the paraxial theory. In the chapters on interference and diffraction, which precede the discussion of aberrations (and in many chapters which follow it), the lenses and optical instruments that are employed are assumed to be perfect. That is to say, it is assumed that the systems have the same properties outside the paraxial region as they have inside it. For example, the optical path from an object point to the image point is the same through all zones of the lens. That is to say, a spherical wave emerges and disturbances from the object arrive exactly in phase at the image, even if the lens has large aperture. In particular, if a plane wave enters a perfect lens a perfect spherical wave emerges and the disturbances arrive in phase at the image point in the focal plane.

3–1. Stops and Diaphragms

It was seen in Chapter II that, in terms of geometrical optics, a system gives perfect imagery within the paraxial region. This means that the imagery is perfect for all object distances. Later it will be shown that it is impossible to secure perfect imagery in this sense with image-forming pencils of large cross-section and objects of finite size. Usually, however, it is found that one can obtain very good imagery for one position of the object plane, but it is always necessary to place some restriction on the size of the object that can be imaged, and on the cross-section of the image-forming pencils from each object point. The necessary restrictions can be introduced by the use of two diaphragms.

Consider the case of a simple lens forming an image of a distant object [Fig. 3–1(a)]. The image of an axial object point can be of good quality if the angle u' is not excessive—one must limit the aperture of the system. This is done by means of the diaphragm A, known as the *aperture stop*. It will be obvious that the aperture stop controls the light-gathering power; it will be seen later that it also limits the resolving power. In designing a lens system, the position of the aperture stop is of paramount importance since, as is seen from the figure, it controls the part of the lens through which oblique image-forming pencils pass.

The presence of the stop A will not prevent the passage of image-forming

* The contributions made by Gauss to the theory of perfect optical systems were so extensive that the term *Gaussian* is frequently regarded as a synonym of *paraxial*.

pencils inclined to the axis at a large angle ω, but it is necessary to do this in order to limit the image size if good images alone are required. It is done by means of a diaphragm known as the *field stop* F which coincides with the image plane. That is to say, the field stop is conjugate to the object. The field stop does nothing to improve the image quality—it merely ensures that only the good images are utilized. In the case of a simple system as shown in Fig. 3–1(*a*), the use of a receiving screen of limited extent is equivalent to the use of a field stop. For example, in the case of a photographic lens, the film or plate holder acts as the field stop.

It will be seen that the aperture and field stops together control the value of the Helmholtz invariant, H, for the system.

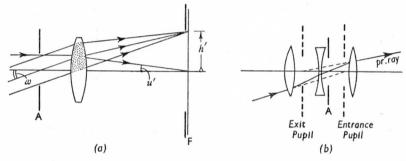

Fig. 3–1. (*a*) Function of aperture and field stops. (*b*) Positions of entrance and exit pupils.

The aperture stop may be anywhere in the optical system or outside it. The image of the aperture stop formed in the object space, i.e. formed by that part of the optical system which is nearer the object is known as the *entrance pupil* [Fig. 3–1(*b*)], and the image of A formed in the image space by that part of the system which is on the image side is known as the *exit pupil*. The pupils therefore lie in conjugate planes of the complete optical system. Either or both of the pupils may be real or virtual images of the aperture stop, and the exit pupil can be either to the left or to the right of the entrance pupil.

In any image-forming pencil of rays that passes through a system there will be one ray which passes through the centre of the aperture stop. This is known as the *principal* (or *chief*) *ray* of the pencil. It will be seen that in the object space the principal ray is directed towards the axial point of the entrance pupil, and that in the image space it emerges from the centre of the exit pupil. Quantities that refer to the principal ray are distinguished by the suffix *pr*.

If the centre of the aperture stop is at a principal focus, one is said to have a *telecentric* system. If the entrance pupil is at infinity, the system is telecentric on the side of the object, and if the exit pupil is at infinity, it is telecentric on the image side. It will be seen that a system cannot be telecentric on the object side if the object is at infinity since A would be located at the plane where the image-forming pencils are focused, and would be unable to control their diameters.

Although, ideally, only two stops are necessary in an optical system, one frequently finds other diaphragms introduced in order to obstruct stray light. In addition, some of the components of the optical system may have inadequate apertures. Fig. 3–2 shows an effect encountered frequently in camera lenses. For image-forming pencils at large angles, the edge of the lens obstructs some of the rays. Often *vignetting* of this kind is introduced in order to remove rays that, owing to aberrations, would spoil the image quality. In a complex system there may be several diaphragms in addition to the nominal aperture and field stops. Consider the image of each stop as formed by that part of the optical system that lies on the object side of it. The stop image that subtends the smallest angle at the centre of the entrance pupil is called the *entrance window* since it determines the field of view if the aperture stop is small. The image of

Fig. 3–2. Vignetting of image-forming pencils.

the entrance window, as formed by the complete system, is called the *exit window*. In the ideal case the entrance window is simply the image of the field stop as formed by that part of the optical system that precedes it.

3–2. The Human Eye

The structure of the human eye is discussed in Chapter XVII. It is sufficient here to regard the eye as a lens system that focuses the image on to a light-sensitive screen, the *retina*. There is an aperture stop, the *iris*, whose diameter varies involuntarily as the intensity of the incident light varies. The entrance pupil is very close to the first principal point. There is no field stop but the resolving power of the retina falls off very rapidly from the centre, so that,

Fig. 3–3. Action of the eye.

although the total field of view is very large, the field of distinct vision is very small. To "look" at an object, the eye is rotated in its socket until the image falls on the central part of the retina where the resolving power is good. The apparent size of the object is determined by the size of the retinal image. Suppose Fig. 3–3 represents, diagrammatically, the formation of an image on the retina. Suppose the object and image (h and h') subtend angles ω and ω' at the first and second principal points of the lens system of the eye.

Helmholtz's equation, applied to imagery in the principal planes, gives

$$n\omega = n'\omega'.$$

In addition one has

$$h' = -l'\omega' = -l'(n/n')\omega \qquad \ldots \ldots \quad (3\text{--}1)$$

so that the apparent size of the object is proportional to the angle that the object subtends at the first principal point.

The power of the lens system may be varied by the observer when it is required to view objects at different distances. This process is known as *accommodation*. During accommodation, the distance l' of the retina from the second principal point of the optical system remains almost constant. In consequence, *the apparent size of an object is proportional to the angle it subtends at the first principal point of the optical system, irrespective of the state of accommodation.*

3–3. Magnifying Power of a Telescope

In a telescopic system, rays that enter the system parallel leave it parallel. Such a system has infinite focal length, and if the object is at infinity the image

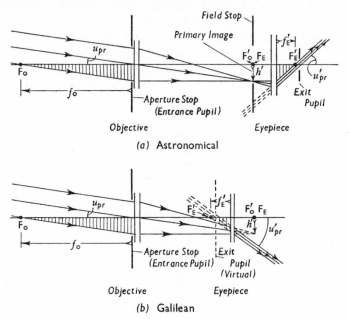

(a) Astronomical

(b) Galilean

Fig. 3–4. Telescopic systems.

is also at infinity. The main use of such systems is the observation of distant objects, but the student should not forget that such a system forms a finite image of a finite object.

A telescopic system can result from the combination of two converging systems, or one converging and one diverging system, such that $g=0$. In the latter case the focal length of the diverging system must be numerically smaller than that of the converging system. An example of the first type is the *astronomical* telescope which, in its simplest form, consists of two single convex lenses. The *Galilean* telescope consists of one convex and one concave lens. The two systems are illustrated in Fig. 3–4. In each case, the lens nearer the object is termed the *objective* and that nearer the observer, the *eyepiece*. Usually the objective itself constitutes the aperture stop and also, therefore, the entrance pupil. It follows that the exit pupil is the image of the objective formed by the eyepiece.

In the astronomical telescope the exit pupil is real and one may place the entrance pupil of the observer's eye at that point (sometimes known as the *eye-point*). In this case the whole field of view is visible at once. The distance from the last surface of the system to the eye-point is called the *eye clearance*. The field stop coincides with the second focal plane of the objective and the first focal plane of the eyepiece, where the objective forms the so-called *primary image* of the object.

In the case of the Galilean telescope the exit pupil is virtual and, since there is no real primary image, there can be no field stop. In consequence, the field of view has no sharp boundary and usually the whole field cannot be seen at once. When the eye is placed just behind the eyepiece, the field of view of such a system is eventually limited by the diameter of the objective. The following discussion applies equally well to either system.

If the telescope is adjusted by the observer to be truly telescopic, the final image is at infinity and the *magnifying power* is defined as the ratio of the apparent size of the image to the apparent size of the object viewed without the telescope. This, as explained in the last section, is the same as the ratio of the angle subtended at the first principal point of the eye by the image, to the angle subtended by the object.

In Fig. 3–4 rays are shown coming from the object at infinity and entering the observer's eye after passing through the telescope. The magnifying power is evidently u'_{pr}/u_{pr} since all the incident and emergent rays corresponding to a single object and image point are parallel, and the object subtends an angle u_{pr} at the eye as well as at the entrance pupil. The figure shows the usual case where the objective itself is the entrance pupil.

Fig. 3–5. Magnification of a telescope.

If h' is the size of the primary image, it can be seen from the shaded triangles that $h'=f_0 u_{pr}=f'_E u'_{pr}$. Hence the magnifying power is given by

$$M=\frac{u'_{pr}}{u_{pr}}=-\frac{f'_0}{f'_E} \quad\quad\quad\quad (3-2)$$

since $-f_0=f'_0$.

It has been shown that the linear magnification is constant for all object and image positions in the case of a telescopic system. The linear magnification is the inverse of the angular magnification so that, for any pair of conjugates,

$$\frac{h'}{h}=-\frac{f'_E}{f'_0}. \quad\quad\quad\quad (3-3)$$

This is seen to be the case for a finite object and image from Fig. 3–5. One may then ask how it is that if the object and image both tend to infinity while $(h'/h)=-(f'_E/f'_0)$ and is constant, the ratio of the apparent sizes can be f'_0/f'_E.

The answer lies in the fact that, as shown by equation (2–22) (p. 26), the ratio of the image and object distances measured from any conjugate reference planes is $(l'_R/l_R)=(h'/h)^2$ if $n'=n$. If l'_R and l_R approach infinity they can be measured from any fixed point in the system without error. One can say that the image and object are distances l'_R and l_R from the observer's eye. Obviously the angular dimensions of the image and object are h'/l'_R and h/l_R and consequently $M=(h'/l'_R)\div(h/l_R)=h/h'$. Thus, when the object and image both tend to infinity, the image does so more slowly, so that although the actual linear magnification or ratio of image to object size is h'/h, the angles subtended at the observer by the image and object are in the ratio h/h'.

3–4. Simple and Telephoto Camera Lenses

Consider the case of a camera lens used to produce an image of a distant object. Equation (2–19) (p. 24) gives the size of the image in terms of the angle

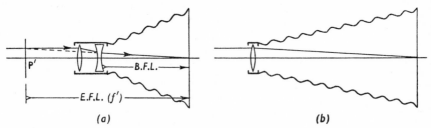

(a)   (b)

Fig. 3–6. Action of a telephoto lens.

subtended at the camera by the object. It follows that to obtain a large scale photograph one requires a lens having a long focal length.

Suppose the separation of the lenses of a Galilean telescope is increased so that g is positive. The image of a distant object will now be formed at a finite distance. The position of the second principal plane of the system is determined by the intersection of a ray parallel to the axis in the object space with its conjugate ray in the final image space (produced if necessary, as it is in this case)— see Fig. 3–6(a). The second principal plane P' is seen to lie some distance to the left of the system so that the equivalent focal length f' is quite large. As a result, the image is as large as it would be if formed by a single convex lens of focal length f'. In this latter case, however, the camera would have to be of length f', whereas in the former case it could be somewhat shorter. (Compare Figs. 3–6(a) and (b).) For this reason the combination of a convex and concave lens system is frequently employed. Such a combination is known as a *telephoto* lens. The ratio of the equivalent focal length to the back focal length is sometimes referred to as the *telephoto magnification*.

The view of a scene which is obtained by a camera lens is that of an eye placed at the first nodal point; that is to say, N is the centre of perspective. Thus the centre of perspective in the image space is N'. Consequently, the photograph is seen in proper perspective only if viewed from a distance equal to that of the plate or film from N'. This is known as the *viewing distance* and, for distant objects, it is simply the focal length of the camera lens. Since the focal length is usually less than D_v, the least distance of distinct vision, one cannot use the correct viewing distance unless the photograph is viewed through a convex lens. One can relax one's accommodation and employ a lens having the same focal length as the camera lens, the photograph being placed in the focal plane. Alternatively one can enlarge the photograph until the viewing distance, which increases in proportion, is equal to or greater than D_v.

With a telephoto lens, the problem is complicated by the fact that the combination of image size and field of view resembles that of a close-up photograph while the perspective corresponds to a camera at the larger distance actually employed; it looks wrong. The perspective would be correct if the proper viewing distance were employed (i.e. f' in most cases) but the advantage of the large image size would then be lost.

3-5. Projection Systems and Enlargers

Figs 3-7(a) and (b) show, diagrammatically, two systems for projecting the image of a transparency on to a screen. In the first, which is used for fairly large

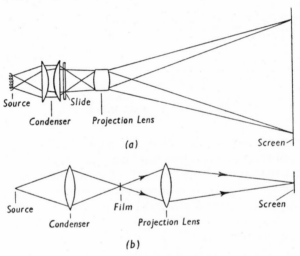

Fig. 3-7. Projection systems. (a) Lantern slides. (b) Ciné film.

slides and a moderately distant screen, the *condenser* images the source in the entrance pupil of the *projection* lens. It will be seen that the conditions of *Maxwellian view* obtain (see §18-7) and, consequently, the screen is evenly illuminated in the absence of the slide. The action of the projection lens resembles that of a camera lens in reverse, although the angular field may be smaller; *Petzval* or *Triplet* type lenses are frequently used (see Chapter XVI). The correction of the condenser is less critical and the system shown is common in the less expensive instruments. Photographic enlargers have a construction which is similar to this projection system; in the cheaper ones the condenser is replaced by a ground glass diffusing screen.

The system shown in Fig. 3-7(b) represents that used in the Kinematograph projector—actually a reflecting condenser is usually employed. The source is an arc and the image is sufficiently large to cover a 35 mm. film. By employing a large aperture condenser and projection lens, one can secure greater illumination on the screen with this system. (If, in the first system, the entrance pupil of the projection lens is as large as the image of the source, an increase in aperture does not give a brighter image. Also, the aperture of the condenser controls the field of view only.)

In the *Episcope*, which is used to project the image of an opaque picture, the major problem is shortage of light. The picture to be projected is illuminated as strongly as possible but, since this light is scattered in all directions, only a small proportion of the total light enters the projection lens. The latter must, therefore, have the largest possible aperture; frequently this is accomplished at the expense of the image quality.

3–6. The Simple Microscope or Hand Magnifier

Consider a single convex lens system used as a hand magnifier. The observer may adjust the final image to be at infinity or at some finite distance not less than the least distance of distinct vision. The magnifying power, M, of such a system is the ratio of the apparent size of the image when using the lens to the apparent size of the object when it is in the best position for observation by the naked eye. That is to say, M is the ratio of the angle subtended at the eye by the final image to the angle subtended by the object when at the least distance of distinct vision, D_v.

Fig. 3–8. Simple microscope.

Consider first the case where the final image is formed at infinity. The object, h, is therefore in the focal plane of the lens. From Fig. 3–8 it is seen that the angle subtended at the eye by the final image at infinity is $\omega = h/f'$.

$$\therefore \quad M = \frac{h}{f'} \div \frac{h}{D_v} = \frac{D_v}{f'}. \qquad \cdots \cdots \quad (3\text{–}4)$$

Suppose, now, that the observer moves the lens closer to the object, so that a magnified virtual image h' is formed by the lens (Fig. 3–9). Suppose object and image are distances l and l' from the lens which may be taken as thin. (If the lens is not thin, l and l' must, of course, be measured from the first and second principal planes.) Since the lens is in air one has

$$\frac{1}{l'} - \frac{1}{l} = \frac{1}{f'}$$

and since the nodal planes coincide with the lens

$$\frac{h'}{h} = \frac{l'}{l} = 1 - \frac{l'}{f'}.$$

If the eye is close to the lens and the observer adjusts the image to be at the least distance of distinct vision, one may put $l' = -D_v$, the negative sign being necessary since l' is negative. In this case

$$M = \frac{h'}{D_v} \div \frac{h}{D_v} = \frac{h'}{h},$$

i.e. $\qquad\qquad\qquad M = 1 + \frac{D_v}{f'}. \qquad \qquad \cdots \cdots \cdots \quad (3\text{-}5)$

Fig. 3-9. Simple microscope.

It is seen that there is a gain in magnification if the image is brought up as close as possible to the eye. If the magnifying power is 10 with the infinity adjustment, for example, the gain in magnifying power is 10%. One may put $D_v = 10''$ so that for the infinity adjustment M is equal to ten times the reciprocal of the focal length in inches. Alternatively, one may take $D_v = 25$ cm. and it will be seen that M is one-quarter of the power of the lens in dioptres.

3-7. The Principle of the Compound Microscope

For very large magnifications the simple magnifying lens is impracticable and a highly magnified image must be produced in two stages. This is done in the *compound microscope* illustrated in Fig. 3-10. The instrument consists of two

Objective   Eyepiece

Fig. 3-10. Compound microscope.

converging systems whose adjacent principal foci are a considerable positive distance apart. The objective, or object glass, produces a real image h' of the object h and this image is further magnified by the eyepiece.

Consider the case where the final image is formed at infinity. The path of the image-forming rays is indicated in the figure. It will be seen that the angle under which the final image is viewed is $\omega = h'/f'_E$. From the figure, since the shaded triangles are similar,

$$\frac{h'}{h} = -\frac{g}{f'_O}. \qquad \cdots \cdots \cdots \quad (3\text{-}6)$$

Consequently the angle subtended at the eye by the final image is $hg/f'_0f'_E$ and the magnifying power is given by

$$M=-\frac{hg}{f'_0f'_E}\div\frac{h}{D_v},$$

$$\therefore\quad M=-\frac{gD_v}{f'_0f'_E}=-\left(\frac{g}{f'_0}\right)\left(\frac{D_v}{f'_E}\right).\quad\ldots\quad(3\text{–}7)$$

This is the *primary magnification*, produced by the objective, multiplied by the *power of the eyepiece*, the eyepiece being looked upon as a simple microscope used to examine the primary image formed by the objective. The negative sign expresses the fact that the image is inverted. (The eyepiece may be considered to act in this way in the case of the astronomical telescope also.) The distance g is called the *optical tube length* of the microscope, and is usually 160 mm.

Although, as stated above, a simple microscope consisting of a single lens is unsuitable for high magnifications, the compound microscope may be considered analytically as a single system of focal length f'. It is just that a compound instrument must be used in order to obtain a sufficiently short focal length. If the final image is formed at infinity, the magnifying power of such a system is given by $M=D_v/f'$. But from equation (2–30) (p. 28) it follows that $f'=-f'_0f'_E/g$ so that

$$M=-\frac{D_vg}{f'_0f'_E}.$$

Many continental writers put $M=\left(\frac{D_v}{f'_0}\right)\left(\frac{g}{f'_E}\right)$ and call D_v/f'_0 and g/f'_E the objective and eyepiece magnifications respectively.

The field stop of a compound microscope is located in the plane of the primary image and the aperture stop is usually in the region of the objective. The exit pupil, therefore, is beyond the eyepiece, a distance slightly greater than f'_E from the second principal plane of the latter. As for a telescope, the eye pupil should be placed as close as possible to the exit pupil of the instrument.

3–8. Chromatic Aberration

The instruments described above are usually used with a source of "white" light such as daylight or an electric lamp. Such light may be looked upon as a mixture of light of many wavelengths. So far, however, the theory has taken no account of the way in which the refractive index of a medium varies with the wavelength of the light. For transparent substances the refractive index decreases with increasing wavelength (see §20–7, Fig. 20–4, p. 452) and a thin lens, for example, will have a shorter focal length for the shorter wavelengths. Consider a point source on the axis of an optical system. In general, the light of each wavelength present in the source will form a separate axial image and there will be no "white" image point. This defect is referred to as *longitudinal chromatic aberration*. Similarly, light of each wavelength will form an image of a finite object, and each image will have a different size—there is said to be a *chromatic difference of magnification*. Thus longitudinal chromatic aberration causes the images to be at different distances along the axis, and chromatic difference of magnification causes the images to have different sizes. These two chromatic aberrations seriously impair the image quality, and one must investigate ways in which their effects may be eliminated or, at any rate, reduced. It should be noted that a purely reflecting system will exhibit no chromatic errors of any kind, and, in view of this fact, reflecting systems start off with an inherent advantage over refracting systems.

Consider the refractive index of a medium at two wavelengths B and R. These letters are chosen for the following reason: in the visible spectrum, the blue end corresponds to the shorter wavelengths and the red end to the longer wavelengths. Thus, while the two wavelengths considered here need not correspond to blue and red light, it is convenient to use the letters B and R to serve as a reminder of which is the shorter of the two. In the same way it is convenient to denote an intermediate wavelength by Y (corresponding to yellow light). With the usual notation, the focal lengths of a thin lens for these three wavelengths are given by

$$\frac{1}{f_B{}'}=(n_B-1)R, \qquad \frac{1}{f_Y{}'}=(n_Y-1)R, \qquad \frac{1}{f_R{}'}=(n_R-1)R,$$

where
$$R=\frac{1}{r_1}-\frac{1}{r_2}.$$

Hence
$$\frac{1}{f_B{}'}-\frac{1}{f_R{}'}=(n_B-n_R)R$$

or
$$\frac{f_R{}'-f_B{}'}{f_B{}'f_R{}'}=(n_B-n_R)R.$$

If $f_B{}'$, $f_Y{}'$, and $f_R{}'$, are not widely different, one may write $f_Y{}'^2$ for $f_B{}'f_R{}'$, so that one has

$$\frac{f_R{}'-f_B{}'}{f_Y{}'}=(n_B-n_R)Rf_Y{}'=\frac{(n_B-n_R)}{n_Y-1}. \qquad \cdots \quad (3\text{–}8)$$

The quantity $\dfrac{n_B-n_R}{n_Y-1}$ is called the *dispersive power* of the medium between wavelengths B and R. Its reciprocal is denoted by V and sometimes is referred to as the *constringence*. It will be seen from (3–8) that the dispersive power of the material of a single thin lens measures the chromatic difference of focal length as a fraction of the mean focal length $f_Y{}'$.

It will be seen below that if it is possible to make lenses of materials which have different dispersive powers, it is possible for the combination of two thin lenses in contact to have the same focal length for two wavelengths. Newton thought that all media had the same dispersive power and therefore thought such a combination was impossible.

3–9. The Thin Achromatic Doublet

Consider two thin lenses in contact. Denote quantities that refer to the separate lenses by suffixes 1 and 2. The powers of the combination for wavelengths B and R are given by

$$F_B=(n_{1B}-1)R_1+(n_{2B}-1)R_2,$$
$$F_R=(n_{1R}-1)R_1+(n_{2R}-1)R_2.$$

If $F_B = F_R$ the combination is said to be *achromatized* for these two wavelengths. Thus for an achromatic combination

$$R_1(n_{1B} - n_{1R}) + R_2(n_{2B} - n_{2R}) = 0,$$

$$\therefore \quad \frac{R_1(n_{1Y} - 1)}{V_1} + \frac{R_2(n_{2Y} - 1)}{V_2} = 0$$

or

$$\frac{F_{1Y}}{V_1} + \frac{F_{2Y}}{V_2} = 0. \quad \cdots \cdots \cdots \quad (3\text{–}9)$$

But

$$F_{1Y} + F_{2Y} = F_Y, \quad \cdots \cdots \cdots \quad (3\text{–}10)$$

where F_Y is the power of the combination for the intermediate wavelength Y.

If V_1 and V_2 are different, these two equations may be satisfied. (If $V_1 = V_2$, then the equations can be satisfied only if $F_Y = 0$.)

It follows that

$$\left. \begin{aligned} F_{1Y} &= F_Y \left(\frac{V_1}{V_1 - V_2} \right), \\ F_{2Y} &= -F_Y \left(\frac{V_2}{V_1 - V_2} \right). \end{aligned} \right\} \quad \cdots \cdots \quad (3\text{–}11)$$

If it is desired to make a combination of given power F_Y using lenses whose materials are characterized by V_1 and V_2, then equations (3–11) give the necessary powers of the components. It must be pointed out at once that the combination is not completely free from chromatic aberration but is achromatic for the two wavelengths B and R which are used in calculating V_1 and V_2. The focal lengths for other wavelengths will be different, and this residual chromatic error is referred to as the *secondary spectrum*.

In the earlier days there were only two main glass types: *crown* and *flint*. A typical pair had refractive indices and V-numbers of about 1·52 and 60, and 1·63 and 35, where the refractive indices are for the Helium d ($\lambda 5876$) line and the V-numbers involve the hydrogen C ($\lambda 6563$) and F ($\lambda 4861$) lines for the "red" and "blue". Using these glasses for a doublet of unit power achromatized for the C and F lines, one has

$$F_{1d} = +2\text{·}4,$$
$$F_{2d} = -1\text{·}4.$$

A doublet achromatized in this way for wavelengths in the red and blue regions has approximately constant focal length over an appreciable range of wavelengths in the middle of the visible spectrum where the eye is most sensitive (see Fig. 16–15, p. 367). There is now a wide range of glass types, the importance of which will be seen in Chapter XVI.

Roughly speaking, glasses which have low dispersions (i.e. high V-numbers) are referred to as crowns and those with high dispersions as flints. However, an achromatic combination may consist of two nominal "crowns" or two "flints" as long as the dispersive powers are *different*. In such a case it is usual to refer to the component having the smaller dispersion as the crown and the other as the flint. It follows from equations (3–11) that for an achromatic doublet of positive power the crown component is of positive, and the flint of negative power. If the adjacent surfaces are given equal curvatures, the components may be cemented together. Many telescopes, low power microscopes, and cheap photographic objectives, consist of doublets (see §§16-8 to 16-11).

3-10. Two Separated Thin Lenses of the Same Material

It is possible to achromatize a system consisting of two separated thin lenses, even when the lenses are made from the same glass. If the lenses are in air the focal length of the combination is given by

$$\frac{1}{f'} = \frac{1}{f_1'} + \frac{1}{f_2'} - \frac{d}{f_1'f_2'}$$

$$= (n-1)R_1 + (n-1)R_2 - d(n-1)^2 R_1 R_2$$

$$\therefore \quad \frac{\partial(1/f')}{\partial n} = R_1 + R_2 - 2d(n-1)R_1 R_2$$

$$= 0 \text{ if } f' \text{ is to be stationary.}$$

$$\therefore \quad R_1 + R_2 = 2d(n-1)R_1 R_2$$

$$\therefore \quad R_1(n-1) + R_2(n-1) = 2d(n-1)R_1(n-1)R_2$$

or
$$\frac{1}{f_1'} + \frac{1}{f_2'} = \frac{f_1' + f_2'}{f_1'f_2'} = \frac{2d}{f_1'f_2'}$$

$$\therefore \quad d = \frac{f_1' + f_2'}{2}. \quad \cdot \quad \cdot \quad \cdot \quad \cdot \quad \cdot \quad (3\text{–}12)$$

If (3-12) is satisfied the focal length of the combination is stationary, but this does not mean that the system can be made entirely free from chromatic error. f_1' and f_2' are different for different wavelengths and hence the lenses can be given the correct separation for only one wavelength; it is only at this wavelength that the focal length of the combination is rendered stationary, and there is a secondary spectrum similar to that described in §16-6.

In view of the discussion of the simple microscope in §3-6 it might be thought that by using the above system one obtains a simple microscope or eyepiece whose magnifying power is achromatized. However, (3-4) holds provided the object is in the focal plane, and the magnifying power would be achromatized only if both f' and the *actual position* of the focal plane were achromatized. But the actual position of the focal plane is not achromatized.

When an eyepiece is used in a compound instrument such as an astronomical telescope, the image-forming rays are obviously restricted to those that pass through the objective (which is the aperture stop and entrance pupil). Only these pencils can enter the eye to enable it to view the primary image with the eyepiece. Now, when an image-forming pencil enters the observer's eye, the direction in which the image appears is determined by the direction of the principal ray of the pencil. The image quality depends on the surrounding rays. Suppose, in the present problem, the principal rays of the pencils are parallel to the axis when entering the eyepiece. Then, if the latter is achromatized for focal length, the angle of emergence of the principal rays is achromatized ($u' = y/f'$). This corresponds to an entrance pupil at infinity, so that (3-12) is the condition for achromatism of the magnifying power. For eyepieces used under different conditions the achromatism condition differs from (3-12).

In practice, many instruments are quite long and there is an approach to the conditions described above. The chromatic difference of magnification introduced by the eyepiece is then small if it consists of two thin lenses separated by half the sum of their focal lengths. It may be noted that for a thin achromatic doublet one may neglect the chromatic differences in the cardinal points and, in particular, for an objective consisting of a thin achromatic doublet which is also the aperture stop, one can say that the image position is achromatized and no chromatic difference of magnification is introduced.

(a)   (b)

Fig. 3–11. Achromatism.

Suppose a system consisting of two separated thin lenses is free from both chromatic aberrations for "red" and "blue" light. Then both "red" and "blue" rays must intersect the axis at the same point; in addition, if the initial and final media are non-dispersing, Helmholtz's equation shows that in order to secure freedom from chromatic difference of magnification they must emerge at equal angles u'. This means that the final paths of the "red" and "blue" rays must coincide, and the two rays must emerge from the second lens at the same height. It is at once evident from Fig. 3–11(a) that *this can occur only if each thin lens is itself achromatic*.

In the case of three separated thin lenses, however, the emergent "red" and "blue" rays may coincide even if the separate lenses are not achromatic. The paths in the system are as shown in Fig. 3–11(b). In this case there is a diverging lens between two converging lenses, the separations of the lenses being determined by the dispersive powers involved.

3–11. Huygens and Ramsden Eyepieces

Since many telescopes and microscopes are quite long, it follows from what has been said above that the chromatic difference of magnification introduced by the eyepiece is small if it consists of two thin lenses separated by half the sum of their focal lengths. Two simple eyepieces in common use employ this principle. They are the *Huygens* and *Ramsden* eyepieces, and each consists of two plano-convex lenses arranged so as to minimize the aberrations. Fig. 3–12(a) shows a Huygens eyepiece, it being

Fig. 3–12. Cardinal points of eyepieces. (a) Huygens. (b) Ramsden.

assumed that the objective lies to the left. That is, the plane surfaces of the eyepiece lenses are towards the eye. The lens nearer the eye, which is known as the *eye lens*, usually has a focal length about half that of the other component.

Suppose that $f_1'=2f_2'=2$. Then, for achromatism of the focal length, $d=3/2$. The focal length of the combination is given by

$$f'=\frac{f_1'f_2'}{f_1'+f_2'-d}=\frac{4}{3}$$

and for the positions of the principal planes one has

$$AP=\frac{df_1'}{f_1'+f_2'-d}=2,$$

$$BP'=-\frac{df_2'}{f_1'+f_2'-d}=-1.$$

In the Ramsden eyepiece [Fig. 3–12(*b*)] the convex surfaces of the components face each other, and the lenses have equal focal lengths. If $f_1'=f_2'=1$, the condition for achromatism gives $d=1$ and one has, in addition, $f'=1$, $AP=1$, $BP'=-1$. The principal and focal points of each eyepiece are shown in the figures.

3–12. The Optical Systems of Telescopes and Microscopes

A simple achromatic doublet serves as an objective for a wide range of telescopes—from astronomical to small laboratory instruments such as those

Fig. 3–13. Passage of rays through eyepieces. (*a*) Huygens. (*b*) Ramsden.

incorporated in spectrometers. Figs 3–13(*a*) and (*b*) show the paths of the image-forming pencils through telescopes employing Huygens and Ramsden eyepieces. In each case the first principal focus of the eyepiece coincides with the second principal focus of the objective. It will be seen that with a Huygens eyepiece the intermediate image is formed between the eyepiece lenses, and that with the Ramsden it coincides with the first lens. Since with a Ramsden eyepiece each image-forming pencil is focused on the first lens, all the rays in a given pencil have the same incidence height and, therefore, are deviated through the same angle. (Deviation$=Fy$.) That is to say, the first lens does not affect the position of the image points. However, the presence of the lens is important because, without it, the pencils would pass more eccentrically through the eye lens and the latter would need to have a larger diameter. A lens that coincides with an intermediate image is known as a *field lens*. In the Huygens eyepiece, the first lens is a considerable distance from the intermediate image and affects the image. However, it does behave as a field lens in the sense that it directs the pencils through the inner zones of the eye lens, and for this reason it is usually referred to as the field lens.

It will be seen that the field lens is in focus when one makes observations through a Ramsden eyepiece. This is a nuisance because any dust that settles on the lens, or any scratches that are made on its surface, appear in focus also. To overcome this it is customary to reduce the separation between the lenses— the focal plane then lies outside the eyepiece. The chromatic correction is less good if the separation of the lenses is reduced but this disadvantage is outweighed by the advantage of having an external focal plane. The freedom from chromatic difference of magnification makes the Huygens eyepiece preferable for visual observations when there is no eyepiece scale.

If a telescope is to be used as a measuring instrument, a graduated scale is placed in the plane in which the intermediate image is formed. With a Huygens eyepiece both lenses are used to view the object but only the eye lens would be used to view the eyepiece scale. Now, although the complete instrument may give a good final image of the object, the eye lens alone does not give a good image of the scale. This may be expressed in another way: the scale is used to measure the size of the intermediate image and, when a Huygens eyepiece is used, this image is of poor quality and cannot be the subject of an accurate measurement. It will be seen that a Huygens eyepiece is not satisfactory if an eyepiece scale is employed. With a Ramsden eyepiece the scale is viewed through the complete eyepiece and can be imaged more clearly. In order to be able to see the scale and the object in focus together

Fig. 3–14. The microscope system.

it is obviously necessary for the intermediate image to be of good quality; image and scale are then viewed with a corrected eyepiece. For more accurate work the simple eyepiece scale is sometimes replaced by a fine wire which can be moved across the image plane by means of a micrometer screw. Such an arrangement is known as a *micrometer eyepiece*. If the telescope carries a simple cross-wire and no eyepiece scale (as in a spectrometer telescope, for example) one requires good definition in the centre of the field of view only. The Ramsden eyepiece is certainly the better.

A Huygens eyepiece is usually employed in microscopes but the objective may be very complex (see §§16–9 and 16–12). High-power microscopes must be equipped with an additional lens system in order to concentrate light on to the object. When the object is not opaque, the extra system is placed on the far side of the slide, co-axial with the objective and eyepiece; it is referred to as the *substage condenser*. Fig. 3–14 represents the system of a typical microscope.

As with telescopes, a scale can be placed in the plane of the intermediate image.

This is satisfactory if the object to be measured can be contained within the field of view of the microscope. Again one should use a Ramsden eyepiece, but one often finds a Huygens eyepiece employed. If the object more than fills the field of view of the instrument, its diameter may be measured by moving the whole microscope and bringing the extremities of the object to the centre of the field in turn. Only a simple cross-wire is required in the focal plane of the eyepiece and a Huygens type is frequently employed because the cross-wire, which is easily damaged, is then enclosed within the eyepiece. The movement of the microscope is measured with the aid of either a vernier or a micrometer screw arrangement. It must be remembered that an eyepiece scale simply gives a measure of the size of the intermediate image and, in order to find the size of the object, one must determine the primary magnification of the instrument. That is to say, one must calibrate the eyepiece scale by viewing a mm. or divided mm. scale; this gives the number of divisions of the eyepiece scale that correspond to 1 mm. in the object plane.

3–13. Terrestrial Telescopes

Most telescopes encountered in physics laboratories are astronomical telescopes. These are of little use in everyday terrestrial observations since the image is inverted. An erect image may be obtained by employing an additional lens system or by using erecting prisms. The action of an *erecting eyepiece* is illustrated in Fig. 3–15. The diaphragm D is conjugate to the aperture stop and helps to reduce stray light.

Fig. 3–15. An erecting eyepiece.

The use of an additional pair of convex lenses in the erecting system has certain very serious disadvantages associated with the aberrations of the instrument (see Chapter XVI) and, in addition, the telescope is made considerably longer.

Fig. 3–16. Action of erecting prisms.

Fig. 3–16 represents the path of the principal rays through a telescope objective forming the inverted image $I_1'I_2'$ of an object I_1I_2. Suppose a right-angled isosceles prism is interposed as shown. The paths of the principal rays will be changed as indicated but the image points $I_1''I_2''$ will still lie on the respective principal rays. It will be seen that the prism has introduced an inversion so that the image is rendered erect. The original image $I_1'I_2'$ formed by the lens is also

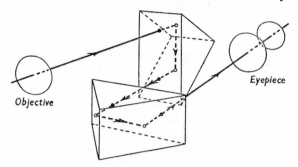

Fig. 3–17. Arrangement of erecting prisms.

reversed left to right, and this latter reversal is not removed by the prism. If, however, a second prism is introduced as indicated in Fig. 3–17, the necessary reversal is secured without interfering with the inversion produced by the first prism. In addition, the final direction of the light is the same as the original. Prism systems of this and similar types are employed in prismatic binocular telescopes and possess distinct advantages over erecting eyepieces.

3–14. Reflecting Systems

Newton supposed that all materials had the same dispersive power and concluded that it was impossible to remove the chromatic aberration of a refracting system. Now the law of reflection does not involve the refractive index, so that a purely reflecting system can give no chromatic aberration. Consequently,

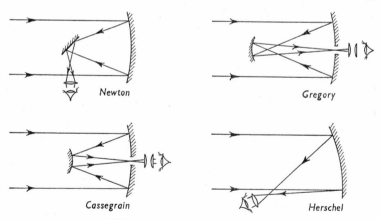

Fig. 3–18. Reflecting telescopes.

many reflecting systems were devised. With the discovery of the possibility of an achromatic lens, interest in reflecting systems decreased, and attention was again focused on refracting systems. Recently, however, there has been a renewed interest in reflecting instruments; some of the later developments are described in §16–13. In the present section a brief description will be given of some of the older reflecting instruments. The chief difficulty encountered is the fact that the direction of the light is reversed at the first mirror so that subsequent optical components constitute an obstruction of the initial incident rays. In particular, the observer's head in a visual instrument, or the plate holder in a photographic instrument, must be placed in such a position as to cause the minimum possible obstruction. The various instruments differ in their methods of reducing these obstructing effects. The telescopes due to Newton, Gregory, Cassegrain, and Herschel, are illustrated in Fig. 3–18. Newton's and Herschel's telescopes are similar in the sense that each consists of a single concave mirror plus an eyepiece. In order to make the image accessible Newton employed a plane mirror and Herschel tilted the concave mirror.

Fig. 3–19. Reflecting microscope.

Newton also suggested the use of a concave mirror as a microscope objective. Amici used an objective which resembled a Newtonian telescope objective in reverse; he viewed the magnified primary image with an eyepiece in the usual way (see Fig. 3–19).

Most of the earlier reflectors were of speculum metal (an alloy of 67% copper and 33% tin) but current practice is to use glass surfaces coated with a suitable metal film.

CHAPTER IV

THE DETERMINATION OF THE PARAXIAL CONSTANTS OF OPTICAL SYSTEMS

I. SIMPLE METHODS FOR MIRRORS AND THIN LENSES

4–1. Neutralization Test for the Power of a Thin Lens

IT was seen in Chapters I and II that the power of two thin lenses in contact is simply the sum of the powers of the separate lenses. Consequently, if two thin lenses having equal and opposite powers are placed in contact, the combination has zero power. A spectacle trial case as used by ophthalmic opticians contains a set of thin lenses whose powers vary from $\pm\frac{1}{4}$ to about ±12 dioptres. Consequently, an approximate value for the power of an unknown lens can be obtained by selecting a lens from the trial case which, when placed in contact with the unknown lens, gives zero power.

Fig. 4–1. The displacement test for the power of a lens.

In order to decide whether the combination has positive, negative, or zero power, it is moved up and down immediately in front of the eye whilst viewing a distant object. It will be observed that the object appears to move. If the lens has negative power (i.e. is a diverging lens) the movement is in the same direction as the movement of the lens, whereas for a positive lens the two movements are in opposite directions. For a combination of zero power there is no apparent movement of the object. The reason for this movement lies in the prismatic effect of a decentred lens and is illustrated in Fig. 4–1. When the power of the combination is numerically small, increased sensitivity may be obtained by holding the lenses farther away from the eye.

4–2. Location of Object and Image

The lens or mirror can be used to form an image of some convenient object, the object and image distances measured, and equations (1–13) or (1–7) used to calculate the focal length. The image of a pin (either real or virtual) may be located by a no-parallax adjustment. For converging systems a real image may be received on a screen. It is assumed that the reader is familiar with these elementary methods.

4–3. Simple Object and Image Coincidence Methods

The radius of curvature of a concave mirror is easily found by using the fact that the object and image coincide when the object is at the centre of curvature. It will be seen from Fig. 4-2 that a similar adjustment is possible using:

(a) A concave mirror.
(b) A plane mirror and a convex lens.
(c) A convex mirror and lens.
(d) A concave mirror and lens.
(e) A convex and a concave lens with a plane mirror.

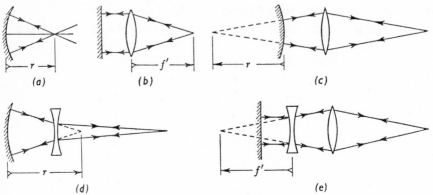

Fig. 4-2. Object and image coincidence methods.

It is obvious that if the focal length of one component in (c), (d), or (e), is known, the other can be found. It should be noted that in (c) the radius of curvature of the mirror must be shorter, and in (d) longer, than the focal length of the lens. If in (e) the lenses are in contact, the method yields the sum of their powers.

4-4. Refractive Index of a Lens

Equation (1–7) shows that if the radii of curvature and the focal length of a lens are known the refractive index may be calculated. Any of the above methods may be used to determine the focal length. The radii of curvature may then be determined fairly easily. Consider the case of a double convex lens [Fig. 4–3(a)]. Suppose rays from the point source B are incident normally on the second surface. The rays then emerge without refraction at that surface and the virtual image point B′ will coincide with the centre of curvature of the second surface C_2. For a thin lens the image distance is given by $l'=r_2$ so that, from equation (1–7),

$$\frac{1}{r_2} - \frac{1}{l} = \frac{1}{f'}, \qquad \cdots \cdots \cdots \quad (4\text{–}1)$$

where, in the figure, r_2 and l are negative. It is easy to decide when the rays do, in fact, emerge along the normal to the second surface. As always, some light is internally reflected and under these circumstances it must retrace its path to B so that a faint image will be seen coincident with the object. Thus, in practice, the object distance is varied until this image is observed and equation (4–1) applied. It should be noted that when using the plane mirror method to find the focal length of a convex lens one is liable to confuse the image formed by internal reflection with that formed after reflection by the mirror. The latter will, of course, disappear if the mirror is removed.

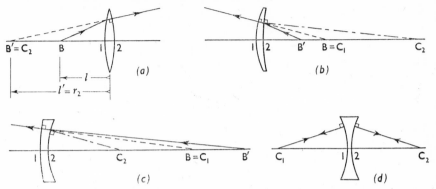

Fig. 4-3. Determination of radii of curvature.

Similar conditions obtain in the case of meniscus lenses. For each meniscus lens there is one surface, and for a double concave lens there are two surfaces, which can be treated as separate concave mirrors [Fig. 4-3(*b–d*)].

4-5. The Liquid Lens

If, in the plane mirror method for a convex lens, the space between the lens and mirror is filled with liquid, the latter constitutes another lens [see Fig. 4-4(*a*)]. The focal length as given by this method will correspond to the combination of liquid lens and glass lens in contact. If the focal length of the glass

Fig. 4-4. Liquid lenses.

lens is known, that of the liquid lens follows from equation (1-12) for two thin lenses in contact, and if the radius r_1 is known, the refractive index of the liquid follows from equation (1-7) since the liquid lens has one face plane.

The refractive index of a liquid may also be found by using a concave mirror as in Fig. 4-4(*b*). From the figure it is seen that a point B may be found where the object and image coincide and the refractive index of the liquid is given by

$$n = \frac{i}{i'} = \frac{r}{l}.$$

II. ACCURATE MEASUREMENT OF RADII OF CURVATURE

4-6. The Spherometer

In Fig. 4–5(a) AB ($=2\varrho$) is the diameter of a "small circle" on the surface of the sphere, centre C, radius r which it is required to find. If the pole P of the sphere is distance h above the plane of the small circle

$$(r-h)^2+\varrho^2=r^2,$$

whence
$$r=\frac{\varrho^2+h^2}{2h}. \quad \cdots \cdots \quad (4\text{-}2)$$

$$r=\frac{\varrho^2+h^2}{2h}$$

$$=\frac{a^2}{6h}+\frac{h}{2}$$

(a)   (b)

Fig. 4–5. The spherometer formulae.

In the ring spherometer shown in Fig. 4–6 an accurately ground metal ring of known radius ϱ fits on to the spherical surface to be measured. The distance h is

measured with a micrometer screw or a spring-loaded plunger whose movement is recorded on a calibrated scale. h is found as the difference between the readings of the screw or plunger scale when the instrument rests on a plane surface and on the surface to be measured. The method applies equally well to convex or concave surfaces which employ the inner and outer radii of the ring respectively. In a common form of spherometer the metal ring is replaced by the tips of three legs located at the vertices of an equilateral triangle. The micrometer screw then moves along the axis of the circumcircle of the

Fig. 4–6. The ring spherometer.

triangle and the radius ϱ now refers to this circumcircle. If a is the distance between adjacent legs of the spherometer it is easily shown that $a=\varrho\sqrt{3}$ [see Fig. 4–5(b)].

$$\therefore \quad r=\frac{a^2}{6h}+\frac{h}{2}. \quad \cdots \cdots \quad (4\text{-}3)$$

If the tips of the legs are ground to a point, the same value of a is used for convex or concave surfaces.

4–7. Microscope Method for Short Radii

For radii of curvature not larger than about 3–4 cm. the best method is probably that illustrated by Fig. 4–7. Light from the source enters the Gauss eyepiece (see §5–5) as shown, and it will be seen from the figure that for either a convex or a concave mirror there are two positions of the mirror which give an image of the cross-wires coincident with the cross-wires themselves. The distance between these positions gives the radius of curvature of the mirror in each case.

4–8. The Knife-Edge Method for Concave Surfaces

This method is particularly useful for shallow surfaces where the quantity h in the spherometer method is very small and therefore difficult to measure with sufficient accuracy. The arrangement is illustrated in Fig. 4–8(a) and consists of a knife edge which can move in the plane of the blade and in a direction perpendicular to the edge, an illuminated pinhole being located in the plane traced out by the knife edge. Suppose the principal axis of the mirror passes approximately midway between the knife edge and the pinhole. If the latter is closer to the mirror than the centre of curvature its image will lie beyond the knife edge as in (b). The opposite conditions are shown in (c).   If the eye is placed just behind the knife edge so as to receive the light from the mirror, the latter will appear to be evenly illuminated. If the knife edge is now moved across the line of sight, a shadow will be seen to cross the mirror from A to B for the condition shown in (b),

Fig. 4–7.
Measurement
of short radii.

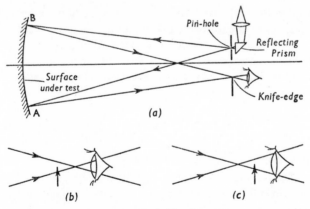

Fig. 4–8. The knife-edge test.

or from B to A for the condition shown in (c). If, however, the centre of curvature lies exactly in the plane of the pinhole and the knife edge, the whole aperture of the mirror will suddenly darken as the knife edge crosses the image of the pinhole. In this way the centre of curvature can be located very accurately.

The whole aperture of the mirror will not darken at exactly the same instant if the mirror is not truly spherical, and the shadow pattern across the mirror yields information concerning the state of perfection of the sphericity and optical polish of the surface. This method of examining the form of a mirror surface is discussed further in § 14–17; it was first used by Foucault in 1859.

4–9. Shallow Surfaces (Convex and Concave)

Consider first the case of a convex surface. A rectangular aperture of width *l* is placed in contact with the surface to be measured (see Fig. 4–9). The eye (or

Fig. 4–9. Measurement of shallow surfaces.

the objective of an observing telescope) is placed at O and the scale S viewed by reflection at the surface. Suppose the length L of the scale is visible. Then the extreme rays are as shown and, from similar triangles if D is large,

$$\frac{l}{r} = \frac{L/2}{r+D},$$

whence

$$r = \frac{2Dl}{L-2l}. \qquad \cdots \cdots \cdots (4\text{--}4)$$

The aperture *l* and the scale S cannot be in focus together, so that if the latter is clear the boundaries of the former are not, and the length L is rather uncertain. This effect can be reduced by placing at O a slit aperture parallel to the rulings of the scale S. This increases the depth of focus of the telescope.

The same method can be used for concave surfaces and the radius is then given by

$$r = \frac{2Dl}{L+2l}. \qquad \cdots \cdots \cdots (4\text{--}5)$$

4–10. Newton's Rings

The radius of curvature of a shallow surface may be measured by observing the interference rings found between it and a known surface. The method will be discussed in Chapter VIII.

III. LOCATION OF THE CARDINAL POINTS OF A THICK LENS OR LENS SYSTEM

4–11. Collimator and Plane Mirror Methods for Principal Foci

By placing a small aperture or pinhole at the principal focus of a well-corrected convex lens, accurately parallel rays are produced. Such a device is called a *collimator,* and the emergent beam is said to be *collimated.* If such parallel rays enter a system parallel to the axis, they will emerge so as to pass through the principal focus which can then be located. Alternatively, the method of so-called *auto-collimation* may be employed which, in principle, is the plane mirror method already referred to in §4–3. In the case of a lens system that is not thin this merely serves to locate the principal focus since the focal length is not simply the distance from the lens to the focus. The knife-edge method may be used to locate the principal focus, but the sudden darkening of the aperture may be upset by the presence of aberrations in the system.

4–12. Location of Principal Planes

Since the principal planes usually lie within the lens system, a real object cannot be placed in one of the planes and a real image received on a screen in the other. By using an auxiliary lens, however, it is possible to project the image

Fig. 4–10. Location of principal planes.

of a scale into any plane within the lens system under test. The image in the conjugate plane can be viewed by means of a low-power microscope. The principal planes may then be located as the planes that give unit magnification. The experimental arrangement is illustrated in Fig. 4–10.

The illuminated object S is imaged at S′ by the auxiliary lens L and the image observed by the low-power microscope M, which contains an eyepiece scale. Suppose the primary image of S′ in the microscope covers n divisions of the eyepiece scale. The lens AB is now interposed as shown and the positions of both AB and M adjusted until the image of S′ again covers n divisions of the eyepiece scale. When this adjustment has been made S′ must lie in the first principal plane of the lens AB and its image S″ in the second principal plane. The microscope is then focused on S″, so that the distance moved by the microscope gives the separation PP′ of the principal planes. (If the principal planes are "crossed", M will have to be moved to the left.) If M is now moved so that dust on the surface B is in focus, the movement of M will give the distance BP′.

Fig. 4–11. The nodal points.

4–13. The Nodal Slide

Consider rays parallel to the axis entering a lens system whose nodal points are N and N′ (Fig. 4–11). Suppose the lens is rotated about N′ so that N rotates to Ñ. The incident rays now constitute an oblique pencil but the emergent rays must still pass through a single image point. Now, the ray incident through N̄ must emerge along N'F' parallel to its direction of incidence. Hence the image point must still lie on N'F', i.e. it does not move laterally. Therefore if a collimated beam enters a lens system, the second nodal point can be located as the point about which rotation of the lens system produces no lateral shift of the image point.

The nodal slide consists of a lens holder in which the lens can be moved along its own axis, the holder itself being capable of rotation about a vertical axis

Fig. 4–12. Auto-collimation method.

which intersects the optical axis of the lens system. By mounting the lens in the nodal slide it is possible to make the adjustment indicated above. Instead of employing a separate collimator, the method of auto-collimation can be employed. A plan of the arrangement is shown in Fig. 4–12. The position of the source S is arranged so that its image S' lies alongside and the position of the lens in the nodal slide is adjusted until rotation about the vertical axis produces no lateral movement of S'. The vertical axis of rotation then passes through the second nodal point N'.

In principle, the same method may be used to find the radius of curvature of a mirror, in which case the nodal points coincide with the centre of curvature. The method is useful for convex mirrors and in that case a real object gives a virtual image which may be observed with a low-power microscope. If the centre of curvature of the mirror lies on the axis of rotation of the nodal slide, the image will obviously remain stationary [see Fig. 4–13(a)]. The mirror is then

Fig. 4–13. Use of nodal slide for mirrors.

moved along the slide parallel to its principal axis until dust particles at the pole of the mirror remain stationary during rotation about the vertical axis [see Fig. 4–13(b)]. The distance moved by the mirror gives the radius of curvature.

IV. INDIRECT DETERMINATION OF FOCAL LENGTH

If the principal planes are known, a simple determination of the object and image distances l and l' will enable the focal length of a system to be calculated. Similarly, if the focal planes are known for a system in air, the focal length may be found from a single determination of the object and image distances x and x'. For a system in air Newton's equation becomes

$$xx' = -f'^2.$$

4–14. Magnification Methods

For a lens system in air

$$\frac{1}{l'} - \frac{1}{l} = \frac{1}{f'}$$

and since the nodal and principal planes coincide the magnification m is simply given by l'/l.

Hence

$$1 - m = \frac{l'}{f'}$$

or

$$l' = f' - f'm. \quad \ldots \ldots \ldots \quad (4\text{–}6)$$

If the magnification is found for two image positions, one has

$$l_1' = f' - f'm_1,$$
$$l_2' = f' - f'm_2,$$
$$\therefore \quad l_1' - l_2' = f'(m_2 - m_1).$$

Hence one needs only the movement of the image plane, and it is not necessary to know the positions of the principal planes. Alternatively, if l' is plotted against m, f' may be found from the slope of the resulting straight line or the intercept on the l' axis. Actually l' cannot be measured unless the position of the second principal plane is known. However, if a scale is fixed along the axis of the lens and C is the reading of the second principal plane, then the scale reading S at the image position will be $(l' + C)$. Equation (4–6) then becomes

$$S - C = f' - f'm$$

or

$$S = -f'm + f' + C, \quad \ldots \ldots \ldots \quad (4\text{–}7)$$

so that *if the lens is not moved* a graph of S against m is also a straight line of slope $-f'$; the position of the second principal plane is not needed in order to find f', but it can be found from the intercept if f' has been found from the slope.

Fig. 4–14. Use of virtual object.

In order to apply this method to a diverging system it is necessary to employ a virtual object as indicated in Fig. 4–14. The object B is imaged at B′ by the auxiliary lens L_1, and the diameter of the image measured. The lens under test (L_2) is then interposed as shown so that B′ becomes a virtual object. Provided $L_2B' < f_2$ a real image B″ is formed and the magnification may be determined.

To change the magnification L_2 must be moved so that in equation (4–7) C is no longer constant. This difficulty is most easily overcome by rewriting the equation in terms of l and m. The movement of L_2 then gives the change in object distance directly.

4–15. The Goniometer

If a scale is placed in the focal plane of a lens system, the image is at infinity and the rays from each object point emerge as a collimated beam. If the object point is a distance h from the axis the collimated beam will be inclined to the axis at an angle $\omega=h/f$, and if this angle can be measured for a given value of

Fig. 4–15. The Searle goniometer.

h, f can be deduced. The goniometer devised by G. F. C. Searle is a simple instrument for measuring this angle, and a plan of the instrument is shown in Fig. 4–15.

It consists of an achromatic objective at whose principal focus a fine vertical wire W is located. The lens and wire are mounted on a wooden base CD capable of rotation about a pivot located beneath the lens. The angle of rotation is measured by recording the linear motion of a pointer P over the scale XY fixed at a known distance from the pivot. CD is adjusted so that the pointer P lies on the zero of the scale XY. The lens L under test is then placed as shown and the scale S adjusted to be in the focal plane by observing when there is no parallax between its image and W. The reading of S is taken in this position and CD rotated until a second point of S is imaged at W. The reading on the scale XY determines the angle ω, and the difference between the readings of the scale S gives the object height h. The focal length of the lens L may then be found.

4–16. Magnifying Power of a Telescope

The most obvious method for finding the magnifying power of a telescope is that of direct comparison. The object viewed directly with one eye is compared with the image viewed through the telescope with the other eye. Many observers have difficulty in making this measurement, and for small terrestrial telescopes the following method is better. It was seen in §§2–11 and 3–3 that a telescopic system forms a finite image of a finite object and that the transverse magnification is the same for all object positions and is equal to the reciprocal of the magnifying power if the indices in the object and image spaces are equal. The magnifying power may therefore be found by finding the transverse magnification for any convenient object. Usually it is convenient to place a scale in front of the objective (which is usually the entrance pupil) and measure the image by means of a low-power microscope. Even if the telescope is focused for viewing a finite object (i.e. is not truly telescopic), the above method is applicable if the object is located in the entrance pupil. This is because the magnifying power can be taken as the angular magnification for the pupil planes; it is the inverse of the transverse magnification for these conjugates if $n=n'$.

4–17. Magnifying Power of a Microscope

The magnifying power of a microscope can be found by measuring the focal lengths of the objective and the eyepiece and applying equation (3–7). It is

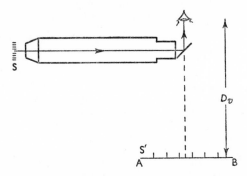

Fig. 4–16. Magnifying power of a microscope.

possible to measure M directly by the method illustrated by Fig. 4–16. A transparent scale S is observed through the microscope via the semi-reflecting plate. (A cover glass forms a suitable reflector.) Assuming that the image is brought to the least distance of distinct vision, a sheet of paper AB is placed a similar distance from the eye. The image S' as seen on AB is then traced with a pencil and the sizes of S' and S compared to give M.

CHAPTER V

PRISMATIC INSTRUMENTS FOR REFRACTOMETRY AND SPECTROSCOPY

5–1. Refraction Through a Prism

IN optics, a prism is a transparent body, two of whose boundaries are non-parallel planes. The nature and shape of the other boundaries do not matter for optical purposes, although the prisms encountered are frequently right prisms

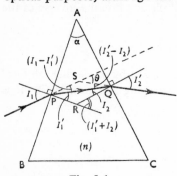

Fig. 5–1.
Path of a ray through a prism.

on triangular bases. The angle included between the plane boundaries or *refracting faces* is the *refracting angle* or simply the *angle of the prism*. The edge along which the refracting faces (produced if necessary) intersect is the *refracting edge*. A plane section of a prism perpendicular to the refracting edge is called a *principal section*. A principal section is perpendicular to both refracting faces so that it follows from Snell's law that a ray incident in a principal section remains in that section during its passage through the prism. The path of a ray

lying in a principal section is shown in Fig. 5–1. Suppose the prism is of index n, has refracting angle α, and is in air. The angle θ between the initial and final directions of the ray is the angle of deviation. It can be shown that θ is a minimum if $I_1=I_2'$, i.e. if the ray travels through the prism symmetrically. If the section of the prism is an isosceles triangle, the ray path in the prism is parallel to the base.

In the figure $\angle APR = \angle AQR = 90°$. Hence APRQ is a cyclic quadrilateral.

$$\therefore \quad \alpha \equiv I_1' + I_2. \quad \ldots \ldots \ldots \quad (5\text{–}1)$$

$\triangle$PSQ gives
$$\theta = I_1 - I_1' + I_2' - I_2,$$

$$\therefore \quad \theta + \alpha = I_1 + I_2'. \quad \ldots \ldots \ldots \quad (5\text{–}2)$$

In addition, Snell's law gives

$$\left. \begin{array}{l} \sin I_1 = n \sin I_1', \\ \sin I_2' = n \sin I_2. \end{array} \right\} \quad \ldots \ldots \ldots \quad (5\text{–}3)$$

Adding the last two equations,

$$\sin I_1 + \sin I_2' = n(\sin I_1' + \sin I_2),$$

i.e. $\quad 2 \sin \tfrac{1}{2}(I_1 + I_2') \cos \tfrac{1}{2}(I_1 - I_2') = n[2 \sin \tfrac{1}{2}(I_1' + I_2) \cos \tfrac{1}{2}(I_1' - I_2)]$

or, from (5–1) and (5–2),

$$\sin \tfrac{1}{2}(\theta + \alpha) = n \sin \tfrac{1}{2}\alpha \cdot \frac{\cos \tfrac{1}{2}(I_1' - I_2)}{\cos \tfrac{1}{2}(I_1 - I_2')}.$$

Suppose $I_2' > I_1$. Then the deviation at the second surface is greater than that at the first surface,

i.e. $$I_2' - I_2 > I_1 - I_1',$$

$$\therefore \quad I_2' - I_1 > I_2 - I_1'.$$

Remembering that $\cos(-x) = \cos x$, it follows that

$$\cos \tfrac{1}{2}(I_1' - I_2) > \cos \tfrac{1}{2}(I_1 - I_2').$$

Similarly, if $I_2' < I_1$, it follows that

$$I_1 - I_1' > I_2' - I_2,$$

$$\therefore \quad I_1 - I_2' > I_1' - I_2$$

and again,

$$\cos \tfrac{1}{2}(I_1' - I_2) > \cos \tfrac{1}{2}(I_1 - I_2').$$

Hence, if $I_2' \neq I_1$,

$$\sin \tfrac{1}{2}(\theta + \alpha) > n \sin \tfrac{1}{2}\alpha.$$

However, if $I_2' = I_1$,

$$\sin \tfrac{1}{2}(\theta + \alpha) = n \sin \tfrac{1}{2}\alpha.$$

Consequently, $\sin \tfrac{1}{2}(\theta + \alpha)$ reaches a minimum value when $I_2' = I_1$. Now, for a given value of α, $\sin \tfrac{1}{2}(\theta + \alpha)$ reaches its minimum value when θ reaches its minimum value. That is to say, when the angle of deviation is a minimum the light passes symmetrically through the prism and one has

$$n = \frac{\sin \tfrac{1}{2}(\theta + \alpha)}{\sin \tfrac{1}{2}\alpha}. \quad \cdot \quad \cdot \quad \cdot \quad \cdot \quad \cdot \quad \cdot \quad (5\text{-}4)$$

Consider the case where α is large. The angle I_2 is reduced to a minimum if I_1' is a maximum (see (5-1)). The maximum possible value of I_1' is the critical angle and there is then grazing incidence at the first surface. When α is equal to twice the critical angle there is also grazing emergence. No rays can be transmitted through prisms of larger refracting angle.

5-2. Formation of a Spectrum

Since the refractive index varies with wavelength (see Fig. 20-4) the angle of deviation will also vary with the wavelength of the light involved. Hence if a beam of light enters a prism and contains disturbances of various wavelengths, the emergent beams for different wavelengths will have slightly different directions. However, these beams will overlap so that no clear spectrum is produced. If one has a slit source perpendicular to the principal section of the prism, an eye which views this source through the prism will see a virtual image of the slit for each wavelength. If the light consists of several discrete wavelengths one sees a line spectrum in which each line is an image of the slit; if the light contains all wavelengths within a certain wide range, a continuous spectrum is seen. If a lens is placed before or after the prism to form a real image of the slit, one will get an image for each wavelength so that a real spectrum is produced and may be received on a screen or viewed with an eyepiece (Fig. 5-2).

4*

A spectrum produced in this way is, however, not of good quality. Consider, for example, monochromatic light diverging from a point on the slit. The constituent rays in the divergent cone are incident at different angles on the prism and are therefore deviated through different angles. Hence they are not concurrent when they emerge from the prism. Consequently, no good image of the slit can be formed by the lens. If the prism is at minimum deviation for the

Fig. 5–2. Production of real spectrum.

central ray of the pencil, one may say that, to a first approximation, the neighbouring rays are deviated by the same amount and emerge as concurrent rays; but this approximation is not sufficiently accurate for most purposes. In addition, the prism can be at minimum deviation for only one wavelength, so that for others the slit image will be more imperfect. However, if one uses only one lens as in Fig. 5–2, the best results are obtained by working near minimum deviation.

In order to secure a spectrum of good quality, it is essential that the beams traversing the prism should be collimated. To produce a real spectrum this necessitates the use of two doublets as in Fig. 5–3. (It should be noted that the use of doublets gives an important improvement in the correction of the monochromatic aberrations—see § 16–6.) For all wavelengths, the beams emerging from the prism will still be collimated, although different wavelengths will give beams at different angles. The spectrum is then formed in the focal plane of the

Fig. 5–3. Production of spectrum of good quality.

second lens. With this system it is not necessary to work near minimum deviation.

Rays from the off-axis parts of the slit do not traverse the prism in a principal section. The deviation for these rays is greater than for those in a principal section and this causes the image of the slit to be curved. It is concave in the direction of increased deviation, i.e. towards the short wavelength end of the spectrum.

5–3. Dispersion of a Prism

For a particular angle of incidence, consider the change in θ consequent upon a small change in the wavelength λ. The quantity $d\theta/d\lambda$ is known as the *angular dispersion* of the prism. Now, one may write

$$\frac{d\theta}{d\lambda} = \frac{d\theta}{dn} \cdot \frac{dn}{d\lambda}.$$

The first term on the right-hand side depends on the geometry of the system (i.e. on the angle of incidence and the angle of the prism) and the second is a property of the material of the prism. $d\theta/dn$ is most easily found by the following method due to Rayleigh.

Consider a collimated beam entering a prism. Suppose that the beam includes wavelengths λ and $\lambda+\delta\lambda$ and that these are deviated through angles θ and $\theta+\delta\theta$. In Fig. 5–4, AB represents the incident plane wave for each wavelength

Fig. 5–4. Dispersion of a prism.

and A′B′ the emergent wave for wavelength λ. If $\delta\theta$ is small, the path taken by the extreme rays of the beam between the planes AB and A′B′ is the same for both wavelengths (to the second order approximation) and the emergent wave-front of $\lambda+\delta\lambda$ is A″B′. Consequently, one may equate the optical paths [A to A′] and [B to B′] for λ and [A to A″] and [B to B′] for $\lambda+\delta\lambda$. If the cross-section of the emergent beam is a, A′A″ $\doteqdot a\delta\theta$, and if the edges of the beam have geometrical paths t_1 and t_2 in the prism and the other distances are as indicated in the figure, one has

$$b + nt_1 + d = c + nt_2 + e$$

and

$$b + (n+\delta n)t_1 + d + a\delta\theta = c + (n+\delta n)t_2 + e.$$

By subtraction, this yields

$$\delta nt_1 + a\delta\theta = \delta nt_2$$

or

$$\frac{d\theta}{dn} = \frac{t_2 - t_1}{a}. \qquad \cdot \quad \cdot \quad \cdot \quad \cdot \quad \cdot \quad \cdot \quad (5\text{–}5)$$

If the beam fills an isosceles prism at minimum deviation, this reduces to

$$\frac{d\theta}{dn} = \frac{t}{a},$$

where t is the length of the base of the prism. Hence the angular dispersion is given by

$$\frac{d\theta}{d\lambda} = \frac{t}{a} \cdot \frac{dn}{d\lambda}. \qquad \cdot \quad \cdot \quad \cdot \quad \cdot \quad \cdot \quad \cdot \quad (5\text{–}6)$$

According to Cauchy's formula, the refractive index of most optical materials can be represented by

$$n = A + \frac{B}{\lambda^2},$$

where A and B are numerical constants (see § 20–7). In this case,

$$\frac{dn}{d\lambda} = -\frac{2B}{\lambda^3}$$

and

$$\frac{d\theta}{d\lambda} = -\frac{2t}{a} \cdot \frac{B}{\lambda^3}. \qquad \cdots \cdots \cdots \quad (5\text{--}7)$$

Thus the angular dispersion varies through the spectrum, being greater at the blue (shorter wavelength) end. The negative sign expresses the fact that θ decreases as λ increases.

In general, the dispersion reaches a minimum value for a particular angle of incidence but it should be noted that this does not occur at the position of minimum deviation.

5–4. Thin Prisms. Combinations of Prisms

If the angle of the prism and the angle of incidence are small, equations (5–3) reduce to

$$I_1 = nI_1',$$

$$I_2' = nI_2$$

and (5–1) and (5–2) give

$$\theta = (n-1)\alpha. \qquad \cdots \cdots \cdots \quad (5\text{--}8)$$

Hence for a thin prism the angle of deviation is independent of the angle of incidence provided the latter is small. The angle of deviation is also small under these circumstances and (5–4) reduces to (5–8) immediately. In addition, it follows at once that the angular dispersion of a thin prism is given by

$$\frac{d\theta}{d\lambda} = \alpha \frac{dn}{d\lambda}.$$

Consider the refraction of rays of light of wavelengths λ_B and λ_R which may be widely different. Let n_B and n_R be the refractive indices for these wavelengths and let the two rays enter the prism along the same path. The angular separation of the emergent rays is given [from (5–8)] by

$$\theta_B - \theta_R = (n_B - n_R)\alpha.$$

The deviation for an intermediate wavelength λ_Y is given by

$$\theta_Y = (n_Y - 1)\alpha.$$

It will be seen that the ratio of the dispersion to the mean deviation gives the dispersive power of the material of the prism.

For a number of prisms in series, the total dispersion and total deviation are given by $\Sigma(n_B - n_R)\alpha$ and $\Sigma(n_Y - 1)\alpha$ respectively. It is possible to combine prisms so that either of these quantities is zero. When applying these expressions to a series of prisms, one must regard inverted prisms as prisms with negative angles. For example, in Fig. 5–5 the middle prism has a negative angle.

Fig. 5–5. Direct vision spectroscope.

If one has a pair of prisms such that

$$(n_{1B}-n_{1R})\alpha_1=(n_{2B}-n_{2R})\alpha_2$$

the combination is achromatic and rays whose wavelengths are λ_B and λ_R are equally deviated.

On the other hand, if the ray of mean wavelength λ_Y is to be undeviated one must have

$$(n_{1Y}-1)\alpha_1=(n_{2Y}-1)\alpha_2.$$

In this case there will, in general, be some dispersion. This is the principle of the direct-vision spectroscope. In this instrument, which is usually pocket-sized, the so-called *Amici prism system* often contains two crown and one flint, or three crown and two flint prisms cemented together so that the mean wavelength of the visible spectrum is undeviated (see Fig. 5–5). (It must be remembered that the prisms in this case are not thin.) The light from the slit S is collimated by the lens L and the virtual spectrum viewed by the unaccommodated eye. The spectrum is of good quality since the beams traversing the prism system are collimated.

5–5. The Simple Table Prism Spectrometer

The optical system of the spectrometer is similar to the one already described for producing a spectrum of good quality, the spectrum being viewed by means

Fig. 5–6. The spectrometer.

of an eyepiece. A plan view of the complete optical system is illustrated in Fig. 5–6. C is a collimator consisting of a slit at the principal focus of an achromatic objective. T is a telescope consisting of an achromatic objective and a Ramsden eyepiece which carries cross-wires in its focal plane. The prism P rests on a table, and can be levelled by means of three screws X, Y, and Z. The telescope and prism table can rotate about the axis of the divided circle S. Usually both are fitted with clamps and fine adjustment screws. As the telescope is swung round, the slit image for each wavelength is brought into coincidence with the cross-wires.

In order to obtain a good spectrum and to be able to apply the simple theory for refraction by a prism as given above, it is essential that the collimator and telescope should be adjusted so that parallel light traverses the prism. In addition, the axis of the telescope must remain in the principal section of the prism during rotation; the axis of the collimator also must lie in this plane, and the scale S must be in a parallel plane. These adjustments are not permanent and must be made before using the instrument. A modified eyepiece known as a *Gauss eyepiece* is very useful in making some of these adjustments. This device usually consists of a Ramsden eyepiece to which has been added a thin

Fig. 5-7. The Gauss eyepiece.

parallel-sided plate of glass (see Fig. 5–7). Light enters through an aperture in the eyepiece tube and is reflected down the axis of the telescope. Suppose that the cross-wires are at the foci of the objective and eyepiece. An eye placed in the usual viewing position will see the cross-wires illuminated, and if a plane reflecting surface is located beyond the telescope objective and is perpendicular to the optical axis, an image of the cross-wires will be seen alongside the cross-wires themselves. Such an eyepiece enables the telescope to be focused and to be placed with its axis perpendicular to a plane surface since it is only when these adjustments have been made that the image of the cross-wires is in focus and correctly positioned in the field of view.

5–6. Adjustment of the Spectrometer

The first adjustment to be made before using the spectrometer is to focus the eyepiece on the cross-wires. After this, in order, it is necessary to adjust the cross-wires to be at the focus of the telescope objective, the slit to be at the focus of the collimator objective, the optical axes of the telescope and collimator to be perpendicular to the axis of rotation, and the refracting edge of the prism to be parallel to this axis. (The axis of rotation of the telescope and prism table is permanently fixed and accurately adjusted to be the axis of the divided circle.)

Focusing of Telescope and Collimator

After focusing the eyepiece, the telescope is focused by moving the complete eyepiece and cross-wires mount. In principle, the simplest method is to view a distant object and to bring the image into focus in the plane of the cross-wires. This may be inconvenient in the laboratory and it may be easier to use the Gauss eyepiece. In this case, using a plane reflecting surface as in Fig. 5–7, the telescope is adjusted until the back-reflected image of the cross-wires is in focus in the plane of the cross-wires themselves. Either of these adjustments brings the cross-wires into the focal plane of the telescope objective. Having adjusted the telescope, the collimator slit is illuminated and, with no prism in position, the telescope is rotated to be co-axial with the collimator. The slit is then moved along the axis of the collimator until its image is in focus in the plane of the cross-wires. The slit then lies in the focal plane of the collimator objective.

Schuster's Method

This is a method of focusing the telescope and collimator simultaneously. The slit must be illuminated by light that yields a line spectrum so that discrete images of the slit can be picked out after dispersion by a prism. The simplest source of light is a bunsen flame coloured by the presence of a sodium salt. The spectrum of this source consists chiefly of a pair of yellow lines lying close

Fig. 5–8. Schuster's method.

together. A sodium or mercury discharge lamp gives a brighter and more steady source. A prism is placed on the prism table and the telescope rotated to view the slit after refraction through the prism, the angle of deviation being considerably greater than the minimum. For a given deviation there will be two possible positions of the prism (see Fig. 5–8). In the first, the width of the emergent beam is greater than that of the incident beam and, for collimator and telescope objectives of equal focal lengths, the slit image is narrower than the slit. In the second, the image is wider than the slit. Thus, when not in the position of minimum deviation, the prism gives a magnification of the image. (It will be seen that the prism behaves like a telescopic system.) Suppose the prism is in the first position and that both telescope and collimator are out of adjustment. The procedure is to adjust the focus of the telescope until the slit image is as clear as possible. The prism is then turned to the second position and the slit image made clear by adjusting the focus of the collimator. The prism is then returned to the first position and the telescope adjusted. This procedure is repeated until the image is clear for both prism positions; the collimator and telescope have then been focused for parallel light. If the telescope and collimator are accidentally adjusted in the wrong order, the adjustments required become very much larger instead of smaller and the error is easily detected.

To understand the principle of Schuster's method, suppose the prism is in the first position and that the collimator is out of adjustment so that a convergent beam is incident at an angle of incidence greater than that for minimum deviation (see Fig. 5–9). Since the angle of deviation gets steadily larger as the angle of incidence differs more widely from that for minimum deviation, ray 2 is deviated more than ray 1. The result is that the convergent beam is rendered more nearly collimated by the prism. Similarly the rays of a convergent beam incident less obliquely than for minimum deviation (position 2) are rendered more strongly convergent by the prism. In addition,

it is easy to see that a divergent pencil is affected in the same way, i.e. is rendered more nearly parallel in position 1 and more divergent in position 2. Suppose, now, that the slit image was last focused by adjusting the collimator with the prism in position 2. Turn the prism to position 1. The emergent beam is now more nearly parallel than the incident beam and therefore more nearly parallel than was the emergent beam in position 2. Consequently, to make the slit image clear the telescope must be adjusted to be more nearly focused for parallel light. When the prism is rotated to position 2, the emergent beam becomes "less parallel" again and the focusing of the slit by means of the collimator must restore the "degree of parallelism", i.e. must make the incident beam more nearly parallel. Therefore the collimator is more nearly in adjustment. Obviously, repetition of these adjustments ultimately causes both collimator and telescope to be adjusted for parallel light.

Fig. 5–9.
Schuster's method.

Adjustment of the Axes of Telescope and Collimator

The adjustment of the telescope is effected by employing the Gauss eyepiece. A piece of parallel-sided plate glass is mounted on the prism table so that, as accurately as can be judged by eye, it is parallel to the axis of rotation of the table and the telescope. Using the Gauss eyepiece, the telescope is turned and, if necessary, focused, so that the image of the cross-wires lies in the plane of the cross-wires themselves, one side of the glass plate being used as a plane mirror. Without moving the glass plate relative to the prism table, the latter is rotated through 180° until the image of the cross-wires again appears in focus. Usually the image now lies at a different height in the field, owing to the fact that the glass plate was not accurately positioned on the table. By using the levelling screws attached to the prism table, the image of the cross-wires is made to lie at the same height in the field of view for both positions of the prism table. The glass plate is then parallel to the axis of rotation of the table and telescope. The inclination of the axis of the telescope can then be adjusted until the cross-wires coincide exactly with the back-reflected image; the axis of the telescope is then normal to the face of the glass plate and therefore perpendicular to the axis of rotation. The axis of the collimator can be adjusted by removing the glass plate, aligning the axes of collimator and telescope, and adjusting the collimator until the image of the slit lies in the middle of the field of view.

Levelling the Prism

The purpose of this adjustment is to ensure that the refracting edge of the prism is parallel to the axis of rotation of the table. It is assumed that the above adjustments of the telescope and collimator axes have been completed. The prism must first be placed on the table so that one of its refracting faces AB is perpendicular to the line joining the levelling screws X and Y (Fig. 5–6). To level the prism, one can proceed in several ways. One method is to employ the Gauss eyepiece and use face AB as a reflecting surface. The levelling screws X and Y are then adjusted until the cross-wires coincide with their image. The prism table is then rotated in order to use face AC. The image of the cross-wires is then adjusted by means of screw Z alone. This tilts the table about the axis XY, so that the face AB is moved in its own plane. Since the axis of the telescope is perpendicular to the axis of rotation, these adjustments cause faces AB and AC, and hence the edge A, to be parallel to this axis.

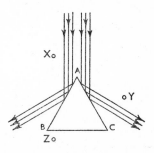

Fig. 5–10. Levelling the prism.

An alternative method is to place the telescope at an angle to the collimator and to rotate the prism table until the slit is visible through the telescope after reflection at face AB. By means of the levelling screws X and Y, the slit is made central in the field of view. The prism table is then rotated so that face AC is employed as reflector, and the same adjustment made by means of screw Z alone.

A similar method is to position the prism table so that the refracting edge A faces the collimator and the collimated beam is reflected by faces AB and AC (Fig. 5–10). The slit is then viewed with the telescope by reflection in face AB and, by means of the levelling screws X and Y, the image centred in the field of view. The telescope is then swung round to receive light reflected at face AC and, by means of Z alone, the slit image is again centred. In all cases it is desirable to return to the first setting to check that the adjustment has not been upset during the second setting. This is necessary because face AB may not be exactly perpendicular to XY.

It is possible that the base of the prism is not exactly perpendicular to the refracting edge, so that it is important to note that these adjustments level the prism and not the prism table. Consequently, once the prism has been levelled, it must not be moved relative to the table during the course of an experiment.

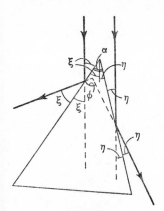

Fig. 5–11.
Measurement of angle of prism.

5–7. Measurement of Refracting Angle and Angle of Deviation

In the first and second methods of levelling the prism, the angle turned through by the prism is $(180°-\alpha)$. In the third method the angle turned through by the telescope is 2α. This follows at once from Fig. 5–11 since one has $\alpha=\xi+\eta$ and $\phi=2\xi+2\eta=2\alpha$. Care must now be taken to set the image of the cross-wires to be in exact coincidence with the cross-wires themselves in each position of the prism (first method), or to set the centre of the slit image to be exactly on the cross-wires (second and third methods).

To find θ, the prism is adjusted in, say, position 1 (Fig. 5–12), so that the deviation is a minimum. This can be done most accurately by using the telescope

Fig. 5–12. Measurement of angle of minimum deviation.

to view the image of the slit whilst the prism table is adjusted, by means of the fine adjustment screw, until the deviation is a minimum. The cross-wires are then set exactly on the slit image. To avoid the necessity of removing the prism, the table is rotated until the prism is in position 2, and the same procedure adopted. The angle turned through by the telescope is 2θ, and the refractive index of the prism may be found from equation (5–4).

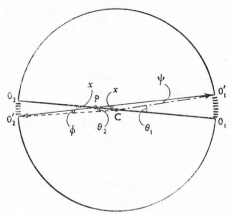

Fig. 5–13. Use of diametrically opposite verniers.

The rotation of the telescope or prism table is indicated on the circular scale S (Fig. 5–6) by means of two diametrically opposite verniers. By taking the mean of the two vernier readings, one can eliminate the error which would otherwise occur if the centre of the divided circle does not pass through the centre of rotation of the instrument. In Fig. 5–13, C is the centre of the divided circle and P is the axis of rotation of the instrument. Suppose the instrument rotates through angle x so that the diameter O_1O_2 rotates to $O_1'O_2'$. On the scale centred at C the difference between the readings at O_1 and O_1' is θ_1 and the difference between the readings at O_2 and O_2' is θ_2. From the figure one has

$$x-\theta_2=\phi=\psi=\theta_1-x,$$
$$\therefore\quad x=\tfrac{1}{2}(\theta_1+\theta_2),$$

i.e. the mean of the two readings gives the actual rotation.

5–8. Use of Hollow Prism for Liquids

The spectrometer may be used to determined the refractive index of a liquid by employing a hollow prism whose faces are parallel-sided plates of glass. The walls of such a vessel have no effect on the angle of deviation, and the angle of the liquid prism is the same as that of the vessel. Hence α and θ can be measured in the usual way.

The refractive index of a prism can be determined to an accuracy of about 0·00001 with a first-class spectrometer (angles being measured to one second). The refractive index of a liquid varies rapidly with temperature and there is usually no point in attempting an accuracy better than 0·0001 in the refractive index unless special care is given to the temperature control.

5–9. Critical Angle Methods Using a Prism Spectrometer

In Fig. 5–14 ABC is the principal section of a prism whose face BC is a ground but unpolished surface. This face is illuminated with monochromatic light, and each point acts as a source sending rays into the prism in all directions. In particular, there will be rays which, after reflection at AB (partial or total, according to the angle of incidence), emerge from AC and enter the telescope T. In the primary image plane of T, each point along the line in the plane of the figure (assumed horizontal) is the focus of rays that emerge from the prism at the same angle. Now if ϕ is positive as shown, larger angles of incidence at face AB correspond to smaller angles of emergence from face AC. Hence, if θ is the critical angle and corresponds to an angle of emergence ϕ, rays emerging at angles less than ϕ are more intense than those emerging at angles greater than ϕ since the latter are only partially reflected at face AB. Thus, along the horizontal line in the field of view of T, the intensity will show a sudden decrease at the point corresponding to the angle of emergence ϕ; the right-hand side of the field seen through the eyepiece will be the brighter. Since the field of view of the telescope is small, the inclination of rays to the principal section may be ignored and it will be seen that a similar argument can be applied to all horizontal

Fig. 5–14. Critical angle method.

lines in the field of T. Consequently, the whole field of view is divided by a vertical demarcation line on the right-hand side of which the field is brighter.

To measure ϕ, the prism is mounted on a spectrometer whose telescope T is adjusted to bring the demarcation line on to the cross-wires. The telescope is then swung round until, using the Gauss eyepiece, it is set with its axis perpendicular to face AC. The angle turned through by the telescope is obviously ϕ.

An alternative method is to position an extended monochromatic source beyond B so that rays fall on face BA in the direction B to A at grazing and near-grazing incidence (see Fig. 5–15). Care must be taken to shield the source from the diffuse surface BC which must remain dark. The rays falling on face BA at

grazing incidence emerge from face AC at angle ϕ, and those incident on BA at angles of incidence less than 90° emerge from AC at angles greater than ϕ. No light emerges at angles less than ϕ. Hence, using the telescope as before, the demarcation line in the field of view will now separate an illuminated area of the field from an area that is completely dark. With the arrangement shown in the figure, it is the right-hand side of the field that is dark. Using this method it is obviously easier to locate the demarcation line and set the cross-wires on it. If the refracting angle is measured in the usual way, the refractive index of the prism can be calculated using the equation (5–10) deduced below.

Fig. 5–15.
Critical angle method for a liquid.

The same method may be employed to determine the refractive index of a liquid of which only a small quantity is available provided the index of the prism is somewhat greater than that of the liquid. A drop of the liquid is placed on face BA and a thin glass plate placed over it. The latter is held in place by capillary action. If the second method for determining ϕ is used, it is advisable to form a wedge of liquid by means of a small piece of glass held in position by capillary action (see Fig. 5–15). In this case, θ is the critical angle for glass to liquid.

If the refractive indices of the prism and liquid are respectively n and n_0 one has

$$n_0 = n \sin \theta \qquad \ldots \ldots \ldots \quad (5\text{–}9)$$

and

$$n \sin \psi = \sin \phi. \qquad \ldots \ldots \ldots \quad (5\text{–}10)$$

In Fig. 5–15 the quadrilateral APQR is cyclic since the angles at P and R are right angles.

$$\therefore \quad \angle PQR = \pi - \alpha.$$

Hence, from the triangle PQR,

$$\pi - \alpha + \theta + \psi = \pi,$$

$$\therefore \quad \alpha = \psi + \theta.$$

Hence, from (5–9),

$$n_o = n \sin (\alpha - \psi)$$
$$= n(\sin \alpha \cos \psi - \cos \alpha \sin \psi)$$

or, from (5–10),

$$n_o = \sin \alpha \sqrt{n^2 - \sin^2 \phi} - \cos \alpha \sin \phi. \quad . \quad . \quad . \quad (5\text{–}11)$$

If there is no liquid on face AB, $n_o = 1$ and one has

$$(1 + \cos \alpha \sin \phi)^2 = \sin^2 \alpha (n^2 - \sin^2 \phi)$$

which reduces to

$$n^2 = 1 + \left(\frac{\sin \phi + \cos \alpha}{\sin \alpha} \right)^2. \quad . \quad . \quad . \quad . \quad (5\text{–}12)$$

If ϕ is measured with the prism alone, (5–12) gives its refractive index. If ϕ is then measured with the liquid on face AB, (5–11) gives the refractive index of the liquid.

5–10. The Auto-collimating Spectrometer

In this instrument, the telescope and collimator are combined into a single unit. The lower half of the primary image plane of the telescope T is occupied

Fig. 5–16. Auto-collimating spectrometer.

by a vertical slit illuminated by means of a reflecting prism (see Fig. 5–16). The prism ABC, whose refractive index is required, is placed on the prism table, and the telescope or prism table is rotated until the image of the slit is observed with the telescope eyepiece to lie vertically above the slit itself. Light is then falling normally on face AC and, from the figure, it will be seen that the prism can be regarded as half the prism ABD of refracting angle 2α. Since the ray path in prism ABC corresponds to symmetrical refraction through ABD, the position of minimum deviation is used automatically in this method. It will be seen that

$$n = \frac{\sin \phi}{\sin \alpha},$$

where ϕ is the angle between the incident/emergent ray and the normal to face AB. This method cannot be used for prisms where α is greater than the critical

angle since the maximum value of sin ϕ is unity (see §5–1). Frequently 30°
prisms are used in refractive index determinations and the spectrometer manufactured by Ross gives n to an accuracy of 0·00001, the angles being measured
to one second of arc. A calibrated fine adjustment on the prism table facilitates
the measurement of the variation of ϕ with wavelength.

5–11. Wollaston's Critical Angle Method

The equations given in §5–9 apply to any prism with refracting angle α. The
special case where α is a right angle is worthy of note. Wollaston employed two
adjacent faces of a right-angled glass block (often a cube). Using a very simple
arrangement, it is possible to find the refractive index of the glass block or of a
liquid to about 0·1%. In Fig. 5–17 ABCD is a right-angled glass block resting

Fig. 5–17. Wollaston's method.

on a film of liquid. XY is a diffusing screen (tissue paper is satisfactory)
illuminated by any convenient source. The principle is the same as in the first
method described in §5–9. Rays from the screen are either partially or totally
reflected at the face AD, and the ray incident on this face at the critical angle
emerges at angle ϕ. Consequently, on looking into the prism from S (usually
with the naked eye), one sees a demarcation line where the brightness of the field
changes suddenly. The figure illustrates a very simple method of measuring ϕ.
A horizontal scratch is made on face AB at P and viewed through a horizontal
slit at S. The cube (mounted on a square of black material such as ebonite) is
then moved along the bench until the demarcation line appears to coincide with
the scratch at P. The path of the critical ray is then PS and the angle ϕ is given
by tan ϕ=SQ/PQ. If the experiment is performed carefully it is possible to
detect the variation of ϕ with wavelength. When a source of white light is used
a coloured demarcation line is seen. From equation (5–9), putting α=90°, the
refractive index of the liquid is given by

$$n_o=\sqrt{n^2-\sin^2\phi}. \qquad \ldots \ldots \quad (5\text{–}13)$$

Alternatively, if the index of the liquid is known, that of the glass is given by

$$n=\sqrt{n_o{}^2+\sin^2\phi}. \qquad \ldots \ldots \quad (5\text{–}14)$$

5–12. The Pulfrich Refractometer

The Pulfrich refractometer frequently employs a right-angled prism as above, but is fitted with a telescope to view the demarcation line. The arrangement is shown diagrammatically in Fig. 5–18(a). T represents the telescope which receives the light emerging from the block of known index n. The instrument can be used to determine the refractive index n_0 of a liquid or of a solid body provided $n_0 < n$. In the case of an unknown solid, at least one surface must be polished flat. To measure the index of a liquid it is simply placed on the top surface of the block; to measure the index of a solid the plane surface of the specimen is placed in contact with the top surface of the block. Frequently, in the latter case, a liquid of index n (or somewhat higher) is placed between the

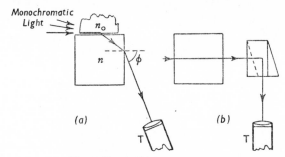

Fig. 5–18. Pulfrich refractometer.

surfaces to reduce the effect of imperfect polish. The theory is as given in the preceding section and the results can be found from equation (5–13). Usually the instrument is supplied with tables to give n_0 in terms of ϕ; alternatively, the arm carrying the telescope can read n_0 directly. The telescope is usually of the auto-collimating type so that, when necessary, ϕ can be measured by setting the telescope normal to the vertical face of the block before the cross-wires are brought on to the demarcation line. In most instruments a reflector is fitted outside the objective of the telescope so that the axis of the latter can be made horizontal. In Fig. 5–18(a) this corresponds to the telescope being perpendicular to the paper; the view from above is then of the form shown in (b). The reflector and telescope can move round a vertical circular scale which indicates the values of ϕ or n_0. When the instrument is to be used solely for liquids, a short length of wide bore glass tube is cemented on to the top surface of the block to form a cell.

In some of the more recent instruments the 90° prism is replaced by one of 60°. In the Bellingham and Stanley instrument a 60° prism is interchangeable with a V-block to convert the refractometer into an instrument of the Hilger-Chance type (see §5–14).

5–13. The Abbe Refractometer

The principle of this instrument is the same as that of the previous critical angle methods. Fig. 5–19 shows the arrangement employed for the measurement of the refractive index of a liquid. P and Q are prisms of high refractive index, and the liquid under test is placed between them. P corresponds to the prism in the total reflection method employing a spectrometer (§5–9). The prism Q and the mirror M simply provide a convenient method of passing light from the liquid into P. (In the dipping refractometer Q is absent and P is dipped into the liquid.) If the top face of Q is not a diffusing surface, an extended diffuse source of light must be used. Light that strikes P at grazing incidence emerges at angle ϕ and the usual demarcation line is viewed by means of the telescope T. As in §5–9, measurement of ϕ would enable the refractive index of the liquid to be calculated from equation (5–11) if α and the refractive index of P are known. Usually T is carried on an arm attached to a scale which is calibrated to read

Fig. 5–19. Abbe refractometer.

directly the index of the liquid. When measuring the refractive index of a solid, Q is removed and a polished face of the solid is placed in contact with P, a small film of high index liquid being interposed as in the Pulfrich refractometer. If white light enters the instrument, rays entering P at grazing incidence will emerge at an angle ϕ which depends upon the wavelength. Consequently, the demarcation line has coloured edges.

In order to enable the instrument to be used with white light, it is usual to place an Abbe compensator before the objective of the telescope. This consists of a pair of Amici direct-vision prisms in series (see §5–4); these can be rotated by equal and opposite amounts about the axis of T. In this way, the dispersion of the combination can be varied until it is sufficient to recombine the rays emerging from P. The demarcation line is then achromatized. Since the compensator is arranged to give no deviation for sodium light, it is for this light that the instrument gives the refractive index of the specimen.

5–14. The Hilger-Chance Refractometer

In the critical angle refractometers the eyepiece cross-wires have to be set on a demarcation line separating bright and dark areas. It is found that the unsymmetrical nature of this setting is responsible for a reduction in the accuracy that an observer can obtain. Further disadvantages of the critical angle methods are: (1) the refractive index of the glass prism must be greater than that of the specimen under test; (2) the measured index corresponds to a surface layer and may differ from that of the main bulk of the specimen. On the other hand, the spectrometer methods require two highly polished surfaces on the specimen. The Hilger-Chance instrument was developed in order to avoid these difficulties. A side elevation of the arrangement is shown in Fig. 5–20(a). The composite glass block B is made by combining two prisms as indicated. The components are united by heat treatment and cannot be separated by any of the usual solvents. The angle between the faces of the V-block is exactly 90°, and the specimen under test is positioned in the groove as indicated. Monochromatic light from the slit S is collimated by C and passes through the V-block and specimen which together resemble an Amici prism system. The direction of the emergent light obviously depends upon the refractive index of the specimen and is measured by means of the telescope T. As in the Pulfrich refractometer, the telescope is fitted with a reflector and has its axis horizontal.

It will be seen that two perpendicular plane surfaces must be produced on the

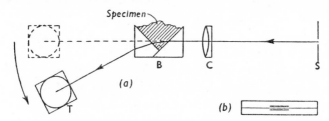

Fig. 5–20. Hilger-Chance refractometer.

specimen, but it is not necessary for these to be of the highest quality since a film of liquid can be placed between the faces of the specimen and the V-block. Since the method is not a critical angle method, the refractive index of the specimen can be greater than or less than that of the V-block. Consequently, the latter can be made of a durable glass of moderate index. In addition, it is obvious that the direction of the emergent beam does not depend solely upon the refractive index of the surface layers. In designing the instrument, special attention was given to the method of setting. The eyepiece carries two short parallel lines in its focal plane, and the setting is made on a fine line which runs along the middle of the wide slit S; the appearance of the field of view is shown in Fig. 5–20(b). The symmetrical nature of this setting, and the care taken to facilitate the reading of the divided circle, are important factors contributing to the accuracy of the instrument. The refractive index of a specimen of glass can be found to an accuracy of 0·00001. The instrument can be used for liquids if the V-block is provided with side plates to form a trough; 2–3 c.c. of liquid are required.

5–15. Refractive Index of Solids of Irregular Shape

The methods described above for the measurement of the refractive index of a solid require the production of at least one polished surface on the solid. This can be avoided as follows: If a transparent solid of irregular shape is immersed in a liquid of the same refractive index, there is no change in index at the boundary of the solid and it becomes invisible. The method consists simply of finding a liquid or mixture of liquids for which the outline of the solid disappears. The index of the liquid can then be measured by one of the methods described above. Frequently, the liquids with suitable refractive indices are volatile, and the different rates of evaporation cause the refractive index of the mixture to change while it is being transferred to the refractometer. This difficulty can be overcome by employing a hollow prism and a spectrometer as described in § 5–8, or by using the Hilger-Chance refractometer. It is then possible to mix the liquids in the vessel containing the irregular solid whilst viewing the slit in the usual way. The slit image will become clear when the refractive index of the liquid is equal to that of the solid, and when this stage is reached the telescope setting is made. If necessary, the evaporation of the liquids can be compensated while making the setting. The refractive indices of most glasses can be matched by a mixture of readily available liquids. These include carbon disulphide (1·632), benzene (1·504), nitrobenzene (1·553), α-monobromnaphthalene (1·658).

5–16. The Simple Spectrograph

Frequently, it is necessary to know the wavelengths present in the light emitted by a source. The spectrum can, of course, be examined visually by

Fig. 5–21. Quartz spectrograph.

means of a spectrometer, but it is sometimes desirable to obtain a permanent record of the spectrum. To do this the telescope is replaced by a camera focused for parallel light, the spectrum being in focus on the plate. If it is necessary to photograph the spectrum in the ultra-violet or infra-red as well as in the visible region, it is obviously necessary to employ lenses and a prism of materials which transmit the wavelengths concerned. A commonly used substance is quartz. Now quartz is birefringent, and it is necessary for the optical axis to be parallel to the direction of the light in the prism. Again, since quartz is also optically active the prism must be made in two halves, one of right-handed and the other of left-handed quartz (see Chapter XXIII). Furthermore, a quartz lens exhibits considerable longitudinal chromatic aberration and, if the spectrum is to be in focus over a wide range of wavelengths, the photographic plate must be inclined to the axis of the camera lens. A typical arrangement is shown in Fig. 5–21.

Quartz is transparent from about $0·19\mu$ to about 4μ. For the farther U.V. one can use prisms cut from *vacuum-grown* crystals of calcium fluoride (fluorite) and lithium fluoride down to $0·125\mu$ and $0·105\mu$ respectively. Substances useful for infra-red spectroscopy include lithium fluoride (up to 6μ), fluorite (up to 9μ), sodium chloride (rock salt) (up to 17μ), silver chloride (up to 25μ), potassium bromide (up to 30μ), and thallium bromide-iodide—42–58% (up to 40μ). It should be noted that some of these substances are very soluble in water and must be protected from the atmosphere. To reduce the number of components made from these rather inconvenient materials, it is usual to employ mirrors instead of lenses.

5–17. The Constant Deviation Spectroscope

In the ordinary spectrometer the telescope is moved in order to view different parts of the spectrum. In the constant deviation instrument the collimator and telescope are fixed at right angles and the prism is rotated. The general arrangement of the instrument is shown in Fig. 5–22. The action of the prism is most easily understood by regarding it as a combination of three parts as indicated in the figure. The slit image for one particular wavelength will coincide with the cross-wires of the telescope, and the path of the principal ray for this wavelength is as shown. It will be seen that the angles of incidence and emergence are equal and opposite, so that the two refractions cause no total deviation. The presence of the reflecting surface, however, causes the two dispersions to be in the same sense.

The prism can be rotated to bring the slit image for any wavelength on to the cross-wires when, for that wavelength, the action of the prism is equivalent to that

Fig. 5–22.
Constant deviation spectroscope.

of a 60° prism at minimum deviation. Usually the prism table is calibrated to enable the wavelength to be read off directly. Frequently a camera attachment replaces the eyepiece and the spectrum, or a region of it, can be photographed. Also, by placing a second slit at the focus of the telescope objective, a narrow region of the spectrum can be isolated. The emergent light is then almost monochromatic and the instrument is referred to as a *monochromator*.

5–18. Other Spectrographs and Monochromators. Spectrophotometers

For a given prism the angular dispersion is fixed, so that the linear dispersion on the photographic plate (that is, the linear separation of slit images for neighbouring wavelengths) will be proportional to the focal length of the camera

Fig. 5–23(a). Littrow spectrograph.

ens. The *Littrow spectrograph* is a convenient arrangement which employs a long focus lens without being unduly cumbersome [see Fig. 5–23(a)]. The light is doubly dispersed by P and the mirror is tilted about a horizontal axis so that the light returns above or below the small prism. Alternatively, the small prism can be moved horizontally a short distance away from the axis of the lens. One can achieve a saving of light (through the elimination of two refractions) at the expense of a loss of dispersion by using a rear-silvered prism as in Fig. 5–16. The dispersion of the original system can be increased by using two (or more) prisms in series.

In some spectral regions it is more convenient to replace the lens with a mirror which has the additional advantage of freedom from chromatic aberration. It is unavoidable that the mirror is used off-axis, and for good definition an off-axis parabola should be used. Some systems use two spherical mirrors—one

Fig. 5–23(*b*). System used by Czerny and Plettig.

for collimating and the other for focusing. To produce sharp spectral lines it is then essential to use the two mirrors off-axis by the same amount in opposite directions. To a first approximation this eliminates unsymmetrical aberration (i.e. coma—see Chapters XV and XVI), but since the correction will apply only to the spectral line at the appropriate distance from the axis of the focusing mirror, the arrangement is more appropriate for a monochromator than for a spectrograph. As was pointed out in §5–2, a prism gives curved spectral lines. In consequence, it is necessary for the exit slit of a monochromator to be curved. There is some difficulty in arranging the layout of the system in such a way that the mirrors are used as close as possible to the axis and the various components do not get in each other's way. Fig. 5–23(*b*) shows the system due to Czerny and Plettig (1930). (When a plane mirror is parallel to the base of a prism at minimum deviation as shown, the light leaving the plane mirror is parallel to that entering the prism.) At first sight the mirrors appear to be off-axis in the same direction, but the plane mirror introduces the necessary reversal.

A photographic plate has spatial discrimination and by using a spectrograph one can record a wide spectrum with a single exposure. This is a satisfactory way of recording the wavelengths present in a spectrum but is less satisfactory if accurate measurements of intensity are required. In a *spectrophotometer* it is better to use a receiver such as a photo-cell or thermopile, and since these detectors do not have spatial discrimination (but have short response times), it is necessary for the detector to scan across the spectrum, recording the intensity at each wavelength as it proceeds. Usually, this is done by using a monochromator in which successive wavelengths are directed to a stationary exit slit behind which the detector is mounted.

In absorption spectrophotometry one uses a source that gives a continuous spectrum and compares the spectral distribution of the light transmitted by the specimen with that of the incident light. A convenient way of doing this is by using a double-beam system. Between the source and the detector the light is passed alternately through the specimen and through a variable aperture (or a variable density filter). If the reduction in intensity is different in the two light paths there is an a.c. component in the output from the detector. A servo-mechanism can then operate the variable aperture or filter until this a.c. signal falls to zero, the setting of the aperture or filter indicating the absorption in the specimen. This can be recorded as the wavelength is varied by means of a monochromator, and the absorption spectrum recorded automatically.

5–19. Geometrical Theory of Rainbows

The main phenomenon consists of either one or two arcs of colour, and can be seen when the observer stands with his back to the sun and looks into falling rain from which the sun is not obscured by cloud. The arcs are concentric and have their common centre on the line joining the sun to the observer, the colour variation occurring in the radial direction.

The appearance of coloured bows under these circumstances can be explained by the refraction and dispersion of the sunlight by the spherical raindrops. The geometrical theory given below is not quantitatively exact and it does not account for certain subsidiary effects. A more complete explanation of the phenomenon can be obtained from an investigation of the shapes of the wavefronts emerging from the raindrops and application of Huygens' principle as formulated in Chapter X.

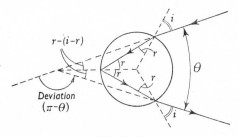

Fig. 5–24.
Refraction and reflection in a raindrop.

Consider the passage of a ray through a spherical raindrop. Fig. 5–24 shows the path of a ray which undergoes one internal reflection. In general, the ray will not lie in a vertical plane. It will be seen that the path of the ray is symmetrical and that the angle between the incident and emergent rays is

$$\theta = 2[r-(i-r)]$$
$$= 4r - 2i.$$

At a stationary value $d\theta/di$ is zero,

i.e. $$4\,\frac{dr}{di}-2=0.$$

Also, since $\sin i = n \sin r$,

$$\frac{dr}{di}=\frac{\cos i}{n\cos r}=\frac{\cos i}{\sqrt{n^2-\sin^2 i}}.$$

Thus, at a stationary value,

$$2\cos i = \sqrt{n^2-\sin^2 i},$$

$$\therefore\quad 4\cos^2 i = n^2-(1-\cos^2 i)$$

or $$\cos i = \sqrt{\frac{n^2-1}{3}}.\qquad \ldots\ldots (5\text{--}15)$$

This specifies the angle of incidence at which the angle of deviation has a stationary value; it is easily shown that θ does, in fact, reach a maximum. The ray is actually rotated $(\pi-\theta)$ so that one has an angle of *minimum deviation* which depends on the wavelength of the light.

Referring to monochromatic light, consider a narrow pencil of parallel rays incident on a raindrop. The separate rays will have slightly different angles of incidence, but if the deviation of the central ray of the pencil is at the stationary value, the rays will emerge nearly parallel. Hence, if the eye looks at the raindrops and receives these rays the field in that direction will appear bright.

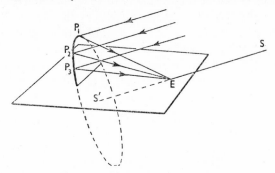

Fig. 5-25. Observation of a rainbow.

In Fig. 5–25 E represents the observer's eye and P_1, P_2, and P_3, are raindrops at which the rays undergo minimum deviation; the eye sees a bright arc $P_1P_2P_3$.

Fig. 5-26. Formation of secondary rainbow.

The angle subtended by the bright arc is about 40°, but will depend on the wavelength so that one sees a radial spectrum. It is easily seen from equation (5–15) that the red is on the outside of this *primary rainbow*. A *secondary rainbow* is similarly formed above the primary one by rays that undergo two internal reflections as in Fig. 5–26. The blue end of the spectrum is then on the outside and it can be shown that the deviation is a minimum when

$$\sin i = \sqrt{\frac{9 - n^2}{8}}.$$

In addition to these two main bows, one frequently sees variations of brightness near the inner edge of the primary bow and, less frequently, at the outer edge of the secondary bow. These *supernumerary* or *spurious bows* cannot be explained in terms of the simple geometrical theory.

THE WAVE THEORY OF LIGHT

Sections 5 to 13 can be omitted on first reading

6–1. The General Equation of Wave Motion and the Principle of Superposition

IT was pointed out in Chapter I that for many purposes the light disturbance at any point can be represented by a single scalar quantity ϕ. It was assumed that the variations of ϕ are propagated in the form of a wave motion, so that for a plane wave of infinite width propagated in the positive x-direction one can write:

$$\phi = a \sin k(ct-x) = a \sin (\omega t - kx) \quad . \quad . \quad . \quad . \quad (6\text{–}1)$$

and for a spherical wave expanding from the origin

$$\phi = \frac{a}{r} \sin k(ct-r) = \frac{a}{r} \sin (\omega t - kr). \quad . \quad . \quad . \quad (6\text{–}2)$$

For a sound wave the particle displacements are always in the direction of propagation and the disturbance at any point is specified completely simply by specifying the magnitude of this particle displacement (or by specifying the excess pressure, condensation, etc.). That is to say, a single scalar quantity adequately specifies the disturbance in a sound wave. In the case of light it is found that a single scalar quantity is not completely adequate. In terms of the old elastic solid theory of the propagation of light, it is found to be necessary to assume that the light disturbance consists of vibrations perpendicular to the direction of propagation. It is then necessary to specify the direction of these vibrations. That is to say, the quantity specifying the light disturbance at any point is a vector quantity. In terms of the electromagnetic theory of light, the vibrating particle is replaced by oscillatory electric and magnetic fields. For example, a transverse linear oscillation of a particle becomes an electric field along a given line (the magnitude varying sinusoidally), plus an associated magnetic field.

An investigation into the propagation of sound waves leads to the general result that the velocity potential satisfies the equation

$$\frac{\partial^2 \phi}{\partial x^2} + \frac{\partial^2 \phi}{\partial y^2} + \frac{\partial^2 \phi}{\partial z^2} = \frac{1}{c^2} \frac{\partial^2 \phi}{\partial t^2}. \quad . \quad . \quad . \quad . \quad (6\text{–}3)$$

This is known as the *general equation of wave motion*. For plane waves of infinite width propagated in the x-direction, ϕ is a function of x only. One has

$$\frac{\partial^2 \phi}{\partial x^2} = \frac{1}{c^2} \frac{\partial^2 \phi}{\partial t^2} \quad . \quad . \quad . \quad . \quad . \quad . \quad (6\text{–}4)$$

and, by direct substitution, it is easily proved that (6–1) is a solution. For spherical waves symmetrical about the origin (6–3) becomes

$$\frac{\partial^2(r\phi)}{\partial r^2} = \frac{1}{c^2} \frac{\partial^2(r\phi)}{\partial t^2} \quad . \quad . \quad . \quad . \quad . \quad (6\text{–}5)$$

and, by comparison with (6–4) and (6–1), it will be seen that (6–2) is a solution of (6–5). Electromagnetic theory shows that the electric and magnetic field vectors also satisfy the general equation of wave motion; in a scalar theory of light the light disturbance must satisfy the same fundamental equation. When thinking in terms of the scalar wave theory, it is not necessary to specify the nature of the scalar quantity which varies—it is simply a quantity which varies sinusoidally and is such that the square of its amplitude is proportional to the intensity of the light.

Frequently it is necessary to find the resultant disturbance at a point when a number of disturbances arrive simultaneously. According to the *Principle of Superposition*, the resultant disturbance is simply the sum of the separate disturbances. It should be noted that since the general equation of wave motion is a linear equation, the sum of any number of solutions is also a solution. If this were not so the principle of superposition would need to be modified. An important result of the principle of superposition is that when beams of light intersect, the propagation of each beam is completely unaffected by the others. Thus after one beam has crossed another it proceeds exactly as it would have done if the other had not been present. Consider, for example, the disturbance at a point where two disturbances of the same frequency arrive with different phases. The separate disturbances can be represented by

$$\left.\begin{aligned}\phi_1 &= a_1 \sin(\omega t - \delta_1), \\ \phi_2 &= a_2 \sin(\omega t - \delta_2),\end{aligned}\right\} \quad \cdots \cdots \quad (6\text{--}6)$$

where δ_1 and δ_2 are sometimes called the phase constants. The resultant disturbance is given by

$$\begin{aligned}\phi &= a_1 \sin(\omega t - \delta_1) + a_2 \sin(\omega t - \delta_2) \\ &= \sin \omega t(a_1 \cos \delta_1 + a_2 \cos \delta_2) - \cos \omega t(a_1 \sin \delta_1 + a_2 \sin \delta_2).\end{aligned}$$

It is convenient to call the first of these brackets $A \cos \delta$ and the second $A \sin \delta$. That is, one puts

$$\left.\begin{aligned}A \sin \delta &= a_1 \sin \delta_1 + a_2 \sin \delta_2, \\ A \cos \delta &= a_1 \cos \delta_1 + a_2 \cos \delta_2.\end{aligned}\right\} \quad \cdots \quad (6\text{--}7)$$

The expression for ϕ then reduces to

$$\phi = A \sin(\omega t - \delta), \quad \cdots \cdots \cdots \quad (6\text{--}8)$$

where
$$A^2 = a_1{}^2 + a_2{}^2 + 2a_1 a_2 \cos(\delta_2 - \delta_1) \quad \cdots \cdots \quad (6\text{--}9)$$

and
$$\tan \delta = \frac{a_1 \sin \delta_1 + a_2 \sin \delta_2}{a_1 \cos \delta_1 + a_2 \cos \delta_2}. \quad \cdots \cdots \quad (6\text{--}10)$$

If $a_1 = a_2$ one has

$$\left.\begin{aligned}A^2 &= 2a^2[1 + \cos(\delta_2 - \delta_1)] \\ &= 4a^2 \cos^2\left(\frac{\delta_2 - \delta_1}{2}\right).\end{aligned}\right\} \quad \cdots \cdots \quad (6\text{--}11)$$

Thus the resultant intensity at the point (A^2) is not simply the sum of the intensities due to the separate disturbances ($a_1{}^2 + a_2{}^2$). The two disturbances are said to *interfere*. In particular, if $a_1 = a_2$ and $(\delta_2 - \delta_1) = \pi$ they interfere destructively to give zero intensity. At first sight this would seem to violate the principle

G. AND P.O.—5

of conservation of energy, but closer inspection shows that whenever there are points where destructive interference causes the resultant intensity to be less than the sum of the separate intensities, there are also other points where constructive interference causes the resultant intensity to be greater than the sum of the separate intensities.

Frequently one is concerned with disturbances that travel from a source to a point via two different routes. They therefore arrive with different phases owing to the different optical paths traversed. Equation (6–9) shows that the superposed disturbances interfere constructively if the phase difference $(\delta_2-\delta_1)$ is an even multiple of π, and destructively if it is an odd multiple of π. Now the phase difference is related to the difference between the optical paths traversed by the two disturbances by the relation

$$\text{phase difference} = (2\pi/\lambda)(\text{optical path difference}).$$

Hence there is constructive interference if the path difference is a multiple of λ, and destructive interference if it is an odd multiple of $\lambda/2$. The analysis can be extended in an obvious manner to the superposition of any number of disturbances.

It must be remembered that the discussion has been concerned with the superposition of disturbances each of which is completely specified by a single scalar quantity. This corresponds to the superposition of simple harmonic oscillations that are along the same straight line. For disturbances that are not along the same straight line it would be necessary to specify the directions of the various oscillations.

The above results give the resultant at any point when two simple harmonic scalar disturbances are superposed there. If one has two progressive waves of the same frequency propagated along the same line, the phase difference is constant at all points along the line, and the resultant disturbance is given by (6–8). For waves of the same amplitude the resultant amplitude is $2a \cos \frac{1}{2}(\delta_2-\delta_1)$, where $(\delta_2-\delta_1)$ is the phase difference. If the waves are propagated in the positive x-direction and one is distance $\varDelta$ ahead of the other, one may write

$$\phi_1 = a \sin (\omega t - kx),$$
$$\phi_2 = a \sin [\omega t - k(x+\varDelta)]$$

and it is easily shown that the resultant is given by

$$\phi = 2a \cos \frac{k\varDelta}{2} \sin \left[\omega t - k \left(x + \frac{\varDelta}{2} \right) \right]. \quad \ldots \quad (6\text{–}12)$$

If $\varDelta = 0$, λ, 2λ, $\ldots$, the crests and troughs of one wave coincide with those of the other and there is maximum constructive interference to give a wave of amplitude $2a$. If $\varDelta = \lambda/2$, $3\lambda/2$, $5\lambda/2$, $\ldots$, the crests of one wave coincide with the troughs of the other and there is complete destructive interference.

6–2. Graphical Method of Adding Disturbances of the Same Frequency

In Fig. 6–1 the disturbances ϕ_1 and ϕ_2 of the previous section are represented by the lines OP and PQ. These have lengths proportional to a_1 and a_2 and are inclined to the x-axis at angles δ_1 and δ_2 respectively. These two lines form the adjacent sides of a parallelogram whose diagonal is inclined to the x-axis at angle δ and is of length A where A and δ are given by equations (6–9) and (6–10). The value of A follows immediately from the triangle OPQ and it is easily seen that the components of A along and perpendicular to the x-axis are given by $A \cos \delta = a_1 \cos \delta_1 + a_2 \cos \delta_2$ and $A \sin \delta = a_1 \sin \delta_1 + a_2 \sin \delta_2$ respectively. That is to say, if the amplitudes and phases of two disturbances of the same frequency are represented by the lengths and directions of two vectors, the amplitude and phase of the resultant is represented by the length and direction of the vector sum. To find the effect of superposing a third disturbance one simply adds the corresponding vector QR. OR then represents the resultant. It is obvious that by proceeding in this way one can use a vector polygon to find the resultant of any number of super-posed disturbances. The resultant intensity depends upon the ampli-tudes and relative phases of the

Fig. 6–1.
Graphical method of adding disturbances.

superposed disturbances and varies from zero, when the polygon is a closed figure, up to a maximum of $(\Sigma a)^2$, when all the disturbances are in phase and the polygon becomes a straight line.

It is worthy of note that if a resultant is built up of a number of superposed disturbances and the phase of each component is changed by the same amount, the phase of the resultant is changed by the same amount, there being no change in amplitude. The change is simply represented by a rotation of the complete vector polygon.

6–3. The Use of Complex Quantities in Wave Theory

The complex quantity e^{ix} has real and imaginary parts given by

$$e^{ix} = \cos x + i \sin x.$$

Hence $a \cos (\omega t - \delta)$ is the real part of the complex quantity $\phi = a e^{i(\omega t - \delta)}$ and, if it is understood that only its real part has physical significance, the latter may be used to represent the disturbance defined by the former. This representation is possible because on adding a number of complex quantities one adds the real and imaginary parts separately. That is to say, the real part of the sum is equal to the sum of the real parts. Therefore to find the resultant of a number of superposed disturbances one can add the corresponding complex quantities and take the real part of the sum. In wave theory such a summation frequently takes the form of an integral which can be evaluated more easily if the complex representation is used. Another advantage of using the complex representation is that the complex quantity that is used to represent a disturbance may be split into its space and time parts to give

$$\phi = a e^{-i\delta} e^{i\omega t}.$$

It is seen to consist of a *complex amplitude*

$$z = ae^{-i\delta}$$

and a harmonic time factor

$$e^{i\omega t}.$$

The modulus and argument* of the complex amplitude give the amplitude and phase of the disturbance represented. When adding a number of disturbances of the same frequency, $e^{i\omega t}$ is a common factor and the sum of the complex amplitudes gives the complex amplitude of the resultant, the modulus and argument respectively giving the amplitude and phase of the resultant disturbance. Frequently one is interested only in the resultant intensity and it is not then necessary to know both the modulus and the argument. The resultant intensity a^2 is obviously given by the product of z and its conjugate complex quantity $\bar{z}$ and this is the usual method of finding the intensity when an expression for z has been obtained.

To illustrate the procedure, consider the superposition of two simple harmonic disturbances. One has

$$a_1 \cos (\omega t - \delta_1) + a_2 \cos (\omega t - \delta_2)$$
$$= (a_1 \cos \delta_1 + a_2 \cos \delta_2) \cos \omega t + (a_1 \sin \delta_1 + a_2 \sin \delta_2) \sin \omega t$$
$$= A \cos \delta \cos \omega t + A \sin \delta \sin \omega t$$
$$= A \cos (\omega t - \delta), \quad \ldots \ldots \ldots \ldots \ldots \quad (6\text{--}13)$$

where

$$A^2 = (a_1 \cos \delta_1 + a_2 \cos \delta_2)^2 + (a_1 \sin \delta_1 + a_2 \sin \delta_2)^2$$
$$= a_1{}^2 + a_2{}^2 + 2a_1 a_2 \cos (\delta_2 - \delta_1)$$

and

$$\tan \delta = \frac{a_1 \sin \delta_1 + a_2 \sin \delta_2}{a_1 \cos \delta_1 + a_2 \cos \delta_2}.$$

In terms of the complex representation, the complex amplitude of the resultant is given by

$$z = a_1 e^{-i\delta_1} + a_2 e^{-i\delta_2}$$

which reduces to

$$z = Ae^{-i\delta} = C + iS,$$

where $C = A \cos \delta$ and $S = A \sin \delta$ and A and δ are given by the above expressions. It will be seen that (6–13) gives the real part of $ze^{i\omega t}$.

Alternatively, if only the resultant intensity is required, one can write at once

$$\text{Intensity} = z\bar{z} = (a_1 e^{-i\delta_1} + a_2 e^{-i\delta_2})(a_1 e^{+i\delta_1} + a_2 e^{+i\delta_2})$$
$$= a_1{}^2 + a_2{}^2 + a_1 a_2 (e^{i(\delta_2 - \delta_1)} + e^{-i(\delta_2 - \delta_1)})$$
$$= a_1{}^2 + a_2{}^2 + 2a_1 a_2 \cos (\delta_2 - \delta_1).$$

The disturbance $a \sin (\omega t - \delta)$ may be represented by the same complex quantity as $a \cos (\omega t - \delta)$ if it is understood that throughout the analysis it is the imaginary part which represents the physical disturbance (see §6–1).

* The modulus $|z|$ of the complex quantity $z = C + iS$ is defined as $\sqrt{C^2 + S^2}$ and the argument θ is given by $\tan \theta = S/C$. If $z = ae^{ix}$, $|z| = a$ and $\arg z = x$. The complex conjugate of z is obtained by substituting $-i$ for i in the expression for z and is written $\bar{z}$. Thus, if $z = C + iS$ $\bar{z} = C - iS$ and $z\bar{z} = C^2 + S^2 = |z|^2$.

6–4. Coherent, Incoherent, and Partially Coherent Disturbances

The discussion in this section applies to non-laser sources—often referred to as *thermal sources*.

An equation of the form $\phi = a \sin k(ct - x)$ represents a continuous train of waves stretching from $x = -\infty$ to $x = +\infty$ and proceeding in the positive x-direction with speed c. That is, if one plots ϕ against x for a given instant of time, one

Fig. 6–2. Sine wave.

has a sine wave stretching from $-\infty$ to $+\infty$ (see Fig. 6–2). The variation with time of the disturbance at any point x is given by imagining the profile of the wave to move along with speed c; it is given by the movement of the point of intersection of the ordinate at x with the sine curve as the latter moves past the former. The disturbance is sinusoidal and continues for ever.

Suppose that at a given point one has two such disturbances of the same frequency superposed. They will not, in general, be in phase, but *the phase difference between them is constant* and the resultant intensity is given by equation (6–9).

Now, as will be seen later, a source of light does not emit a continuous train of waves but can be said to emit a succession of wave trains of finite length, there being no fixed phase relation between successive wave trains. That is, the disturbance emitted by a source exhibits random abrupt variations of phase; these changes occur at the rate of 10^8 or more per second. When the disturbances from two independent sources are superposed, the instantaneous intensity is still given by equation (6–9) but $\cos (\delta_2 - \delta_1)$ will vary rapidly in the range between -1 and $+1$. Now the eye and most existing physical receptors cannot appreciate such rapid variations in intensity and the effective intensity is given by the average value of A^2 over a period of time which includes many variations. If the phase changes are random the mean value of $\cos (\delta_2 - \delta_1)$ will be zero and the mean value of A^2 is $a_1^2 + a_2^2$. If there is a constant phase relation between two or more disturbances they are said to be *coherent* and if there is no fixed phase relation they are *incoherent*. When disturbances are added and the time average of the resulting intensity is different from the sum of the separate intensities the disturbances are said to interfere. That is to say, coherent disturbances interfere and incoherent disturbances do not. It will be seen that to add coherent disturbances one adds the complex amplitudes, and to add incoherent disturbances one adds the intensities. Since every source exhibits random changes of phase, disturbances from different sources (or different points of an extended source) are incoherent.

Suppose light from a single point source is divided into two parts (by a half-silvered mirror for example) and that after traversing slightly different optical path lengths these disturbances are superposed. The disturbances superposed at any instant will have originated in the source at only slightly different times so that the abrupt changes of phase which occur in one of the disturbances will occur almost simultaneously in the other. Consequently, the phase difference between them is constant and equal to $(2\pi/\lambda)$(optical path difference). The disturbances are coherent and can interfere. On the other hand, if disturbances traverse widely different optical path lengths before being brought to the same point, they must have been emitted by the source at widely different times, and light belonging to one wave train from the source is superposed with light from another. There is then no fixed phase relation between them—they are incoherent and do not interfere.

Between the two extreme examples quoted in the above paragraph, there is the possibility that the superposed disturbances are *partially coherent*. Thus, suppose that the path difference is increased from zero until it is such that the abrupt changes in one disturbance occur about half-way between those of the other. Then for half the time the superposed disturbances are derived from the same wave train and for half the time they belong to different wave trains. When averaging over a relatively large period of time one could say that the disturbances are half coherent and half incoherent, i.e. they are partially coherent. Thinking in terms of propagation of wave trains of finite length, one may say that in an interference experiment in which light is divided into two beams, each finite wave train is divided into two similar wave trains. If these are superposed after traversing similar optical path lengths, they overlap along their entire length and interference effects can be observed. If they traverse widely different optical paths before passing along the same path, the whole of one wave train will have passed by before the other has arrived, and obviously they cannot interfere. On the average there is no interference between wave trains that have not been derived from the same original wave train so that no interference effects will be observable. Between these two extremes it may happen that if they have traversed moderately different optical path lengths, the wave trains partially overlap and the overlapping portions interfere. With such an arrangement it is only for part of the time that one has overlapping wave trains derived from the same original one. The average intensity over a relatively large period of time shows the effect of interference but the effect is less marked than when the wave trains overlap along their entire length.

For any source the average length of a wave train is called the *coherence length*, and the time taken by light to travel this distance (i.e. the interval of time during which the mean wave train is emitted) is called the *coherence time*.

The above discussions show that the transition from coherence to incoherence is a gradual one, and explain why the interference effects which can be observed when disturbances from the same source are superposed become less distinct as one increases the differences between the optical paths traversed by the disturbances. As the path difference is increased the disturbances may be said to be coherent over a smaller fraction of the total time and the time average of the intensity gradually changes from $[a_1{}^2+a_2{}^2+2a_1a_2 \cos{(2\pi/\lambda)}\text{(path difference)}]$ to $(a_1{}^2+a_2{}^2)$.

From what has been said above it will be seen that a truly simple harmonic wave extends to infinity, and hence one can never have a source of truly monochromatic light. However, light from a single line in a line spectrum can correspond to very long wave trains (a million or more wavelengths), and it will be shown in §6–7 that this is equivalent to a mixture of monochromatic disturbances, most of which have wavelengths close to a mean value. Thus many laboratory sources are referred to as *quasi-monochromatic*, and have a single wavelength λ associated with them.

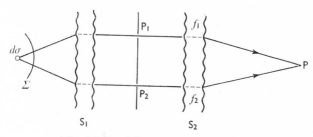

Fig. 6–3. Partially coherent disturbances.

Suppose, now, that light from an extended quasi-monochromatic source falls on two points P_1 and P_2 whose distances from the source are not widely different (i.e. differ by much less than the coherence length). Disturbances from any one element of the source are coherent, whilst those from different elements are incoherent. That is to say, part of the light at P_1 is coherent with part at P_2, and the total disturbances at P_1 and P_2 are partially coherent. It is now necessary to have some way of describing the *degree of coherence* between these disturbances. Consider, for example, the arrangement shown in Fig. 6–3. Light from the extended quasi-monochromatic source Σ passes through the optical system S_1, through the two pinholes P_1 and P_2, through the system S_2, and arrives at the point P. The disturbances at P are partially coherent and one needs to be able to calculate the total intensity at P. The treatment given here and in §11–12 follows that given by Hopkins (1951). Consider the effect of a small source element $d\sigma$. This produces at P_1 and P_2 intensities proportional to $d\sigma$, i.e. amplitudes proportional to $\sqrt{d\sigma}$. Suppose, then, that complex amplitudes $u_1\sqrt{d\sigma}$ and $u_2\sqrt{d\sigma}$ emerge from P_1 and P_2 respectively. Suppose disturbances of unit amplitude and zero phase at P_1 and P_2 produce complex amplitudes f_1 and f_2 respectively at P. Then light passing from $d\sigma$ to P via P_1 and P_2 gives complex amplitudes $u_1 f_1 \sqrt{d\sigma}$ and $u_2 f_2 \sqrt{d\sigma}$, and since these are coherent the resultant complex amplitude at P due to $d\sigma$ is $(u_1 f_1 + u_2 f_2)\sqrt{d\sigma}$, and the intensity, δI_p, is given by

$$\delta I_p = (u_1 f_1 + u_2 f_2)(\bar{u}_1 \bar{f}_1 + \bar{u}_2 \bar{f}_2)d\sigma.$$

Now, for any two complex quantities, z_1 and z_2, $z_1 \bar{z}_2 + \bar{z}_1 z_2 = 2\mathrm{R}\{z_1 \bar{z}_2\}$, where R denotes "real part of".

$$\therefore \ \delta I_p = |u_1|^2 d\sigma |f_1|^2 + |u_2|^2 d\sigma |f_2|^2 + 2\mathrm{R}\{u_1 \bar{u}_2 d\sigma f_1 \bar{f}_2\}.$$

Now since different source elements are incoherent, the total intensity at P due to the extended source Σ is given by

$$I_p = \iint_{\Sigma} \delta I_p$$

$$= (\iint_{\Sigma} |u_1|^2 d\sigma)|f_1|^2 + (\iint_{\Sigma} |u_2|^2 d\sigma)|f_2|^2 + 2R\{(\iint_{\Sigma} u_1 \bar{u}_2 d\sigma)f_1 \bar{f}_2\}$$

Now $\iint_{\Sigma} |u_1|^2 d\sigma(=I_1)$ and $\iint_{\Sigma} |u_2|^2 d\sigma(=I_2)$ are the total intensities emerging from P_1 and P_2. One puts

$$I_{12} = \iint_{\Sigma} u_1 \bar{u}_2 d\sigma$$

where I_{12} is called the *mutual intensity* and one puts

$$\gamma_{12} = \frac{I_{12}}{\sqrt{I_1 I_2}} \qquad \cdots \cdots \quad (6\text{--}14)$$

where γ_{12} is called the *phase coherence factor* or the *complex degree of coherence*. One has

$$I_p = I_1|f_1|^2 + I_2|f_2|^2 + 2\sqrt{I_1 I_2} R\{\gamma_{12} f_1 \bar{f}_2\} \quad \cdots \cdots \quad (6\text{--}15)$$

One denotes $|\gamma_{12}|$ by V_{12} and arg γ_{12} by β_{12}, i.e. $\gamma_{12} = V_{12} e^{i\beta_{12}}$. One can put $f_1 = g_1 e^{i\delta_1}$ and $f_2 = g_2 e^{i\delta_2}$, where δ_1 and δ_2 are the phase delays corresponding to the optical paths from P_1 to P and P_2 to P. Then $|f_1|^2 = g_1^2$, $|f_2|^2 = g_2^2$, and $f_1 \bar{f}_2 = g_1 g_2 e^{i(\delta_1 - \delta_2)}$. If a_1^2 and a_2^2 are the total intensities at P due to light that has travelled via P_1 and P_2 respectively, then $a_1^2 = g_1^2 I_1$ and $a_2^2 = g_2^2 I_2$, and one has

$$I_p = a_1^2 + a_2^2 + V_{12}.2a_1 a_2 \cos(\delta_1 - \delta_2 + \beta_{12}). \qquad \cdots \quad (6\text{--}16)$$

It will be seen that when $V_{12} = 0$ the result corresponds to complete incoherence between the disturbances arriving at P, and that when $V_{12} = 1$ and $\beta_{12} = 0$ the result corresponds to complete coherence. In general, V_{12} measures the extent to which the interference term is involved and is reasonably called the *degree of coherence*. It will be seen that when partially coherent disturbances are added there is, in effect, an additional phase difference β_{12} between them, although it simply becomes either zero or π in an axially symmetrical arrangement. The degree of coherence between points illuminated by an extended source is calculated in §11–12.

It will be seen from the discussions given above that for disturbances to be coherent they must have been emitted from the same source element at approximately the same time. Disturbances at different distances from a given source element are partially coherent owing to the finite coherence length which, as shown in §6–7, is related to the spectral impurity of the source. It will be seen in §8–10 that this has been studied with the Michelson interferometer. Disturbances arriving at neighbouring points from an extended quasi-monochromatic source are also partially coherent as indicated above and this effect has been studied with the Michelson stellar interferometer (see §§11–12 and 11–13). In the discussions given here the effect of the finite extent of the source is neglected when the finite coherence length (spectral impurity) is discussed, and the spectral impurity is neglected when discussing a source of finite extent. The complete theory deals with extended polychromatic sources.

It follows from the discussion of §11–12 that to illuminate a wide area coherently, using a quasi-monochromatic non-laser source, it is necessary to employ a pinhole source, with the result that one cannot obtain a high intensity. A discussion of the coherence properties of *lasers* (see §20–5) is beyond the scope of this book but it can be noted here that lasers give very long coherence lengths and, by avoiding the need for a pinhole, produce high-intensity coherent wavefronts, thus enabling wide areas to be coherently illuminated with high intensity.

6–5. Fourier Series*

In its simplest and most commonly quoted form, Fourier's theorem states that any periodic function can be expressed as the summation of a series of simple harmonic terms having frequencies that are multiples of that of the given function. (Actually the function must not have an infinite number of discontinuities during one period.) One refers to the function as being *analysed* into its simple harmonic components; the function is the *synthesis* of those components. To give some idea of what is involved, one simple example will be quoted. It can be shown that the rectangular wave form illustrated in Fig. 6–4(*a*) (which extends from $x=-\infty$ to $x=+\infty$) can be analysed into a series of sine waves, and can be expressed as the following summation:

$$y=\frac{4a}{\pi}\left(\sin x+\frac{1}{3}\sin 3x+\frac{1}{5}\sin 5x+\ldots\right).$$

Each of the first three terms is represented by a dotted curve in the figure and the sum of these three terms can be seen by inspection to be represented by the full curve. Fig. 6–4(*b*) shows the resultant of the first fifteen terms. It can be

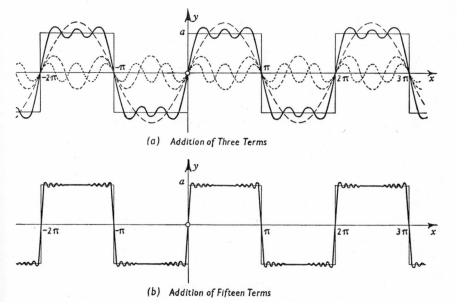

(*a*)   Addition of Three Terms

(*b*)   Addition of Fifteen Terms

Fig. 6–4. Analysis of a square wave.

* A rigorous discussion of Fourier series and Fourier Integrals is beyond the scope of this book. The present discussion merely serves to introduce the results that are required.

5*

seen that as more terms in the series are included in the summation, the resultant approaches the rectangular wave form more closely. In this example, the Fourier analysis of the function contains only sine terms which are initially in phase and which have frequencies which are odd multiples of that of the function represented. In general the series also contains cosine terms (which is equivalent to saying that it contains sine terms with various initial phases) and there are terms with every integral multiple of the original frequency. In general there is also a constant term.

This way of analysing a periodic function into simple harmonic components can be extended to non-periodic functions in the following manner. Suppose that the non-periodic function $y=f(x)$ has the form represented by the full line in Fig. 6-5. Let $\phi(x)$ be the periodic function which is identical to $f(x)$ in the region $-\pi \leqslant x \leqslant +\pi$ but which repeats itself outside that region as indicated by the dotted curve in the figure. Then, according to Fourier's theorem as stated above, the function $\phi(x)$ can be analysed into a series of simple harmonic terms. It is obvious that within the range $-\pi \leqslant x \leqslant +\pi$ the series also represents $f(x)$. By proceeding in this way one can represent any non-periodic function over any desired range by an appropriate series of simple harmonic terms. Obviously

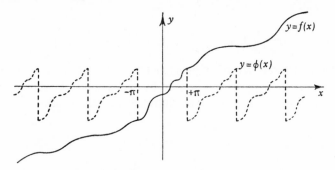

Fig. 6-5. Analysis of a non-periodic function over a limited range.

these terms have frequencies which are multiples of that of $\phi(x)$. In particular one can say that in the range $-\pi$ to $+\pi$ the function $f(X)$ can be written

$$f(X)=a_o+\sum_{n=1}^{n=\infty} a_n \cos nX+\sum_{n=1}^{n=\infty} b_n \sin nX. \quad . \quad . \quad (6\text{--}17)$$

Now $\int_{-\pi}^{+\pi} \cos n_1 X \cos n_2 X dX=0$ if $n_1 \neq n_2$, and $=\pi$ if $n_1=n_2$. In addition, $\int_{-\pi}^{+\pi} \cos n_1 X \sin n_2 X dX=0$ for all values of n_1 and n_2. Hence by integrating each side of (6–17) between $-\pi$ and $+\pi$ one has

$$a_0=\frac{1}{2\pi}\int_{-\pi}^{+\pi} f(X)dX.$$

Similarly, by multiplying each side of (6–17) by cos nX and integrating, one has

$$a_n = \frac{1}{\pi} \int_{-\pi}^{+\pi} f(X) \cos nX \, dX$$

and, by multiplying each side of (6–17) by sin nX and integrating, one obtains

$$b_n = \frac{1}{\pi} \int_{-\pi}^{+\pi} f(X) \sin nX \, dX.$$

It is convenient to transform (6–17) into a summation of complex exponential terms. One has

$$\cos nX = \tfrac{1}{2}(e^{inX} + e^{-inX}) \quad \text{and} \quad \sin nX = \tfrac{i}{2}(e^{-inX} - e^{inX}).$$

$$\therefore \quad a_n \cos nX + b_n \sin nX = \frac{a_n}{2} e^{inX} + \frac{a_n}{2} e^{-inX} - \frac{ib_n}{2} e^{inX} + \frac{ib_n}{2} e^{-inX}$$

$$= c_n e^{inX} + c_{-n} e^{-inX},$$

where $c_n = \tfrac{1}{2}(a_n - ib_n)$ and $c_{-n} = \tfrac{1}{2}(a_n + ib_n)$.

Hence, putting $a_0 = c_0$, one can write

$$f(X) = \sum_{n=-\infty}^{n=+\infty} c_n e^{inX}, \quad \ldots \ldots \quad (6\text{–}18)$$

where c_{-n} and c_n are conjugate complex quantities and

$$c_n = \frac{1}{2\pi} \int_{-\pi}^{+\pi} f(X) e^{-inX} dX. \quad \ldots \ldots \quad (6\text{–}19)$$

6–6. Extension of the Range. The Fourier Integral

Equation (6–18) shows that over the range $-\pi \leqslant X \leqslant +\pi$ the non-periodic function $f(X)$ may be represented as the summation of an infinite series of simple harmonic terms whose amplitudes are given by (6–19). It will now be shown that the range can be extended as far as may be desired and that it can be made to extend from $-\infty$ to $+\infty$. In the latter case the function is expressed as a *continuous* series of simple harmonic terms whose frequencies have every possible value between $-\infty$ and $+\infty$.

To show that the range can be extended and that $f(x)$ can be represented over the range $-l \leqslant x \leqslant +l$, put $x = lX/\pi$. Then (6–18) and (6–19) give

$$f(x) = \sum_{n=-\infty}^{n=+\infty} c_n e^{\left(\frac{in\pi x}{l}\right)}, \quad \ldots \ldots \quad (6\text{–}20)$$

where

$$c_n = \frac{1}{2l} \int_{-l}^{+l} f(x) e^{-\frac{in\pi x}{l}} dx. \quad \ldots \ldots \quad (6\text{–}21)$$

If one introduces the dummy variable x' in place of x in (6–21) one can write

$$f(x)=\sum_{n=-\infty}^{n=+\infty}\frac{1}{2l}\int_{-l}^{+l}f(x')e^{\frac{in\pi}{l}(x-x')}dx'\qquad \ldots \quad (6\text{–}22)$$

and the summation on the right-hand side represents $f(x)$ in the range $-l<x<+l$. In (6–22) l may be made as large as one pleases and it can be shown that one can extend the range in this way to $\pm\infty$. Now the nth harmonic in the series has wavelength $\lambda_n=2l/n$ and in terms of the wavelength constant $k=2\pi/\lambda$ one has $k_n=n\pi/l$. Similarly $k_{n+1}=(n+1)\pi/l$. Hence $k_{n+1}-k_n=\pi/l=\Delta k$ (say). One may then write (6–22) in the form

$$f(x)=\frac{1}{2\pi}\sum_{n=-\infty}^{n=+\infty}\Delta k\int_{-l}^{+l}f(x')e^{i\{n\Delta k(x-x')\}}dx'.\qquad \ldots \quad (6\text{–}23)$$

Now $n\Delta k$ is simply k_n and as $l\to\infty$ $\Delta k\to 0$. (6–23) then leads to the *Fourier Integral*:

$$f(x)=\frac{1}{2\pi}\int_{-\infty}^{+\infty}dk\int_{-\infty}^{+\infty}f(x')e^{ik(x-x')}dx'.\qquad \ldots \quad (6\text{–}24)$$

Hence one can write

$$f(x)=\frac{1}{\sqrt{2\pi}}\int_{-\infty}^{+\infty}g(k)e^{ikx}dk,\qquad \ldots \ldots \quad (6\text{–}25)$$

where

$$g(k)=\frac{1}{\sqrt{2\pi}}\int_{-\infty}^{+\infty}f(x)e^{-ikx}dx.\qquad \ldots \ldots \quad (6\text{–}26)$$

This shows that the function $f(x)$ is represented by a continuous series of simple harmonic terms whose amplitudes are given by (6–26). When two functions f and g are related in this way, each is said to be the *Fourier Transform* of the other. By writing (6–20) as $\sum_{n=-\infty}^{n=+\infty}c_{-n}e^{-\frac{in\pi x}{l}}$, one can reverse the signs in the exponents of (6–25) and (6–26), but there must always be $+i$ in one and $-i$ in the other.

The factor $1/\sqrt{2\pi}$ can be replaced by $1/2\pi$ in (6–25) and omitted from (6–26). If one then puts $k'=k/2\pi$, $dk=2\pi dk'$, and one has

$$f(x)=\int_{-\infty}^{+\infty}g(k')e^{2\pi ik'x}dk',\qquad \ldots \ldots \quad (6\text{–}25a)$$

where

$$g(k')=\int_{-\infty}^{+\infty}f(x)e^{-2\pi ik'x}dx.\qquad \ldots \ldots \quad (6\text{–}26a)$$

k' $(=1/\lambda)$ is now the number of cycles per unit of x. Thus, if one is thinking of a complicated motion as the superposition of simple harmonic motions, x is time, λ is period, and k' is frequency; $f(x)$ is the displacement as a function of time, and $g(k')$ is the amplitude of the simple harmonic component of frequency k'. If one is analysing a complicated variation of some quantity with distance, x is distance, λ is wavelength, and k' is known as *spatial frequency*.

Equation (6–25a) can be written

$$f(x) = \int_0^\infty g(k')e^{2\pi i k'x}dk' + \int_0^\infty g(-k')e^{-2\pi i k'x}dk'$$

$$= \int_0^\infty [g(k')+g(-k')]\cos 2\pi k'x dk' + i\int_0^\infty [g(k')-g(-k')]\sin 2\pi k'x dk'.$$

Similarly, (6–26a) gives

$$g(k') = \int_0^\infty [f(x)+f(-x)]\cos 2\pi k'x dx - i\int_0^\infty [f(x)-f(-x)]\sin 2\pi k'x dx,$$

and $g(-k') = \int_0^\infty [f(x)+f(-x)]\cos 2\pi k'x dx + i\int_0^\infty [f(x)-f(-x)]\sin 2\pi k'x dx.$

Suppose, now, that $f(x)$ is real and an even function, i.e. $f(-x)=f(x)$. Then $g(-k')=g(k')$ and one has

$$f(x) = 2\int_0^\infty g(k')\cos 2\pi k'x dk' \quad \ldots \ldots \quad (6\text{--}25b)$$

and

$$g(k') = 2\int_0^\infty f(x)\cos 2\pi k'x dx. \quad \ldots \ldots \quad (6\text{--}26b)$$

Each is referred to as the *Fourier cosine transform* of the other.

6–7. Wave Trains of Finite Length

As has already been pointed out, $\phi=a\sin k(ct-x)$ represents a simple harmonic disturbance of wavelength $2\pi/k$ travelling in the positive x-direction with speed c. At any instant the wave extends from $x=-\infty$ to $x=+\infty$, and at any given value of x the disturbance continues from $t=-\infty$ to $t=+\infty$. The wave can be represented by Fig. 6–6(a). At a given instant the disturbance in space is represented by having x as the abscissa, and the disturbance at a given position in space is represented by having t as the abscissa. The disturbance represented in (b) is *not* a simple harmonic wave since it follows a sine curve over a certain range only and is zero beyond that range. Strictly speaking, then, ϕ is a non-periodic function—it does not repeat itself to infinity. Consequently, it can be represented as the summation of a continuous series of simple harmonic terms by an expression of the form of (6–25), the relative amplitudes of the components being defined by (6–26). It can be shown that the frequency distribution for a sharply limited sine wave of this type is of the form shown in Fig. 6–6(c). The train of waves from a source is unlikely to be of this form, being more likely to start and stop gradually as in (d). It can be shown that the frequency distribution is then of the form shown in (e). Further analysis shows that the longer is the *wave group* shown in (d), the sharper is the maximum in (e). Thus for a long train of waves most of the energy is concentrated into a small range of wavelengths. This is the form of the disturbance from a so-called monochromatic source. It will be seen that no source is truly monochromatic since this would imply that it has radiated, and will radiate, for ever.

Now the discussion of § 6–4 shows that if one is to obtain interference between disturbances that have traversed widely different optical path lengths, the wave

Fig. 6–6. Analysis of finite wave trains.

groups must be long. This means that the energy must be concentrated into a narrow band of wavelengths—a more nearly monochromatic source is required. The frequency distribution of light emitted from a nominally monochromatic source can be deduced from observations of the way in which the visibility of the interference phenomena decrease as the optical path difference between the interfering disturbances is increased. (See § 8–10.)

With a source emitting what is known as a line spectrum one has, in crude terms, the emission of a number of discrete wavelengths; actually one has the emission of a number of sharp frequency distributions.

In a source emitting "white light" spectroscopic analysis shows that the energy is fairly evenly distributed over a wide range of wavelengths. From

Fig. 6–7. A single pulse.

(6–25) it can be shown that the synthesis of such a distribution is a short *pulse* such as that represented in Fig. 6–7(a). In Fig. 6–6 this corresponds to the extreme case of the frequency distribution in (e) becoming very broad and the wave train (d) becoming very short. Fig. 6–7(b) illustrates how a continuous distribution of wavelengths gives a pulse. It is only at O that curves of every wavelength are in phase. As one moves away from this point the waves gradually get more and more out of phase to give destructive interference. With a number of discrete wavelengths the waves would begin to get in phase again later, but with a continuous distribution of wavelengths they never give constructive interference again. It can also be seen from this figure that when most of the energy is concentrated into a relatively small range of wavelengths one can move farther from O before one gets destructive interference and the resultant is a wave group of the form shown in Fig. 6–6. Fig. 6–7(*b*) can also be used to represent the way in which interference fringes for different wavelengths gradually get out of step away from the zero order fringe so that only the latter can be observed with white light. (See Chapter VII.)

In the past there have been many arguments on the question of whether white light "really consists" of a series of pulses or a mixture of disturbances of all wavelengths. It will be seen that the two are synonymous.

In many experiments it is found to be possible to obtain interference effects with white light by arranging that disturbances from the source are superposed after traversing almost equal optical path lengths. The necessity of having the paths almost equal can be explained by the fact that disturbances from the same pulse must overlap or by saying that the interference fringes for all wavelengths must coincide.

6–8. Group Velocity

In all the above discussions it has been assumed that simple harmonic waves are propagated with a speed c which is independent of the frequency—there is no dispersion. When this is so every component of a wave group travels at the same speed. This means that the whole group also travels at that speed and is completely unchanged during its passage through the medium. It can be shown that if there is dispersion the wave group constituting the disturbance of finite length travels at a speed which differs from that of any of the component simple harmonic waves. This phenomenon can be observed with the waves spreading across the surface when a stone is dropped into still water. A group of waves is observed to spread out across the water surface but, in the group, waves can be seen to be moving faster than the group itself. These waves appear at the rear of the group, travel through it, and die out at the front. It is found that for any type of wave motion the *group velocity* is less than the velocity of individual waves (the *wave velocity*) if the dispersion is such that the wave velocity increases with wavelength.

Suppose one has two superposed simple harmonic waves, with equal amplitudes and slightly different frequencies and velocities, propagated in the positive x-direction. The resultant is given by

$$\phi = a \cos \frac{2\pi}{\lambda}(ct-x) + a \cos \frac{2\pi}{\lambda+\delta\lambda}[(c+\delta c)t-x]$$

$$= 2a \left\{ \cos \pi \left[\left(\frac{c}{\lambda} + \frac{c+\delta c}{\lambda+\delta\lambda} \right) t - \left(\frac{1}{\lambda} + \frac{1}{\lambda+\delta\lambda} \right) x \right] \right.$$

$$\left. \times \cos \pi \left[\left(\frac{c}{\lambda} - \frac{c+\delta c}{\lambda+\delta\lambda} \right) t - \left(\frac{1}{\lambda} - \frac{1}{\lambda+\delta\lambda} \right) x \right] \right\}.$$

If $\delta\lambda \ll \lambda$ one can write λ^2 in place of $\lambda(\lambda+\delta\lambda)$ so that one has

$$\frac{1}{\lambda} - \frac{1}{\lambda+\delta\lambda} = \frac{\delta\lambda}{\lambda^2} \quad \text{and} \quad \frac{c}{\lambda} - \frac{c+\delta c}{\lambda+\delta\lambda} = \frac{c\delta\lambda - \lambda\delta c}{\lambda^2}$$

and

$$\phi = 2a \cos\frac{2\pi}{\lambda}(ct-x) \cos\frac{\pi\delta\lambda}{\lambda^2}\left(\frac{c\delta\lambda - \lambda\delta c}{\delta\lambda}t - x\right). \quad . \quad (6\text{--}27)$$

At a given instant the variation of ϕ with x is of the form shown in Fig. 6–8. The wave shown as a full line corresponds to the first term in (6–27) and is modulated by the slowly varying envelope which corresponds to the second term.

Fig. 6-8. Wave groups.

The first term defines a wave of the same speed and wavelength as the original waves but the envelope has wavelength $2\lambda^2/\delta\lambda$ and speed $(c\delta\lambda - \lambda\delta c)/\delta\lambda$. Thus the wave is divided up into groups which travel with the group velocity v given by

$$v = c - \lambda\frac{dc}{d\lambda}. \quad . \quad . \quad . \quad . \quad . \quad (6\text{--}28)$$

As the disturbance is propagated, the wave shown as a continuous line in Fig. 6–8 moves along with velocity c while the envelope moves with velocity v.

This example involves the superposition of only two waves. It has already been seen that if one has a continuous series of waves they form only one group and (6–28) shows that this has a unique group velocity only if the dispersion term $\lambda\,dc/d\lambda$ is constant. If the wave group is mainly confined to a narrow range of frequencies, the dispersion term is usually almost constant so that there is a unique group velocity. Equation (6–28) shows that the group velocity is smaller than the wave velocity if the latter increases with wavelength, is greater than the wave velocity if $dc/d\lambda$ is negative, and is equal to the wave velocity if there is no dispersion.

It is sometimes convenient to have alternative expressions for the group velocity. For example, if ω is the pulsatance and f is the frequency, one has

$$\omega = 2\pi f = \frac{2\pi c}{\lambda} = ck,$$

$$\therefore \quad \frac{d\omega}{dk} = c + k\frac{dc}{dk} = c - \lambda\frac{dc}{d\lambda},$$

i.e.

$$v = \frac{d\omega}{dk}. \quad . \quad . \quad . \quad . \quad . \quad . \quad (6\text{--}29)$$

Now $(d\omega/dk) = (d\omega/df)(df/d\lambda)(d\lambda/dk)$, where $d\omega/df = 2\pi$ and $dk/d\lambda = -2\pi/\lambda^2$.

$$\therefore \quad v = -\lambda^2\frac{df}{d\lambda}. \quad . \quad . \quad . \quad . \quad . \quad (6\text{--}30)$$

If c_0 is the velocity of light in a vacuum the refractive index of the medium is defined by $n=c_0/c$. From (6–29) one has

$$\frac{1}{v}=\frac{dk}{d\omega}=\frac{d}{d\omega}\left(\frac{\omega}{c}\right)=\frac{1}{c}-\frac{\omega}{c^2}\frac{dc}{d\omega},$$

whence
$$\frac{1}{v}=\frac{1}{c}+\frac{\omega}{c_0}\frac{dn}{d\omega}.\qquad\ldots\ldots\quad(6\text{–}31)$$

6–9. Passage of a Pulse Through a Diffraction Grating

In this section (and in § 6–11) it is assumed that the reader is familiar with the elementary properties of diffraction gratings. These are discussed in detail in

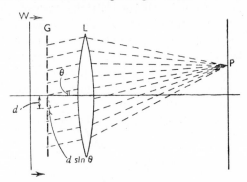

Fig. 6–9. Passage of a pulse through a grating.

Chapter XII where it is convenient to consider the incident light resolved into its simple harmonic components. It is convenient to discuss here the passage of a pulse through a grating. It has already been seen that a pulse can be analysed into waves whose frequencies are evenly distributed over a wide range and it is easy to see how a grating performs this analysis to give a continuous spectrum. In Fig. 6–9 a plane pulse W is incident on a grating G which consists of narrow slits. Thus a single pulse emerges from each slit and these pulses arrive at regular intervals at the point P in the focal plane of the lens L. There is thus a periodic disturbance at P. Referring only to the first order spectrum, the number of pulses arriving at P per second gives the frequency of the disturbance found at P, the wavelength being equal to the path difference from P to successive slits in the grating. This path difference is $d \sin \theta$, so that the wavelength of the disturbance found at P is given by $\lambda=d \sin \theta$, which agrees with the result obtained in §12–1. The number of pulses involved gives the number of waves in the train at P. This is equal to the number of slits in the grating, i.e. to the resolving power of the grating in the first order (see §12–6).

6–10. Passage of a Pulse Through a Prism

In Fig. 6–10 P is the centre of the spectral line for monochromatic light of wavelength λ. The optical path from A to A′ is then equal to that from B to B′. Thus disturbances travelling with the wave velocity throughout take equal times to travel from A to A′ and B to B′. If AB now represents a pulse entering the prism, it can be resolved into a broad spectrum of simple harmonic waves, but only those within a small range of wavelengths give an appreciable amplitude at P. Suppose that the group velocity for these waves in the prism is v. Now disturbances passing from A to A′ travel with the wave velocity throughout but

Fig. 6-10. Passage of a pulse through a prism.

the relevant disturbance from B to B′ travels at the relatively slow group velocity through a thickness t of the prism. This causes the time taken for the path t in the prism to be t/v instead of t/c. The time taken for the disturbance to travel from B to B′ therefore exceeds the time taken for the pulse to travel from A to A′ by an amount $(t/v-t/c)$ and the disturbance at P continues for this period of time. (The effect of dispersion in the lens is ignored.) Suppose that during this time N waves of frequency f pass. Then

$$N=\left(\frac{t}{v}-\frac{t}{c}\right)f.$$

Inserting the value of $1/v$ from (6–31) one has

$$N=\frac{tf\omega}{c_o}\frac{dn}{d\omega}$$

and if λ is now the wavelength in a vacuum one has

$$\omega=\frac{2\pi c_o}{\lambda} \quad \text{or} \quad \frac{d\omega}{d\lambda}=-\frac{2\pi c_o}{\lambda^2},$$

$$\therefore \quad N=-t\frac{dn}{d\lambda}. \quad \quad \ldots \ldots \quad (6\text{–}32)$$

N is positive since, as has already been pointed out, $dn/d\lambda$ is negative when $v<c$. Again the number of waves in the wave train is equal to the resolving power. (See §11–5.)

6–11. Talbot's Bands

Suppose white light enters a prism spectroscope to form a continuous spectrum. In 1837 Talbot discovered that if a thin glass plate is placed across one half of the aperture of the prism as indicated in Fig. 6–11(a), a series of dark bands appears across the spectrum. It is found that the bands are most distinct for a certain thickness of the plate and that they cannot be observed at all if the plate has more than twice this thickness. It is also found that the same bands are formed whether the plate is placed before or after the prism or immediately in front of the observer's eye, provided that the disturbances that pass through the plate are those that pass through the thinner part of the prism. No bands are formed if the plate covers the other half of the prism aperture. Similar bands are observed in the continuous spectrum formed by a grating if the plate covers half the width of the grating as in Fig. 6–11(*b*), but again no bands are formed if the plate covers the other half of the aperture.

The formation of the bands can be explained quite simply by saying that the plate introduces a path difference between disturbances traversing the two halves of the aperture and that for some wavelengths one will have destructive interference. However, this does not explain why there is an optimum thickness for the plate nor why no bands are formed when the plate covers the other half of the aperture. These facts are easily explained if the white light which enters the prism or grating consists of a series of pulses. The arrangement involving a grating will be considered first. If there are N slits in the grating, each half of the

Fig. 6–11. Observation of Talbot's bands.

grating gives a wave train containing $N/2$ waves. It follows that two wave trains, each $N\lambda/2$ in length, pass through the appropriate point P in the focal plane of the telescope objective. If there is no plate in position, the wave train from the lower half of the grating arrives first at P and is immediately followed by the wave train from the upper half of the grating. Consequently, if the wave train from the lower half of the grating is retarded by the plate, it can overlap the other and the two can interfere. It is obvious that the wave trains cannot be made to overlap by retarding that from the upper half of the grating. This explains why the bands can be produced by interposing the plate across one half of the aperture but not the other. It is also obvious that the interference will be most marked when the thickness of the plate is just sufficient to make the wave trains overlap along the whole of their length, and that no bands will be produced if the retardation in the plate is increased until the wave trains are again prevented from overlapping. That is to say, the bands have maximum visibility when the plate produces a retardation of $N/2$ wavelengths and the visibility falls to zero if the retardation exceeds $N\lambda$.

A similar explanation is possible with the arrangement involving a prism. It was shown in §6–10 that a train of $-t\,dn/d\lambda$ waves arrives at a point in the spectrum and that the initial disturbance arrives from the apex of the prism. That is to say, the plate must be inserted as indicated by Fig. 6–11 in order to retard the first half of the wave train until it overlaps the second half. The optimum retardation is obviously $-\tfrac{1}{2}t\,dn/d\lambda$.

The formation of Talbot's bands has also been explained as follows. The plate and the space beside it can be looked upon as constituting an *echelon grating* of two elements. The properties of these gratings are discussed in Chapter XII and it is shown that one can observe only one principal maximum for those wavelengths for which the optical path difference introduced by the plate is an integral number of wavelengths. For other wavelengths two maxima are always contained beneath an envelope whose minima are only twice as far apart as the principal maxima. Suppose, then, that light is incident normally on an aperture of which half is occupied by a plate. Looking against the oncoming light, the

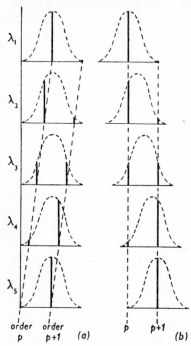

positions of the principal maxima for a number of slightly different wavelengths will be as indicated in Fig. 6–12(*a*) if $\lambda_1 > \lambda_2 > \lambda_3$, etc., and the plate covers the left-hand side of the aperture. If a prism is now inserted with its apex to the left, the light is deviated to the right and the deviations for $\lambda_1, \lambda_2, \lambda_3, \ldots$, are progressively larger. For a suitable combination of plate and prism the result is the superposition of the *p*th and (*p*+1)th orders as shown in Fig. 6–12(*b*). In the spectrum these give adjacent maxima between which there is a minimum. Throughout the banded spectrum, light with a narrow distribution of wavelengths collects in the maxima. If the prism had been reversed so that the plate covered the other half of its aperture, the principal maxima would not have been collected together in this way and the bands would not be observed. Since inadequate dispersion by the prism for a given plate thickness corresponds to excessive thickness of the plate for a given

Fig. 6–12. Talbot's bands with a prism.

prism, one can also explain how (for a given prism) it is possible for the plate to be too thick for the bands to be formed.

The envelopes shown in Fig. 6–12 represent the central maxima in the diffraction pattern for monochromatic disturbances when using half the aperture of the prism and no plate. If the full aperture is used the width of these maxima is halved and becomes equal to the separation of the Talbot's bands which were obtained with the plate in position across half the aperture. That is, the separation of the Talbot's bands which are obtained at a given point in the spectrum with a given spectroscope is equal to twice the distance from the centre of the maximum to the first minimum in the ordinary spectral line for one wavelength.

6–12. Stationary Waves

It was shown in §6–1 that when one superposes two simple harmonic waves of the same frequency travelling in the same direction the resultant is a similar wave. An interesting result is produced by superposing two waves of the same frequency travelling in opposite directions. The waves can be represented by

$$\phi_1 = a \sin k(ct-x),$$
$$\phi_2 = a \sin k(ct+x),$$

and the resultant is

$$\phi = 2a \cos kx \sin kct. \quad \ldots \ldots \quad (6\text{–}33)$$

This does not represent a progressive wave. That is to say, its profile does not move along; it is known as a *stationary* or *standing wave*. At all points along the x-direction the disturbance is simple harmonic with frequency $ck/2\pi$, the amplitude at any point being $2a \cos kx$. It will be seen that the disturbance has maximum amplitude at $kx=p\pi$ (p integral) but has zero amplitude at $kx=(p+\frac{1}{2})\pi$. The points where the disturbance is zero are called *nodes,* and those where the disturbance has maximum amplitude are called *antinodes.* The distance between adjacent nodes or adjacent antinodes is given by

$$k(x_2-x_1) = p\pi - (p-1)\pi,$$

or

$$x_2 - x_1 = \frac{\lambda}{2}.$$

The occurrence of stationary waves on a finite stretched string is well known. The interference of light waves to give stationary waves has also been confirmed experimentally (see § 21–10). The phenomenon is more difficult to observe with light waves because the wavelength is very short.

6–13. The Doppler Effect

If there is relative motion between a source and a receiver, the frequency measured by an observer moving with the receiver differs from that measured by an observer moving with the source. If the source approaches the receiver the frequency observed by the receiver is higher than that for an observer at the source, and if the observer moves away from the source the apparent frequency is lower than that of the source. This explains the sudden fall in the apparent pitch of the whistle when a railway engine passes the observer. It will be shown below that the fractional change in frequency is given by the ratio of the velocity of the source relative to the observer, to the velocity of the waves. For light the velocity of the waves is very large and this ratio is usually very small.

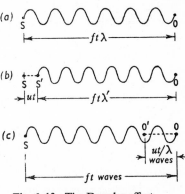

Fig. 6–13. The Doppler effect.

In Fig. 6–13(*a*) S is a stationary source of sound of frequency f and O is the stationary observer. Suppose that a disturbance passes from S to O in time t. Then ft waves are emitted during this time and occupy the space between S and O. If λ is the wavelength $SO=ft\lambda$. Suppose now that the source moves towards O with speed u. In time t the source moves a distance ut to S' and ft waves are emitted. Since these waves now occupy the distance S'O the new wavelength is λ', where $ft\lambda'=$S'O$=$SO$-ut$,

i.e.
$$ft\lambda'=ft\lambda-ut,$$

$$\therefore\ \lambda'=\lambda-\frac{u}{f}.$$

Now if f' is the frequency measured at O and c is the velocity of the waves through the air, one has $f'\lambda'=f\lambda=c$.

Hence
$$\lambda'=\lambda\left(1-\frac{u}{c}\right),\qquad\ldots\ldots\ldots\quad(6\text{--}34)$$

or
$$f'=\frac{f}{1-\dfrac{u}{c}}.\qquad\ldots\ldots\ldots\quad(6\text{--}35)$$

Suppose now that the source is stationary and that the observer moves towards the source with velocity u. During time t the observer moves from O a distance ut to O' [Fig. 6–13(c)]. ft waves pass O during this time but the observer also receives the ut/λ waves which lie between O and O'. The total number of waves received is therefore $t(f+u/\lambda)$ and the apparent frequency is $f''=f+u/\lambda$. Since $\lambda=c/f$ this gives

$$f''=f\left(1+\frac{u}{c}\right).\qquad\ldots\ldots\ldots\quad(6\text{--}36)$$

In the above discussion the waves are assumed to be propagated with definite velocity in a fixed medium with respect to which the motion of the source and the observer can be specified. According to the theory of relativity light waves are not propagated in a medium which can be said to be at absolute rest and with respect to which the absolute motion of a source or observer can be specified. The theory shows that the only movement which can be recognized is the *relative* motion of source and observer. It shows that there can be no distinction between the two cases discussed above and leads to the result

$$f'=f\sqrt{\frac{1+\dfrac{v}{c}}{1-\dfrac{v}{c}}},\qquad\ldots\ldots\ldots\quad(6\text{--}37)$$

where c is the velocity of light and v is the relative velocity of source and observer towards one another.

The Doppler effect has been observed in light from the sun, the spectral lines from an approaching edge being of slightly shorter wavelength than those from a receding edge. In the laboratory the effect has been observed by using rotating mirrors to produce a virtual source in motion. Much more rapidly moving sources have been obtained in the laboratory by accelerating hydrogen ions and then neutralizing them without slowing them down appreciably. If the atoms are then excited and emit light, one can observe a Doppler shift in the wavelengths of the spectral lines emitted. Owing to the fact that the atoms in the source are always in motion, the Doppler effect causes all spectral lines to cover a range of frequencies (see § 8–10).

One important application of the Doppler effect is in the discovery of double stars that are so close that they cannot be resolved with a telescope. If one has a bright star and a dark star rotating round one another the observed spectral lines exhibit a periodic shift about a mean position, moving to the shorter wavelengths when the bright star is approaching the observer and to the longer wavelengths when it is receding. If one has two stars of similar brightnesses rotating round one another the observed spectral lines become double and single periodically. They are double when the line joining the stars is perpendicular to the line of sight since one star is approaching and the other is receding. When one star is behind the other, they are both moving across the line of sight and the spectral lines are single.

6–14. Malus' Experiment. Malus' Law

In all the above discussions it has been assumed that the light disturbance at any point can be represented by a single scalar quantity. Malus' experiment is one of the simplest experiments which show the inadequacy of a scalar wave theory of light. The arrangement is shown in Fig. 6–14. P_1 and P_2 are glass plates on which light is incident at an angle of about 57°. (The significance of this particular angle of incidence will be seen later.) When the planes of the plates are parallel as indicated in the figure the light is reflected as shown. If, however, the plate P_2 is rotated about the ray 2 as axis, it is found that as the reflected ray 3 swings out of the plane of the figure its intensity decreases. The intensity of ray 3 falls to zero when P_2 is rotated 90°. The ray reappears as one continues to rotate P_2 and its intensity rises to a maximum when the rotation of P_2 reaches 180°. Its intensity falls to zero again when the rotation reaches 270°, and returns to its original maximum value at 360°. Thus the intensity of ray 3 is a maximum when the planes of incidence at P_1 and P_2 are parallel, and falls to zero when the planes of incidence are at right angles. If either of the angles of incidence is not 57° the intensity of ray 3 varies between maximum and minimum values but does not fall to zero. The reason for this will be seen later. One is led to the conclusion that under certain circumstances the intensity of a ray reflected from a glass plate varies as the incident ray is rotated relative to the plate about itself as axis. Obviously there is something unsymmetrical about such a ray. This behaviour cannot be explained in terms of a scalar wave theory. For example, the phenomenon is not observed with sound waves. In the case of sound the vibrations are known to be along the direction of propagation and can therefore be specified by a single scalar quantity. In order to explain the effect it is necessary to assume that light waves are transverse waves. For example, if the disturbance at any point consists of linear simple harmonic vibrations, these must be perpendicular to the direction of propagation or must

Fig. 6–14.
Malus' experiment.

have a component in that direction. To specify the disturbance completely, it is then necessary to specify the direction of the vibrations as well as the amplitude and frequency, i.e. one must use a vector. A beam of light obtained direct from the sun or from an ordinary filament lamp does not exhibit this non-symmetrical nature although it does show the effect after it has been reflected from a glass plate. Light showing this non-symmetrical property is said to be *polarized* and direct sunlight is *unpolarized*. In Malus' experiment the reflection from the plate P_1 causes ray 2 to be polarized and P_1 is referred to as the *polarizer*. The fact that the ray *is* polarized is shown by its behaviour at P_2. P_2 is called the *analyser*. The eye cannot differentiate between polarized and unpolarized light.

Malus' experiment can be explained if it is assumed that in the light reflected from P_1 the disturbances take the form of linear simple harmonic motions in a direction perpendicular to the direction of propagation. The fact that no effect is produced by changing the separation of P_1 and P_2 leads to the conclusion that these transverse vibrations remain in the same plane as the disturbance progresses. Such light is said to be *plane-polarized*. It can be assumed that when the angle of incidence is 57° the light reflected from a glass plate is plane polarized with the vibrations perpendicular to the plane of incidence, and that with this angle of incidence a plate cannot reflect light whose vibrations are *in* the plane of incidence. This accounts for the fact that ray 3 is absent when the planes of incidence at P_1 and P_2 are at right angles. An equally good assumption would be that for ray 2 the vibrations are parallel to the plane of incidence at P_1 and that there is no reflection if the vibrations are perpendicular to the plane of incidence. For the present purposes it does not matter which of these assumptions is made but the former will be adopted. The vibration direction then becomes the direction of the electric displacement in the electromagnetic theory, and it will be seen later that this is an advantage. One can therefore define the *plane of vibration* of plane polarized light as the plane of incidence at a glass plate at which, for an appropriate angle of incidence, there is no reflection. In the past, the term *plane of polarization* has been used for the plane of vibration as defined here or, more often, for the plane at right angles to it. The term will not be used in this book.

In Malus' experiment (still using angles of incidence of 57°) it is found that as P_2 is rotated about ray 2 as axis the intensity of ray 3 is proportional to $\cos^2 \theta$, where θ is the angle between the planes of incidence at P_1 and P_2. This is known as *Malus' law* and can be explained in the following way. It is assumed that the vibrations in ray 2 can be resolved into components in and perpendicular to the plane of incidence at P_2 and that the light corresponding to the component in the plane of incidence cannot be reflected from P_2 when the angle of incidence is 57°. On the other hand, light corresponding to the component perpendicular to the plane of incidence is reflected with a reflection factor which is constant for that particular angle of incidence. Now the vibrations in ray 2 are perpendicular to the plane of incidence at P_1 so that when the angle between the planes of incidence at P_1 and P_2 is θ a vibration of amplitude a in ray 2 has component $a \cos \theta$ perpendicular to the plane of incidence at P_2. This component can be reflected and ray 3 has amplitude $ra \cos \theta$, where r is a reflection factor. This means that as P_2 is rotated the intensity of ray 3 is proportional to $\cos^2 \theta$.

6-15. Brewster's Law

If direct sunlight or light from an ordinary filament lamp falls on a glass plate, it is found that the intensity of the reflected beam does not vary as the plate is rotated about an incident ray as axis—even if the angle of incidence is 57°. This implies that (at least when averaged over a finite period of time) the vibrations in the incident light have equal components in all directions and can be resolved into components of equal amplitude in any two mutually perpendicular directions. The light is unpolarized. (There is an alternative possibility as will be seen later.) A mixture of unpolarized light and plane polarized light is referred to as *partially plane polarized.* If it falls on a glass plate at 57°, the intensity of the reflected beam varies between a maximum and a minimum as the mirror is rotated about an incident ray as axis (instead of between a maximum and zero as it is does when the incident light is plane polarized).

It is found that when unpolarized light is incident on the surface of any transparent material, the reflected and refracted beams are partially plane polarized. For a particular angle of incidence known as the *polarizing angle,* the reflected beam becomes completely plane polarized with the plane of vibration perpendicular to the plane of incidence. (It will be seen in Chapter XXI that there are, in practice,

Fig. 6–15. Brewster's law.

small deviations from this condition, but they can be ignored in the present discussions.) Brewster discovered that when light is incident at the polarizing angle the plane polarized reflected beam is at right angles to the partially plane polarized refracted beam. Fig. 6–15 shows light incident at the polarizing angle I_p. The fact that in the reflected light the vibrations are perpendicular to the plane of incidence is denoted by the dots. The lines and dots on the incident and refracted rays denote that in these rays the vibrations have components both in and perpendicular to the plane of incidence. Snell's law of refraction gives

$$\frac{\sin I_p}{\sin I'_p} = n$$

and since the reflected and refracted rays are at right angles,

$$I'_p = \frac{\pi}{2} - I_p,$$

i.e. $\tan I_p = n.$ . . . . (6–38)

This is known as *Brewster's Law.* It is now possible to see the origin of the mysterious 57° which has been referred to frequently when dealing with glass plates. The refractive index of hard crown glass is about 1·52 and since $\tan^{-1} 1·52$ is 56·7° it will be seen that 57° is an approximate value for the polarizing angle. When the refractive index is increased to 1·7 the polarizing angle increases to about 59·5°; i.e. it is not widely different for different glasses.

The polarization resulting from reflection and refraction can be explained by assuming that the reflection coefficient for light whose vibrations are in the plane of incidence is different from that for light whose vibrations are perpendicular to the plane of incidence and that for the former it falls to zero at the polarizing angle. This is confirmed experimentally. Unpolarized incident light can then be resolved into two components: one with vibrations in, and the other with them perpendicular to, the plane of incidence, and these are reflected and refracted in the same way as independent plane polarized beams. Thus the reflected light is plane polarized when the angle of incidence is equal to the polarizing angle, and partially plane polarized for other angles of incidence. If one has plane polarized incident light and the plane of vibration is inclined to the plane of incidence, it can be resolved into components in the same way. One can see at once that if the angle of incidence at either of the plates in Fig. 6–14 is not equal to the polarizing angle, the intensity of ray 3 will vary between a maximum and a minimum but will never fall to zero.

Now when unpolarized light is incident on a glass plate only half the energy is represented as having its vibrations perpendicular to the plane of incidence, and only about 15% of this is reflected at the polarizing angle. On the other hand, *all* the light whose vibrations are in the plane of incidence is refracted. If the light is passed through a series of parallel plates, some of the light with vibrations perpendicular to the plane of incidence is removed at each reflection and, apart from absorption losses, all the light polarized at right angles is transmitted. Thus the larger is the number of plates the more nearly is the transmitted light plane polarized, and very little of this light is lost. In a more detailed study it is, of course, necessary to take into account the multiple reflections between the various surfaces.

6–16. Superposition of Beams of Polarized Light

It is shown in Chapter XXII that if light is passed through a calcite crystal there are, in general, two emergent rays. Both these rays are plane polarized and their planes of vibration are at right angles. If the incident light is unpolarized the two emergent rays have equal intensities, and if the incident light is plane polarized the relative intensities of the emergent beams depends on the orientation of the plane of vibration of the incident light with respect to the crystal structure. These two plane polarized beams can be superposed after being made to traverse different optical paths. It is possible to rotate their planes of vibration before superposing them but the way in which this is done need not be discussed here. (See Chapters XXII and XXIII.) In this way it is possible to study the effects of superposing plane polarized disturbances under various conditions. The conditions under which it is possible to obtain interference fringes with the polarized disturbances are summarized in the *Fresnel-Arago laws*:

(1) Two plane polarized beams whose vibration directions are at right angles cannot give interference fringes, i.e. they cannot give destructive interference.

(2) Two plane polarized beams whose vibration directions are the same interfere under the same conditions as two similar beams of unpolarized light, provided they are originally derived from the same beam of plane polarized light or from the same plane polarized component of unpolarized light.

(3) Two plane polarized beams which are derived from perpendicularly polarized components of unpolarized light never produce interference fringes, even if their planes of vibration have been rotated until they are the same.

Results 1 and 2 are what one might expect, since the two transverse vibrations are obviously unable to interfere destructively when they are at right angles, and are able to do so when they are in the same straight line unless something has occurred to upset their coherence. For example, if the two beams had traversed widely different optical paths, they would in any case be unable to interfere. The third law given by Fresnel and Arago indicates that the perpendicularly polarized components into which unpolarized light can be resolved must always be regarded as being incoherent. This result will be discussed again later.

The first of the Fresnel-Arago laws does not imply that there is no interaction when one superposes two perpendicularly polarized beams which are derived from the same plane polarized beam; it simply says that interference fringes cannot be produced. Consider now the form which the interaction does take. If the two beams are produced from a single plane polarized beam by means of a calcite crystal as described above they will not, in general, have the same amplitude. Let their amplitudes be denoted by a_1 and a_2. Suppose that, before being superposed, the beams traverse unequal optical paths with the result that there is a phase difference δ between their vibrations. The problem, then, is to find the resultant of two simple harmonic vibrations of the same frequency at right angles. The vibrations can be assumed to occur in the yz plane and to be represented by

$$\left.\begin{aligned} y &= a_1 \sin \omega t, \\ z &= a_2 \sin (\omega t + \delta). \end{aligned}\right\} \quad \cdots \cdots \quad (6\text{–}39)$$

If these are imagined as components of the motion of a particle, the path of the resultant motion of the particle is given by eliminating t from this pair of equations. One has

$$z = a_2 \sin \omega t \cos \delta + a_2 \cos \omega t \sin \delta$$

$$= a_2 \frac{y}{a_1} \cos \delta + a_2 \left(\sqrt{1 - \frac{y^2}{a_1^2}} \right) \sin \delta$$

or

$$\left(z - a_2 \frac{y}{a_1} \cos \delta \right)^2 = a_2^2 \left(1 - \frac{y^2}{a_1^2} \right) \sin^2 \delta,$$

which reduces to

$$\sin^2 \delta = \frac{y^2}{a_1^2} + \frac{z^2}{a_2^2} - \frac{2yz}{a_1 a_2} \cos \delta. \quad \cdots \cdots \quad (6\text{–}40)$$

The curve represented by this equation is, in general, an ellipse. It is plotted in Fig. 6–16 for various values of δ. In general, the angle θ between the co-ordinate axes and the axes of the ellipse is given by

$$\tan 2\theta = \frac{2a_1 a_2 \cos \delta}{a_1^2 - a_2^2}. \quad \cdots \cdots \quad (6\text{–}41)$$

The axes of the ellipse become parallel to the y and z axes when $\delta = \pi/2$, $3\pi/2$, $5\pi/2$, . . ., and the curve reduces to a straight line when $\delta = 0$, π, 2π, ... By inspection of the original equation it is easy to see that the direction in which the particle traverses each path is as indicated.

Thus when $\delta = 0, \pi, 2\pi, \ldots$, the two superposed plane polarized beams give a plane polarized resultant. For other values of δ the resultant is an elliptic motion and one is said to have *elliptically polarized light*. If $a_1 = a_2$ the resultant reduces to a circle when $\delta = \pi/2, 3\pi/2, \ldots$, and one has *circularly polarized light*. It should be noted that although both circularly polarized and unpolarized light can be resolved into components of equal amplitude in any two mutually perpendicular directions, the components of the former are coherent and those of the latter must be considered to be incoherent. In the old elastic solid theory

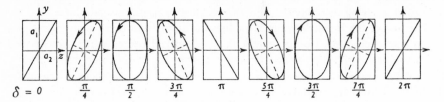

$$\delta = 0 \qquad \frac{\pi}{4} \qquad \frac{\pi}{2} \qquad \frac{3\pi}{4} \qquad \pi \qquad \frac{5\pi}{4} \qquad \frac{3\pi}{2} \qquad \frac{7\pi}{4} \qquad 2\pi$$

Fig. 6–16. The combination of two S.H.M.'s of the same frequency at right angles (z leads).

the disturbances in a light wave were thought of as the motion of a particle. This executed linear S.H.M. when the light was plane polarized, or traversed an ellipse or a circle for elliptically and circularly polarized light. In terms of the electromagnetic theory, the light disturbance consists of rapidly varying electric and magnetic fields. For example, in plane polarized light the electric displacement at a given point is always along the same straight line but its magnitude varies sinusoidally. That is to say, the end-point of the electric displacement vector executes linear S.H.M. For elliptically and circularly polarized light the end-point of the vector traverses an ellipse and a circle respectively.

The states of polarization shown in Fig. 6–16 are produced by the superposition of two components at right angles, and since there is no destructive interference each diagram represents light of the same intensity. Thus the total intensity is always equal to the sum of the intensities of the components, i.e. $a_1^2 + a_2^2$. It is in any case fairly obvious that this gives the intensity of the plane polarized resultant since it is simply the square of the amplitude. For elliptically polarized light the intensity is given by the sum of the squares of the semi-axes, and for circularly polarized light it is given by twice the square of the radius.

6–17. Polarized and Unpolarized Light

It has already been seen that the vibrations in unpolarized light can be resolved into equal transverse linear components in any two mutually perpendicular directions, and that these components must be considered to be incoherent. Now when two disturbances are incoherent the phase difference between them is constantly changing in a random fashion. At any given instant the two components of unpolarized light correspond to a particular elliptical polarization. That is, unpolarized light can be regarded as elliptically polarized light in which the shape and orientation of the ellipse is constantly changing, circularly and plane polarized light being included as special cases. No matter what phase difference is introduced between the components of unpolarized light after they have been separated, the resultant will always be unpolarized light if the components are recombined.

It has already been shown that strictly monochromatic light is represented by an infinite train of waves. In general, the disturbance is represented by the resultant of two vectors in perpendicular planes and the variation of each of these vectors must be represented by an expression of simple harmonic form. Since each of these expressions must be valid from $-\infty$ to $+\infty$, there is a systematic phase relation between them. That is to say, a perfectly monochromatic beam must be completely polarized. Obviously the state of polarization varies as the phase difference between the components varies, but the polarization is complete.

CHAPTER VII

INTERFERENCE OF TWO BEAMS.
DIVISION OF WAVEFRONT

7–1. Classification of Interference and Diffraction Phenomena

As stated in Chapter I, each point on a wavefront may be regarded as a source of secondary waves. To account for the rectilinear propagation of light through large apertures it was assumed that these secondary waves produce an effect only on their forward envelope. However, careful investigation shows that the passage of light through a finite aperture is not completely in accordance with the idea of rectilinear propagation. It is found that some light always appears within the geometrical shadow. This complex behaviour of light on passing through an aperture is known as diffraction. In order to explain the observed intensity patterns it is necessary to assume that the secondary waves interfere with one another according to the principle of superposition. This subject will be discussed in detail later (Chapter X), but it will be seen that every optical problem involving apertures is, strictly speaking, a problem in interference and diffraction.

One frequently has to deal with arrangements in which light from a source is separated into two or more beams by some suitable optical system, the separate beams being superposed subsequently. If the apertures of the system are sufficiently large, the amount of light involved in the departure from rectilinear propagation through the apertures is small, and the primary phenomenon is the subsequent interference of the separate beams of light. Thus in the majority of what are classed as interference phenomena, the behaviour of the light before the superposition of the beams is roughly in accordance with the principles of geometrical optics. The chief exception in this method of grouping is the case where two narrow slits are employed. These are simply regarded as sources of light and the diffraction mechanism is ignored.

The light may be divided into separate beams or waves by employing apertures and other optical components to separate neighbouring parts of the wavefront (division of wavefront) or by employing partial reflection to divide a single beam (division of amplitude). In the present chapter arrangements involving division of wavefront will be discussed. They always require the use of a point or line source.

The Rayleigh Refractometer and the Michelson Stellar Interferometer are sometimes included in discussions of two beam interference by division of wavefront but these are more conveniently discussed in Chapter XI. In the same way a diffraction grating could be regarded as a case of multiple division of the wavefront, especially when the apertures are narrow; in this case the chief phenomenon is associated with the interference between disturbances from different apertures. Diffraction gratings are discussed in Chapter XII.

7–2. Young's Experiment

One of the earliest experiments involving interference was that described by Thomas Young in 1807. Sunlight from a single pinhole P (Fig. 7–1) was allowed

126

to fall on two pinholes P_1P_2. According to Huygens' principle P acts as a point source so that a spherical wave emerges and falls on P_1 and P_2. These two pinholes act as point sources emitting fresh spherical waves which spread out from P_1 and P_2 as indicated. In the space beyond P_1 and P_2 these secondary waves become superposed. Since P_1 and P_2 are illuminated by the same spherical wave, the superposed disturbances are coherent and the intensity at any point will depend on their relative phases. For example, assuming P_1 and P_2 are equidistant from P, the intensity will be a maximum for light of wavelength λ at any point X whose distances from P_1 and P_2 differ by $p\lambda$, where p is an integer. For a given value of p the locus of the point X is an hyperboloid of revolution having P_1 and P_2 as foci. (An hyperboloid may be defined as the surface generated by

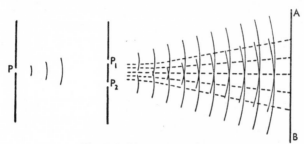

Fig. 7-1. Young's experiment.

a point which moves in such a way that the difference between its distances from two fixed points is a constant.) Other hyperboloidal surfaces of maximum intensity correspond to other values of p and similar surfaces of zero intensity will be generated by points which move in such a way that their distances from P_1 and P_2 differ by an odd multiple of $\lambda/2$. Since light passes through the pinholes in only one direction the complete pattern in space cannot be observed. Fig. 7-1 shows the intersection of the surfaces of maximum intensity with the plane PP_1P_2. As one recedes from P_1P_2 these hyperbolae quickly approximate to straight lines, and over the region near the middle of the screen AB the variations in intensity give a set of approximately linear fringes.

In the original experiments sunlight was used, so that the fringe systems for many wavelengths were superposed. In consequence, fringes could be observed near the centre of the field only (see below).

The amount of light that emerges from the pinhole P is very small and the fringes are rather faint and difficult to observe on a screen. However, they can be observed quite easily by looking at a small (preferably monochromatic) source and holding a double pinhole in front of the eye.

7-3. Elementary Discussion of Young's Experiment Using Slits

Fringes are more easily observed if monochromatic light is used and the pinholes replaced by parallel slits. The disturbances from the slits now have cylindrical envelopes and there will be symmetry about any plane perpendicular to the three slits. Consequently, it is usual to restrict the analysis to one of these planes. The interference pattern will consist of straight fringes parallel to the slits. The use of slit sources and apertures in diffraction experiments is discussed further in §§ 11–4, 13–7.

In Fig. 7–2 it will be assumed that the slits S_1 and S_2 are equidistant from S so that S_1 and S_2 act as coherent sources in the same phase; if they are of the same width, they will emit disturbances of equal amplitudes. These disturbances are superposed at P and since S_1P and S_2P are not widely different each disturbance may be assumed to have the same amplitude a at P. The path difference (S_2P-S_1P) causes the disturbances from S_1 and S_2 to be out of phase at P by an amount $\delta=(2\pi/\lambda)(S_2P-S_1P)=(2\pi/\lambda)(S_2A)$, where λ is the wavelength of the light concerned. Thus, one has, at P, two superposed disturbances of the same

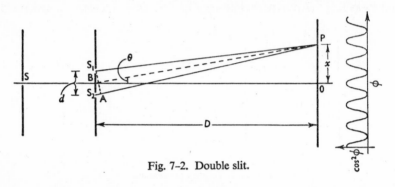

Fig. 7–2. Double slit.

frequency differing in phase by an amount δ. From equation (6–11) it will be seen that the resultant intensity at P is given by

$$I=2a^2(1+\cos\delta). \qquad \ldots \ldots \quad (7\text{–}1)$$

The intensity at P is therefore a maximum if $\cos\delta=+1$ and zero if $\cos\delta=-1$. That is, for a bright fringe $\delta=0, 2\pi, 4\pi, 6\pi, \ldots$, and for a dark fringe $\delta=\pi, 3\pi, 5\pi, \ldots$.

From the figure, if $D\gg d$ or x, triangles BOP, S_1S_2A are similar so that

$$S_2A=\frac{dx}{D}.$$

Therefore for a bright fringe

$$\delta=\frac{2\pi}{\lambda}\cdot\frac{dx}{D}=0, 2\pi, 4\pi, 6\pi, \ldots =2p\pi,$$

and for a dark fringe

$$\delta=\frac{2\pi}{\lambda}\cdot\frac{dx}{D}=\pi, 3\pi, 5\pi, \ldots =(2p+1)\pi,$$

where p is an integer.

That is, for a bright fringe

$$x=p\frac{\lambda D}{d}, \qquad \ldots \ldots \ldots \quad (7\text{–}2)$$

and for a dark fringe

$$x=(p+\tfrac{1}{2})\frac{\lambda D}{d}. \qquad \ldots \ldots \ldots \quad (7\text{–}3)$$

p is called the *order* of the fringe. For example, the bright fringe which is at distance $x=2\lambda D/d$ from the axis is the second order bright fringe. As defined here p is an integer but, in general, the phase difference as a multiple of 2π is called the *order of interference* and is not necessarily integral.

When, as assumed above, $x \ll D$, the distance between successive maxima and minima is $\lambda D/d$ and is constant across the screen. Consequently, by measuring the fringe spacing, one can find λ. The intensity at any point is given [from (7–1)]

by
$$I=4a^2 \cos^2 \left(\frac{\delta}{2}\right)$$

$$=4a^2 \cos^2 \left(\frac{\pi d}{\lambda D} \cdot x\right). \quad \cdots \cdots \quad (7\text{–}4)$$

Such fringes are referred to as $\cos^2$ fringes. The intensity distribution in the fringes is illustrated in Fig. 7–2. It will be seen that the bright and dark fringes have equal widths. At the minima the intensity is zero and at the maxima it is $4a^2$ but the average intensity over the fringe system is $2a^2$, which is the sum of the intensities due to the disturbances from S_1 and S_2 considered separately. Hence, as always in interference phenomena, the principle of conservation of energy is not violated although a redistribution of the energy occurs.

If light of several wavelengths is present, each wavelength produces its own fringe system. For all wavelengths the central fringe is at O which is optically equidistant from S_1 and S_2. The next bright fringe is formed where the disturbances from S_1 and S_2 are 2π out of phase, i.e. where the path difference is λ. It will therefore be formed a distance x from O where x depends on λ [see equation (7–2)]. Thus for white light the central fringe is white whilst higher order maxima at first show coloured edges and then appear drawn out into spectra. Eventually, the maxima for various orders and different wavelengths overlap to give a white continuum where no fringes are observable.

If the primary slit S is wide each element of it gives fringes in different positions, and if S_1 and S_2 are wide corresponding elements act as separate slits and also give overlapping fringe systems. Thus to observe the above fringes clearly it is important to employ narrow slits. (See also §11–12.)

The fringes discussed above are formed by the superposition of two coherent cylindrical wave envelopes diverging from line sources a short distance apart. The same conditions may be produced in several ways by dividing a single . expanding wavefront into two parts and causing the parts to become superposed.

7–4. Fresnel's Biprism

Although its function is that of a pair of thin prisms whose bases are cemented together, the biprism usually consists of a single isosceles prism whose apex A is just less than 180°. Light from a slit source is refracted through the prism as shown in Fig. 7–3 so that cylindrical wave envelopes diverge from S_1 and S_2. A convenient source is a slit illuminated by light from a gas discharge lamp. The waves become superposed in the region beyond the biprism to give fringes of the same type as in the modified form of Young's experiment. The virtual slit images S_1 and S_2 replace the two slits used in that experiment but the interference effects are the same. The effects are, of course, present only in the region XY where the waves overlap. Examination of the fringes shows an effect which is absent from the simple fringe system obtained in Young's experiment. Superposed on the main interference fringes there is a more gradual variation of intensity as shown in Plate I(a). The two cylindrical wave envelopes are of finite extent in this experiment, being limited on one side by the extreme edges of the biprism and on the other by the vertex A. The intensity variation that is superposed on the interference pattern is caused by the limitation of the divergent waves by the vertex A and is characteristic of diffraction by a straight edge [see Chapter XIII and Plate III(g)]. If the biprism is distance D_1 from the slit whose

Fig. 7–3. Fresnel's biprism.

virtual images S_1S_2 are distance d apart, the fringe separation at distance D_2 from the biprism is given by

$$x = \frac{\lambda(D_1 + D_2)}{d},$$

and, by measuring x, λ may be determined if d can be found. This can be done in several ways. If α is the refracting angle of each thin prism which effectively forms half of the biprism, and n is the refractive index, it is easily proved that

$$d = D_1\theta$$
$$= D_1 2(n-1)\alpha,$$

and n and α can be measured with a spectrometer.

Alternatively, the angle θ can be measured directly with a spectrometer by passing parallel light from the collimator through the biprism and measuring the angle θ between the two emergent pencils by means of the telescope. Another method, usually more convenient in practice, is to employ a convex lens to form two real images of the slit (i.e. images of S_1 and S_2) on a screen. The distance from S to the screen must be greater than four times the focal length of the lens. For a given position of the screen there are two possible positions for the lens. If the separations of the slit images for the two lens positions are d_1 and d_2, it can be shown that $d = \sqrt{d_1 d_2}$. (See §1–16.)

To observe the fringes and measure x, d_1, and d_2, it is usual to replace the screen by a micrometer eyepiece. It must be remembered that d_1 and d_2 must be measured with the same value of $(D_1 + D_2)$ and with the same value of D_1 as is used when x is measured. In performing the experiment it is necessary to ensure that the edge A of the biprism is accurately parallel to the slit S. A single point on S will give a complete set of approximately linear fringes parallel to the edge

A of the prism. If S is not parallel to A the fringes for a neighbouring point on S are slightly displaced laterally. Since the maxima of these two fringe systems do not coincide, the contrast in the resultant pattern is reduced. The fringes corresponding to other points on S reduce the contrast further and, unless the angle between A and S is very small, no fringes can be seen with the complete slit source.

7–5. Fresnel's Double Mirror

If light from a slit source S (Fig. 7–4) is reflected from two slightly inclined mirrors whose line of intersection is accurately parallel to S, the reflected light

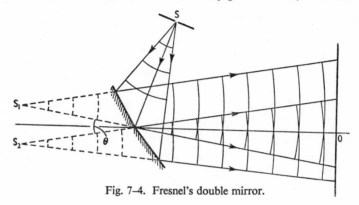

Fig. 7–4. Fresnel's double mirror.

consists of two cylindrical wave envelopes diverging from S_1 and S_2, the images of S formed by the mirrors. The conditions are obviously similar to those obtaining in the biprism experiment, and similar interference fringes are formed. The angle θ is now twice the angle between the mirrors.

7–6. Lloyd's Mirror

Similar fringes may be obtained with only one mirror used at almost grazing incidence (see Fig. 7–5). In this case, the interference is between the direct and

Fig. 7–5. Lloyd's mirror.

reflected disturbances. The slit must be exactly parallel to the plane of the mirror in order to render parallel the slit and its image. It will be seen from the diagram that the central fringe can be observed only by placing the receiving screen in contact with the end of the mirror. Lloyd found that this zero path difference fringe was dark instead of bright; this confirms the existence of the phase change of π undergone by light reflected at a denser medium. (See §21–4.)

7-7. Other Arrangements

Two arrangements for producing a similar fringe system are the Billet split lens (Fig. 7-6) and the biplate (Fig. 7-7). In the former, two real images $S_1 S_2$ of the slit S are formed by separating the halves of the lens and cylindrical wave envelopes diverge from these images. In the biplate one again has two real images of the slit from which cylindrical envelopes diverge. In all these arrangements the same interference effects are observed, and in all cases the separation of the effective sources involved may be found by using a convex lens as described for the biprism.

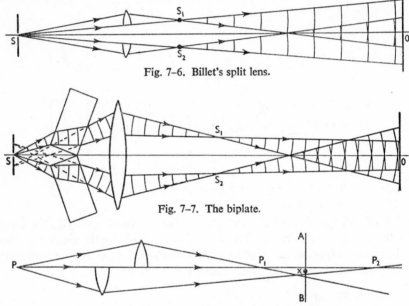

Fig. 7-6. Billet's split lens.

Fig. 7-7. The biplate.

Fig. 7-8. Halves of split lens separated axially.

Fig. 7-8 shows an interesting variation of the split lens arrangement. One now has a point source P and the halves of the lens are separated along the axis and not transversely so that the images P_1 and P_2 also are separated along the axis. It must be noted that one does not have interference between waves diverging from P_1 and P_2 and the surfaces of constant intensity are no longer hyperboloids of revolution about $P_1 P_2$ as described in § 7-2, but are ellipsoids.

It will be seen that the disturbances associated with P_1 and P_2 are superposed only in the region between P_1 and P_2 and only on one side of the plane through $P_1 P_2$ perpendicular to the diagram. Here interference occurs between one diverging and one converging spherical wave. The optical path difference between PP_2 and PP_1 is simply $P_1 P_2$, so that at X the difference between the paths traversed by the superposed disturbances is $P_1 X - (P_1 P_2 - P_2 X)$ and a surface of constant intensity is generated if X moves and maintains this quantity constant. Thus $(P_1 X + P_2 X)$ must remain constant, i.e. the locus of X is an ellipsoid with P_1 and P_2 as foci. The surfaces of maximum or minimum intensity consequently form a family of ellipsoids and these intersect a plane such as AB in a family of circles. Actually it can be shown that there is a phase change of π when a wave passes through a focus. This has occurred to one of the superposed waves so that a path difference of $p\lambda$ corresponds to a minimum. Since, as pointed out above, disturbances are not superposed over the whole plane AB, only approximately semi-circular fringes can be observed.

7-8. Achromatic Fringes with Lloyd's Mirror

Using a slit illuminated with white light, the fringes obtained with Lloyd's mirror (and similar arrangements) rapidly blend into a uniformly illuminated

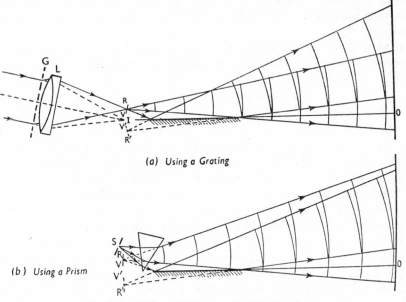

(a) Using a Grating

(b) Using a Prism

Fig. 7–9. Achromatic fringes with Lloyd's mirror.

field because the fringe separation varies with wavelength. Now the fringe separation depends also on the separation of the effective sources and if the source consists of a short spectrum with its blue end towards the mirror the effective sources have different separations for different wavelengths. If the dispersion in the spectrum is such that the distance from the mirror to any point in the spectrum is proportional to λ, the separation of the effective sources is also proportional to λ, and the fringe separations will be the same for all wavelengths. In this achromatic system the fringes are black and white. It is shown in Chapter XII that the dispersion given by a diffraction grating is almost exactly what is required in this case. The arrangement is given in Fig. 7–9(a). A collimated beam of white light is incident on the grating G which forms the usual spectra in the focal surface of the lens L. It is essential that there is no overlapping of orders and usually one of the first order spectra RV is employed. It is shown in Chapter XII that the distance from the zero order image to a first order maximum is proportional to λ so that if the zero order image I lies in the plane of the mirror the separation of the effective sources is proportional to λ and the achromatic fringes are formed.

The dispersion in the spectrum formed by a prism does not satisfy the requirements exactly, but for a prism of fairly small angle the approximation is sufficiently close for an appreciable number of white light fringes to be observable. The arrangement is shown in Fig. 7–9(b).

7–9. General Theory of Achromatic Fringes

In Young's experiment, the path difference at the centre of the fringe system is zero for all wavelengths and a white light maximum can be observed. Away from the centre no white light fringes are observed so that the pattern contains only one achromatic fringe. With the grating arrangement described in the preceding paragraph it is possible to secure a perfectly achromatic *system* of fringes.

In general one may say that at any point in a fringe system the order (not necessarily integral) usually depends on λ; if p is independent of λ one has a perfectly achromatic fringe and if this is true at every point in the pattern one has a perfectly achromatic *system* of fringes. Conditions of less complete achromatism can occur as follows:

If at any point in the pattern $\partial p/\partial \lambda = 0$ for any wavelength, then there is an appreciable range of wavelengths for which the variation of order is small and one is said to have an achromatic fringe at that point. This fringe is not perfectly achromatic and the notation is similar to that employed in geometrical optics. (A lens is said to be achromatic if $\partial f'/\partial \lambda$ is zero for one value of λ since f' is then approximately constant for a finite range of wavelengths; for a perfectly achromatic lens f' would have to be completely independent of λ.)

If at the same point in the pattern $\partial/\partial x(\partial p/\partial \lambda)$ is also zero (where x denotes position in the pattern), then $\partial p/\partial \lambda \doteqdot 0$ over a finite region of the pattern and one has a number of approximately achromatic fringes; one is said to have an achromatic system of fringes. It will be seen that the conditions for perfect achromatism may be expressed analytically as $\partial p/\partial \lambda = 0$ for all values of λ and $\partial^2 p/\partial x \partial \lambda = 0$ for all values of λ and x. Using Lloyd's mirror and a prism, one can obtain an achromatic system of fringes, but to obtain perfect achromatism a grating must be used. As stated above, a single perfectly achromatic fringe is obtained in Young's experiment.

7–10. Introduction of a Thin Transparent Plate

In Young's experiment or in one of its derivatives using monochromatic light, suppose that a transparent plate of thickness t and refractive index n is introduced in front of one of the real or virtual sources (e.g. in front of one half of the biprism). An extra optical path, $(n-1)t$, is then introduced in one of the interfering beams. This will cause the fringes to move across the field and, for example, the zero order fringe will move to the position formerly occupied by the fringe corresponding to a path difference of $-(n-1)t$, i.e. will move to the position formerly occupied by a fringe of order $p=(n-1)t/\lambda$. Since with monochromatic light it is impossible to distinguish one fringe from another, n cannot in general be found from this experiment.

If white light is used and the material of the plate is non-dispersive, the zero order fringe will remain perfectly achromatic and n may be found by observing the displacement of this fringe; it will simply move to the place which is optically equidistant from the two sources. If, however, the plate is dispersive then, for any point in the pattern, the optical distance from one source is independent of wavelength while that from the other is not. Consequently there can be no *completely* achromatic fringe. The central ("achromatic") fringe can be said to be located at the point P where $\partial p/\partial\lambda=0$ for the central wavelength in the range present. (For the wavelength to which the eye is most sensitive in the case of visual observations with white light.) This is the point of maximum agreement of order and therefore of phase difference, and is not the place where the path difference is zero for the central wavelength. Suppose the path from the source S to P is in air and of length l and let $(L-t)$ be the part of the other path which is in air, the dispersive part being of geometrical length t. Then the optical path difference at P is $(L+(n-1)t-l)$ and this divided by λ gives the order. Differentiating with respect to λ and equating to zero one has, when P is the central fringe,

$$\frac{\partial}{\partial\lambda}\cdot\frac{1}{\lambda}[L+(n-1)t-l]=0=-\frac{(L-l-t)}{\lambda^2}+\frac{t}{\lambda}\cdot\frac{\partial n}{\partial\lambda}-\frac{nt}{\lambda^2},$$

$$\therefore\quad l-L=\left(n-\lambda\frac{\partial n}{\partial\lambda}-1\right)t,\qquad \ldots\ldots\quad (7\text{-}5)$$

and the achromatic fringe is moved to P, a point such that $(l-L)$ is given by equation (7-5). This corresponds to a shift of $(l-L)/\lambda$, i.e. $(1/\lambda)(n-\lambda\,\partial n/\partial\lambda-1)t$ fringes of wavelength λ. Now the zero order fringe of wavelength λ is moved a distance $(n-1)t/\lambda$ fringes so that the distance, in terms of fringes of wavelength λ, from the achromatic fringe to the zero order fringe for wavelength λ is $t\,\partial n/\partial\lambda$.

INTERFERENCE OF TWO BEAMS.
DIVISION OF AMPLITUDE

INTERFERENCE frequently results from the recombination of the two parts of a beam of light which is divided by partial reflection and refraction in a thin plate or film. The interference phenomena are of two main types: those observed with parallel-sided, moderately thin plates and those observed with very thin plates of varying thickness.

8-1. Parallel-sided Plates

Consider a ray SA from a monochromatic point source S entering a parallel-sided plate of glass of index n and thickness d (see Fig. 8-1). At each of the

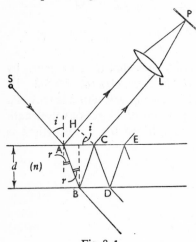

points A, B, C, D, E, etc., a small proportion of the light is reflected and the rest is refracted. Consequently, the rays emerging at A and C have intensities which are not widely different, each having undergone one reflection. Rays from E and points farther to the right have rapidly decreasing intensities and can be ignored in a first approximation. If the disturbances travelling along the rays emerging from A and C enter the lens L they will be superposed at P in the focal plane. When these disturbances are superposed they will be out of phase by an amount determined by the optical path difference [ABC]−[AH]. The lens L may be the eye of an observer and, if the

Fig. 8-1.
Reflections in a parallel-sided plate.

accommodation is relaxed, P will be on the retina and the resultant intensity at P will determine the brightness of the field of view in the direction concerned.

The optical path difference (o.p.d.) between the superposed disturbances is given by

$$(\text{o.p.d.}) = n(\text{AB}+\text{BC})-\text{AH}$$

$$= \frac{2nd}{\cos r} - \text{AC} \sin i,$$

where i and r are the angles of incidence and refraction of the ray SA as in the figure. Now $\sin i = n \sin r$ and $\text{AC} = 2d \tan r$.

$$\therefore \quad (\text{o.p.d.}) = \frac{2nd}{\cos r} - \frac{2nd \sin^2 r}{\cos r} = 2nd \cos r. \quad . \quad . \quad (8\text{-}1)$$

Now it is known that when there is reflection at a denser medium there is a phase change of π (see §21-4). Here the phase change occurs at A so that the

136

condition for the disturbances to be in phase and to give a maximum becomes

$$2nd \cos r = (p + \tfrac{1}{2})\lambda,$$

and for a minimum, ... (8–2)

$$2nd \cos r = p\lambda,$$

where p is an integer.

If the lens L has a large aperture, pairs of rays may enter after being reflected from widely different parts of the plate [Fig. 8–2(a)]. Associated with each pair of rays, there will be an optical path difference given by equation (8–1), where r is the angle of internal reflection in the plate of the ray so reflected. The constituent rays of each pair are superposed at a point in the focal plane of L so that there will be a variation of intensity across this plane. Now the usual laws of

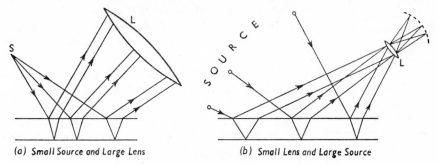

(a) Small Source and Large Lens   (b) Small Lens and Large Source

Fig. 8–2. Arrangements for observing fringes of equal inclination.

reflection must be obeyed at the plate so that, using a point source and a lens of small aperture such as the eye, the rays that can be collected are confined to a small range of directions. If one has an extended source, however, light from each point of the source enters the eye in a separate direction and, if the accommodation is relaxed, rays in each pair are brought together at a different point on the retina [Fig. 8–2(b)]. Associated with each pair of rays there is again a certain o.p.d. and this determines the brightness of the field of view in the direction concerned. To prevent obstruction of the incident light by the observer, it is obviously desirable to employ a reflector plate as indicated in Fig. 8–3. (To simplify the diagram refractions in the plane parallel plate and in the reflector have been neglected.) This figure also shows that by using a subsidiary lens S.L. it is possible to use an observing lens of small aperture (e.g. the eye) with a small source, the latter being imaged at the observing lens to give the condition known as *Maxwellian view* (see § 18–7). It is easily seen from the diagram that if the subsidiary lens is removed an extended source is required.

For a particular bright or dark fringe the o.p.d. between the two superposed disturbances is constant so that one must have r=constant; the fringes are therefore known as fringes of equal inclination. Thus the fringes form a series of concentric circles in the focal plane of the observing lens, i.e. they are seen clearly in this form by an unaccommodated eye and may be said to be at infinity. Fringes of equal inclination may be seen also by transmission as indicated by Fig. 8–3 but the contrast in these fringes is poor because the ray which has undergone two reflections is much less intense than the other. The fringes

6*

by transmission are complementary to those observed by reflection but with a uniform intensity added. The fringes viewed near normal incidence are called *Haidinger fringes*.

If, in equation (8–2), p has the value p_1 for the innermost fringe, it has value (p_1-1) for the next and (p_1-j+1) for the jth fringe where the fringes are numbered from the centre. If r is small one may write $\cos r = 1-(r^2/2)$ and, for the jth dark fringe by reflection, one has

Source

S.L.

$$2nd\left(1-\frac{r_j^2}{2}\right)=(p_1-j+1)\lambda,$$

so that, since for small angles $i=nr$, the squares of the angular diameters of the fringes vary linearly with the fringe numbers. This result applies also to the bright fringes and to the fringes viewed by transmission. The fringes viewed by reflection have an appearance similar to the fringes shown in Plate I(b) and the fringes seen by transmission resemble those shown in Plate I(c) (see § 8–4).

With thick plates the fringes become very close together and it becomes necessary to observe them with the aid of a telescope of suitable magnifying power. For example, with a plate 1 cm. thick of refractive index 1·5 the angular separation of the fringes for green light is about 1′ when $r=3°$. With very thick plates the distance CH (Fig. 8–1) may be larger than the diameter of the eye pupil, and for visual observation it is necessary to employ a telescope whose objective admits the two rays. If M is the magnifying power of the telescope, the emergent rays will be distance CH/M apart and this must be smaller than the diameter of the eye pupil. If the surfaces of the plate are semi-silvered, the telescope objective must admit rays emerging from E and points farther to the right (Fig. 8–1).

Fig. 8–3. Arrangement for observing complete fringe system.

Referring again to Fig. 8–3, it will be seen that whenever the fringes are observed with a point source the rays traversing the plate at a given angle pass through a particular part of the plate, so that variations in plate thickness will distort the fringes. When the plate is very thin the effect of variation in direction becomes negligible and, even with an extended source, the intensity at a given point in the pattern characterizes the local thickness of the plate. Fringes of this type are discussed in the following sections.

8–2. Interference in Very Thin Films

If d is very small it may become impossible for $\cos r$ to vary sufficiently to make the variations in $2nd \cos r$ appreciable. Certainly this will be so if only a moderately extended source is employed. If the variations of $2nd \cos r$ are small compared with λ, the field of view will be of uniform intensity.

Now if d is very small the distance AC (Fig. 8–1) is very small and the total disturbance consists of two superposed wave trains along closely neighbouring paths. They may be said to interfere at what is now the single point of reflection and the resultant may be regarded as a single ray whose intensity is given by the superposition of the internally and externally reflected disturbances. (Notice here that it is convenient to combine the terminologies of ray and wave optics.)

If d varies across the plate, the o.p.d. introduced between the internally and externally reflected rays will depend upon the thickness of the film at the point of reflection and will be independent of the angle of emergence. The resulting intensity will therefore be characteristic of the local thickness of the film. This discussion is satisfactory for thin films whose thickness undergoes abrupt changes so that it consists of a number of adjacent parallel-sided films. Such films may consist of the air gap between an optical flat and, for example, the surface of a sheet of mica which exhibits abrupt changes of level.

In the case of films of continuously varying thickness, such as a wedge, the internally and externally reflected rays are not parallel and the formation of the fringes is more easily understood by considering the wavefronts reflected at the two surfaces of the film.

8–3. The Wedge Film

A common arrangement for observing the so-called *Fizeau fringes* is shown in Fig. 8–4(*a*). This is a particular case of the use of Maxwellian view, the wave-

Fig. 8–4. Fringes of equal thickness in a wedge

fronts incident on the film being plane. The arrangement can be used with a point or moderately extended source which ensures that the variation of cos r is small. For a point source two plane waves leave the wedge, one being reflected from each surface. Fig. 8–4(*b*) shows the reflected waves in the region between the wedge and the lens; the full lines denote crests and the broken lines troughs. Along the lines A the crests and troughs of one wave train coincide with the crests and troughs of the other. Along the lines B the crests of one wave train coincide with the troughs of the other and vice versa. Thus along the lines A the disturbances associated with the two wave trains are in phase and there is constructive interference, whereas there is destructive interference along the lines B. It follows that in any plane XY there is a fringe system, the maxima and minima occurring where the loci A and B, etc., intersect it. The loci of maxima and minima intersect the film where the thickness is given by $2nd=(p+\frac{1}{2})\lambda$ and $2nd=p\lambda$, respectively. These thicknesses cause a relative retardation of one wavefront with respect to the other of odd and even multiples of $\lambda/2$ which respectively give maxima and minima since there is the usual phase change of π at the upper surface. Beyond the lens L the interfering wavefronts are, of course, spherical.

With an extended source each point of the source gives a pair of coherent waves which interfere in this way and the loci of the maxima and minima emanate from the points on the film as defined above. Thus *it is only at the film itself that all the fringe systems coincide,* and it is here that the aggregate fringe system is located. The fringes are said to be *localized* in this plane and may be observed conveniently with a low-power microscope as in Fig. 8–5. If the source is not at the focus of a lens, spherical waves are reflected by the wedge. These interfere in the same way as plane waves to give the same fringe system, provided the curvature of the spherical waves is not sufficient to give an appreciable variation in r. These *fringes of equal thickness* will be equally spaced straight lines parallel to the edge of the wedge and will be contours of the wedge thickness; the latter increases by $\lambda/2$ in going from one dark or bright fringe to the next. Using these fringes, one can measure the angle of a very thin wedge-shaped sheet of any transparent material or the wedge-shaped air gap between two slightly inclined plates. These fringes are frequently viewed with a small but finite source and, although they are localized in the plane of the wedge, the depth of focus is large, i.e. they are not sharply localized. With a true point source the fringes are not localized in this sense but still characterize the local thickness of the wedge. If observations are made at oblique incidence, variations in r may become important and the fringes may become curved and less distinct —particularly in the thicker parts of the wedge. Plate I(f) shows the fringes viewed by reflection with an air wedge between two optical flats. The fringes viewed by transmission have very poor contrast (see § 8–1); it is similar to that of the fringes shown in Plate I(c).

Fig. 8–5. Observation of localized fringes of equal thickness.

8–4. Newton's Rings

If an optical flat is placed in contact with a shallow convex spherical surface, a thin air film of varying thickness results (see Fig. 8–6). This film is, of course, symmetrical about the point of contact so that the localized interference fringes, which are contours of the air film thickness, become concentric circles centred on the point of contact. These fringes were first observed by Newton and are known as *Newton's rings*. One has, here, interfering spherical wavefronts and the fringes of equal thickness will again be non-localized for point sources and sharply localized for extended sources.

If R is the radius of the spherical surface and d is the thickness of the air film a distance r from the point of contact,

$$R = \frac{r^2 + d^2}{2d}.$$

Fig. 8–6. Observation of Newton's rings.

If R is large $d^2 \ll r^2$ and one has

$$d = \frac{r^2}{2R}. \quad \cdots \cdots \quad (8\text{–}3)$$

Since the film is thin, any departure from normal incidence can be ignored. The film is of air so that $n=1$ and, remembering that there is a phase change of π at the lower surface, the conditions for a maximum or minimum are:

for a minimum $2d = p\lambda$,

for a maximum $2d = (p + \tfrac{1}{2})\lambda$.

Therefore the radii of the bright and dark fringes are given [from (8–3)] by

$$\left. \begin{array}{ll} \text{(dark)} & r^2 = pR\lambda, \\ \text{(bright)} & r^2 = (p + \tfrac{1}{2})R\lambda. \end{array} \right\} \quad \cdots \cdots \quad (8\text{–}4)$$

Hence if λ is known the radius of curvature of the spherical surface may be determined by measuring the radii of the rings.

It will be seen that when contact at the centre is perfect p is zero at the centre and the squares of the radii of successive dark rings are proportional to the natural numbers. On plotting r^2 against the ring number for either dark or bright fringes, one obtains a straight line of slope $R\lambda$. It will be seen that the relationship between the ring numbers and ring diameters is the same as for the fringes of equal inclination described in §8–1. Since, to a first approximation, both sets of fringes result from the interference of only two beams, the fringes are similar in appearance. They are shown in Plate I(*b*). As before, the fringes viewed by transmission have poor contrast; they are shown in Plate I(*c*). It must be pointed out that although the fringes are similar in appearance they are somewhat different in origin. In Newton's rings the order increases as one moves away from the centre of the pattern, and in Haidinger's fringes the order decreases as one moves outwards across the fringes.

The effect of imperfect contact between the surfaces is simply to alter the intercept on the r^2 axis. This is easily shown since equation (8–3) becomes

$$d = \frac{r^2}{2R} + d_0$$

where d_0 is the separation of the surfaces at the centre. The fact that with good contact the central fringe (viewed by reflection) is dark, is an important confirmation of the existence of the phase change of π associated with reflection at the denser medium. The arrangement is a special case of two spherical surfaces of different radius of curvature in contact and, in general, the radius of one surface can be found if that of the other is known. One has

$$2d = r^2 \left(\frac{1}{R_1} \pm \frac{1}{R_2} \right).$$

The spherical surface in Fig. 8–6 is part of a lens, but the effect of the latter on the size of the rings can be ignored since it is in contact with the plane of the fringes and the magnification is unity.

At the point of contact in the Newton's rings arrangement (or at the edge of the wedge), the phase difference is simply π for all wavelengths so that, using white light, an achromatic dark fringe can be observed. As the thickness of the film increases, the phase difference varies with wavelength and (as shown by equation (8–3)) the rings for different wavelengths have different radii. Thus the first few bright rings are drawn out into spectra with the shorter wavelengths inside, and after a few orders the bright fringes of various colours and orders intermingle to give a white continuum as in Young's experiment (see Chapter VII). Thus for films whose thickness is not greater than a few wavelengths, polychromatic localized fringes can be observed. Such *interference colours* are frequently seen in films of oil on water or in the films of a soap bubble.

8–5. Non-reflecting Films

At each refracting surface in an optical system some light is reflected. If this light does not subsequently reach the image plane, the effect is simply a reduction

Fig. 8–7.
Non-reflecting film.

in image brightness and, for most purposes, no great harm is done. Frequently, however, this light reaches the image plane and causes an overall reduction in image contrast and/or local bright patches or *glare spots*. The amount of light reflected at any surface can be reduced considerably by coating the surface with a thin film of transparent material such that the internally and externally reflected rays interfere destructively (see Fig. 8–7). Obviously the destructive interference will be complete if the rays have equal amplitudes and are π out of phase. For a given angle of incidence, the relative amplitudes of the two rays depend on the refractive indices of the glass and thin film, and the phase difference depends on the optical thickness of the film. Now when light is incident normally on a surface separating dielectrics whose indices are n and n', the ratio of the reflected and incident amplitudes is $(n'-n)/(n'+n)$ (see § 21–3). Suppose, then, that a disturbance of unit amplitude is incident on the film. Most of the light is transmitted at the interface between air and the film so that the amplitude of the light incident on the glass is approximately unity. Again, most of the light reflected at the glass surface emerges from the film. Consequently, the amplitudes of the externally and internally reflected rays are, to a first approximation, $(n_F-1)/(n_F+1)$ and $(n_G-n_F)/(n_G+n_F)$ respectively. It is easily shown that these are equal if $n_F = \sqrt{n_G}$ and this determines the necessary index for the film. The thickness of the film is determined by the fact that for a phase difference of π or an odd multiple of π

$$2n_F d = (2p+1)\frac{\lambda}{2}.$$

It should be noted that these conditions can be satisfied exactly for only one angle of incidence and one wavelength but the intensity of the reflected light is small for an appreciable range of angles and wavelengths. A surface treated in this way is said to be *bloomed*.

For a glass of index 1·5 one requires a layer of material of index 1·22. In addition, the film must be durable. No completely satisfactory material has been found and those frequently employed are magnesium fluoride and cryolite whose indices are 1·38 and 1·36 and are, of course, better for the denser glasses. These materials are usually deposited by evaporation in a vacuum. A bloomed surface reflects less than 1% of the incident white light. Non-reflecting films have been produced also by chemically attacking the surface of the glass, leaving a layer of lower index.

It is possible to produce anti-reflecting films that are efficient over a wide range of wavelengths by depositing several layers whose indices decrease progressively from the supporting medium towards the air. Highly reflecting films can also be produced. Many of these employ multiple reflections and the subject is discussed further in §9–16.

8–6. Further Applications of Localized Fringes

The localized fringes observed in thin films provide a simple method of testing the accuracy of optical components. The surface under test is placed in contact with a standard *test plate*. The correctness of the fit is indicated by the number of fringes of equal thickness which can be seen. On pressing the surfaces together, the air gap, if present, tends to be reduced; since a given fringe corresponds to a given air-film thickness, the fringes will move to places where the air film is relatively thicker. For example, if contact is at the centre the fringes will move outwards when the surfaces are pressed together.

The wedge fringes are used in precision engineering for comparing end gauges. An end gauge consists of an accurately known length of steel rod whose ends are polished flat and parallel. Such gauges have two important advantages when compared with the older line gauges consisting of two rulings on a metal bar. Firstly, the length of an end gauge can be measured more accurately than the distance between two rulings; and secondly, by "wringing" a number of end gauges together, a compound gauge can be made. This is done by pressing the gauges together—sometimes with a minute film of paraffin between them. If the ends of the gauges are clean and flat, they will be held together by atmospheric pressure.

In order to test an end gauge (slip gauge), the ends are first examined by means of a test plate as indicated above. If the ends are flat, one end is wrung on to the polished surface of a flat steel plate alongside a standard gauge as in Fig. 8–8. A glass optical flat is then placed across the top of the gauges as shown. If the gauges are not exactly equal in length, wedges of air occur between the gauges and the plate. If l is the separation of the appropriate edges of the gauges and

Fig. 8–8. Testing a slip gauge.

m is the number of fringes per cm. in the wedge above the standard, the difference in height between the gauges is given by

$$\delta h = \frac{m\lambda l}{2}.$$

This assumes that the ends of the standard gauge are exactly parallel. The fringes above the gauge under test will, of course, yield the same result if this gauge also has parallel ends. End gauge interferometers are discussed further in § 8–16.

In a similar way one can measure small movements of one surface towards or away from a standard surface and this has obvious applications to the measurement of small elastic deformations or thermal expansions.

8–7. The Michelson Interferometer

The essential feature of the formation of fringes in parallel-sided plates and wedges is the division of a beam of light by partial reflection at the first surface, and the subsequent superposition of the two disturbances after they have traversed unequal optical paths. In the Michelson interferometer the beam is divided (i.e. the amplitude is divided) into two beams of equal intensity by the plate A (Fig. 8–9) which is half-silvered on its rear surface. The beams are reflected at the front silvered mirrors M_1 and M_2 and recombine at plate A. The unsilvered compensating plate C is identical to A and parallel to it and is employed so that the separate beams have equal paths in glass. For the reasons given in § 7–9 this is important when white light fringes are required. Let M_2' be the virtual image of M_2 formed by reflection at the plate A. Then the conditions obtaining in the beam that has undergone reflection at M_2 are exactly the same as they would be after reflection by a mirror located at M_2'. Hence the fringes will be similar to those that would be obtained if M_1 and M_2' were reflecting surfaces enclosing the air gap which lies between them. That is to say, if A is at 45° to the incident beam and M_1 and M_2 are perpendicular and placed so that $[AM_1]$ and $[AM_2]$ are slightly different, the fringes are similar to those of a parallel-sided plate where the plate consists of air. Hence, with an extended monochromatic source the fringes are the usual concentric fringes of equal inclination and can be viewed with a telescope or unaccommodated eye. As

Fig. 8–9. The Michelson interferometer.

before, it is necessary to use a telescope when the "plate" is thick.

In the direction inclined to the normal to M_1 at angle θ, the path difference between the superposed disturbances is [from equation (8–1)] $2d \cos \theta$, where d is the separation $M_1 M_2'$, i.e.

$$\text{phase difference} = \delta = \frac{2\pi}{\lambda} \cdot (2d \cos \theta).$$

Thus, if each beam is of amplitude a, the resulting intensity is [from equation (6–11)] given by

$$I = 2a^2(1 + \cos \delta)$$

$$= 4a^2 \cos^2 \left(\frac{\delta}{2}\right), \quad \cdots \cdots \quad (8\text{–}5)$$

I reaches a maximum value when $\delta = 2p\pi$ and is zero where $\delta = (2p+1)\pi$ (p an integer). Thus maxima and minima occur at values of θ given by $\cos \theta = p\lambda/2d$ and $\cos \theta = (p+\frac{1}{2})\lambda/2d$ respectively and, as for the fringes observed with a plane parallel plate, the squares of the fringe diameters vary linearly with the fringe numbers when θ is small. As is pointed out above, these two fringe systems are formed in a similar manner but the Michelson fringes, being formed by the interference of two beams, are $\cos^2$ fringes whereas the others are only approximately $\cos^2$ fringes since disturbances undergoing additional reflections are involved. In the foregoing paragraphs the effect of the additional beams was neglected; they do not affect the positions of the maxima and minima but, as will be seen in Chapter IX, they increase the sharpness of the fringes.

Newton's rings (which are fringes of equal thickness and are formed in a rather different manner from the fringes discussed above) are also approximately $\cos^2$ fringes when viewed by reflection with unsilvered surfaces, and again the effect of silvering is an increased sharpness of the fringes. With Newton's rings it has already been seen that, if the fringes are numbered outwards from the centre, the squares of the fringe diameters vary linearly with the fringe numbers so that Newton's rings are similar in appearance (although not in origin) to the fringes of equal inclination discussed above. It has already been pointed out that with Newton's rings the order increases as one moves outwards from the centre of the pattern whereas for the fringes of equal inclination the order is a maximum at the centre. The appearance of all three fringe systems is represented qualitatively by Plate I(b) which is actually a photograph of Newton's rings by reflection.

Now, in general, if the phase difference between two superposed disturbances is $p \cdot 2\pi$, p is called the order of interference and is not necessarily integral. With the Michelson fringes, as has just been pointed out, the order is a maximum at the centre of the pattern. Suppose, now, that the mirror M_1 is moved continuously so that d is decreased. Then the path difference is decreased over the whole field of view and a fringe of given order (i.e. corresponding to a given path difference) will move towards the centre of the pattern and disappear. A fringe will disappear each time $2d$ is decreased by λ. As d is decreased steadily, θ must decrease more and more rapidly to maintain the order. The result is that the fringes become more widely spaced (for adjacent maxima $\cos \theta_p - \cos \theta_{p-1} = \lambda/2d$). When d is zero the whole field of view is of uniform intensity and is occupied by the zero order fringe. If one continues to move the mirror so that d increases fringes appear from the centre of the pattern and spread across the field of view, becoming closer together (a) toward the edge of the field and (b) as d increases.

It is assumed here that the beams undergo identical phase changes at the plate A. The phase changes depend on the nature of the semi-reflecting surface, and if a phase difference is introduced between the beams, the fringes are displaced. In practice there is often a phase difference of approximately π, giving a minimum when the path difference is $p\lambda$.

8–8. Localized Fringes. White Light

When d is very small, suppose that one of the mirrors is tilted so that M_1 and M_2' are inclined at a small angle. The fringes will then be those of a thin wedge and, with an extended source, are straight fringes parallel to the line of intersection of M_1 and M_2' and localized in the plane of the wedge. As d is increased, the fringes move towards the thin end of the wedge. Another effect is the introduction of a variation of path difference with θ. This causes the fringes to become curved. Since a fringe is a line of constant optical path difference, and since the path difference is smaller for larger values of θ, the fringes will curve towards the thicker part of the wedge in the outer part of the field. In Fig. 8–10

Fig. 8–10. Appearance of fringes when M_1 and M_2' form a thin wedge.

AB is the line of intersection of M_1 and M_2'; it is vertical and to the left of the field of view so that the fringes are drawn to the thicker parts of the wedge at X and Y (where θ is largest) and are thus concave towards the thicker part of the wedge. Only the zero order fringe, which lies along the line of intersection of M_1 and M_2' is exactly straight; if this lies in the field of view and the compensating plate is in position, the localized fringes can be observed with white light. This is possible because the path difference is zero for all wavelengths if it is zero for one. Thus the zero order fringe is a white light achromatic fringe. The fringes are coloured on each side of this central white light fringe, the maxima for shorter wavelengths being on the inside; in the outer part of the field of view the fringes disappear into a white continuum. The importance of the white light fringes lies in the fact that they indicate when M_1 actually intersects M_2' and therefore provide a very sensitive indicator of the position of the movable mirror M_1.

8–9. Adjustment of the Michelson Interferometer

Both mirrors can be adjusted with levelling screws and M_1 is carried on a nut threaded on an accurate screw thread so that it can be moved along the line AM_1 (Fig. 8–9). To adjust the instrument for the formation of the circular fringes of equal inclination, it is necessary to make M_2' parallel to, and a short distance from, M_1. These adjustments are carried out as follows:

1. The movable mirror M_1 is set so that $AM_1=AM_2$ to within a millimetre or so.

2. Using a small source such as an illuminated pinhole, one looks into the instrument from the usual position of observation. The direction of vision should be roughly normal to M_1 and frequently this is ensured by looking through a suitably positioned aperture fixed to the instrument. Several images of the source might be seen but, of these, two are brighter than the others. These are formed by light which has traversed the paths indicated; the others are formed by reflections at the unsilvered surfaces of A. The levelling screws of mirror M_2 are then adjusted until these two images appear to coincide. Adjustment of M_1 may be necessary in some cases. This makes M_2' parallel to M_1 within about one minute of arc.

3. Using an extended monochromatic source, fringes should now be visible although, if the previous adjustment was not performed sufficiently accurately, further adjustment of M_2 may now be necessary before fringes are seen. Further adjustment of M_2 is now required in order to secure circular fringes centred at the centre of the field. If M_2 is adjusted in the direction which broadens the fringes, this state will be reached eventually. M_2' is then parallel to M_1. When M_2' is almost exactly parallel to M_1 the fringes are almost circular and the departure from true circular shape is too small to be noticed. However, a lateral movement of the eye will move the centre of the observed pattern to a different part of M_1 and if there is a change in $M_2'M_1$ the fringes will open out or close in since the diameters of the rings depend on this distance. M_2 must then be adjusted until the fringes do not move in this way.

4. To obtain localized fringes, $M_2'M_1$ is made to approach zero. This broadens the circular fringes and, when only one or two fill the field of view, M_2 is tilted and the eye focused on M_1. The gap between M_1 and M_2' is now wedge shaped but usually M_2' does not intersect M_1 within the field of view and the fringes are curved as in Fig. 8–10. M_1 is then moved until the fringes are almost straight and, using white light, movement of M_1 is continued in the same direction until the central white light fringe is found and brought into the field. It will be obvious that the optical quality of the mirrors and the plates A and C is important since any departure from flatness or (in the case of A and C) homogeneity will introduce optical path differences and distort the fringes.

8–10. Visibility of the Fringes. Structure and Width of Spectral Lines

As remarked above, the circular fringes with a monochromatic source are of good contrast. Michelson defined the *visibility* of the fringes by the relation

$$V = \frac{E_{max} - E_{min}}{E_{max} + E_{min}}, \quad \cdots \cdots \cdots \quad (8\text{–}6)$$

where E_{max} and E_{min} are the relative intensities of a bright fringe and the neighbouring dark fringes. For a monochromatic source equation (8–5) shows that the visibility of the fringes is unity and is constant over the field of view.

Suppose now that the source gives two slightly different wavelengths (e.g. a sodium flame). For certain values of d the path difference $2d \cos \theta$ is an integral number of wavelengths for both the wavelengths emitted by the source, and for separations of M_1 and M_2' in this region the fringes for the two wavelengths coincide over an appreciable range of angles θ. The combined effect is a set of fringes of good visibility. For intermediate values of d the fringes for one wavelength will be exactly complementary to those for the other wavelength (supposing the two wavelengths are emitted with equal intensity) and the fringe visibility falls to zero. By increasing d from zero and noting the values of d corresponding to maximum and minimum visibility, the ratio of the two wavelengths may be determined. If the two wavelengths are not emitted with equal intensity, the minimum visibility is not zero; if it is measured, the relative intensities of the two wavelengths can be found. If the amplitudes of the wavelengths are a_1 and a_2, $V_{min}=(a^2_1-a^2_2)/(a^2_1+a^2_2)$. This method was used by Michelson to investigate the structure of spectral lines but has now been superseded. (For a fuller account see §§ 9–4 and 9–5.)

For sources giving a single spectral line it is found that the visibility of the fringes decreases steadily as d is increased and made very large. Now it was shown in Chapter VI that no source emits completely monochromatic light and that a nominally monochromatic source actually emits light with a frequency distribution of the form shown in Fig. 8–11. Since most of the energy is concentrated into a narrow band of wavelengths, the fringe systems for the various wavelengths will be almost coincident for small values of d. As d is increased, the slightly different wavelengths produce fringe systems that are not quite coincident—the maxima for the various wavelengths gradually get out of step. When one has a continuous distribution of wavelengths, the fringes never

·0065 Angstroms

Fig. 8–11. Energy distribution in a spectral line.

become in step again so that a continued increase in d causes a steady decrease in the visibility of the fringes. The decrease in visibility is often explained by saying that a source of light emits wave trains of finite length and that there is no fixed phase relation between successive trains. If d is large, this would mean that light of one wave train is superposed on light of another so that there is no fixed phase relation and fringes cannot be seen. It was shown in Chapter VI that these two explanations are really the same.

By careful observation of the visibility of the fringes obtained with the red cadmium line, Michelson showed that the energy distribution of this line approximated to a Gaussian distribution with a *half-width* of 0·0065 angstrom. (The half-width is here defined as the distance from the mean wavelength at which the energy falls to half its maximum value; the *half-value width* is twice this.) It can be shown that the corresponding length of the finite wave trains is about 50 cm., i.e. each wave train contains about a million waves.

The finite width of a spectral line is due to three main causes: natural damping, the Doppler effect, and pressure broadening. As the atomic oscillator radiates, it loses energy and therefore its amplitude decreases. This causes the amplitude of the wave to decrease as it is emitted, so that it is not a simple harmonic wave. The Doppler effect causes a variation of frequency since the radiating atoms are not stationary. Pressure broadening is associated with the fact that at high pressures other atoms disturb the radiating atom, so that the radiation is not simple harmonic. At low pressures the Doppler effect is the most important factor. This will be reduced if the speed of the atoms is reduced, so that the most highly monochromatic sources are low-pressure discharge lamps operated at low temperatures.

8–11. Fourier Transform Spectroscopy

Suppose a Michelson interferometer, adjusted for fringes of equal inclination, is used with a polychromatic source. Suppose the spectral distribution of the source and the various losses (absorption, reflection, etc.) within the interferometer are such that each of the emerging beams has intensity $B(v)dv$ in the wave-number range v to $v+dv$. (Wave number=1/wavelength.) Then, if the interferometer introduces an optical path difference $\triangle$ between the beams, the phase difference is $(2\pi/\lambda)\triangle$, i.e. $2\pi v \, \varDelta$, and the resultant intensity of the light in this spectral range is (from equation 8–5)

$$dI=2B(v)dv(1+\cos 2\pi v\varDelta).$$

The total intensity is simply the sum of the intensity contributions from the various spectral regions so that

$$I=2\int_0^\infty B(v)dv+2\int_0^\infty B(v)\cos 2\pi v\varDelta dv.$$

The first term is constant and the second term varies as the optical path difference varies; the second term is, in fact, the Fourier cosine transform of the spectral distribution in each emergent beam. That is, if

$$\phi(\varDelta)=2\int_0^\infty B(v)\cos 2\pi v\varDelta dv,$$

then $$B(v)=2\int_0^\infty \phi(\varDelta)\cos 2\pi v\varDelta d\varDelta. \quad . \quad . \quad . \quad . \quad . \quad (8\text{–}7)$$

[See equations (6–25b) and (6–26b)].

It follows from (8–7) that if one measures the resultant intensity in the emergent light as a function of the path difference, one can calculate the spectral distribution of the source by taking the transform of $\phi(\varDelta)$. For light emerging parallel to the axis of the system the path difference is $2d$ (§8–7). One can simply receive this light on a photo-cell or, for measurements in the infra-red, on a thermal detector and measure the variation of the intensity as the movable mirror of the interferometer is displaced. It should be noted that in practice there is an upper limit to the path difference that can be introduced and this means that, in effect, one takes $\phi(\varDelta)=0$ above a certain value of $\varDelta$. The effect of taking the transform of this truncated function is that there is a limit to the fine detail that can be shown in the calculated spectral distribution, i.e. the system has a finite resolving power. (Chromatic resolving power is defined in §11–5).

The method of Fourier transform spectroscopy has certain photometric advantages compared with the direct recording of a spectral distribution by simply scanning the spectrum. This advantage is particularly important in the far infra-red where the sources tend to be weak.

The Fourier transform method described above is related to Michelson's method of deducing spectral line profiles from fringe visibility measurements. With the usual arrangement of the interferometer for visual observation light emerges in various directions and there is an extended field of view. The path difference Δ is $2d \cos \theta$ and varies across the field, but if the source distribution $B(\nu)$ extends over a wide spectral range, $\phi(\Delta)$ has a complicated form and does

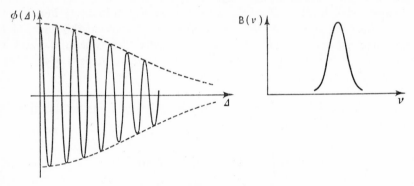

Fig. 8–12. Single spectral line.

not show a simple periodic variation, i.e. there are no fringes. However, if the source emits a narrow spectral line $\phi(\Delta)$ shows a periodic variation—there is a periodic variation of intensity across the field and fringes are seen. Fig. 8–12 shows $\phi(\Delta)$ for a single spectral line having a Gaussian profile (ϕ has a Gaussian envelope).

Fig. 8–13. Complicated spectrum.

Michelson observed the reduction in fringe visibility corresponding to the decrease in amplitude of ϕ with increasing path difference, and deduced the line profile $B(\nu)$. Fig. 8–13 shows the kind of curve one obtains for $\phi(\Delta)$ and $B(\nu)$ with a broad spectral distribution.

8-12. The Twyman and Green Interferometer

The interferometer is illustrated in Fig. 8–14(a). It will be seen to resemble a Michelson interferometer in which the extended source is replaced by a monochromatic point source S at the principal focus of a well corrected objective L_1. Single plane waves are therefore reflected at M_1 and M_2 which, if the half-silvered mirror A is at 45°, are accurately perpendicular. The plane waves are superposed and brought to a focus at E by the second objective L_2. The eye is placed at this focus so that the conditions of Maxwellian view obtain. In order to adjust the instrument, images of an illuminated pinhole at S are received alongside the

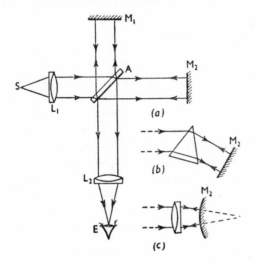

Fig. 8–14. The Twyman and Green interferometer.

pinhole itself, and also on a screen at E. The mirrors are adjusted until the two images at S coincide with the pinhole at the same time as the two images at E coincide. Frequently, one adjusts a Michelson interferometer by converting it into a Twyman and Green instrument by means of two lenses and proceeding in this way. With the mirrors adjusted as described, the superposed plane waves are exactly parallel so that, across the whole field of view, there is a constant phase difference between the superposed disturbances. The field is therefore of uniform intensity. This intensity is determined by the difference between the paths AM_1A and AM_2A and is obviously a maximum when these are equal or differ by an integral number of wavelengths. It will be seen that, with this form of Maxwellian view, different directions of the field of view do not correspond to different angles of incidence on the mirror. In consequence, the circular fringes of the Michelson interferometer are absent. By tilting M_1 or M_2, it is possible to observe the wedge fringes, but these are not localized in the sense of being in focus only in the plane of M_1. If, when M_1 and M_2 are perpendicular, the plane mirror M_2 is replaced by an optically perfect prism plus a plane mirror, or a perfect lens and spherical mirror, as suggested by Fig. 8–14(b) and (c), the field of view will remain of uniform intensity. If, however, the prism or lens is not perfect (the mirrors M_2 being perfect), the wave returning to A no

longer will be plane and the phase difference between the superposed disturbances will vary across the field of view and fringes will be seen (see Fig. 8–15).
These fringes, being lines of equal phase difference, are contours of the distorted
wavefront, so that the imperfections of the prism or lens are found at once in
terms of the wavefront aberration which they introduce (see Chapter XV). This
method was originally used in the manufacture of prisms, the errors caused by
inhomogeneity of the prism being corrected by local *figuring* of the surface of
the prism until the field of view in the interferometer was of uniform intensity.
As stated above, the fringes are not in focus in any particular plane but, if the
eye is focused on a prism face as viewed through L_2, it is possible to see the
fringes clearly and mark on the face the areas which must be figured. In order
to see whether a fringe system such as that shown in Fig. 8–15 corresponds to an
additional optical path or the reverse, it is only necessary to
press on the mounting of the mirror M_2 so as to increase
the path AM_2 slightly. The fringes will then move to
points corresponding to relatively smaller optical paths so
that if the ring system corresponds to additional retardation
the rings will open out. By mounting a lens under test on
a nodal slide which automatically maintains the centre of
curvature of M_2 (Fig. 8–14) at the Gaussian focus of the
lens, it is possible to find the aberrations present at any
point of the field of the lens. It is frequently convenient
to. adjust the interferometer to give the linear fringes

Fig. 8–15.
Appearance of a
defect.

referred to above. An imperfection in the system under test then distorts the
fringes.

It is interesting to note that the use of Fizeau fringes with a test plate enables
the optical quality of the surface of a component to be measured, whereas the
Twyman and Green interferometer tests the optical path *through* the component.

A modified form of the Twyman and Green interferometer can be used for
testing end gauges. The method is better than that described in §8–6 because it
is not necessary to wring gauges on to a third surface. This is a distinct advantage since frequent wringing of one surface against another involves a risk of
damage to the surfaces, especially if dust settles on them. A compensating plate
is placed in the arm AM_2 so that white light fringes can be employed, and the
mirror M_2 is replaced by the polished ends of two gauges which are to be
compared. The mirror M_1 is tilted to give wedge fringes and adjusted until the
central fringe falls across the ends of the gauges. When these ends are co-planar
the sections of each fringe will be collinear. A similar procedure is carried out
when viewing the other ends of the gauges which must, of course, be left undisturbed. By measuring the new positions of the central fringe on the ends of
the gauges it is possible to find the difference between the lengths of the gauges.
Other methods of comparing end gauges are described in §§8–16 and 9–9.

8–13. The Jamin Interferometer

A plan of the instrument is shown in Fig. 8–16(*a*). The glass blocks P and Q
are as nearly identical as possible and are silvered on their rear surfaces. Rays
from an extended source S are amplitude-divided at A and the component rays

are recombined at D. The disturbances traversing the ray paths ABCD and AEFD are obviously coherent and can interfere at D. If the faces of the blocks P and Q are parallel, the optical paths ABCD and AEFD are equal and this equality will hold for the component parts of all rays from S which are divided by P. The components of all rays thus interfere constructively at D to give emergent rays of equal intensity. The field of view of the telescope T is therefore of uniform brightness.

Suppose the blocks are rotated through equal and opposite small angles about horizontal axes parallel to their respective faces. Equal optical paths are now traversed by parallel rays that lie in a horizontal plane in the space between the blocks. Now parallel rays in a given direction are focused at a point in the primary image plane of T, and the rays in different directions in a horizontal

Fig. 8–16. The Jamin interferometer.

plane between the blocks are focused at points along a horizontal line in the image plane. That is, each point along this line corresponds to a zero path difference between rays internally reflected in P and those reflected in Q; the line is therefore a zero order bright fringe. Rays that are focused at points along another horizontal line in the image plane of T have optical path differences introduced between the components that entered P and the ones that entered Q. Since they are not horizontal between the blocks they make different angles with the two blocks and therefore have unequal paths in them. The rays that are focused at a non-central point on the line have optical paths that are different from those for rays that are internally reflected in the same block but are focused at the mid-point of the line, and the differences are proportional to the paths of the rays focused at the mid-point. This means that the path differences between rays internally reflected in P and those internally reflected in Q are not the same as the difference for rays focused at the mid-point. That is, the horizontal line is not a line of constant phase difference—it is not a fringe. However, the path differences between rays focused at the mid-point of the line are already small and the discrepancy between these differences and those for rays focused at other points along the line are very small. That is to say, one has a system of approximately linear horizontal fringes in the focal plane of T. A similar effect occurs with two Fabry-Perot etalons in series (see §9–7).

Owing to the considerable thickness of the blocks, the beams are sufficiently separated to be passed through the identical gas or liquid containers X and Y. These tubes have optically flat windows at each end and vary in length from about 10 cm. upwards. Any path difference introduced between the component rays to be recombined at D will cause a movement of the fringe system. If p fringes traverse the cross-wires and l is the length of the tubes, the difference δn between the refractive indices of the contents of the tubes is given by

$$l\delta n = p\lambda.$$

Since the o.p.d. cannot easily be introduced gradually, p cannot be found directly by observing the passage of the fringes across the field of view of the telescope. To overcome this difficulty, Jamin employed a compensator of the form shown in Fig. 8–16(b). Two glass plates H and K are fixed to a common axis LM and are inclined to one another at a small angle. The arrangement can be rotated as a whole about LM and the rotation is indicated on a circular scale. The compensator is mounted as indicated in Fig. 8–16(a) such that LM is horizontal and one plate lies in the path of each of the beams traversing the gas tubes. It will be seen that if the rays pass through the plates at different angles an o.p.d. is introduced and this is varied as the compensator is rotated as a whole. By employing monochromatic light and observing the passage of fringes across the field of view as the compensator is rotated, the scale can be calibrated to read o.p.d.'s in terms of wavelengths. By varying the angle between the compensator plates, the sensitivity of the device is changed, being greater when the inclination between the plates is reduced since a larger rotation is required to introduce a given o.p.d.

To determine the refractive index of a fluid, the tubes X and Y are evacuated and, using white light, the central fringe is brought on to the cross-wires by adjusting the compensator. The fluid is then introduced into one of the tubes and the compensator adjusted to return the central fringe to the cross-wires. The o.p.d. introduced by the fluid is then indicated on the scale of the compensator, and the required index can be found since o.p.d.$= (n-1)l$. It is, of course, necessary to employ white light since it is only in this way that the zero order fringe can be identified.

If the second plate Q is rotated about a vertical axis vertical fringes are formed, but white light fringes can be seen only by using the compensator and there will be no truly achromatic central fringe if the dispersions of the blocks and compensator plates are different (see §7–10). A similar difficulty may occur when the dispersion of the specimen under test is very different from that of the compensator plates. It is then necessary to perform a preliminary experiment with shorter tubes or a smaller concentration of fluid in order to identify the central fringe.

One of the most important disadvantages of the Jamin interferometer has been the expense involved in obtaining identical glass blocks, accurately worked and homogeneous. This difficulty has been overcome by Kuhn and Wheatley (1945) by employing air-spaced reflecting surfaces at P and Q. This overcomes the chief disadvantage that the Jamin interferometer had compared with the Rayleigh interferometer (see §11–14).

8–14. The Mach-Zehnder Interferometer

Fig. 8–17 shows the optical system of the Mach-Zehnder interferometer. It will be seen that the instrument is related to the Jamin and Michelson instruments. S is a moderately extended source of monochromatic light. M_1 and M_2

are front-silvered mirrors and P_1 and P_2 are semi-silvered plates. The fringes are observed from O. It will be seen that the beams are widely separated, and this has recently proved a useful feature in the study of gas flow in such apparatus as wind tunnels. One beam is made to pass through the gas to be investigated at G while the other is passed through a pair of plates C which compensate for the windows of G. It can be shown that when the paths $P_1M_1P_2$, $P_1M_2P_2$ are equal a suitable adjustment of the mirrors gives localized fringes of the type observed with the Michelson interferometer. In the present case a suitable adjustment of the mirrors causes the (virtual) fringes to be localized in a chosen plane in the vessel G in which the variations of gas pressure are to be investigated. It is this ability to localize the fringes in a chosen plane

Fig. 8–17.
The Mach-Zehnder interferometer.

which is the chief advantage of the Mach-Zehnder over the Michelson interferometer. Several modified forms of the interferometer have been used to study the gas flow in the region of projectiles and aircraft.

8–15. The Wavefront Shearing Interferometer

In a Twyman and Green interferometer the wavefront under test is compared with a reference wavefront and, to produce the latter, it is necessary to employ a dividing mirror A and comparison mirror M_1 (Fig. 8–14) which are highly corrected over an aperture equal to that of the optical system under test. This may become an insuperable difficulty when it is desired to test very large aperture astronomical telescope objectives. In the *wavefront shearing interferometer* this difficulty is overcome. When one part of a wavefront is under test, a different part of the same wavefront acts as the reference wavefront. The principle of the method is as follows.

In Fig. 8–18 AB represents a wavefront which should be spherical but in fact exhibits a local error at E. A'E'B' is an identical wavefront which is displaced circumferentially a distance δs. If the wavefronts are coherent, they will interfere and in the region of E and E' will give patterns similar to those observed in the Twyman and Green interferometer. If the wavefronts are tilted through equal and opposite small angles about the chord AB, an eye viewing the waves under conditions of Maxwellian view will see a series of fringes parallel to AB, the

Fig. 8–18. Principle of the wavefront shear-ing interferometer.

fringes being distorted in the region of E and E'. As in the Twyman and Green interferometer, measurement of these fringes enables the nature of the error E to be calculated. In the wavefront shearing interferometer the interfering wavefronts are obtained by amplitude division of the wave emerging from the optical system under test. The components are recombined in such a way that one is sheared a distance δs relative to the other. Bates (1947) used the optical system of the Mach-Zehnder interferometer to effect the division and recombination of the disturbances. With this arrangement a shear can be introduced by rotating the plate P_2 (Fig. 8–17). A slit source can be used, the slit being narrow in the direction parallel to the direction of shear.

(a) Plan (b) Section along A-B

Fig. 8–19. Interferometer with fixed shear and tilt.

Since the interferometer can be placed close to the focus of the wavefront under test, it is not necessary to have wide aperture mirrors. For example, Brown (1954) has described an instrument measuring only $2 \times 1\frac{1}{2} \times 1\frac{1}{8}$ inches. This follows a principle suggested by Drew (1951) but gives a fixed shear and tilt to the wavefront. The components can then be mounted rigidly and the instrument becomes much easier to use. The arrangement is shown in Fig. 8–19; it forms a single cemented unit. The plate D plays the part of the beam splitter

(a) Gauge in position

(b) Appearance of Fringes

Fig. 8–20.
Principle of the
N.P.L. gauge testing
interferometer.

and recombiner of the Mach-Zehnder system. S_1 and S_2 are glass spacers. The angle α controls the shear and β controls the tilt.

8–16. Gauge Measuring Interferometers

Fig. 8–20(a) shows the principle of the interferometer used at the N.P.L. for measuring slip gauges. The gauge G is wrung to a base plate B and, viewing from above, one observes monochromatic fringes formed between the semi-reflecting glass plate P and the gauge, and between P and B. The plate P is tilted to obtain linear fringes across G and B as in (b). If the faces of G are parallel, the two sets of fringes are parallel and equally spaced. By observing the misfit of the fringes for four wavelengths, the thickness of the gauge can be obtained using the method of exact fractions (see §9–5).

Kösters' comparator employs a modification of the Twyman-Green arrangement (see Fig. 8–21). The gauge G is wrung to the mirror M_2 and the position of M_1 adjusted so that its virtual position M_1' is across the middle of the gauge. If M_1 is then tilted, equally clear linear mono-chromatic fringes can be seen across G and M_2. The mis-fit of the fringes is again found for several wavelengths and the method of exact fractions used. Since M_1' is approximately half-way along the gauge, the optical path differences involved in this method are only half those involved in the previous method. In consequence, the Kösters interferometer can be used for longer end gauges than can the above N.P.L. arrangement. In both these instruments the gauge must be wrung to a plate, with a consequent risk of damage to the surfaces. This difficulty is overcome in

Fig. 8–21.
Principle of the Kösters interferometer.

Dowell's interferometer. As will be seen from Fig. 8–22, this is another adaptation of the Twyman-Green instrument. Fringes can be seen across the ends of G_1 and G_2 in an obvious manner. If the gauges are symmetrically located between the mirrors, white light fringes can be used to compare them, fractions being estimated with monochromatic light. This instrument may be modified

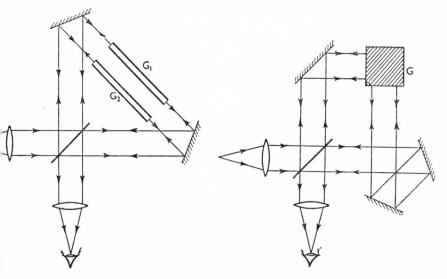

Fig. 8–22. Dowell's interferometer.   Fig. 8–23. Angle-gauge interferometer.

to give an angle-gauge interferometer—Fig. 8–23 shows the arrangement for comparing a right-angle gauge G with a standard. The standard is put in position at G and the mirrors adjusted until the field of view is of uniform brightness. The standard is then replaced by the gauge under test, when the spacing of the fringes observed indicates the error in the gauge.

The measurement of an end gauge will now be used to explain the principle of another method of using a Michelson interferometer to measure distances. The gauge G is wrung to a mirror M_2 as in Fig. 8–21. M_1 is tilted slightly and moved until the zero order white light fringe is observed across M_2. This indicates that M_1' intersects M_2. M_1 is then moved to the left and its movement measured by counting monochromatic fringes—at any point in the field of view the passage of one fringe indicates a movement of $\lambda/2$. M_1 is then moved until the white light fringe is seen across the upper surface of G, indicating that M_1' intersects this surface. In this way one can find the length of G in wavelengths. This is the basis of the method used by Michelson and Benoît to find the number of wavelengths of the red cadmium line in the length of the standard Metre. Since the source was not sufficiently monochromatic for fringes to be observed with a path difference of 1 metre, they built up to 1 metre by means of a step by step process. The determination of the Metre is discussed in §§9–9 and 9–10.

CHAPTER IX

MULTIPLE BEAM INTERFEROMETRY

THE present chapter is concerned with arrangements involving multiple reflections. Those involving multiple division of wavefront (e.g. the echelon) are discussed in Chapter XII. It will be shown that, in general, the effect of employing high reflectivity and therefore multiple beams is to cause a sharpening of the fringes.

Unless otherwise stated, wavelengths are measured in air.

9–1. Multiple Beam Fringes of Equal Inclination

The discussion of § 8–1 was concerned with the fringes that may be observed with a parallel-sided plate or film when the surfaces have low reflectivity. In

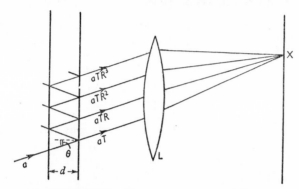

Fig. 9–1. Multiple reflections in a parallel-sided plate.

that case the interference was substantially between only two beams and the fringes observed by transmission were found to be of very poor contrast. When the boundary surfaces have higher reflectivity it is easily shown that the fringes are sharper and that those viewed by transmission have good contrast. In this case beams undergoing many internal reflections contribute to the pattern. The most important fringes are those associated with an air space between two reflecting surfaces; usually these surfaces consist of metal films deposited on glass plates. In developing the theory, the existence of the plates can be ignored because (a) their outer surfaces have low reflectivity, and (b) if the plates are plane-parallel, they will introduce no deviation in the rays.

Fig. 9–1 illustrates the successive partial reflections of a ray between two reflecting surfaces in air. If the reflections occur at a denser dielectric, there is a phase change of π at each reflection. The difference between the paths traversed by successive beams in passing to X, in the focal plane of L, is $2d \cos \theta$. Hence the phase difference at X between successive beams is

$$\delta = \frac{2\pi}{\lambda}(2d \cos \theta) + 2\pi$$

159

where the term 2π can, of course, be omitted. If the reflections occur at metal surfaces the phase changes are not π but the effect can be ignored in a first treatment. If T and R are the fractions of the incident energy which are transmitted and reflected at each surface, the fractional amplitudes are $T^{\frac{1}{2}}$ and $R^{\frac{1}{2}}$ and successive emergent rays have amplitudes aT, aTR, aTR^2, aTR^3, etc., where a is the amplitude of the initial incident ray. Thus if the first transmitted beam is assumed to have zero phase, the disturbances superposed at X may be represented by

$$aTe^{i\omega t}, \quad aTRe^{i(\omega t-\delta)}, \quad aTR^2e^{i(\omega t-2\delta)}, \text{ etc.} \ldots \quad (\text{see } \S 6\text{--}3).$$

The complex amplitude of the resultant is therefore given by

$$z = aT(1 + Re^{-i\delta} + R^2e^{-2i\delta} + R^3e^{-3i\delta} + \ldots)$$

$$= \frac{aT}{1 - Re^{-i\delta}}.$$

Hence the resultant intensity is (see $\S 6$--3)

$$I = z\bar{z} = \frac{a^2T^2}{1 + R^2 - 2R\cos\delta},$$

i.e. $$I = \frac{a^2T^2}{(1-R)^2} \cdot \frac{1}{1 + \dfrac{4R}{(1-R)^2}\sin^2\dfrac{\delta}{2}}. \quad \ldots \quad (9\text{--}1)$$

Fig. 9–2 shows the variation of I with δ for various values of R when the maxima have the same intensity (see below). It will be seen that the sharpness

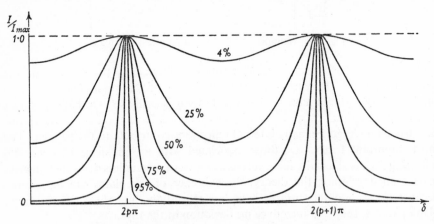

Fig. 9–2. Intensity distribution in multiple beam fringes.

of the fringes increases as the reflecting power of the films is increased. For all values of R and T, the maxima and minima occur at $\cos\delta = +1$ and $\cos\delta = -1$ respectively, i.e. at $\delta = 2p\pi$ and $(2p+1)\pi$ (p an integer).

Plate I(e) shows a photograph of the fringes viewed by transmission. (The multiple-beam fringes can also be observed by reflection; they are shown in

Plate I(d) beneath fringes resembling those obtained with a Michelson inter-ferometer. It will be seen that the spacing of the maxima is the same in each case but the multiple beam fringes are very much sharper than the Michelson fringes which are formed by the interference of two beams and are the usual $\cos^2$ fringes.)

From equation (9–1), on putting $\delta = 2p\pi$, one has, for the intensity of the maxima,

$$I_{max} = \frac{a^2 T^2}{(1-R)^2}, \qquad \ldots \ldots \quad (9\text{--}2)$$

and, putting $\delta = (2p+1)\pi$,

$$I_{min} = \frac{a^2 T^2}{(1+R)^2}. \qquad \ldots \ldots \quad (9\text{--}3)$$

If a fraction A of the incident energy is absorbed at each reflecting surface, one has $A+T+R=1$. When there is no absorption, $T=1-R$ and

$$I_{max} = a^2,$$

$$I_{min} = a^2 \left(\frac{1-R}{1+R}\right)^2.$$

Whilst the absolute values of I_{max} and I_{min} depend on the absorption at each reflecting surface, it will be seen from equation (9–1) that the general shape of the fringes is unaffected. In particular, the ratio I_{max}/I_{min} is independent of A and is given by

$$\frac{I_{max}}{I_{min}} = \left(\frac{1+R}{1-R}\right)^2, \qquad \ldots \ldots \quad (9\text{--}4)$$

and the visibility of the fringes is given by

$$V = \frac{I_{max}-I_{min}}{I_{max}+I_{min}} = \frac{2R}{1+R^2}. \qquad \ldots \ldots \quad (9\text{--}5)$$

For unsilvered glass plates $R \doteqdot 4\%$ and $V \doteqdot 0.08$. V reaches 0.8 when $R \doteqdot 50\%$ and approaches unity as R approaches 100%. Although the absorption does not affect the sharpness of the fringes, it does control the absolute intensity in the pattern, and it is important to select reflecting surfaces whose absorption is as low as possible. The surfaces consist of a metal film deposited on a glass surface and are usually formed by evaporation in a vacuum. Silver and aluminium are probably the most widely used materials. The former is the better in the visible and infra-red regions but the latter is better in the ultra-violet because silver has an absorption band in the region of $\lambda 3000$ angstroms. Aluminium is frequently used in the visible region also because it is cheaper and does not tarnish easily.

The way in which an increase of the reflectivity causes a sharpening of the fringes is easily understood if one uses the graphical method of summing the disturbances. Although, in fact, a large number of disturbances is superposed, a sufficiently good indication of the state of affairs is obtained when the discussion is restricted to the interference of ten beams with two values of the reflectivity. At a maximum the vector diagrams in each case will be straight lines composed of the vectors, representing separate beams, lying end to end (see Fig. 9–3). For the higher reflectivity the lengths of the vectors decrease less rapidly, but the total lengths of the resultants will be equal if there is no absorption since, in this case, the maxima are equally bright. At a point a short distance away from the centre of a maximum the superposed disturbances are slightly out of phase, the

Lower Reflectivity   *(a)*   Higher Reflectivity

(b)

Fig. 9–3. The effect of increased reflectivity.

phase difference between successive disturbances being constant. The vector diagrams take the form indicated in Fig. 9–3(*b*) where the angles between successive vectors are equal and are the same for both values of the reflectivity. It will be seen that the resultant is very much smaller in the case of higher reflectivity, showing that as one moves away from the centre of a maximum the intensity falls off more rapidly.

The above discussion has related to the distribution across the fringes as illustrated in Fig. 9–2 where intensity is plotted against δ, the phase difference between successive rays. It is instructive to think, now, of the pattern actually formed in the focal plane of the lens in Fig. 9–1.

At the centre of a fringe all disturbances arrive in phase (i.e. with phase differences that are integral multiples of 2π). A fringe is sharp if the intensity falls off rapidly as one moves away from the maximum, and this will happen if

(a)

Small
source

Telescope

(b)

Extended
source

Fig. 9–4. Experimental arrangement.

strong disturbances get out of phase rapidly. The requirement is, then, that for a small displacement away from a maximum the largest possible phase difference should arise between the first transmitted ray and the last ray of appreciable amplitude. This corresponds to the largest possible plate separation and the highest possible reflectivity.

Unless the reflecting surfaces are very close together, it is necessary to use an observing telescope in order to collect sufficient multiply reflected rays (see §8-1) and one may again employ a small source under conditions resembling Maxwellian view [Fig. 9-4(a)] or an extended source with or without a collimating lens [Fig. 9-4(b)]. With no lens a very large source is required. It should be noted that the presence and position of any lenses on the source side of the film make no difference to the fringes in the region in which they can be seen, the lenses simply cause light to traverse the reflecting plates at various angles and enter the observing lens, thus increasing the field of view over which fringes can be seen. The fringes are always in focus in the focal plane(s) of whatever lenses follow the reflecting plates.

9-2. The Fabry-Perot Interferometer and Etalon

In the Fabry-Perot interferometer the separation between two semi-silvered glass plates can be varied. One plate remains stationary with respect to the frame of the instrument whilst the other is mounted on a nut threaded on an accurate screw. The nut is constrained to move exactly linearly so that, once the plates are adjusted to be parallel, they remain parallel as the separation is altered. The instrument is difficult to manufacture and must now be considered obsolescent.

The etalon consists of two semi-silvered plates rigidly held a fixed distance apart. This is obviously much more easily manufactured and serves many useful purposes. In both instruments the reflecting surfaces must be very accurate optical flats and, to keep the fringes sharp and truly circular, it is necessary for the reflecting surfaces to be flat to a small fraction of a wavelength. An accuracy of approximately $\lambda/100$ can be achieved. It is usual for the glass plates of the instruments to be slightly wedge shaped so that the outer, unsilvered, faces of the plates are not exactly parallel to the inner, silvered, faces. The wedge angle is usually between 1 and 10 minutes of arc. This is desirable in order to reduce the effect of the interference patterns formed by reflections at the unsilvered faces. The observed fringe system is not materially affected.

The adjustment of the Fabry-Perot interferometer is in many ways similar to that of the Michelson. Using a small separation, the plates are made roughly parallel by viewing a small source through the plates. The plates are adjusted until the images of the source, formed by multiple reflections, appear collinear. Next, using a monochromatic source, the mirrors are adjusted to give circular fringes centred at the centre of the field as with the Michelson interferometer. Since the plate separation is small, these can be seen with the naked eye. As before, exact parallelism of the plates is secured by adjusting the mirrors until a lateral movement of the eye does not cause the fringes to open out or close in.

One simple application of the etalon can be mentioned here: the measurement of the refractive index of air (or any other gas). The optical path difference between successive beams emerging from the etalon is $2nd \cos \theta$, where n is the refractive index of the gas between the plates. If the space between the plates is evacuated, the path difference becomes $2d \cos \theta$. That is, the optical path difference is decreased by $2(n-1)d \cos \theta$. If λ_0 is the wavelength in a vacuum, $[2(n-1)d \cos \theta]/\lambda_0$ is the change in path difference in wavelengths and is equal to the number of fringes which cross the field of view. By counting this number, n can be found if d and λ_0 are known.

9-3. Resolving Power of Fabry-Perot Instruments

As for a spectral line (§8–10) the sharpness of a fringe can be indicated by stating the half-value width, i.e. the width of the fringe at $I=\frac{1}{2}I_{max}$. In Fig. 9–5 I/I_{max} is plotted against order; referring to the fringes shown by the unbroken

Fig. 9–5. Fringes for neighbouring wavelengths.

lines, the order p is an integer at the centre of a fringe and increases by $\delta p_{\frac{1}{2}}$ as I/I_{max} falls to $\frac{1}{2}$. The half-value width in terms of order is $2\delta p_{\frac{1}{2}}$. Equation (9–1) (known as Airy's formula) gives

$$I= \frac{I_{max}}{1+F\sin^2(\frac{\delta}{2})},$$

where $\qquad F=4R/(1-R)^2$ and $\delta=(2\pi/\lambda).2d\cos\theta=2\pi p$

$$\therefore \frac{I}{I_{max}} = \frac{1}{1+F\sin^2\pi p}.$$

When $I=\frac{1}{2}I_{max}$, $p=$integer$+\delta p_{\frac{1}{2}}$ and $\sin\pi p=\sin\pi\delta p_{\frac{1}{2}}$.

$$\therefore \frac{1}{2}=\frac{1}{1+F\sin^2\pi\delta p_{\frac{1}{2}}},$$

or $\qquad F\sin^2\pi\delta p_{\frac{1}{2}}=1.$

If the reflectivity is high, F is large, $\delta p_{\frac{1}{2}}$ is small, and the angle may be equated to its sine.

$$\therefore (\pi\delta p_{\frac{1}{2}})^2 =\frac{1}{F},$$

or $\qquad \delta p_{\frac{1}{2}}=\frac{1}{\pi\sqrt{F}}.$

$$\therefore \text{ Half-value width}=2\delta p_{\frac{1}{2}}=\frac{2}{\pi\sqrt{F}}.$$

The ratio: $\dfrac{\text{separation of successive orders}}{\text{half-value width}}$ is called the *finesse*.

Now, *in terms of order* the separation of successive orders is simply unity, so that the finesse is simply the reciprocal of the half-value width:

$$\text{Finesse} = \frac{1}{2\delta p_{\frac{1}{2}}} = \frac{\pi\sqrt{F}}{2}.$$

(Fabry and Perot called F the coefficient of finesse.)

Suppose, now, that two wavelengths λ, $\lambda+\delta\lambda$, are emitted by the source with equal intensities. The bright fringes of each wavelength will be formed alongside one another as in Fig. 9–5. As $\delta\lambda$ decreases, the maxima overlap to a greater extent, and when the fringes are just resolved (i.e. just distinguishable), $\lambda/\delta\lambda$ is, as usual, referred to as the *chromatic resolving power*. The subject of resolving power is discussed more fully in §§11–5 and 11–6 and it is seen that when investigating the resolving power of prism spectroscopes Rayleigh formulated a very simple criterion for deciding when two slit images are resolved. However, the intensity distribution in the Fabry-Perot fringes is quite different from that in diffraction slit images and the simple statement of the criterion as given in §11–5 cannot be applied here. When expressed in terms of intensity in the pattern, the *Rayleigh criterion* implies that two patterns may be said to be resolved if, midway between their centres, there is a reduction of intensity to about 81% of that occurring at the centre of each separate image. Although this latter is the correct criterion to adopt here in order to be able to compare the resolution of a Fabry-Perot instrument with that of a prism or a grating, it leads to a fairly complicated calculation; the *Taylor criterion* is a useful alternative which is in the spirit of Rayleigh's, being simple in statement and giving simple results rather than being precise in the sense of being based on a careful consideration of what variations in intensity can be detected in particular circumstances. The Taylor criterion states that there is a just-detectable drop in intensity between two fringes, so that they can be said to be resolved, if the separate intensity curves intersect at $I=\frac{1}{2}I_{max}$, i.e. if the separation of the maxima is equal to the half-value width.

It has been pointed out by Tolansky that the spectroscopist is usually concerned with the wave number $\nu=1/\lambda$ rather than the wavelength of a line, and that when two lines are very close it is $\delta\nu$ rather than $\delta\lambda$ that has significance. The value of $\delta\nu$ when two fringes are just resolved Tolansky calls the *resolving limit*; it is easily obtained from the classical resolving power. One has $\nu\lambda=1$,

$$\therefore \frac{\lambda}{\delta\lambda} = -\frac{\nu}{\delta\nu}, \qquad \cdots \cdots \quad (9\text{–}6)$$

$$\therefore \delta\nu = -\frac{\nu}{(\lambda/\delta\lambda)}. \qquad \cdots \cdots \quad (9\text{–}7)$$

The minus sign has no importance and will be dropped when the result is applied below. The value $\delta\nu$ is a direct measure of the power of the instrument to separate close components.

Suppose, now, that at the pth order maximum for $\lambda+\delta\lambda$ the order for λ is $p+\delta p$. Since this corresponds to a given point in the pattern,

$$2d\cos\theta=(p+\delta p)\lambda=p(\lambda+\delta\lambda),$$

whence

$$\frac{\lambda}{\delta\lambda}=\frac{p}{\delta p}. \qquad\qquad\qquad (9\text{--}8)$$

Now, at the limit of resolution the Taylor criterion gives

$$\delta p=2\delta p_{\frac{1}{2}}.$$

$$\therefore\quad \frac{\lambda}{\delta\lambda}=\frac{p}{2\delta p_{\frac{1}{2}}}=p.\frac{\pi\sqrt{F}}{2}=p\times\text{Finesse,}$$

whence

$$\delta\sqrt{}=\frac{2}{\lambda p\pi\sqrt{F}}$$

or, since $\lambda p=2d$ if θ is small,

$$\delta\nu=\frac{1}{\pi d\sqrt{F}}.$$

In order to be able to compare the resolution of a Fabry-Perot instrument with that of a prism or a grating, the Rayleigh criterion will now be applied as indicated above. As before, the order at a short distance from a maximum is an integer $+\delta p$ and the intensity is given by

$$I=\frac{I_{\max}}{1+F\sin^2(\pi\delta p)}.$$

Fig. 9–6 shows the appearance of two maxima at the limit of resolution. The total intensity is indicated by the full line and, according to the criterion given above, falls at the midpoint to 0·81 of its maximum value. It will be seen that the maximum reached by the total intensity is greater than $I_{\max}$ for a single fringe because the intensity due to the adjacent fringe does not fall to zero. However, if it is assumed that at the centre of one fringe the intensity due to the other may be neglected, the total intensity midway between the maxima is simply $0\cdot81I_{\max}$, and the intensity at this point associated with each fringe is $0\cdot405I_{\max}$. Now, if p is the order at the centre of the maximum and δp is the smallest resolvable change in order, the order for wavelength λ at the centre of the maximum for wavelength $\lambda+\delta\lambda$ is $p+\delta p$ and that midway between the maxima is $p+\frac{1}{2}\delta p$. Thus at the mid-point one may write, for a first approximation,

$$I=\frac{I_{\max}}{1+F\sin^2\frac{1}{2}\pi\delta p}=0\cdot405I_{\max},$$

Fig. 9–6. Fringes at limit of resolution.

$$\therefore\quad \sin^2\tfrac{1}{2}\pi\delta p=\frac{1-0\cdot405}{0\cdot405F}=\frac{1\cdot469}{F}.$$

If the reflectivity of the surfaces is large, F is large and the angle may be equated to its sine. Whence

$$\delta p = \frac{1}{1 \cdot 301 \sqrt{F}} \cdot$$

If allowance is made for the fact that the intensity in one fringe is not zero at the centre of the other, it can be shown that one obtains, as a better approximation,

$$\delta p = \frac{1}{1 \cdot 49 \sqrt{F}} \cdot$$

Hence the resolving power is given by

$$\frac{\lambda}{\delta \lambda} = \frac{p}{\delta p} = p \, 1 \cdot 49 \sqrt{F}. \quad \ldots \ldots \quad (9\text{–}9)$$

The resolving limit is given by

$$\delta v = \frac{v}{(\lambda / \delta \lambda)} = \frac{1}{\lambda p \, 1 \cdot 49 \sqrt{F}}$$

or, since $\lambda p = 2d$ when θ is small,

$$\delta v = \frac{1}{2d \, 1 \cdot 49 \sqrt{F}} \cdot \quad \ldots \ldots \quad (9\text{–}10)$$

As will be seen in Chapter XII, the resolving power of a diffraction grating is the product of the order and the total number of apertures; for the reflection echelon the latter is the total number of plates. In comparing the properties of the echelons and the Fabry-Perot instruments it is possible, in view of equation (9–9), to regard $1 \cdot 49 \sqrt{F}$ as the effective number of reflections in the latter instruments. It is easily shown that this increases from 8·3 when $R = 70\%$ to 28·3 when $R = 90\%$ and reaches 58 when $R = 95\%$, so that the attainment of a higher reflectivity is an important factor in these instruments. As $R \to 1$, $F \to 4/(1-R)^2$ and the effective number of reflections is given approximately by $3/(1-R)$. This gives 50 for $R = 94\%$ and 60 for $R = 95\%$.

It is interesting to note that all spectral lines have a width which depends on the conditions obtaining in the source, so that resolution of smaller intervals is useless. With non-laser sources the maximum resolving power which can be employed usefully is about 10^7 and this is obtained with an etalon of thickness about 20 cm. when the reflectivity of the surfaces is about 80%.

Usually one is interested in examining neighbouring spectral lines over a finite range of wavelengths. The possibility then arises of the extreme wavelengths in the range being sufficiently different to cause the maximum of a certain order of one to overlap that of the next order of another. This, of course, renders examination difficult and it is important to know the *spectral range* over which an instrument can be used without this overlapping of orders. To examine a larger spectral range one would have to employ an auxiliary dispersion system to isolate manageable regions. If $\Delta \lambda$ is the difference between two wavelengths such that the pth order of one coincides with the $(p+1)$th order of the other, one has from equation (9–8) since $\delta p = 1$,

$$\Delta \lambda = \frac{\lambda}{p} = \frac{\lambda^2}{2d} \quad \ldots \ldots \quad (9\text{–}11)$$

or, in terms of wave numbers,

$$\Delta\nu = \frac{\nu}{p} = \frac{1}{2d}.$$

It follows at once from (9–9) and (9–11) that

$$\frac{\Delta\lambda}{\delta\lambda} = \frac{1}{\delta p}.$$

Now, using the Taylor criterion, $\delta p = 2\delta p_{\frac{1}{2}}$ so that, in terms of either wave numbers or wavelengths,

$$\frac{\text{spectral range}}{\text{smallest resolvable increment}} = \frac{\Delta\nu}{\delta\nu} = \frac{\Delta\lambda}{\delta\lambda} = \text{Finesse.}$$

It is the relatively small free spectral range and the consequent need of a premonochromator to isolate this range that is the chief disadvantage of Fabry-Perot instruments. It seems likely that the recent improvements in the production of diffraction gratings will lead to their use in place of etalons in many applications, but the etalon remains the only practical instrument for resolving powers much above 10^6.

The relative merits of the various high resolution instruments are discussed on p. 274.

9–4. Comparison of Wavelengths. Method of Coincidences. Hyperfine Structure

If the source emits two wavelengths λ_1 and λ_2, two sets of fringes will be observed with a Fabry-Perot interferometer. Suppose that, in a direction θ, the maxima for λ_1 and λ_2 coincide when the plate separation is d_1. Then

$$2d_1 \cos \theta = p\lambda_1 = q\lambda_2, \quad \cdot \quad \cdot \quad \cdot \quad \cdot \quad \cdot \quad (9\text{--}12)$$

where p and q are integers. Thus $\lambda_1/\lambda_2 = q/p$. Proceeding outwards from the centre of the pattern, the condition for the next maxima to coincide is $\lambda_1/\lambda_2 = (q-1)/(p-1)$. Now since p and q are large ($p = 40,000$ when $\theta = 0$, $d = 1$ cm., $\lambda = 5000$ angstroms), the ratios q/p and $(q-1)/(p-1)$ are nearly equal. Therefore the maxima will coincide over a considerable range of angles—certainly over the field of view of the observing telescope, i.e. the complete ring systems will appear coincident.

Suppose the plate separation is increased until the two sets of fringes again coincide. The order of λ_1 has then increased by k and that of λ_2 by $k+1$ so that

$$2d_2 \cos \theta = (p+k)\lambda_1 = (q+k+1)\lambda_2.$$

Hence, from equation (9–12),

$$2 \cos \theta(d_2 - d_1) = k\lambda_1 = (k+1)\lambda_2, \quad \cdot \quad \cdot \quad \cdot \quad (9\text{--}13)$$

$$\therefore \ (\lambda_1 - \lambda_2) = \frac{\lambda_2}{k} = \frac{\lambda_1}{k+1}, \quad \cdot \quad \cdot \quad \cdot \quad \cdot \quad (9\text{--}14)$$

or, writing $\cos \theta = 1$,

$$\lambda_1 - \lambda_2 = \frac{\lambda_1 \lambda_2}{2(d_2 - d_1)}. \qquad \ldots \ldots \quad (9\text{-}15)$$

One can proceed as follows: k may be found by counting the number of λ_1 (or λ_2) fringes which pass an instrumental mark (or arise from the centre of the pattern). Equation (9–14) then gives λ_1/λ_2 or, if one of the wavelengths is known, $(\lambda_1 - \lambda_2)$ may be found. If the change in mirror separation is given by the instrument, equation (9–13) can be used to give k if λ_1 or λ_2 is known or to find λ_1 and λ_2 if k is found by counting. Alternatively, if approximate values of λ_1 and λ_2 are available, equation (9–15) gives a value for $(\lambda_1 - \lambda_2)$ which is more accurate than that known from the approximate values of the wavelengths.

For widely different wavelengths, k is relatively small and several coincidences should be recorded. The method is then very accurate but has the disadvantage of employing the costly interferometer and of requiring individual measurements for every spectral line examined. The method of exact fractions described in the next section uses the cheaper etalon and enables numerous lines to be examined relatively quickly.

One of the most common applications of Fabry-Perot instruments is to the investigation of the hyperfine structure of spectral lines. In this work one measures the small difference in wave numbers ($\Delta\nu$) between the satellite and the main line. If θ_1 and θ_1' are the angular radii of the main line and the satellite for order p_1, and θ_2 is the angular radius for the main line of order p_2, one has, if the angles are small,

$$1 - \frac{\theta_1^2}{2} = \frac{p_1}{2\nu d}, \quad 1 - \frac{\theta_2^2}{2} = \frac{p_2}{2\nu d}, \quad 1 - \frac{\theta_1'^2}{2} = \frac{p_1}{2\nu' d},$$

where ν and ν' are the wave numbers of the main line and the satellite respectively. If θ_1 and θ_2 correspond to adjacent maxima, $p_2 = p_1 - 1$. The above equations then give

$$\frac{\theta_2^2 - \theta_1^2}{2} = \frac{1}{2d\nu} \quad \text{and} \quad \frac{\theta_1'^2 - \theta_1^2}{2} = \frac{p_1}{2d}\left(\frac{1}{\nu} - \frac{1}{\nu'}\right) = \frac{p_1}{2d} \cdot \frac{\Delta\nu}{\nu\nu'},$$

$$\therefore \quad \frac{\theta_1'^2 - \theta_1^2}{\theta_2^2 - \theta_1^2} = \frac{p_1 \Delta\nu}{\nu'}$$

or, since $\Delta\nu$ is small,

$$\Delta\nu \fallingdotseq \left(\frac{\theta_1'^2 - \theta_1^2}{\theta_2^2 - \theta_1^2}\right)\frac{\nu}{p_1} \fallingdotseq \left(\frac{\theta_1'^2 - \theta_1^2}{\theta_2^2 - \theta_1^2}\right)\frac{1}{2d}.$$

9–5. Method of Exact Fractions

Given an etalon whose plate separation is known approximately, and given a number of accurately known wavelengths, the method of exact fractions enables one to find the plate separation more accurately and to determine other wavelengths.

For any wavelength λ, the order of interference at the centre of the Fabry-Perot fringes is not usually an integer and may be written $(p + \varepsilon)$ where p is the order of the first bright ring and is, of course, integral. If one has, for example,

7*

three accurately known wavelengths λ_1, λ_2, λ_3, one may write, for the orders at the centre of their respective fringe systems, $(p_1+\varepsilon_1)$, $(p_2+\varepsilon_2)$, $(p_3+\varepsilon_3)$, and one has

$$2d=\lambda_1(p_1+\varepsilon_1)=\lambda_2(p_2+\varepsilon_2)=\lambda_3(p_3+\varepsilon_3). \quad \ldots \quad (9\text{--}16)$$

The fractions ε_1, ε_2, ε_3, can be found from observation of the fringe systems (see below), but if d is unknown the values of the integers p_1, p_2, p_3, are unknown since there will be an infinite number of sets of values which will satisfy equation (9–16). However, if an approximate value of d is available, this will give a range of possible values for, say, p_1. One can then take values of p_1 within this range and, using the observed value of ε_1, calculate $(p_2+\varepsilon_2)$ and $(p_3+\varepsilon_3)$ from equation (9–16) until a value of p_1 is found which yields the observed values of ε_2 and ε_3. If the approximate value of d is very unreliable it may be found that equation (9–16) can be satisfied for more than one value of p_1 lying within the possible range. This difficulty is easily overcome since values of p_1 that satisfy equation (9–16) become less frequent as the number of standard wavelengths is increased. Thus one must measure the fractions for additional standard wavelengths until the values of p_1 satisfying equation (9–16) become sufficiently infrequent for only one value to lie within the range of possible values. In this way the value of p_1 can be found exactly. The value of ε_1 can be found to an accuracy of about $\pm 0\cdot 01$ so that if, for example, λ_1 is 6438 angstroms (cadmium red light) d can be determined to an accuracy of about $0\cdot 0000003$ cm. If another wavelength is known with sufficient accuracy to determine the integral part of the order at the centre, measurement of the exact fraction as described below yields a more accurate value for the wavelength. By proceeding subsequently to thicker etalons, wavelengths can be determined with still greater accuracy (e.g. to about $\pm 0\cdot 0001$ angstrom with a 10 cm. etalon). To justify the use of the thicker etalons it is, of course, necessary to have a source of light yielding very sharp spectral lines.

9–6. Measurement of the Fractions

In order to measure the fractional orders at the centres of the fringe systems for several different wavelengths, it is convenient to employ a prism spectrometer

arrangement in which the etalon is placed between the telescope and collimator. For each wavelength present in the source (or successive sources) the arrangement is equivalent to that illustrated in Fig. 9–4(b) with the exception that, apart from the slit width, the source extends in one direction only. Thus in the focal plane of the telescope one gets a vertical section across a diameter of the fringe system for each wavelength, the width of the section being equal to that of the slit image. The appearance of each spectral line is therefore as shown in Fig. 9–7. If j is the ring number going out from the centre of the pattern and p is the order for the first ring, the order for the jth ring is $(p-j+1)$ and one has

Fig. 9–7. Fringes across image of slit.

$$\frac{2d \cos \theta_j}{\lambda} = p - j + 1,$$

$$\therefore \quad (p + \varepsilon) \cos \theta_j = p - j + 1,$$

where θ_j is the angular radius of the jth ring before subsequent magnification.

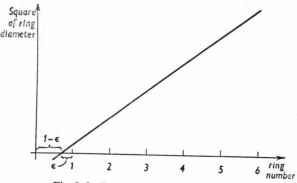

Fig. 9–8. Determination of the fraction.

The ring diameters may be measured directly using a telescope with a micrometer eyepiece. Alternatively the fringes may be photographed and the ring diameters measured on the plate or film. If, in any suitable units, D_j is the diameter of the jth ring, one may write $mD_j = 2\theta$, where m is a magnification constant. This is justifiable since the angular diameters of the observed rings are small. In addition one may write

$$\cos \theta_j = 1 - \frac{\theta_j^2}{2} = 1 - \frac{m^2 D_j^2}{8},$$

$$\therefore \quad (p + \varepsilon) - (p + \varepsilon)\frac{m^2 D_j^2}{8} = p - j + 1,$$

or

$$\left(\frac{p + \varepsilon}{8}\right) m^2 D_j^2 = j + \varepsilon - 1,$$

so that when $D_j = 0$, $j = 1 - \varepsilon$, and a graph of (ring diameter)² v. (ring number) is a straight line, the intercept on the ring number axis being $(1 - \varepsilon)$ (see Fig. 9–8).

9–7. Brewster's Fringes

Fig. 9–9(a) shows a plan view of two equal etalons A and B whose normals are inclined at equal and opposite small angles, $\pm\alpha$, to the axis of the telescope T. S is an extended source of white light.

Rays directed from S parallel to the axis are amplitude-divided at the various semi-silvered surfaces. In particular, ignoring refractions in the glass plates, there will be disturbances along paths of the types (1) and (2). Such disturbances will arrive in phase in the primary image plane of T. Rays traversing the etalons in this and similar ways may be divided into pairs, one of which undergoes p reflections in A and $(p+2)$ in B (p even) and the other $(p+2)$ in A and p in B. Those of type (1) have an extra path $2d \cos \alpha$ in B, and those of type (2) an equal extra path in A. Rays not parallel to the axis but inclined at angle ϕ and lying

Fig. 9–9. Formation of Brewster's fringes.

in vertical planes that are parallel to the axis will pass obliquely through the etalons [see Fig. 9–9(*b*)]. Members of each pair of rays in a particular direction will again have equal optical paths through the etalons and will arrive in phase at a single point in the primary image plane of T. Those in different directions ϕ will arrive in phase at different points along the central vertical line in the image plane. Thus there is constructive interference for all wavelengths along the central vertical line in the field of view of T and this line will be a white light maximum.

Consider horizontal rays inclined at angle θ to the axis of the telescope. These and all parallel rays pass through A at angle $(\theta-\alpha)$ and through B at angle $(\theta+\alpha)$ (or vice versa). Thus for a ray of type (1) the extra path in B is $2d \cos (\theta+\alpha)$, and differs from the extra path $2d \cos (\theta-\alpha)$ in A traversed by a ray of type (2). Thus, at the appropriate non-central point on the central horizontal line in the primary image plane of T, the members of each pair arrive with a phase difference of

$$\frac{2\pi}{\lambda} 2d \left[\cos (\theta-\alpha)-\cos (\theta+\alpha)\right] = \frac{8\pi d}{\lambda} \sin \theta \sin \alpha.$$

Consider, now, rays inclined at the same angle θ to the vertical plane containing the axis but inclined also at angle ϕ to the horizontal. The additional paths through the appropriate etalons of the members of each pair are now given by multiplying the above values by $\cos \phi$. The resulting phase difference between the members of a pair is also given by multiplying the previous value by $\cos \phi$. Rays traversing the etalons at the same angle θ but with different values of ϕ come to a focus at points along a vertical line in the primary image plane of T, and at each point the phase difference between the members of a pair of rays is that given above. Consequently, along such a vertical line the order of inter-

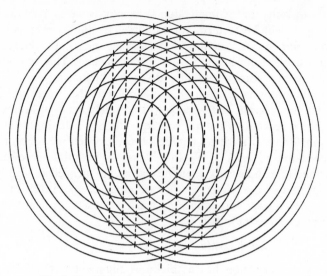

Fig. 9–10. Monochromatic fringes of superposition.

ference between the members of a pair of rays is not exactly constant. However, the variation is small since ϕ is small, and for low orders the variation is completely negligible. Thus in the field of view of T one sees a series of vertical fringes. They are known as *Brewster's fringes*.

At a maximum, the phase difference between the disturbances in each pair is $2j\pi$ (j an integer) i.e. at a maximum

$$\frac{8\pi d}{\lambda} \sin \theta \sin \alpha = 2j\pi,$$

or, since θ and α are small,

$$\theta = \frac{j\lambda}{4d\alpha}, \qquad \ldots \ldots \quad (9\text{--}17)$$

so that the angular separation of the fringes is $\dfrac{\lambda}{4d\alpha}$.

With white light one sees a well defined central maximum, a number of coloured fringes as the maxima for various wavelengths intermingle, and finally a white background. With monochromatic light high order fringes of superposition can be observed; these, as shown above, are curved. With monochromatic light one can see the Fabry-Perot fringes for each etalon as in Fig. 9–10 and the difference fringes appear where the two circular fringe systems are superposed; they are indicated by the dotted lines.

The fringes described above are a special case and, in general, fringes of superposition will be formed by interference between disturbances undergoing p reflections in A and $(p+q)$ in B and those undergoing $(p+q)$ in A and p in B (p and q even integers). The path difference between such disturbances is $qd[\cos(\theta-\alpha)-\cos(\theta+\alpha)]$ i.e. $2qd \sin \theta \sin \alpha$ and this is $j\lambda$ at a maximum. Thus, in general, the fringe separation is given by $\theta = \lambda/2qd\alpha$. In each case the central white light maximum occurs at $\theta = 0$.

It is fairly obvious that if one etalon is exactly twice as thick as the other, Brewster fringes will be formed, for example, by the interference of disturbances undergoing $(p+4)$ reflections in the thinner and p in the thicker and those undergoing p in the thinner and $(p+2)$ in the thicker. This can obviously be extended to cover any case where the ratio of the thicknesses is N_1/N_2, where N_1 and N_2 are small integers. If N_1 and/or N_2 are large, the fringes will be of poor contrast since the relevant interference will be solely between beams that have undergone many reflections and are consequently of small amplitude.

In addition, Brewster's fringes can be observed when the ratio of the thicknesses of the etalons is *nearly* N_1/N_2. In this case the path difference between rays of types (1) and (2) can be zero when the etalons are inclined at slightly different angles to the axis of the telescope. For example, the path difference between disturbances which have undergone $2N_2$ extra reflections in A and those which have undergone $2N_1$ extra in B is

$$2N_2d_1 \cos (\theta-\alpha_1)-2N_1d_2 \cos (\theta+\alpha_2).$$

In particular, if one etalon has a thickness slightly less than that given by $d_1/d_2=N_1/N_2$, the fringes will be seen when this etalon is placed perpendicular to the axis of T and the other is tilted. For example, suppose that, when d_1/d_2 is slightly less than N_1/N_2, the first etalon is co-axial with the telescope and the second is tilted through angle α_2. The path difference between disturbances undergoing $2N_2$ extra reflections in the first etalon and those undergoing $2N_1$ extra in the second is

$$2N_2d_1 \cos \theta-2N_1d_2 \cos (\theta+\alpha_2).$$

On putting $\theta=0$ it follows that the zero order white light maximum will be central in the field of view of the telescope if

$$2N_2d_1-2N_1d_2 \cos \alpha_2=0,$$

i.e. if $\qquad\qquad\qquad N_2d_1=N_1d_2 \cos \alpha_2. \qquad \ldots \ldots \quad (9\text{--}18)$

For a first order maximum

$$2N_2d_1 \cos \theta-2N_1d_2 \cos (\theta+\alpha_2)=\lambda,$$

or, from (9–18),

$$2N_1d_2 \sin \theta \sin \alpha_2=\lambda,$$

or, since θ and α_2 are small,

$$\theta= \frac{\lambda}{2N_1d_2\alpha_2}, \qquad \ldots \ldots \quad (9\text{--}19)$$

and this will be the angular separation of the Brewster fringes. Alternatively, in terms of d_1 and d_2 one has [from (9–18)]

$$\theta= \frac{\lambda}{\sqrt{8N_1d_2(N_1d_2-N_2d_1)}}. \qquad \ldots \ldots \quad (9\text{--}20)$$

On comparing the fringes described above with those formed in the Jamin refractometer, it will be seen that the latter can be regarded as a special case of

Brewster's fringes, being formed by reflection instead of transmission, the interference being between disturbances undergoing a single internal reflection in one plate.

9–8. Central Spot Scanning

Originally, Fabry-Perot instruments were used in the visible and near U.V. regions and the fringes were observed visually or photographed so that the complete fringe system in the focal plane of the lens (or a section across it) was observed or recorded simultaneously. For work in the I.R., particularly in the far I.R., other detectors must be used (e.g. photo-conductive cells or thermal detectors) and none of these give the spatial discrimination necessary for the whole fringe pattern to be recorded simultaneously. However, these detectors

Fig. 9–11. Central spot scanning.

do give good temporal discrimination—which the photographic plate obviously does not—so that the appropriate method of examining the fringe system is by scanning across it and recording the variations of intensity with time. In fact, of course, the photographic method involves recording first and scanning (of the photograph) later, whilst what is here called the scanning method involves simultaneous scanning and recording.

Now the condition for a maximum is

$$2nd \cos \theta = p\lambda_o,$$

λ_o being the vacuum wavelength. Hence for a fixed etalon the maxima for different wavelengths in a given order are found at different positions in the pattern, and this is the basis of the photographic method. In principle, it is possible to make this the basis of a scanning method in which a small scanning aperture is moved across the fringe system and the intensity variations are recorded. However, it is more convenient to use the fact that at a given point in the pattern (θ constant) different wavelengths will appear for different values of the etalon spacing d, or for different values of the refractive index n. In order to achieve maximum photometric efficiency one would need to use an annular aperture so that the detector could receive all the light corresponding to a given path difference. It is more usual to record the intensity at the centre of the pattern and vary either n or d—the former by varying the pressure of the air in the etalon, and the latter by displacing one of the plates. This is referred to as *central spot scanning* and the optical system is shown in Fig. 9–11. In principle it is not necessary to employ both pinholes, but if both are used there is a reduction in the amount of stray light reaching the detector. One is here measuring the intensity at the centre of the Fabry-Perot fringe system, but with the system shown in Fig. 9–11 no actual fringe system is formed in space; one can be said to be using the etalon as a filter and measuring the intensity of the transmitted wavelength. The use of an etalon as a filter is discussed further in §9–16. The character of the available detectors enforced the use of the scanning method in the I.R. but central spot scanning has advantages in all spectral regions:

1. It is much easier to get reliable intensity measurements—photography is a good method of recording positions but a relatively poor method of measuring intensities. Moreover, the photometric efficiency of the system is high.

2. One naturally obtains a linear scale of wavelengths—$\lambda_o \infty n$ or $\lambda_o \infty d$. (The dispersion is, of course, not linear across the spatial fringe pattern.)

3. There is often a gain in resolution since, specially for thick etalons, an inadequate aperture can cause the loss of multiply reflected oblique beams after relatively few reflections.

Now for normal incidence

$$2nd = p\lambda.$$

Hence, if d is constant $n\alpha p$, and if n is constant $d\alpha p$, so that the abscissus of Fig. 9–5 is effectively n if d is constant, or d if n is constant. If, then, Δn or Δd denotes the spectral range, i.e. the increment corresponding to a change of one order for wavelength λ_o, and if δn or δd gives the increment corresponding to the smallest resolvable difference in wavelength, $\delta\lambda_o$, one has

$$\frac{\Delta n}{\delta n} = \frac{\Delta d}{\delta d} = \text{Finesse}.$$

Since $\Delta p = 1$ one has

$$\Delta n = \frac{\lambda_o}{2d} \ \& \ \Delta d = \frac{\lambda_o}{2n}.$$

In addition,

$$\delta n = \frac{p\delta\lambda_o}{2d} \ \& \ \delta d = \frac{p\delta\lambda_o}{2n},$$

so that for pressure scanning and for mechanical scanning one has, for the resolving power using the Taylor criterion,

$$\frac{\lambda_o}{\delta\lambda_o} = p.\frac{\Delta n}{\delta n} = p.\frac{\Delta d}{\delta d} = p \times \text{Finesse},$$

i.e. the same result as before.

Pressure scanning is often achieved by evacuating the space between the etalon plates and allowing the air to re-enter slowly—slowly in order to avoid heating effects. Mechanical scanning has been attempted by a number of methods, including the use of piezo-electric spacers in the etalon. Tolansky and Bradley (1959) have successfully used the system illustrated by Fig. 9–12 to oscillate one etalon mirror.

It will be seen at once that a displacement of $\lambda/2$ is sufficient to scan the free spectral range. In fact, this system enabled 26 orders to be scanned before the lack of parallelism became of the same order as the non-flatness of the plates (approximately $\lambda/80$). Rapid scanning is possible and repetitive frequencies up to 1000 cycles per sec were used, corresponding to a time resolving limit of 4 μsec. for a scan of 5 orders.

For pressure scanning over a range of one atmosphere the change in index is limited to 2.7×10^{-4} with the result that if the wavelength is too long or the plate separation (i.e. resolution) is too small it may be impossible to cover the full spectral range ($\Delta n = \lambda_\circ / 2d$).

Fig. 9–12. Mechanical scanning.

As usual with a Fabry-Perot system, it may be necessary to employ an auxiliary dispersion system (premonochromator) to isolate a range of wavelengths not exceeding $\Delta\lambda$. The need to use an auxiliary instrument such as a grating monochromator markedly reduces the photometric efficiency of the system. Nevertheless, until recently the Fabry-Perot spectrometer was photometrically superior to a large grating spectrometer and was virtually the only instrument available for very high resolution spectroscopy. It has been pointed out by Stroke (1963) that there has been a radical change in the situation since recent improvements in the production of gratings have put them in the 10^6 resolving power class. The relative merits of gratings and interferometers are discussed further in § 12–15.

9–9. Comparison of Wavelengths with Mechnical Standards of Length; Method of Sears and Barrell

Prior to 1960 the legal metrical standard of length consisted of a platinum-iridium bar on which were engraved two lines whose distance apart was defined as one metre; practical measuring scales were derived from this by processes of comparison and sub-division. When interferometers such as the Michelson and Fabry-Perot instruments became available it became possible to measure distances in terms of wavelengths, and obviously it became necessary to obtain accurate determinations of the number of wavelengths in the length of the standard Metre. It was realized that the possibility would then arise of adopting the wavelength of some convenient spectral line as the ultimate standard of

Fig. 9–13. Determination of the metre by Sears and Barrell.

length, and eventually this was done in 1960. (It was, in fact, Babinet who, as early as 1829, first suggested using a wavelength as a standard of length.)

The first attempt to relate the wavelength of a spectral line to the standard Metre was made by Michelson and Benoît, using a method based on the fact that the Michelson interferometer provides a means of measuring displacements in terms of wavelengths (see §8–16). Kösters and Lampe also used the Michelson interferometer and other workers, following Fabry, Perot, and Benoît, have used methods employing Fabry-Perot etalons. The determinations to be discussed in detail here were made by Sears and Barrell from 1933 onwards.

The method of exact fractions described in §9–5 enables one to find the thickness of an etalon in terms of wavelengths of light, so that if one could use an etalon with a plate separation of a metre one could make the required determination. Unfortunately, when this determination of the Metre was made it was impossible to observe fringes with a plate separation of a metre because there was no light source that was sufficiently monochromatic for such large path differences to be used. In consequence, the determination was carried out in three stages employing etalons whose thicknesses were approximately 1 metre, $\frac{1}{3}$ metre, and either $\frac{1}{9}$ or $\frac{1}{12}$ metre:

1. The determination of the thicknesses of the two smallest etalons in terms of the red cadmium line using the method of exact fractions.

2. The comparison of the two smallest etalons with the $\frac{1}{3}$ metre, and of the $\frac{1}{3}$ metre with the 1-metre etalon, using Brewster's fringes.

3. The comparison between the thickest etalon and the standard Metre.

The whole apparatus was made very compact and the temperature was measured to an accuracy of 0·001°C. The general arrangement is shown in Fig. 9–13. The main telescope was employed to observe the circular fringes used in the measurement of the smallest etalons and also to observe the Brewster fringes when comparing etalons. The former measurement required cadmium red light with other cadmium and krypton lines as auxiliaries, and the latter required white light. The positions of the lamps and mirrors are indicated in the figure; it will be seen that the smallest etalon could be moved aside when comparing the other two etalons. In each comparison it was the $\frac{1}{3}$-metre etalon which was tilted.

In order to obtain a rigid etalon with a small expansion coefficient, a hollow invar cylinder was used as spacer in each case. The ends were made accurately parallel, and since it is difficult to obtain a clean optically polished surface on invar, they were chromium plated before being polished optically flat. Partially silvered glass or quartz plates were then wrung on to the ends of the cylinder to make an airtight joint so that the etalon could be evacuated. Quartz plates were used for the largest etalon because they were less likely to be damaged by the repeated wringing which is necessary (see below). Adjustment for parallelism and for small changes in length could be made

Fig. 9–14. Etalon used by Sears and Barrell.

by means of invar straining rods joining two flanges on the sides of the cylinder. Fig. 9–14 shows a scale drawing of the $\frac{1}{3}$-metre etalon.

Comparison of largest etalon with Metre

This comparison is made difficult by the fact that the standard Metre is a line gauge. The comparison was made in three stages.

Inside the largest etalon there was fitted an end gauge whose cross-section was a rectangular cross (see Fig. 9–15). This was only slightly shorter than the etalon and had optically polished ends. It was supported inside the etalon in such a way as to avoid flexure of the gauge. The gaps between the ends of this X-gauge and the etalon mirrors were measured using monochromatic fringes. These were viewed by reflection by means of the east and west telescopes, the etalon being displaced sideways to the dotted position (see Fig. 9–13). The X-gauge remained in the etalon during the earlier part of the experiment when the white light fringes were observed in the four channels alongside the X-gauge.

The X-gauge was then compared with a composite end gauge carrying rulings whose separations could be related to the overall length of the gauge. The length of this line gauge was then compared with the standard Metre using travelling microscopes. Part of the composite gauge consisted of a rod of circular cross-section and of length approximately half an inch less than 1 metre, the ends being optically polished and perpendicular to the axis of the rod. In addition there were two parallel-faced rectangular blocks each half an inch in thickness with sides equal respectively to the radius and diameter of the rod. At the middle of the half-inch face of each block a fine line was ruled parallel to the longer edge. By wringing one block on to one end of the rod, an approximately one-metre end gauge was formed, and by wringing a block on each end of the rod, a one-metre line gauge was obtained (see Fig. 9–15). The composite end gauges were compared with the X-gauge by an extension of the method used for comparing the latter with the largest etalon. The principle is as follows. If the X-gauge is placed between a pair of parallel semi-silvered mirrors, the sizes of the gaps can be measured using monochromatic fringes. If, keeping the mirrors fixed, the composite end gauge is substituted for the X-gauge and the new gaps similarly found, the difference between the gauges is obtained. Using this method, the X-gauge was compared with the composite end gauges formed by wringing each block, in turn, each way round on each end of the rod. The mean of these readings gave the difference between the length of the X-gauge and the length of the rod plus half the sum of the end blocks. (The thickness of the wringing film between the rod and a block can be neglected; it has been shown

X end Gauge

nominally 1 metre

1 metre–½ inch

Composite Gauge

½"

Fig. 9–15. Subsidiary gauges.

to be about 50 angstroms.) These measurements were made with the gauges occupying the position of the displaced etalon (Fig. 9–13) utilizing the east and west telescopes.

A block was then wrung on each end of the rod and the resulting line gauge compared with the standard Metre. By reversing each block in turn and then both together three more gauges were formed and the mean of the four comparisons gave the difference between the Metre and the length of the rod plus half the sum of the blocks—the length previously compared with the X-gauge. In this way the X-gauge and therefore the longest etalon was compared with the Metre. It should be noted that the lengths of the components of the composite gauge are eliminated and need not be known precisely. Comparisons between line gauges involve setting microscopes on rather broad and diffuse images and it was necessary in this investigation to take the mean of the results obtained by several observers.

Results

Sears and Barrell measured the number of wavelengths of the red cadmium line in the standard metre in a vacuum and in dry air free from CO_2 at 15° C. and 20° C. Their results were:

1. In a vacuum,   1,552,734·52 ($\therefore$ λ=6440·2510 × 10⁻¹⁰ metre).

2. In air at 15° C., 1,553,163·76 ($\therefore$ λ=6438·4711 × 10⁻¹⁰ metre).

3. In air at 20° C., 1,553,156·33 ($\therefore$ λ=6438·5019 × 10⁻¹⁰ metre).

These results are quoted to an accuracy justified by the optical part of the experiments. The purely metrological part reduces the accuracy so that the wavelengths are probably correct to about ±0·001 × 10⁻¹⁰ metre.

The number of wavelengths in the yard was also found:

1. In a vacuum,   1,419,818·31.
2. In air at 15°C.,   1,420,210·81.
3. In air at 20°C.,   1,420,204·02.

Sears and Barrell went on to measure the refractive index and dispersion of ir. This was done by viewing Brewster fringes with a series of monochromatic ources using two etalons, each approximately 67 cm. in length. The principle is s follows: suppose both etalons are evacuated and that one is slightly longer than e other. If one observes along the normal to the thinner etalon the zero order ero path difference) Brewster fringe can be brought to the centre of the field of iew by tilting the thicker etalon (see §9–7). If air is now admitted to the thinner talon, the optical path difference in this etalon changes from $2d$ to $2nd$, so that r the disturbances forming the Brewster fringes an optical path difference of $(n-1)d$ is introduced. If p fringes move across the centre of the field as the air introduced one has

$$2(n-1)d=p\lambda.$$

Ience, by counting fringes $(n-1)$ can be found. The method has an important dvantage over the simple method described in §9–2 where one simply observes e Fabry-Perot rings in a single etalon as it is evacuated. In the present method ne has the same *change* in the optical path difference as air is introduced, but is not added to the already very large optical path difference between the isturbances forming the rings in the evacuated etalon. In consequence one can se a much longer etalon giving much greater accuracy since many more fringes re counted; each etalon can be so long that the path difference is too great for ne to see the Fabry-Perot rings for the individual etalons.

–10. Summary of Results of All Determinations. The New Metre

In 1948 Barrell gave a summary of the results obtained in the various determi- ations of the Metre, the wavelength of the red cadmium line being corrected vhere necessary to correspond to air under standard conditions, i.e. 15°C., 60 mm. pressure (g=980·665 cm. sec.$^{-2}$), and containing 0·03% by volume of CO_2. The table shows $\lambda \times 10^{10}$ in metres. It is an odd coincidence that the mean f all the above results is the same as the result announced by Benoît, Fabry, nd Perot, and already accepted internationally for many purposes, although it s now known that the original result should have been given as shown in the able. It seems to be agreed that the differences between the various determina- ions are due partly to differences between the conditions obtaining in the various ources used, and partly to differences between various copies of the Metre; orobably the least accurate part of each experiment is the setting of the micro- cope cross-wires on the rather diffuse images of the terminal marks of the line standards.

In 1907 the angstrom was defined by taking the result of Benoît, Fabry, and Perot, i.e. by defining the wavelength of the cadmium line to be 6438·4696 angstroms, and this has since served as the spectroscopic unit.

In 1927 the cadmium line was accepted as the provisional metrologica! standard and its use then became a permitted alternative to direct reference to

Date	Observers	Result	Difference from Mean
1892–3	Michelson and Benoît	6438·4691	−0·0005
1905–6	Benoît, Fabry, and Perot	6438·4703	0·0007
1927	Watanabe and Imaizumi	6438·4682	−0·0014
1933	Sears and Barrell	6438·4713	0·0017
1933	Kösters and Lampe	6438·4689	−0·0007
1934–5	Sears and Barrell	6438·4709	0·0013
1934–5	Kösters and Lampe	6438·4690	−0·0006
1937	Kösters and Lampe	6438·4700	0·0004
1940	Romanova, Varlich, Kartashev, & Batarchukova	6438·4687	−0·0009

Mean Value 6438·4696

the prototype Metre or its authorized copies. The search then continued for th
source that would give the narrowest possible spectral line with the highe
degree of reproducibility. Now a single isotope with even atomic mass an
charge (zero nuclear spin) emits a line free from hyperfine structure and eventu
ally, in 1957, it was decided to recommend the use of the orange-red line produce
by a hot cathode lamp employing the krypton 86 isotope. This lamp wa
perfected by Engelhard and is operated at the triple point of nitrogen (63°K).

It was decided to maintain continuity with the provisional definition throug
the intermediary of the wavelength of the cadmium line in standard air, and th
mean value of $6438·4696 \times 10^{-10}$ metre was accepted. (Hart and Baird (196.
have since reconsidered the results given in the table and have concluded tha
some of them require slight modification to take account of what is now know
about the various factors affecting the results. Fortunately, the net result is tha
the mean value remains almost unchanged: it becomes 6438·4695.) Since the ne
standard would involve a vacuum wavelength it was necessary to specify
dispersion formula for air, and that due to Edlén (1953) was adopted. Edlé
derived his formula by using the absolute values of Sears and Barrell for th
index and dispersion of air, in combination with the relative measurements b
Traub and by Koch in the visible and U.V. For standard air Edlén's formul
gives $n = 1·000276381$ so that the vacuum wavelength for the cadmium line i
$6440·2490_7 \times 10^{-10}$ metre.

Comparisons between the cadmium and krypton lines were made in fiv
different laboratories, using the Engelhard krypton lamp and the cadmium lam
specified by the International Committee in 1935. The results for the wave
length of the krypton line are given in the second table.

Laboratory	BIPM	PTB	NPL	CIIWM	NRC	NRC	Mean
Interferometer used	M & F–P	M	F–P	F–P	F–P	M	
Vacuum Wavelength 6057·80....	21	23	21	21	21	19	6057·8021

Wavelength in Standard air = 6056·1252.

he laboratories were:

BIPM—Bureau International des Poids et Measures, Sèvres.
PTB—Physikalisch-Technische Bundesanstalt, Braunschweig.
NPL—National Physical Laboratory, Teddington.
CIIWM—Central Inspection Institute of Weights and Measures, Tokyo.
NRC—National Research Council, Ottawa.

At the NPL the Fabry-Perot etalon, with a path difference of 125 mm., was
luminated with the cadmium and krypton lamps simultaneously and was used
a series with a prism spectrograph in order to photograph the fringes for the
arious spectral lines. The wavelengths were compared by using the method of
xact fractions to find the orders at the centres of the patterns. Settings on fringes
ere made in two ways: (1) using a microscope to make visual settings and (2)
sing a microdensitometer. As a result of the above measurements it was recom-
ended in 1957 that the Metre should be defined as "the length equal to
,650,763·73 wavelengths in vacuum of the radiation corresponding to the
ansition between the levels $2p_{10}$ and $5d_5$ of the atom of krypton 86". This was
ormally adopted by the General Conference on Weights and Measures in 1960.
he angstrom was then defined as 10^{-10} metre and subsequently, in 1964, the
ard was defined as 0·9144 metre.

In addition to the measurement of the orange-red krypton 86 line in terms of
he red cadmium line, a number of other krypton and cadmium lines were
easured, together with lines in the mercury 198 spectrum, and in 1962 the
econdary standards shown in angstroms in the third table were recommended.

Kr^{86}	Hg^{198}	Cd^{114}
6458·0720	5792·2683	6440·2480
6422·8006	5771·1983	5087·2379
5651·1286	5462·2705	4801·2521
4503·6162	4359·5624	4679·4581

After correction for departures from the specified ideal conditions of excita-
ion, the Engelhard lamp gives a wavelength that is reproducible to about 1 part
n 10^9 but practical calibrations of existing end standards and line standards of
metre length in terms of the krypton line are probably not better than 10 parts
n 10^9—about one order of magnitude better than can be obtained with material
tandards of the Metre. It will be appreciated that end standards are much easier
o check interferometrically than line standards, although the accuracy of
etting on line standards has been improved in recent years by employing photo-
lectric microscopes.

When the krypton standard was adopted it was realized that an atomic beam
ource using a pure isotope would be expected to give highly monochromatic
adiation but it was decided to adopt the krypton standard in view of the urgent
eed for a new definition. A relevant development since that time is the laser;
his gives very highly monochromatic light, enabling interference effects to be
bserved with path differences far in excess of any used previously. It is, however,
roving difficult to achieve the required reproducibility in the wavelength emitted.

9–11. Two Fabry-Perot Instruments in Series

If two Fabry-Perot instruments in series are arranged to be exactly paralle
light will be transmitted only in directions which correspond to maxima for bot
instruments.

For a single instrument, maxima are found when $2d \cos \theta = p\lambda$, so that th
angular separation of orders is given by $(d/dp)(\cos \theta) = \lambda/2d$. Thus the maxim
of the thinner interferometer are more widely spaced, and maxima associate
with the thicker instrument are suppressed when they do not coincide with thos
of the thinner. The increased range without overlapping of orders is an in
portant advantage of the arrangement. The resolving power of the compoun
interferometer is better than that of the thicker component and better than eac
component when the components are the same. (This is fairly obvious sinc
if the maximum of one component coincides with a maximum of the other, th
ordinates of the intensity curve of one are modified by those of the other with
consequent steepening of the intensity curve.) It can be seen also that, since th
dispersion $(d/d\lambda)(\cos \theta) = p/2d = (\cos \theta)/\lambda$ is independent of d, a change in λ cause
the same change in θ for each instrument so that a complete line pattern is eithe
transmitted or cut out. (Alternatively, all maxima of a given *order* are trans
mitted or cut out.)

The compound interferometer has, however, some disadvantages. Betwee
maxima, the intensity transmitted by a Fabry-Perot interferometer does not fa
completely to zero so that the intermediate orders of the thicker interferomete
are not completely suppressed. These *spurious* maxima may obscure wea
satellites in a line or cause difficulty in identification. The latter should not b
regarded as a serious difficulty because the position of the unsuppressed maxim
are accurately known. Since four silvered surfaces are employed, it is essentia
to have reflecting films of very low absorption if weak lines are to be examined
With metal films this may necessitate a reduction in the reflectivity of eac
surface. The latter would cause a loss in resolving power and also a brightenin
of the spurious maxima since the intensity curve for the thinner interferomete
would not fall to a low minimum.

9–12. Method of Edser and Butler for Calibration of a Spectroscope

The arrangement, first used by Esselbach in 1856, is illustrated in Fig. 9–16
S is a source of white light focused on to the spectroscope slit by means of th

Fig. 9–16. Position of etalon for Edser and Butler fringes.

lens L. E is an etalon which, in practice, is sufficiently thin for variations i
obliquity to be ignored. Although it is usually placed in the position shown, th
thin etalon may be placed anywhere between the source and the observer. As
suming normal incidence, the condition for a maximum by transmission throug
an etalon is $2d = p\lambda$ (p an integer), and for a minimum $2d = (p+\frac{1}{2})\lambda$. Thus in th

focal plane of the spectroscope the spectrum consists of lines at those wave-lengths satisfying the first equation.

Let λ_0 be a wavelength at the red end of the spectrum at which a maximum occurs. Suppose successive maxima on the blue side of λ_0 are numbered, and let λ_j be the wavelength at which the jth bright fringe occurs. Then if p_0 is the order for λ_0, (p_0+j) is the order for λ_j and one has

$$2d = p_0\lambda_0 = (p_0+j)\lambda_j,$$

$$\therefore \quad \lambda_0 = \lambda_j + \frac{j\lambda_j}{p_0} = \lambda_j + \frac{j\lambda_j\lambda_0}{2d},$$

$$\therefore \quad \frac{1}{\lambda_j} = \frac{j}{2d} + \frac{1}{\lambda_0}.$$

Suppose a line spectrum containing a number of known lines lies alongside the white light spectrum. Then, in general, the spectral lines will not fall exactly opposite a maximum and so will correspond to non-integral values of j. If these values of j are observed (by estimating fractions of a fringe separation) for a number of known wavelengths and $1/\lambda_j$ plotted against j, a straight line will result. The slope of this line is $1/2d$ so that the thickness of the etalon may be found. Also, if the value of j is observed for any unknown line, the wavelength may be found from the graph. It will be seen that the fringes constitute a scale which can be calibrated to indicate wavelengths—obviously they give a linear scale of wave numbers or of frequency.

9–13. The Lummer-Gehrcke Interferometer

If a thick, parallel-sided glass plate (i.e. an all-glass Fabry-Perot etalon) is used near grazing emergence, it is possible to secure multiple beam fringes of equal

Fig. 9–17. Lummer-Gehrcke interferometer.

inclination without employing silvered surfaces. This is possible because the reflectivity of a glass to air surface increases for angles of incidence near the critical angle. However, this means that if a simple glass plate is used near grazing incidence, a rather small amount of light will enter the plate initially. In the Lummer-Gehrcke interferometer (introduced in 1903) the light is passed into the plate as in Fig. 9–17(a) or, better, by means of an auxiliary prism as in 9–17(b). The most useful plates are those made of quartz and in this case the auxiliary prism is wrung on to the plate, thereby overcoming the difficulty of finding a cement which is transparent throughout a large spectral range.

As in the etalon, the multiple beam fringes of equal inclination can be ob served in the focal plane of the lens L, and if the source is a wide vertical slit, the pattern takes the form indicated. Owing to the way in which the light is passed into the plate, emerging beams on the two sides have comparable intensities and identical patterns are formed on the two sides of the plate.

As usual for an etalon, the condition for a maximum is

$$2nd \cos \theta = p\lambda, \qquad (p \text{ an integer}),$$

but the complete theory of the Lummer plate is complicated by the fact that (1) the medium between the reflecting surfaces is dispersive and (2) there is a finite number of beams to be superposed, the number depending on the length of the plate. To a first approximation the resolving power of a Lummer plate is proportional to its length. For a given resolving power a Lummer plate can give a free spectral range greater than that of an etalon, and the theoretical superiority of a Lummer plate over an etalon is greater for thinner plates and shorter wave lengths. However, the advantages of Lummer plates are outweighed by their disadvantages: the surfaces must be plane to at worst $\lambda/80$; the material must be homogeneous if ghosts are to be avoided; strains from the supports must be avoided; and the temperature should be controlled with an accuracy approach ing $0.01°$C. Owing to the high cost and the inconvenience, high resolution Lummer plates are now virtually obsolete, although those fortunate enough to possess good plates might continue to use them.

9–14. Multiple Beam Fringes of Equal Thickness

It was seen earlier in the chapter that by silvering the reflecting surfaces it i possible to improve the sharpness of the fringes of equal inclination which are observed with parallel-sided plates. In addition it becomes possible to observe the fringes by transmission. By silvering the relevant surfaces of a thin wedge film the same effect is produced in the localized fringes of equal thickness. For example, multiple beam Newton's rings by transmission resemble Fabry-Pero fringes [Plate I(e)]; those seen by reflection resemble the fringes shown in (d) These multiple beam Fizeau fringes have an important application in th examination of surface topography. The surface to be examined is used as one face of the wedge and an optical flat is used for the other. The structure of the surface under examination introduces differences of thickness in various part of the wedge and these cause a distortion of the localized fringes observed in the wedge. The movement of the fringes at various points enables the topography of the surface to be examined. The use of the sharp multiple beam fringe improves the accuracy of measurement since relatively small movements of th fringes can be measured. Plate I(g) shows the interference pattern obtained between an optical flat and a sheet of mica. If the wedge angle is vanishingl small a maximum occupies a wide region and variations in the surface unde test cause a measurable change in intensity.

Fig. 9–18 shows an air wedge between two semi-silvered plane surfaces (a and (b), the outer faces of the plate being omitted for simplicity. W is a plane wave incident normally on surface (a). The figure shows the paths of a numbe of internally reflected rays associated with W. As the disturbances undergo repeated internal reflections between the surfaces they move across the wedg towards the thicker side. Consequently the phases of the various disturbances that are superposed at P are characteristic of the wedge thickness *at* P only if the angle of the wedge is very small and/or the wedge is very thin. In order to study local variations in the height of, say, the second surface, it might be necessary to have the ordinary wedge fringes fairly close together. Thus an appreciable wedge angle must be used and this may be increased when necessary by tilting the reference plate or specimen. In addition, the specimen itself may show steep wedge-like structures. In consequence, it is essential in this work to employ very thin wedges. Since the disturbances move across the wedge each time they are internally reflected, the phase difference between beams undergoing successive numbers of reflections is not constant. This causes the high order beams to begin to interfere destructively with those of low order, thereby reducing the sharpness of the fringes. Since the beams will get out of phase more rapidly with thicker wedges, this effect places an upper limit on the value of d which can be used when a given number of multiply reflected beams is to be superposed. It can be shown that the path difference between the first and nth beams is approximately $[2nd - (4/3)n^3\theta^2 d]$, where θ is the wedge angle and d the thickness at the point of

Fig. 9–18. Reflections in a wedge film.

emergence of the disturbances. The second term in this expression must not exceed $\lambda/2$ if the nth beam is not to be destructive.

The higher is the reflectivity of the surfaces, the less rapidly does the intensity of the beams decrease and the larger is the number of reflections before the intensity is reduced to a negligible value. In practice the reflectivity of the surfaces is such that it may be assumed that about 60 disturbances give appreciable contributions to the resultant. Thus, assuming that the 60th beam has a path difference of $\lambda/2$, the maximum permissible value of d is given by

$$\frac{4}{3}(60)^3\theta^2 d_{max} = \frac{\lambda}{2}. \qquad \cdots \cdots \cdots \quad (9\text{--}21)$$

If there are X fringes per cm. across the wedge, $\theta = \lambda X/2$ so that, taking $\lambda = 5\cdot5 \times 10^{-5}$ cm. (green light), d_{max} is given by

$$d_{max} = \frac{1}{7\cdot92X^2}. \qquad \cdots \cdots \cdots \quad (9\text{--}22)$$

Thus d_{max} is 0·0012 cm. when X is 10 and falls to 0·000012 cm. when X is 100.

As seen above, the higher order beams superposed at P have passed through a part of the wedge progressively farther from P. To a first approximation it can be shown that the linear separation on the wedge between the points of entry and emergence of the nth beam is

$$l_n = 2n^2\theta d.$$

If the fringes are to give reliable information regarding the detailed topography of a small surface area it is obviously necessary for l_{60} to be as small as possible so that the intensity at any point in the fringe system is characteristic of the local height of the surface studied. If the thickness of the wedge is the maximum permitted by the phase condition discussed above, then from equation (9–21) one has, for the 60th beam,

$$l_{60} = \frac{1}{40X} = \frac{1}{40} \text{ (distance between fringes)}.$$

l_{60} is reduced to 1/2000 cm. if the wedge angle is adjusted to give 50 fringes per cm. and the wedge thickness used is the maximum permitted by the phase condition (i.e. 5×10^{-5} cm. or about one wavelength). Assuming normal incidence, the angle of emergence of the 60th beam is 120θ, where θ is the wedge angle. If λ is $5 \cdot 5 \times 10^{-5}$ cm. the angle of emergence is about 10°. If this beam is to enter the microscope used to examine the fringes, the numerical aperture of the objective must be about 0·17. This is roughly what can be obtained using a nominal 2-inch objective. In normal microscopy one would employ a magnifying power of 50 with such an instrument so that on the photo-micrograph the fringes would be about 1 cm. apart. It is interesting to note that the conventional limit of resolution of this microscope is 0·0002 cm. and is less than l_{60} (0·0005 cm.).

Tolansky (1948) has summarized the conditions under which sharp multiple beam Fizeau fringes can be employed as follows:

1. The surfaces must be coated with a highly reflecting film of minimal absorption.

2. The film must contour the surface exactly and be highly uniform in thickness.

3. Monochromatic light or at most a few widely spaced monochromatic wavelengths should be used.

4. The interfering surfaces must be separated by at most a few wavelengths of light.

5. A parallel beam should be used. (Within 1°–3° tolerance.)

6. The incidence should preferably be normal.

With regard to the second condition, it has been shown that an evaporated silver film can be made uniform and the top surface can be made to follow the surface on which the film is deposited, even if the thickness of the film exceeds considerably the changes in height involved.

The importance of a very thin wedge has already been pointed out. Now the chromatic resolution of a Fabry-Perot instrument obviously becomes very poor if the surfaces are very close together. In this work the low chromatic resolution is an advantage since it means that the fringes will not be broadened by the use of rather broad spectral lines. Thus very intense sources can be used, very thick silvering of the surfaces can be tolerated, and high power microscopes can be employed.

Using a thin wedge of vanishingly small angle the changes in intensity across the interference pattern can be measured. It can be shown that differences in level of the order of 3 angstroms can be measured easily; this is far better than the accuracy of measurement employing a phase contrast microscope. Thus one has extremely good resolution *in depth* although, as indicated by the value of l_{60} the lateral resolution is not always good.

9–15. Fringes of Equal Chromatic Order

In Fig. 9–19 S is a source of white light illuminating a small circular aperture A. Light from A passes through L_1 and falls near normal incidence on a thin air wedge W between semi-silvered optical flats. A magnified image of the wedge film is projected on to the slit of the spectroscope by means of the achromatic lens L_2, the line of intersection of the flats being parallel to the slit. Now along each line parallel to the edge of the wedge the latter passes only those wavelengths that satisfy the condition

$$2d=p\lambda \qquad (p \text{ integral}). \quad . . . (9\text{–}23)$$

Hence the light entering the slit consists of the wavelengths satisfying (9–23), d being the thickness of the strip of the wedge that is imaged on to the slit. Consequently the pattern observed through the spectroscope consists of a series

Fig. 9–19. Observation of fringes of equal chromatic order.

of spectral lines resembling the Edser-Butler bands. If the wedge film is rotated about the axis of the collimator the strip imaged on to the slit has a thickness that increases along its length with the result that as one moves along the length of the slit there is a gradual change in the series of wavelengths received, i.e. for each value of the integer p there is a gradual change in λ as one moves along the slit. Each value of p corresponds to a fringe and, since the wavelength varies in the horizontal direction in the field of view, the fringes observed through the spectroscope are inclined to the vertical. The same effect is observed with the arrangement shown in Fig. 9–16 when E is a wedge film and is close to the slit.

Suppose now that one of the boundary surfaces of the air film is not a plane. Again the film thickness varies along the length of the strip that is imaged at the slit and for each value of p there is a variation in the wavelength entering the slit.

In general d does not vary linearly along the strip of the film and hence the wavelength does not vary linearly with distance along the slit. In general, therefore, each fringe observed through the spectroscope will be curved, the wavelength varying along it. Since p is constant along any fringe, d/λ is constant. The fringes, which are known as *fringes of equal chromatic order* (hence sometimes as FECO fringes), reveal the topographical features of the strip of the film that is imaged on to the spectroscope slit. One application is to the measurement of small surface angles giving rise to very small wedge angles. Thus an increase of $\lambda/2$ in film thickness in distance y along the strip (wedge angle $\lambda/2y$) gives a horizontal movement of one fringe width (x) in a vertical distance my in the field of view, m being a magnification factor determined by lens L_2 and the spectroscope. The inclination of the fringe to the vertical is x/my, so that the angle of the wedge is effectively magnified by $(x/my) \div (\lambda/2y) = 2x/m\lambda$, and this can be made very large—for the middle of the visible region 10^4 is typical.

9–16. Interference Filters

If a single collimated beam of light is incident normally on a Fabry-Perot etalon, only those wavelengths are transmitted which satisfy the relation $2d=p\lambda$. As d is reduced, the transmitted wavelengths become widely spaced. When d is between 2×10^{-5} and 6×10^{-5} cm. it is easily verified that the film transmits only one maximum in the visible region. For example, if $d=5000$ angstroms the fringes are at $\lambda\lambda$ 10,000, 5000, 3333 of which only $\lambda5000$ is in the visible region. With a reflectivity of 0·94 for the surfaces of the etalon, it follows from the discussions of §9–3 that the fringe half-value width is about 1/50th of an order. Hence the half-value width of the transmitted maximum in the visible region is about 50 angstroms.

If the source of light contains only a few lines, it is frequently possible to separate very close components by employing a rather larger value of d in order to reduce the fringe width, care being taken to ensure that the other transmitted wavelengths do not coincide with lines emitted by the source. For example, it

Fig. 9–20. Interference filter.

is possible to separate the two mercury yellow lines which are 20 angstroms apart, transmitting one and cutting out the other together with the green line. It is worthy of note that it is not necessary to adjust the etalon thickness precisely since, if it is made slightly larger, the effective thickness $d\cos\theta$ can be reduced to the desired value by tilting. (N.B.—it cannot be *increased*.) Colour filters of this type may be made by employing a layer of cryolite between reflecting surfaces instead of an air-spaced etalon. A silver film is first evaporated on to a glass plate followed by a layer of cryolite and then a second silver film. It is not necessary for the glass plate to be an optical flat because the evaporated layers follow the contours of the glass, the layers remaining of uniform thickness. By using two filters in series, the narrow transmission band of the thicker can be coupled with the small number of bands associated with the thinner. By evaporating first a dielectric layer and then a semi-reflecting metal film on to a perfectly reflecting mirror, a reflection filter can be produced and this can have a zero reflectivity for chosen wavelengths.

In using etalons as filters, it is obvious that in order to obtain a filter that will transmit very narrow bands of wavelengths, it is necessary to employ surfaces of very high reflectivity. This necessitates a rather thick metal film and the esulting absorption causes the overall transmission to be rather small. The olution to this problem is to replace the metal film by highly reflecting films of lielectrics.

It was pointed out in §8–5 that the reflection losses from an air-glass surface an be reduced by employing a thin film of a material of low refractive index. `he minimum reflectivity is obtained when the film is a quarter of a wavelength hick and has a refractive index equal to the geometric mean of the indices for ir and the glass concerned. If one employs a quarter-wave film whose refrac- ive index is higher than that of glass, the internally and externally reflected rays re in phase because the phase change of π on reflection occurs only at the outer urface. For example, it can be shown that when a quarter-wave film of index ·5 is deposited on a glass of index 1·5, the reflectivity is increased to 0·38 for the avelength concerned.

More recent work has shown that by depositing several films whose indices ecrease progressively from the glass towards the air, it is possible to secure anti- eflection films that are effective over a wide range of wavelengths, and that by epositing films of alternatively high and low index, the reflectivity can rise to ery high values. For example, using alternate layers of zinc sulphide (index ·3) and cryolite (index 1·35) it is possible to secure reflectivities of 0·6, 0·8, and ·9 by using 3, 5, and 7 layers respectively. In such dielectric layers the absorp- on losses are very small.

Fig. 9–20 shows an example of a suggested compound filter employing, in ffect, two etalons whose reflecting surfaces consist of dielectric films with efractive indices $n_1 = 1·4$ and $n_2 = 1·8$, the index of the glass being 1·6 (note air $= n_1 \lambda_1 = n_2 \lambda_2$).

The outer surfaces of the glass plates are bloomed for low reflectivity and the entral glass plate is made wedge-shaped to reduce reflections etween the two halves of the filter. The difficulty of djusting the air film is overcome if the filter can be con- ructed entirely of dielectric layers that can be deposited by vaporation. One example of an all-dielectric filter has a otal of 15 layers. Layers 1–7 and 9–15 play the part of two eflecting surfaces and the 8th layer is the spacer. The odd yers are of zinc sulphide and the even layers are of cryolite. ach layer is $\lambda/4$ thick except the spacer whose thickness is a ultiple of $\lambda/2$ according to the order required (the higher rder giving narrower but more closely spaced maxima). When larger number of dielectric layers is employed it becomes ore difficult to secure layers of the desired thickness.

An alternative method of securing high reflectivity with- ut absorption is the use of frustrated total reflection. The ectromagnetic theory of light indicates that when light is cident at an angle greater than the critical angle from the

Fig. 9–21. Frustrated total reflection filter.

enser side of a boundary between two media, energy penetrates a short distance to the second medium (see §21–6). It is found that if a second high-index edium is brought close to the first, light passes into the last medium. The inner is the layer of low index, the larger is the transmitted fraction of the incident energy. One is said to have *frustrated total reflection*. If the second high index layer is followed by another low-index layer and another high-index medium, these give a second partial reflection. Therefore the high-index layer is effectively between two partially reflecting films, the reflectivities of which depend on the thicknesses of the low-index layers. Such an arrangement can be used as a filter in the same way as an etalon. The band width is determined by the reflectivity of the surfaces and in this case is obviously controlled by the thicknesses of the low-index films. The transmitted wavelengths are controlled by the thickness of the high-index layer which plays the part of the air space of the etalon. A frustrated total reflection filter is illustrated in Fig. 9–21.

9–17. Summary of Types of Fringes

In this section there is given a brief summary of the conditions giving rise to the various types of fringes in systems employing division of amplitude. One has, in effect, interference between disturbances reflected from the two boundary surfaces of a medium, and the basic equation is

$$2nd \cos \theta = p\lambda,$$

the symbols having their usual meanings. Usually, this equation corresponds to a maximum or a minimum, depending on the phase changes that occur at the various reflecting surfaces in the system, but it is possible that a further effective path difference has to be added. In any system a fringe is the locus of point corresponding to a constant phase difference. In each case the use of highly reflecting surfaces results in a multiple beam system, giving sharper fringes. The following possibilities arise:

1. λ, n, and d are constant. θ varies

One has monochromatic light incident on a film of constant thickness. The path difference depends on θ and one has fringes of equal inclination, such as the circular fringes in the Michelson or Fabry-Perot interferometers. The fringes observed with the Lummer plate are also of this type. When d is large slightly different wavelengths correspond to significantly different values of θ and this is why these fringes are useful in high resolution spectroscopy.

2. d and θ are constant. λ (and hence n) varies

One has collimated polychromatic light incident on a film of constant thickness. The phase difference depends on λ and one has the basis of an interference filter. Edser-Butler fringes demonstrate this. If d is large one has maxima for closely spaced wavelengths, and if d is small one has maxima for widely separated wavelengths.

3. λ, n, and θ are constant. d varies

One has collimated monochromatic light incident on a film whose thickness varies from point to point. The path difference depends on d and one has fringes of equal thickness such as those obtainable with a wedge film, e.g. with Michelson interferometer with inclined plates; Newton's rings are of this type. If d is very small moderate variations in θ have little effect. The fringes are contour lines of the film thickness and are the ones used in studying surface topography.

4. θ is constant. d and λ (and hence n) vary

One has collimated polychromatic light incident on a film whose thickness varies from point to point. Along any fringe p is constant, and hence nd/λ is constant. One refers to fringes of equal chromatic order.

HUYGENS' PRINCIPLE AND THE SCALAR THEORY OF DIFFRACTION

10–1. Early Geometrical Picture

IN order to explain the propagation of a disturbance as a wave motion, Huygens assumed that each point on a wavefront becomes the source of so-called secondary waves, and that the effect of these waves is mainly confined to their forward envelope. As shown in §§1–5, 1–6, 1–7, this simple picture is sufficient to account for the passage of light through very small holes, the approximately rectilinear propagation of light through large apertures, and the classical laws of reflection and refraction. It is not sufficient, however, to explain in detail the departures from exactly rectilinear propagation of light which are encountered in cases of diffraction. It is not, of course, made clear in the simple theory why the secondary sources produce no effect in the reverse direction (e.g. on the backward envelope), but it must be remembered that at the time of Huygens light was thought of as a disturbance in an aether consisting of closely packed perfectly elastic spheres; the impact of one sphere on another would then result in the total forward transfer of momentum.

10–2. Fresnel's Extension

As originally propounded (c. 1678), Huygens' principle was meant to apply to isolated waves or pulses. In order to extend the principle to cover the propa-

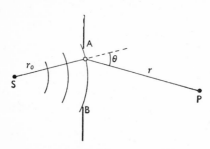

Fig. 10–1. Passage of a wave through an aperture.

gation of an extended train of simple harmonic waves, Fresnel (1815–18) assumed that the secondary waves interfere with one another according to the principle of superposition. In the case of the passage of light through an aperture in a screen (see Fig. 10–1), Fresnel simply assumed that each element of that part of the wave which is not obstructed acts as a secondary source. The secondary disturbances from these sources are then superposed at P to give the resultant disturbance. If the secondary disturbances are simple harmonic waves, and the sources are in phase on the primary wavefront, the phase of each disturbance when it arrives at P will depend on the optical path from P to the point on the wavefront concerned. It follows that there may be a maximum or a minimum at P, according to the degree of constructive or destructive interference which occurs. In this way it is possible to account for the so-called diffraction fringes which are observed.

Fresnel assumed that the amplitude of the disturbance at P due to the sources in any elementary area of the primary wavefront is:

1. Proportional to the amplitude of the disturbance at the element.
2. Proportional to the area of the element.
3. Inversely proportional to the distance from the element to P.

In addition, it was found necessary to assume that the contribution of the sources in any elementary area depends on the angle θ between the normal to the primary wavefront and the direction of P. This *obliquity* or *inclination factor* is essential to the theory as will be shown below. The phase of the disturbance at P due to any element of the wavefront was assumed to be that of a disturbance which has travelled the total distance from the source to P via the element of wavefront concerned.

The next six sections can be omitted by the student whose mathematics is weak. A simplified discussion of Fresnel's method is given in Chapter XIII.

10–3. Propagation of a Spherical Wave

The disturbance from a point source in an isotropic medium consists of expanding spherical waves, and the most obvious test to apply to the Fresnel

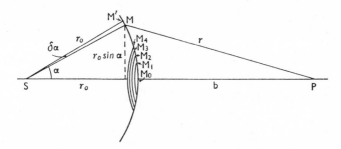

Fig. 10–2. Half-period zones.

theory is to see whether the secondary sources located on a spherical wavefront at one instant produce a similar wave of larger radius at a subsequent time.

As was seen in §1–3, a spherical wave expanding from the monochromatic point source S (Fig. 10–2) may be represented by

$$\phi = \frac{a}{r_0} \cos k(ct - r_0). \quad \cdots \cdots \quad (10\text{--}1)$$

Each point on the wavefront (radius r_0 at time t) is, according to Fresnel, to be considered as a source of disturbances which interfere according to the principle of superposition to yield the subsequent disturbance. To calculate the disturbance at P, Fresnel divided the wavefront into annular zones centred on the axis SP as illustrated in the figure. The central zone extends to M_1, where $r_1 = M_1P = M_0P + \lambda/2 = b + \lambda/2$. The next zone extends from M_1 to M_2, where $r_2 = M_2P = r_1 + \lambda/2 = b + \lambda$, and so on, such that the boundaries of successive zones are $\lambda/2$ farther from P. These zones are called *Fresnel zones* or *half-period zones*. The disturbance at P is calculated in two stages. Firstly, that due to the sources in each zone is found, and secondly, the effects of the various zones are summed.

Any area over which the factors enumerated in the previous section are constant can be taken as an elementary area, and to find the effect of the nth Fresnel zone, one may take, as an element of that zone, an elementary annulus which subtends an angle $\delta\alpha$ at S. The boundaries of this element are represented by M and M', where MP$=r$, and M'P$=r+\delta r$. It is assumed that the obliquity factor is a slowly varying factor and that it may be assumed to be approximately constant over a single half-period zone. The contribution of the sources within this elementary area to the disturbance at P is, therefore,

$$d\phi = \frac{a}{r_o} \cdot d\sigma \cdot \frac{1}{r} \cdot f_n(\theta) \cdot \cos k[ct-(r_o+r)], \qquad . \quad . \quad (10\text{-}2)$$

where $f_n(\theta)$ is the obliquity factor for the nth zone, and $d\sigma$ is the area of the elementary annulus; the term (r_o+r) occurs because the phase must be appropriate to the total distance SMP traversed.

Now,
$$d\sigma = 2\pi(r_o \sin \alpha)r_o d\alpha.$$

But, from $\triangle$SMP,

$$r^2 = r_o{}^2 + (r_o+b)^2 - 2r_o(r_o+b) \cos \alpha,$$

$$\therefore \quad 2rdr = 2r_o(r_o+b) \sin \alpha d\alpha,$$

$$\therefore \quad d\sigma = \frac{2\pi r_o r}{r_o+b} dr,$$

$$\therefore \quad d\phi = 2\pi f_n(\theta) \frac{a}{r_o+b} \cos k[ct-(r_o+r)]dr.$$

Hence the disturbance due to the nth zone is given by

$$\phi_n = \int_{n\text{th zone}} d\phi = \frac{2\pi f_n(\theta)a}{(r_o+b)} \int_{r_{n-1}}^{r_n} \cos k[ct-(r_o+r)]dr$$

$$= \frac{f_n(\theta)a\lambda}{(r_o+b)} \left\{ \sin k[ct-(r_o+r_{n-1})] - \sin k[ct-(r_o+r_n)] \right\},$$

since $2\pi/\lambda = k$. By expanding the sines separately and putting

$$r_{n-1} = b + (n-1)\frac{\lambda}{2},$$

$$r_n = b + \frac{n\lambda}{2},$$

it is easily shown that this reduces to

$$\phi_n = (-1)^{n+1} \cdot \frac{2f_n(\theta)a\lambda}{(r_o+b)} \sin k[ct-(r_o+b)]. \qquad . \quad . \quad (10\text{-}3)$$

That is, ϕ_n is positive or negative when n is odd or even respectively. The importance of the obliquity factor now becomes evident because, in its absence, successive zones would, according to (10–3), give alternately positive and negative contributions of equal magnitude and the total disturbance would oscillate between 0 and ϕ_n according to the number of zones summed; it would never agree with the known disturbance at P as given by the appropriate form of equation (10–1).

Fresnel assumed that $f_n(\theta)$ gradually decreases as θ (and therefore n) increases until it is zero when $\theta=90°$. Thus one must construct Fresnel zones in the wavefront (Fig. 10–2) until PM is tangential to the wavefront. The disturbance at P is then given by the sum of the finite series $\Sigma\phi_n$ where, although it may not be known how many terms are taken, it is known that $|\phi_n|$ steadily decreases to zero.

The series to be summed is

$$\phi_p=|\phi_1|-|\phi_2|+|\phi_3|-|\phi_4|+ \dots , \quad \dots \quad (10\text{–}4)$$

and in order to perform this summation it is necessary to rearrange the terms of the series. For example, if n is odd, the series is written in the forms

$$
\left.
\begin{aligned}
\phi_p &= \frac{|\phi_1|}{2} + \left(\frac{|\phi_1|}{2} - |\phi_2| + \frac{|\phi_3|}{2}\right) + \left(\frac{|\phi_3|}{2} - |\phi_4| + \frac{|\phi_5|}{2}\right) \\
&\quad + \dots + \left(\frac{|\phi_{n-2}|}{2} - |\phi_{n-1}| + \frac{|\phi_n|}{2}\right) + \frac{|\phi_n|}{2}, \quad (a) \\
\text{or} \quad \phi_p &= |\phi_1| - \frac{|\phi_2|}{2} - \left(\frac{|\phi_2|}{2} - |\phi_3| + \frac{|\phi_4|}{2}\right) - \left(\frac{|\phi_4|}{2} - |\phi_5| + \frac{|\phi_6|}{2}\right) \\
&\quad - \dots - \left(\frac{|\phi_{n-3}|}{2} - |\phi_{n-2}| + \frac{|\phi_{n-1}|}{2}\right) - \frac{|\phi_{n-1}|}{2} + |\phi_n|. \quad (b)
\end{aligned}
\right\} \quad (10\text{–}5)
$$

Now it is not clear exactly how $f_n(\theta)$ must vary with n and two possibilities arise: either $|\phi_j|$ is greater than, or it is less than, the arithmetic mean of $|\phi_{j-1}|$ and $|\phi_{j+1}|$, and each case must be considered.

(a) If $|\phi_j|>\frac{1}{2}(|\phi_{j-1}|+|\phi_{j+1}|)$, each bracket in (10–5(a) and (b)) is negative, i.e.

$$\phi_p< \frac{|\phi_1|}{2} + \frac{|\phi_n|}{2}$$

and

$$\phi_p>|\phi_1| - \frac{|\phi_2|}{2} - \frac{|\phi_{n-1}|}{2} + |\phi_n|.$$

If it is assumed that $f_n(\theta)$ varies slowly, $|\phi_j|$ and $|\phi_{j-1}|$ are never widely different. These inequalities indicate that ϕ_p is only slightly smaller than $\frac{1}{2}(|\phi_1|+|\phi_n|)$. Consequently, to a first approximation one may write

$$\phi_p= \frac{|\phi_1|}{2} + \frac{|\phi_n|}{2}. \quad \dots \dots \quad (10\text{–}6)$$

(b) If $|\phi_j|<\frac{1}{2}(|\phi_{j-1}|+|\phi_{j+1}|)$ the above inequalities are reversed and again yield

(10-6). If n is even, a suitable rearrangement of terms in the series gives, in a similar way,

$$\phi_p = \frac{|\phi_1|}{2} - \frac{|\phi_n|}{2}. \qquad \ldots \ldots \ldots \text{(10-7)}$$

If it is assumed that Fresnel zones are constructed until $\theta = 90°$ (when $f_n(\theta) = 0$), one has $\phi_n = 0$, and $\phi_p = \frac{1}{2}\phi_1$. Thus the disturbance at P is half that due to the first Fresnel zone. In this sense it is possible to look upon the energy as travelling along SP, i.e. along the ray. It will be possible to look at the problem in this way provided one can draw the necessary number of Fresnel zones so that $\phi_n \doteq 0$. This will be possible only if P is not in the vicinity of a focus. If P is at or near the focus of a converging wave (see Fig. 10-3), all points on the wavefront are approximately equidistant from P, the obliquity factor is almost constant over the whole wave, and it is impossible to construct the necessary zones.

Fig. 10-3.
Converging wave.

10-4. Defects of Fresnel's Theory

Returning to an expanding spherical wave, it will be seen that the present theory gives, for the disturbance at P (Fig. 10-2),

$$\phi_p = \frac{f_1(\theta)a\lambda}{(r_o+b)} \sin k[ct-(r_o+b)]. \qquad \ldots \ldots \text{(10-8)}$$

But, on replacing r_o by (r_o+b), equation (10-1) must give

$$\phi_p = \frac{a}{(r_o+b)} \cos k[ct-(r_o+b)]. \qquad \ldots \ldots \text{(10-9)}$$

On comparing equations (10-8) and (10-9), the following difficulties are encountered:

1. In order to get the correct amplitude one must put $f_1(\theta) = 1/\lambda$, but it is difficult to justify an obliquity factor which is not unity when the obliquity is zero. The alternative seems to be to retain $f_1(\theta) = 1$ and assume that the secondary sources radiate with an amplitude $1/\lambda$ times the amplitude of the primary disturbance which excited them.

2. The theory yields the wrong phase for the disturbance at P since the sine occurs in place of the cosine. This could be put right by assuming that the secondary sources vibrate a quarter of a period ahead of the primary disturbance.

3. To these difficulties regarding the nature of the secondary sources there is added the difficulty of explaining the existence of the obliquity factor and, in particular, why the sources do not radiate backwards.

In spite of these difficulties the Fresnel theory does yield results which are in very good agreement with experimental observations in many diffraction problems. The reasons why the above defects do not show up are that one is not normally interested in absolute intensities in a pattern nor in the absolute phases of the disturbances which are superposed, but only in relative intensities and phases. In addition, one can easily "forget" the backwave.

10–5. Circular Aperture. Circular Obstacle. Irregular Obstacle

For a circular aperture or obstacle, the results given by Fresnel's theory are contrary to the idea of rectilinear propagation. At first it was claimed that this disposed of the theory, but experiment confirmed the predictions. For an irregular obstacle, the principle of rectilinear propagation is less noticeably violated.

Suppose that an opaque screen is interposed between S and P and that it contains a circular aperture, equal in size to the central zone, and centred on SP. From the Fresnel theory one would expect the whole of the central zone to be active so that the presence of the screen causes the disturbance at P to be doubled and, consequently, the intensity to be increased fourfold.

If a circular obstacle is placed centrally on SP, construction of the half-period zones may be commenced at the edge of the obstacle and the disturbance at P will be half that due to the new first zone. Hence, for any circular obstacle centred on SP, there will be a finite intensity at all points on SP beyond the obstacle.

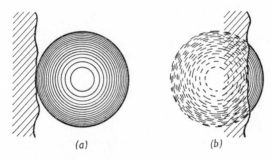

(a)   (b)

Fig. 10–4. Irregular obstacle.

Suppose now that an irregular obstacle is interposed between S and P. Figure 10–4 shows the appearance of the wave, divided into Fresnel zones and viewed from P. In (a) P is inside and in (b) it is outside the geometrically illuminated area. In (a) the central zones are unaffected and the outer zones are partially obstructed so that their contribution to the disturbance is reduced. This causes higher terms in series 10–4 to decrease in magnitude and the intensity at P is not appreciably affected. In (b), however, the central zones are obstructed and the next zones are partially obstructed by decreasing amounts so that the terms in the series now decrease in magnitude at both ends and the sum is nearly zero. Thus when P is in the geometrical shadow the intensity at P is small, and when it is in the geometrically illuminated area the intensity is almost unaffected by the presence of the obstacle. This is roughly in accordance with the principle of rectilinear propagation.

The Fresnel theory was very successful in explaining these and other simple diffraction phenomena but there remain fundamental objections to the theory as described above. Kirchhoff gave an analytical formulation of Huygens' principle which overcomes most of these difficulties. The theory is based on the general equation of wave motion which must be satisfied by the function used to represent the light disturbance.

10-6. Kirchhoff's Formulation of Huygens' Principle

It is assumed that the disturbance can be represented by a single scalar function ϕ, which satisfies the general equation of wave motion:

$$\nabla^2\phi = \frac{1}{c^2}\frac{\partial^2\phi}{\partial t^2}, \qquad \cdots \cdots \cdots \quad (10\text{-}10)$$

where ∇^2 is the operator $\left(\dfrac{\partial^2}{\partial x^2} + \dfrac{\partial^2}{\partial y^2} + \dfrac{\partial^2}{\partial z^2}\right)$ and c is the speed of propagation of the disturbance. If the disturbance is not monochromatic it may be resolved into its components, each of which satisfies (10-10). Consider, then, the component of frequency n, wavelength $\lambda = 2\pi/k$. As shown in § 6–3, one may split the disturbance into its space and time parts and write

$$\phi = \psi(x, y, z)e^{ikct},$$

where ψ is the complex amplitude, and the physical disturbance is now the real part of ϕ.

$$\therefore \quad \nabla^2\phi = e^{ikct}\nabla^2\psi.$$

Also

$$\frac{\partial\phi}{\partial t} = \psi ikce^{ikct},$$

$$\therefore \quad \frac{1}{c^2}\frac{\partial^2\phi}{\partial t^2} = -\psi k^2 e^{ikct}.$$

Thus, from (10-10),

$$\nabla^2\psi = -k^2\psi. \qquad \cdots \cdots \cdots \quad (10\text{-}11)$$

If ψ_1 and ψ_2 are any two continuous single-valued functions whose derivatives are continuous, Green's theorem states

$$\iiint (\psi_2\nabla^2\psi_1 - \psi_1\nabla^2\psi_2)dv = \iint \left(\psi_2\frac{\partial\psi_1}{\partial n} - \psi_1\frac{\partial\psi_2}{\partial n}\right)dS,$$

where the volume integral extends over the volume enclosed by the closed surface S, and $\partial/\partial n$ denotes differentiation along the outward normal.

Fig. 10-5. Exclusion of P from volume of integration.

Suppose one requires the disturbance at the point P. One can take the closed surface S to surround P and put $\psi_1 = \psi$, the complex amplitude. ψ_2 may be any well-behaved function; it proves convenient to put $\psi_2 = e^{-ikr}/r$, where r is measured from P as origin. This at once causes some difficulty since ψ_2 becomes infinite at P and, in order to apply Green's theorem, P must be excluded from the volume of integration. To do this, take a small sphere Σ centre. P. Green's theorem may now be applied to ψ_1 and ψ_2, where the volume of integration is the volume enclosed between S and Σ which, together, constitute the surface of integration (see Fig. 10-5).

It is easily shown that $\nabla^2\psi_2 = -k^2\psi_2$. To verify this, consider first $\partial^2\psi_2/\partial x^2$.

Now
$$\frac{\partial}{\partial x} = \frac{\partial r}{\partial x} \cdot \frac{\partial}{\partial r} = \frac{x}{r}\frac{\partial}{\partial r} \quad \text{since} \quad r^2 = x^2 + y^2 + z^2.$$

$$\therefore \quad \frac{\partial \psi_2}{\partial x} = -\frac{ikxe^{-ikr}}{r^2} - \frac{xe^{-ikr}}{r^3},$$

whence

$$\frac{\partial^2 \psi_2}{\partial x^2} = -\frac{k^2 x^2 e^{-ikr}}{r^3} + \frac{2x^2 ike^{-ikr}}{r^4} - \frac{ike^{-ikr}}{r^2} + \frac{x^2 ike^{-ikr}}{r^4} + \frac{3x^2 e^{-ikr}}{r^5} - \frac{e^{-ikr}}{r^3}$$

with similar expressions for $\partial^2\psi_2/\partial y^2$ and $\partial^2\psi_2/\partial z^2$. On collecting terms and simplifying, it follows that

$$\nabla^2\psi_2 = -k^2\psi_2. \quad \ldots \ldots \quad (10\text{–}12)$$

This result follows much more easily if one writes ∇^2 in spherical polar co-ordinates. For a function such as ψ_2, where there is symmetry about the origin, one has $\nabla^2\psi_2 = \partial^2\psi_2/\partial r^2 + (2/r)\partial\psi_2/\partial r$.

On substituting the values of $\nabla^2\psi_1$ and $\nabla^2\psi_2$ from (10–11) and (10–12), the volume integral in Green's theorem becomes zero. Hence the surface integral is zero.

Consider the surface integral over Σ. Over this surface the external normal from the volume of integration is, of course, towards P so that $\partial/\partial n$ becomes $-\partial/\partial r$.

$$\therefore \quad \iint_{\Sigma}\left(\psi_2\frac{\partial\psi_1}{\partial n} - \psi_1\frac{\partial\psi_2}{\partial n}\right)dS = \iint_{\Sigma}\left\{\frac{e^{-ikr}}{r}\left(-\frac{\partial\psi}{\partial r}\right) - \psi\left[-\frac{\partial}{\partial r}\left(\frac{e^{-ikr}}{r}\right)\right]\right\}dS$$

$$= \iint_{\Sigma}\left\{\frac{e^{-ikr}}{r}\left(-\frac{\partial\psi}{\partial r}\right) - \psi\left(\frac{e^{-ikr}}{r^2} + \frac{ike^{-ikr}}{r}\right)\right\}dS.$$

Suppose the surface element dS on Σ subtends, at P, a solid angle $d\omega$. Then $dS = r^2 d\omega$,

$$\therefore \quad \iint_{\Sigma} = \int_{\text{round P}}\left\{re^{-ikr}\left(-\frac{\partial\psi}{\partial r}\right) - \psi e^{-ikr} - r\psi ike^{-ikr}\right\}d\omega.$$

Assuming ψ is always finite, only the second term in the integrand does not approach zero as $r \to 0$. If Σ collapses round P, the value of ψ on and inside Σ may be assumed to be constant and equal to ψ_P, its value at P. Then

$$\iint_{\Sigma} \to -\psi_P\int e^{-ikr}\,d\omega$$

$$= -\psi_P\int d\omega \quad \text{since } e^{-ikr} \to 1 \text{ as } r \to 0$$

$$= -4\pi\psi_P.$$

Now since $\iint_{S+\Sigma}$ is zero it follows that $\iint_{S} = +4\pi\psi_P$, i.e.

$$4\pi\psi_P = \iint_{S}\left\{\frac{e^{-ikr}}{r}\cdot\frac{\partial\psi}{\partial n} - \psi\frac{\partial}{\partial n}\left(\frac{e^{-ikr}}{r}\right)\right\}dS$$

$$= \iint_{S}\left\{\frac{e^{-ikr}}{r}\cdot\frac{\partial\psi}{\partial n} - \psi e^{-ikr}\frac{\partial}{\partial n}\left(\frac{1}{r}\right) + \frac{ik\psi e^{-ikr}}{r}\cdot\frac{\partial r}{\partial n}\right\}dS. \quad (10\text{–}13)$$

This equation is frequently referred to as Helmholtz's equation (c. 1859).

8*

Since $\phi = \psi e^{ikct}$,

$$\phi_P = \frac{1}{4\pi} \iint_S \left\{ \frac{e^{ik(ct-r)}}{r} \cdot \frac{\partial \psi}{\partial n} - \psi e^{ik(ct-r)} \frac{\partial}{\partial n}\left(\frac{1}{r}\right) + \frac{ik\psi e^{ik(ct-r)}}{r} \cdot \frac{\partial r}{\partial n} \right\} dS,$$

$$\text{. . . (10-14)}$$

and this expression gives the disturbance at P at time t. In the integrand the factor $\psi e^{ik(ct-r)}$ can be written $\psi e^{ikc(t-r/c)}$. Obviously, it is the value of ϕ at the element dS at time $(t-r/c)$; it is referred to as the *retarded value* of ϕ and is written $[\phi]_{t-r/c}$. In the same way the first and third terms may be written in terms of the retarded values of $\partial\phi/\partial n$ and $\partial\phi/\partial t$. One has

$$\phi_P = \frac{1}{4\pi} \iint_S \left\{ \frac{1}{r}\left[\frac{\partial\phi}{\partial n}\right]_{t-r/c} - \frac{\partial}{\partial n}\left(\frac{1}{r}\right)[\phi]_{t-r/c} + \frac{1}{cr}\frac{\partial r}{\partial n}\left[\frac{\partial\phi}{\partial t}\right]_{t-r/c} \right\} dS,$$

$$\text{. . . (10-15)}$$

which is usually known as Kirchhoff's formula.

Thus the disturbance at P can be calculated from a knowledge of the conditions obtaining over the closed surface S. Physically, one may say that since the conditions at any element dS can affect ϕ_P only by means of a disturbance which travels from dS to P, the value of ϕ_P at any time t depends on the disturbance at dS at the previous time $(t-r/c)$, r/c being the time taken for a disturbance to travel the distance r from dS to P. Thus the appearance of the retarded values is explained.

10-7. Application to Spherical Waves

Equation (10-15) was derived for a surface S which enclosed the point P but

not the source (since it was assumed in applying Green's theorem that ψ remains finite throughout the volume of integration). It can be shown that the same result follows if S encloses the source but not the point P. Thus in the case of a single point source the closed surface S may be taken as a spherical wavefront.

Consider first the case of a point source at O (Fig. 10-6), where S is any surface enclosing O. (n is the outward normal from the space containing P.) One may put

Fig. 10-6. Expanding spherical wave.

$$\phi = \frac{a}{r_0} e^{ik(ct-r_0)},$$

where r_0 is the radius vector from O as origin.

Thus
$$\psi = \frac{a}{r_0} e^{-ikr_0}.$$

One has $\dfrac{\partial\psi}{\partial n} = \dfrac{\partial\psi}{\partial r_0} \cdot \dfrac{\partial r_0}{\partial n}$, where $\dfrac{\partial r_0}{\partial n} = \cos\theta_0$. Also, $\dfrac{\partial r}{\partial n} = \cos\theta$.

In equation (10–14), one has

$$\frac{e^{ik(ct-r)}}{r} \cdot \frac{\partial \psi}{\partial n} = -\cos\theta_o \cdot \frac{a}{rr_o} \cdot ike^{ik[ct-(r_o+r)]} - \cos\theta_o \cdot \frac{a}{rr_o{}^2} \cdot e^{ik[ct-(r_o+r)]},$$

$$-\psi e^{ik(ct-r)} \cdot \frac{\partial}{\partial n}\left(\frac{1}{r}\right) = +\cos\theta \cdot \frac{a}{r^2 r_o} e^{ik[ct-(r_o+r)]},$$

$$ik\psi \frac{e^{ik(ct-r)}}{r} \cdot \frac{\partial r}{\partial n} = +\cos\theta \cdot \frac{ika}{rr_o} e^{ik[ct-(r_o+r)]}.$$

Whence $\phi_P = \dfrac{1}{4\pi}\displaystyle\int\int_S e^{ik[ct-(r_o+r)]} \cdot \dfrac{a}{r_o r}\left\{\cos\theta\left(ik+\dfrac{1}{r}\right) - \cos\theta_o\left(ik+\dfrac{1}{r_o}\right)\right\}dS.$

If $\lambda \ll r_o$ or r, one may neglect $1/r_o$ and $1/r$ in comparison with k so that

$$\phi_P = \frac{1}{4\pi}\int\int_S \frac{ika}{r_o r}(\cos\theta - \cos\theta_o)\, e^{ik[ct-(r_o+r)]} dS. \qquad . \quad (10\text{–}16)$$

Now $k = 2\pi/\lambda$ and $e^{i\pi/2} = i$, and *if S is taken to be a wavefront*, $\cos\theta_o = -1$.

$$\therefore \quad \phi_P = \int\int_S \frac{a}{r_o} \cdot \frac{1}{r} \cdot \frac{1}{\lambda}\left(\frac{1+\cos\theta}{2}\right)e^{ik[ct-(r_o+r)]+i\frac{\pi}{2}} dS. \qquad . \quad (10\text{–}17)$$

It will be seen that this integral has the form of a summation of disturbances at P due to sources distributed over the surface S. Now it will be recalled that in the simple theory of Fresnel, difficulties were encountered concerning the amplitude and phase of the disturbance at P, and that an obliquity factor was introduced in a rather arbitrary manner (see § 10–4). These difficulties could be resolved only by making certain assumptions regarding the nature of the secondary sources. Examination of equation (10–17) reveals that these difficulties no longer exist.

1. The integrand includes an obliquity factor $\frac{1}{2}(1+\cos\theta)$ which is unity in the forward direction ($\theta=0$) and zero in the reverse direction ($\theta=\pi$). The amplitude factor $1/\lambda$ is also present as was seen to be necessary.

2. The presence of the factor $i\pi/2$ in the exponent indicates that the secondary sources vibrate a quarter of a period ahead of the primary disturbance, as was seen to be necessary to account for the phase of the disturbance at P.

3. The absence of the direct backwave is taken care of by the obliquity factor, although it is interesting to notice that the disturbance becomes zero only when $\theta=\pi$ (not when $\theta=\pi/2$ as assumed earlier).

If the above expression for ϕ_P is evaluated for an expanding spherical wave by means of Fresnel's zones, it is obvious that the result will be similar to that obtained in § 10–4 but with the correct phase and amplitude.

10–8. Kirchhoff's Diffraction Formula. St. Venant's Principle

One is frequently interested in the passage of light through an aperture or a number of apertures in an opaque non-reflecting screen. Usually the screen can be assumed to extend to infinity and then to enclose P, in which case the surface S in (10–14, 15, and 16) can be taken to consist of the screen plus open surfaces which bridge the diffracting apertures. According to St. Venant, one may assume that ψ and $\partial\psi/\partial n$ are zero over the part of S covered by the screens, and that over the surfaces which bridge the gaps they have the values which would obtain in the absence of the screens. Although this is a natural assumption to make, it is fundamentally unsound since it implies that ψ and $\partial\psi/\partial n$ are discontinuous at the edges of the apertures. This is physically impossible and contrary to the assumptions made when applying Green's theorem. Nevertheless, it leads to many results that are in agreement with observation. Experimental diffracting screens are not totally non-reflecting but the dark side of an opaque screen will give a completely negligible contribution and the remote surface enclosing P can be the non-reflecting walls of the laboratory.

For diffraction of light from a point source one then obtains

$$\phi_P = \int\int_\Sigma \frac{a}{2\lambda r_o r} (\cos\theta - \cos\theta_o)e^{ik[ct-(r_0+r)]+i\frac{\pi}{2}} dS, \quad . \quad (10\text{–}18)$$

where the integral is taken over any surfaces Σ which bridge the gaps in the diffracting screen. This is the Kirchhoff diffraction integral (1883).

10-9. Classification of Diffraction Patterns

In terms of the simple Fresnel theory, the disturbance at any point in the presence of a diffracting aperture is given by the summation of the effects of the secondary sources over the unobscured part of the wavefront or over any convenient surface which bridges the aperture. The contribution of any element of the wavefront has an amplitude proportional to the area of the element dS, proportional to the disturbance at the element (a/r_0), inversely proportional to the distance r of the element from the point in the pattern, and dependent on an inclination factor. The phase of the contribution is appropriate to the total distance (r_0+r) from the source to the field point in the pattern via the wavefront element. The Kirchhoff theory shows the nature of the obliquity factor and confirms the fact that this simple Fresnel theory will give the correct relative intensities in the pattern.

The most important diffraction patterns result from diffraction by an opaque plane screen containing one or more apertures. It will be assumed that the screen lies in the xy plane. Frequently, the surface Σ over which the diffraction integral is taken will simply be that part of the xy plane not covered by the screen; sometimes it is the unobstructed part of a wavefront. Usually the variations of r and r_0 are very small compared with r and r_0, and the amplitude term $1/r_0 r$ may be taken to be constant. This means that, apart from the effect of the obliquity factor, equal areas dS give contributions with equal amplitudes. Small variations in (r_0+r) can make a significant difference to the phase factor since (r_0+r) is multiplied by the large quantity $k(=2\pi/\lambda)$—it is obvious that a change in (r_0+r) of only a fraction of a wavelength will significantly affect the phase of the contribution from any element.

In general there may be a lens system between the source and the diffracting screen, and between this and the receiving screen. In this case (r_0+r) in the phase term becomes the optical path from the source to dS plus that from dS to P, the field point in the pattern. This is denoted by $[r_0+r]$ and will depend upon the co-ordinates (x, y) of the element dS. The quantity $[r_0+r]$ may be expressed as a power series in these variables. If $[r_0+r]$ is a linear function of x and y the pattern is referred to as a *Fraunhofer pattern*; otherwise it is a *Fresnel pattern*. It will be shown in the next section that patterns formed in planes conjugate to the source are Fraunhofer patterns; they were observed by Fraunhofer in 1821. As a special case, Fraunhofer patterns are formed when, in the absence of lenses, the source and receiving screen are infinitely distant from the diffracting screen. The Fresnel patterns usually discussed are those observed when there are no lens systems involved and the source and/or receiving screen are at finite distances from the diffracting screen. It is very often stated that in Fraunhofer diffraction the wavefronts incident on the diffracting screen must be plane so that the source and receiving screen are at infinity or in the focal planes of two

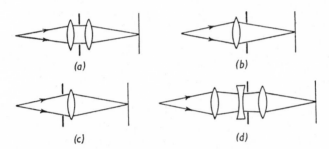

(a)   (b)

(c)   (d)

Fig. 10–7. Formation of Fraunhofer patterns.

lenses between which lies the diffracting screen [see Fig. 10–7(a)]. This restriction is not necessary, however, and the arrangements in (b), (c), and (d), would give similar patterns in the plane conjugate to the source (assuming the lenses are perfect). It will be seen that images formed by optical instruments are, in fact, Fraunhofer diffraction patterns. One has, in the image space, a converging spherical wave diffracted by the exit pupil.

Further investigation quickly shows that for any particular point in a Fraunhofer pattern, the inclination factor is constant over the whole surface Σ if this is taken to be a wavefront, whereas this is never (strictly) true in Fresnel patterns.

The above theory is found to yield results which are in good agreement with observation for moderate angles of diffraction and the Fraunhofer patterns predicted by the theory agree with the observed patterns for systems of moderate aperture. But it has been assumed that the light disturbance at any point can be represented adequately by a single scalar quantity ϕ, whereas it follows from the electromagnetic theory of light that in order to specify the disturbance one must specify the six components of the electric and magnetic field vectors. A scalar theory cannot, for example, take any account of the phenomenon of polarization. However, within the limitations mentioned above, the scalar theory of diffraction does yield a useful first approximation.

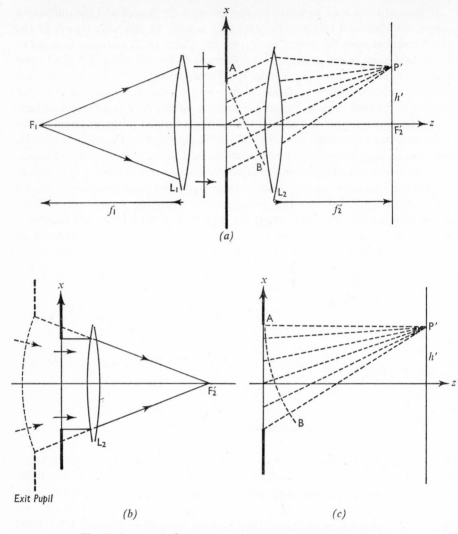

Fig. 10–8. Fraunhofer and Fresnel patterns for a single aperture.

10–10. Fresnel and Fraunhofer Patterns for a Single Slit

In Fig. 10–8(a) there is a point source at the first principal focus F_1 of lens L_1 so that a plane wave is incident on a rectangular aperture extending from $x=-a/2$ to $x=+a/2$ and from $y=-b/2$ to $y=+b/2$. Now, within the limits of paraxial theory, a converging lens causes *any* incident plane wave to converge towards a point focus. Hence, within these limits, for *any* point P' in the focal plane of L_2 there will be a plane AB such that all points on AB are optically equidistant from P'. It will be seen at once that the optical distance from P' to a point in the aperture in the xy plane is linearly dependent on the co-ordinate x of the latter point (and independent of y) so that the pattern in the second focal plane of L_2 is a Fraunhofer pattern. Furthermore, the figure shows that the obliquity factor is the same for all points in the aperture.

In terms of geometrical optics, F_2' is conjugate to F_1 so that the Fraunhofer pattern centred on F_2' constitutes the image of the point object at F_1. In the image space of the lens system one has a spherical wave converging towards the geometrical image point F_2', and this is diffracted by the exit pupil of the system [Fig. 10–8(b)]. This is also the situation in the image space of each of the arrangements illustrated in Fig. 10–7, and exactly similar conditions obtain in the image space of any lens system forming the image of a point source. This can be extended to any form of source (object) and it follows that any optical image is, in fact, a Fraunhofer diffraction pattern. Referring again to Fig. 10–8(a), it will be seen that in the optical space in which the diffracting aperture is situated both the source and the receiving screen are at infinity. Thus if L_1 and L_2 are removed and the source and receiving screen placed at large distances from the aperture, the diffraction pattern approximates to the Fraunhofer pattern. One sometimes refers to the *far-field* pattern—and it may be more useful to express the intensity in the pattern as a function of direction from the aperture rather than position in a receiving screen.

Suppose now that lens L_2 is removed. Fig. 10–8(c) shows that the distance from P′ to a point on the wave passing through the aperture is no longer linearly dependent on x. Points on the arc AB are equidistant from P′ and it is easily shown that if h' is small compared with the distance from the aperture to the receiving screen, the distance from P′ to a point in the aperture is dependent on $(h'-x)^2$, i.e. x^2 if the origin is moved to A. It follows that one has a Fresnel pattern, and it will be seen from the figure that the obliquity is not constant across the aperture. However, the obliquity factor varies only slightly and the variation is neglected in the discussion given below. With both lenses removed from Fig. 10–8(a) one has a diverging spherical wave incident on the aperture and it is obvious that one again has a Fresnel pattern.

The optical distance from P′ to any elementary area in the aperture affects both the amplitude and the phase of the disturbance at P′ due to the element. It has already been pointed out that small variations in this distance produce a negligible effect on the amplitude but an important effect on the phase. To find the disturbance at P′ one may divide the aperture into any convenient elementary areas and sum their contributions. Suppose that for the arrangements shown in Fig. 10–8(a) and (c) the aperture is divided into very narrow equal strips parallel to the y axis. If the variations of the obliquity factor can be ignored, it may be assumed that each strip produces a contribution of the same amplitude at P′, and that this is the same for all positions of P′ near the z axis.

In the case of the Fraunhofer pattern, the phase of the disturbance due to any strip is linearly dependent on x so that the phase difference between successive strips is constant. (If $l=ax+b$, $dl/dx=a$.) In the Fresnel case, with an appropriate choice of origin, the phase corresponding to each strip is proportional to x^2 so that the increment in phase in going from one strip to the next is proportional to x. [$(d/dx)(kx^2)=2kx$.] It follows that if one uses the graphical method to sum the contributions of the various strips, one gets an equilateral equiangular vector polygon in the Fraunhofer case [Fig. 10–9(a)]. In the Fresnel case the polygon is equilateral but not equiangular, the angle between successive vectors being proportional to x, or to the strip number if the strips are numbered from the origin of x [Fig. 10–9(b)]. If the strips in each case are made infinitesimally small, the vector polygons become arcs of a circle and a spiral respectively.

Fig. 10–9. Vector polygons for Fraunhofer and Fresnel patterns.

The more complicated geometrical figure that results in the Fresnel case makes this pattern more difficult to analyse.

10–11. Fresnel and Fraunhofer Patterns for a Double Slit

Further aspects of the relationship between Fresnel and Fraunhofer patterns may be seen by brief consideration of the patterns formed with two slits, using a slit source.

Figs 10–10(a) and (b) illustrate respectively the formation of the Fresnel and Fraunhofer patterns with a so-called double slit S_1S_2. For one narrow slit the

Fig. 10–10. Fresnel and Fraunhofer patterns for a double slit.

Fresnel pattern can be shown to consist of a central maximum on either side of which there are subsidiary maxima of rapidly decreasing intensity. (The intensity does not fall completely to zero between the maxima.) Using a double slit, the pattern associated with each slit is centred on the line through the source and diffracting slit as indicated in the figure. The outer maxima of the two patterns will obviously overlap and in this region the light in the two patterns can interfere. Consequently, superposed on the overlapping diffraction patterns, there will be the usual double slit interference fringes [see Plate III(i)]. The separate patterns actually extend to infinity so that interference does occur in the central maxima. This may pass unobserved because the intensity associated with one pattern may be very small at the centre of the other.

When the lens is used as in Fig. 10–10(b), the Fraunhofer pattern for each slit is centred on the geometrical image of the source slit. In general, the Fraunhofer pattern for a single slit is quite different from the Fresnel pattern but for very narrow slits the two patterns are similar [see Chapters XI and XIII, and Plates

II(b) and III(d)]. The main difference then is that the intensity falls to zero at the minima of a Fraunhofer pattern. Now it is obvious from the figure that one may look upon the lens as bringing the separate patterns together so that the central maxima coincide. The interference fringes again occur in the region in which the patterns due to the separate slits overlap so that they are now observed in the central maximum—see Plate II(d). The pattern formed on a screen held fairly close to the lens is again due to overlapping Fresnel patterns, and by examining the pattern in planes at increasing distances from the lens, it is possible to observe the transition from the Fresnel to the Fraunhofer double slit pattern. The patterns are discussed further in Chapters XI and XIII.

With the arrangement of Fig. 10–10(a), diffraction causes fringes to appear at the edges of the geometrical shadows which are cast by the boundaries of the apertures. This effect is particularly noticeable when the apertures are fairly large—see § 13–9. In the arrangement of Fig. 10–10(b) one has fringes around the geometrical image of the source. These effects—fringed shadows and fringed images—are characteristic of Fresnel and Fraunhofer diffraction respectively.

10–12. Babinet's Principle

Two screens, S_1 and S_2, are said to be *complementary* if S_2 is the screen which is formed when the transparent parts of S_1 are made opaque and the opaque parts made transparent. If P is a point at which, in the absence of any diffracting screens, the disturbance is zero, then Babinet's theorem states that the intensity at P caused by the introduction of S_1 is the same as that caused by the introduction of S_2. In other words: apart from the direct light, complementary screens produce identical diffraction patterns.

This theorem is easily proved as follows. Let ϕ_1 and ϕ_2 be the disturbances at P in the presence of screens S_1 and S_2 respectively. The disturbances are due to the light which passes through the apertures of these screens so that if the apertures of both screens are present simultaneously, the disturbance at P would be $\phi_1+\phi_2$. But if both sets of apertures are present at once, there are no opaque portions, i.e. there is no diffracting screen. Hence by assumption, the disturbance, $\phi_1+\phi_2$, at P is zero, i.e.

$$\phi_1=-\phi_2 \quad \text{or} \quad |\phi_1|^2=|\phi_2|^2,$$

so that the intensities at P associated with patterns due to S_1 and S_2 are equal.

It would seem that there is no *exact* application for Babinet's principle because if no diffracting obstacles of any kind are present, a single source will illuminate all space. However, when one has an optical system of large aperture, the intensity is very small at points outside the geometrical image of the source and, apart from the region near this image, approximately equal intensity distributions result from the successive interposition of complementary screens.

10–13. Young's Edge-Wave Interpretation of Diffraction

Before Fresnel advanced his very successful formulation of Huygens' principle, Young had suggested that the incident light undergoes some kind of reflection at the edge of a diffracting aperture. He assumed that the diffraction pattern was then the result of the interaction between the unobstructed light and an *edge wave* or *boundary wave* which can be regarded as originating from the rim of the aperture.

As a result of experimental investigations, Fresnel concluded that the diffraction pattern did not depend upon the degree of polish or sharpness of the edge and the success of Fresnel's theory caused Young's ideas to be forgotten for a time. Many years later work by Sommerfeld and by Rubinowicz put Young's ideas on to a firm basis.

For any diffracting aperture, the surface Σ in the Kirchhoff integral [equation (10–18)] can be any surface which bridges the aperture. That is to say, the only requirement is that the rim L of the open surface Σ must be the boundary of the aperture. Consequently, the integral depends only upon the curve L and it must be possible to transform the surface integral over Σ into a line integral round L. This transformation has been effected by Rubinowicz and the result indicates that within the geometrical shadow the disturbance can be regarded as being due to radiation from the boundary of the aperture. In the geometrically illuminated region the disturbance is due to the superposition of the edge wave and the disturbance which would be present in the absence of the diffracting screen. The effect of the edge wave is discussed further in §§ 13–8, 9, 10, and 14–13.

CHAPTER XI

FRAUNHOFER DIFFRACTION PATTERNS

11–1. Rectangular Aperture and Point Source. Location of the Minima

WHEN investigating the patterns formed by diffraction at a rectangular aperture, it is usually convenient to employ a slit source parallel to one of the edges of the aperture. It must be pointed out that each point of the slit source emits spherical waves and, although these have a cylindrical envelope, the resultant is

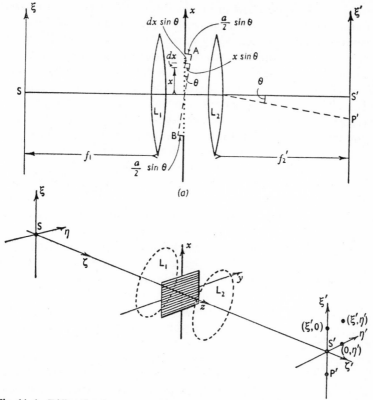

Fig. 11–1. Diffraction by a rectangular aperture. Path difference for extreme strips

$$2\frac{a}{2}\sin\theta = a\sin\theta.$$

not a cylindrical wave. A true cylindrical wave is produced by placing a point source at the focus of a cylindrical lens; it is seldom encountered in practice. For this reason it is necessary to commence the analysis with an investigation of the pattern formed when a point source is used.

Suppose that the monochromatic point source S (Fig. 11–1) is at the principal focus of a perfect lens L_1 and that the receiving screen is in the focal plane of a second lens L_2, the diffracting aperture being located between the lenses and centred on their common optical axis. As was shown in § 10–10, this

211

arrangement of the lenses is not essential and the same pattern results whenever the screen is conjugate to the plane of the source.

With the present arrangement a plane wave is incident on the rectangular aperture which will be assumed to have limits $x = \pm a/2$, $y = \pm b/2$. The elements of the wave which lie within these limits act as secondary sources, and it is necessary to find their combined effect at the point P' on the receiving screen. Initially it is assumed that P' lies in the plane of diagram (a). As shown in § 10–10, all points on the plane AB [Fig. 11–1(a)] are optically equidistant from P', and there occur only small variations in the optical paths from P' to points on the wavefront. Consequently, it may be assumed that equal elementary areas of the wavefront give disturbances of equal amplitude at P'.

Suppose the unobstructed part of the wavefront is divided into narrow strips parallel to the y-axis. Points on a single strip are optically equidistant from P' and are sources of coherent secondary waves. Consequently, each strip gives a disturbance at P' whose amplitude is proportional to the area of the strip. It follows that if the strips are of equal width they contribute disturbances of equal amplitude at P', the phase of the contribution of any strip depending on its optical distance from P'. The positions of the minima are easily found as follows. When θ is such that the difference between the paths from P' to the strips at the edges of the aperture is λ, the path difference for the first strip and the first past the middle is $\lambda/2$. At P' these strips then give contributions of equal amplitude but opposite phase; they therefore interfere destructively. Similarly, the disturbance from the second strip and the second past the middle cancel, and so on. Thus the resultant at P' is zero. Now, from Fig. 11–1, it is seen that the path difference for extreme strips is $a \sin \theta$, so that a minimum occurs where $a \sin \theta = \lambda$. By a similar argument it can be shown that another minimum occurs when $a \sin \theta = 2\lambda$. In this case the aperture can be divided into two halves. *For each half* the optical distances from P' to the extreme strips differ by λ so that the disturbance from the first strip interferes destructively with that from the first

strip past the middle, and so on. By an obvious extension it can be shown that minima occur when $a \sin \theta = p\lambda$, where p is an integer.

In Fig. 11–1 the receiving screen is conjugate to the plane containing the source and, as has been pointed out before, the Fraunhofer diffraction pattern constitutes the image of the source. In the image space one has a converging spherical wave which is diffracted by the rectangular exit pupil. Obviously these conditions will obtain whenever one has an optical system with a rectangular

Fig. 11–2.
Diffraction of wave in image space.

aperture stop. Fig. 11–2 illustrates the diffraction of the wave in the image space for any system of this type. When P' is at the first minimum in the pattern the distances of the extreme edges of the wave from P' differ by λ. If all points on AB are the same distance from P', and θ and U' are small, one may write

$$h' = R\theta = R\frac{\lambda}{a},$$

where R is the radius of the converging wave. As usual, U' is the angular semi-aperture in the image space; one has

$$\frac{a}{2} = R \sin U'.$$

Whence

$$h' = \frac{\lambda}{2 \sin U'}.$$

In this equation λ is the wavelength in the image space. If n' is the refractive index of this space and λ is the wavelength in a vacuum, one has

$$h' = \frac{\lambda}{2n' \sin U'}. \qquad \cdots \cdots \quad (11\text{–}1)$$

11–2. Intensity Distribution. Use of the Graphical Method

For a detailed examination of the complete pattern it is convenient to take the central strip as giving a contribution of zero phase at P' (Fig. 11–1). This is justified because only relative phases are important. Since points on AB are optically equidistant from P' it is obvious that the strip at x is $x \sin \theta$ farther from P' than is the central strip, so that the former gives, at P', a contribution whose phase is $(2\pi/\lambda)x \sin \theta$. If each strip is of width dx, the difference between the phases of the contributions of adjacent strips is $(2\pi/\lambda)dx \sin \theta$, and is constant. If the contributions of the strips are added by means of the graphical method, the vector polygon is an equilateral figure since each strip gives a vector of the same length; the angle between successive vectors is constant and equal to $(2\pi/\lambda)dx \sin \theta$. The total number of sides in the polygon is equal to the total number of strips; i.e. it is determined by a, the total width of the aperture. In the limiting case where the strips are made infinitesimal in width, the polygon becomes the arc of a circle, the length of the arc being proportional to a (Fig. 11–3). The resultant amplitude is given, as usual, by the length of the chord, and

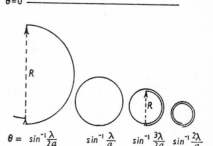

Fig. 11–3. Vibration curves.

the intensity is the square of that length. Since the number of unobstructed strips is constant, the arc length is constant for all field points P'. For different positions of P' the curvature of the arc varies, being determined by the increment in phase between successive strips. Thus when $\theta = 0$ P' is on the axis and the arc commences as a straight line since, in this position, all points on the wavefront are optically equidistant from P'. As θ increases, the curvature of the arc increases. When $(2\pi/\lambda)a \sin \theta = 2\pi$ (i.e. $a \sin \theta = \lambda$) the first and last strips in the aperture give contributions which are 2π out of phase, and the arc is bent into a complete circle. As θ increases further, the arc executes more than one complete revolution; it again becomes a closed curve when $a \sin \theta = 2\lambda$ and, in general, when $a \sin \theta$ is an integral number of wavelengths (see Fig. 11–3).

$\therefore$ at a minimum $\sin \theta = \dfrac{p\lambda}{a} (p \text{ integral}).$ . . . . . (11–2)

For certain intermediate values of θ the disturbance reaches maximum values. Fig. 11–3 shows the vibration curves midway between the minima, but the maxima do not lie *exactly* midway between the minima. It can be seen at once that successive maxima are weaker as P' recedes from the axis because the vibration curve winds up. When $\theta = 0$ the vibration curve is simply a straight line, so that if one takes the central maximum to have unit amplitude, the length of the arc is fixed as unity. As the arc becomes curved, the angle subtended at the centre is the phase difference between contributions from extreme strips of the aperture and is $\delta = (2\pi/\lambda)a \sin \theta$. The radius of the arc is given by

$$r = (\text{arc length}) \div (\text{angle at centre})$$

$$= \frac{1}{(2\pi/\lambda)a \sin \theta}.$$

The resultant is defined by the chord and (see Fig. 11–3) is given by

$$R = 2r \sin \frac{\delta}{2}$$

$$= 2 \cdot \frac{1}{\dfrac{2\pi a \sin \theta}{\lambda}} \cdot \sin \frac{\pi a \sin \theta}{\lambda}$$

$$= \frac{\sin \left(\dfrac{\pi a \sin \theta}{\lambda} \right)}{\left(\dfrac{\pi a \sin \theta}{\lambda} \right)}.$$

$\therefore$ Intensity $= \left[\dfrac{\sin \left(\dfrac{\pi a \sin \theta}{\lambda} \right)}{\left(\dfrac{\pi a \sin \theta}{\lambda} \right)} \right]^2 = (\text{say}) \left(\dfrac{\sin \alpha}{\alpha} \right)^2.$ (11–3)

This gives the intensity at any point along a line through S' parallel to the x-axis (i.e. along the ξ'-axis). An exactly similar expression (in which a is replaced by b and θ by ϕ, the corresponding angle in the yz plane) gives the intensity along the η'-axis.

The minima occur when the numerator in (11–3) is zero, i.e. when α is an integral multiple of π. That is, minima occur at angles given by

$$\theta = \sin^{-1} \frac{p\lambda}{a} (p \text{ integral}),$$

which is the result given above [equation (11–2)].

The positions of the maxima may be found by equating $dI/d\alpha$ to zero. One has

$$\frac{dI}{d\alpha} = 2\left(\frac{\sin\alpha}{\alpha}\right)\left[-\frac{\sin\alpha}{\alpha^2} + \frac{\cos\alpha}{\alpha}\right] = 0.$$

Hence at a maximum

$$\tan\alpha = \alpha.$$

This equation may be solved graphically by plotting $y = \alpha$ and $y = \tan\alpha$ and finding the points of intersection of the two curves (see Fig. 11–4). It is found

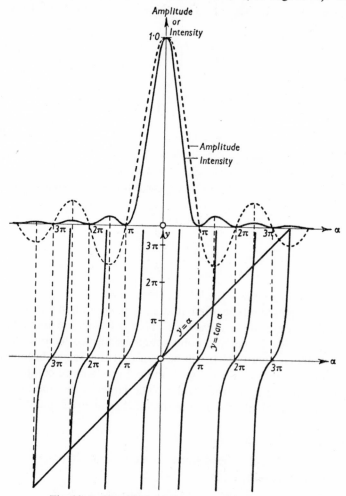

Fig. 11–4. Graphical solution for single slit pattern.

that the maxima occur at $\alpha = 0$, 1.4303π, 2.4590π, 3.4707π. . . . The amplitude and intensity distributions are shown in the figure. It will be seen that after the first few the maxima are approximately midway between the minima.

It should be noted that the obliquity factor has been neglected so that the above results are not accurate for large values of θ. The intensity should be multiplied by $\frac{1}{4}(1 + \cos\theta)^2$.

Suppose now that each of the strips of the unobstructed part of the wavefront is divided into elements by means of lines parallel to the x-axis. The difference between the disturbances at the points $(\xi',0)$ and $(0,0)$ is due to the phase differences introduced between elements whose y co-ordinates are the same. When P' moves from $(0,\eta')$ to (ξ',η') the same phase differences are introduced. Thus the variations of relative intensity are the same along all lines parallel to the ξ'-axis. By a similar argument it follows that the variations of intensity along any line parallel to the η'-axis is given by an equation of the same form as (11–3), a and θ being replaced by b and ϕ. Thus the general expression for the intensity in the $\xi'\eta'$ plane is

$$I = \left[\frac{\sin\left(\dfrac{\pi a \sin \theta}{\lambda}\right)}{\left(\dfrac{\pi a \sin \theta}{\lambda}\right)} \right]^2 \left[\frac{\sin\left(\dfrac{\pi b \sin \phi}{\lambda}\right)}{\left(\dfrac{\pi b \sin \phi}{\lambda}\right)} \right]^2 . \qquad (11\text{–}4)$$

θ and ϕ are, of course, measured in the $\xi'\zeta'$ and $\eta'\zeta'$ planes respectively. A photograph of the pattern is shown in Plate II(a). The lines of zero intensity are at $\theta = \sin^{-1} p\lambda/a$ and $\phi = \sin^{-1} p\lambda/b$ where p is an integer. For small angles one has $\theta = p\lambda/a$, $\phi = p\lambda/b$, i.e. in the $\xi'\eta'$ plane the lines of zero intensity are given by

$$\xi' = p \cdot \frac{f_2'\lambda}{a},$$

$$\eta' = p \cdot \frac{f_2'\lambda}{b},$$

where f_2' is the focal length of the lens L_2 (Fig. 11–1).

The pattern is centred on the origin in the $\xi'\eta'$ plane and, in terms of geometrical optics, this is conjugate to the source. That is to say, the above Fraunhofer pattern is the physical image of a point source as formed by an optical system having a rectangular aperture. It will be seen that this image becomes smaller as the size of the aperture is increased—the pattern is more compressed in the direction in which the aperture is wider. The larger is the aperture the more closely does the pattern approximate to the ideal geometrical point image.

11–3. Use of the Kirchhoff Integral

Equation (11–4) can also be deduced directly from Kirchhoff's diffraction integral. Equation (10–18) gives

$$\phi_{P'} = \int\int_{\Sigma} \frac{a}{2\lambda} (\cos \theta - \cos \theta_0) \frac{e^{ik[ct-(r_0+r)]+i\frac{\pi}{2}}}{rr_0} \, dS,$$

where Σ can be any surface which bridges the aperture and, in the present case, is taken to be simply the unobstructed part of the wavefront. In the exponential r_0 and r become, respectively, the optical paths from the source, and from the field point P' to the current point on Σ, r_0 becoming a constant. It may be assumed, as above, that the obliquity factor is constant and that the amplitude term,

$1/r_0r$, also becomes a constant. In addition, the phase factor $i(\pi/2)$ may be omitted since only relative phases are important. The complex amplitude is then given by

$$\psi_{P'} = (\text{constant}) \int\!\!\int_{\Sigma} e^{-ikr} dS.$$

Using the complex representation of disturbances, this equation also follows from the simple Fresnel theory since it corresponds to a summation of the effects of the secondary sources distributed over the exposed part of the wavefront.

If the optical path from the centre of the aperture to P' is denoted by R,

$$r = R + x \sin\theta + y \sin\phi \qquad \text{(see Fig. 11-1).}$$

If the edges of the aperture are $x = \pm a/2$, $y = \pm b/2$, and the constant term is omitted, one has

$$\psi_{P'} = \int_{-a/2}^{+a/2} e^{-ikx \sin\theta}\, dx \int_{-b/2}^{+b/2} e^{-iky \sin\phi}\, dy$$

$$= \left(\frac{e^{\frac{i\pi a \sin\theta}{\lambda}} - e^{\frac{-i\pi a \sin\theta}{\lambda}}}{2 \frac{i\pi \sin\theta}{\lambda}} \right) \left(\frac{e^{\frac{i\pi b \sin\phi}{\lambda}} - e^{\frac{-i\pi b \sin\phi}{\lambda}}}{2 \frac{i\pi \sin\phi}{\lambda}} \right)$$

$$= \left(\frac{i \sin\left(\frac{\pi a \sin\theta}{\lambda}\right)}{\frac{i\pi \sin\theta}{\lambda}} \right) \left(\frac{i \sin\left(\frac{\pi b \sin\phi}{\lambda}\right)}{\frac{i\pi \sin\phi}{\lambda}} \right),$$

so that if the expression is *normalized* to give unit intensity at the centre of the pattern, one has

$$\text{Intensity} = \left[\frac{\sin\left(\frac{\pi a \sin\theta}{\lambda}\right)}{\left(\frac{\pi a \sin\theta}{\lambda}\right)} \right]^2 \left[\frac{\sin\left(\frac{\pi b \sin\phi}{\lambda}\right)}{\left(\frac{\pi b \sin\phi}{\lambda}\right)} \right]^2,$$

which is the result obtained in §11-2.

11-4. Slit Aperture and Slit Source

If, in the above example, there are other point sources along the η-axis, each will give a pattern centred on its geometrical image point on the η'-axis. For a large number of closely spaced point sources along the η-axis, the patterns will overlap and there will be no variation of intensity along lines parallel to the η'-axis. Along lines parallel to the ξ'-axis, however, the variation in intensity will still be given by an equation of the form of (11-3). For example, the lines of zero intensity parallel to the η'-axis are the same for each point source. Thus a slit or line source along the η-axis gives linear fringes parallel to the η'-axis, the intensity distribution across the fringes being given by (11-3). Moreover, the relative intensities along a line across the fringes are independent of the length of the aperture in the y-direction. This result justifies the common procedure of restricting the discussion for slit source and aperture to one plane. A photograph of the fringes obtained with a narrow slit source parallel to a single diffracting slit or rectangular aperture is shown in Plate II(b).

If the width of the source slit is increased, each line element produces the above pattern so that the combined effect is the superposition of a number of fringe systems at slightly different positions along the ξ'-axis. It follows that if the slit source is too wide the overlapping fringes produce a continuous band of light and no fringes are distinguishable.

11–5. Chromatic Resolving Power of a Prism Spectroscope. The Rayleigh Criterion

Fig. 11–5 shows the optical system of a simple prism spectroscope. If the narrow slit S is illuminated by a source which emits a number of discrete wavelengths, a line spectrum is formed in the focal plane of L_2. If the rectangular

Fig. 11–5. Prism spectrum.

cross-section of the prism constitutes the limiting aperture of the system, each line in the spectrum is a Fraunhofer pattern for a slit source and rectangular aperture. Suppose the source emits wavelengths λ and $\lambda+\delta\lambda$ with equal intensities, and that S_1' and S_2' are the geometrical line images for these wavelengths. The two wavelengths must have been emitted by different sources (on the atomic scale) so that the disturbances are incoherent. Consequently, the total intensity at any point in the focal plane of L_2 is simply the sum of the intensities for each wavelength. (It will be appreciated that it is impossible to distinguish any colour difference between λ and $\lambda+\delta\lambda$.)

Fig. 11–6. The Rayleigh criterion for resolution.

If $\delta\lambda$ is fairly large, $S_1'S_2'$ is large and the central maxima of the diffraction patterns are clearly distinguishable [see Fig. 11–6(a)]. They are said to be resolved. If, however, $\delta\lambda$ is very small, the separate patterns may overlap to such an extent that the total intensity shows no drop between S_1' and S_2' [Fig. 11–6(b)]. It is then impossible, by casual observation, to see whether the pattern corresponds to a single line or to two neighbouring lines—the lines are not resolved. Obviously it is important to know how close the lines can be before they cease to be resolved. That is, one needs to know the minimum separation of S_1' and S_2' for which there is a just perceptible decrease in intensity between them. According to Rayleigh, it is just possible to see, by casual observation, that the resultant pattern consists of two overlapping patterns if the centre of one pattern falls on the first minimum of the other [Fig. 11–6(c)]. It will be appreciated that by careful analysis of the intensity distribution, it is possible to detect the existence of two overlapping patterns when their centres are closer than this, but the Rayleigh criterion provides a useful simplification of the problem.

When the lines are just resolved, the intensity I midway between S_1' and S_2' may be found from equation (11–3). It is twice the intensity in each central maximum midway between its centre and its edge, and if the intensity at the centre of each pattern is unity, $I=0.81$. When the intensities of the two spectral lines are different, the Rayleigh criterion as stated above is not directly applicable. That is, when the first minimum of one pattern falls on the centre of the other there might not be an easily detectable drop in intensity between the patterns. In such cases it is usually assumed that the patterns are resolved if, at any point between the maxima, the intensity falls to about 0.81 of that of the weaker maximum. This latter criterion is also used when discussing overlapping interference fringes (see §9–3). If the spectral lines for wavelengths λ and $\lambda+\delta\lambda$ are just resolved, $(\lambda/\delta\lambda)$ is the *chromatic resolving power*. Its reciprocal is the fractional difference in wavelength between the two lines when they are just resolved.

When the lines are just resolved, the separation of their centres (the geometrical line images) is equal to the distance from the centre to the first minimum of one of the lines. It was shown in §11–1 that the angular separation of the first minimum and the centre of the pattern is $\theta=\sin^{-1}(\lambda/a)$, or λ/a if the angle is small. Consequently, the spectral lines are resolved if the angular separation of S_1' and S_2' is given by

$$\delta\theta = \frac{\lambda}{a}. \qquad \cdots \cdots \quad (11–5)$$

The separation of the geometrical images is, of course, due to the dispersion of the prism. Now [from equation (5–6)] the angular dispersion of a prism is given by

$$\frac{\delta\theta}{\delta\lambda} = \frac{t}{a} \cdot \frac{dn}{d\lambda},$$

where n is the refractive index of the prism and t is the length of its base. Hence, from (11–5),

$$\frac{\lambda}{\delta\lambda} = t \cdot \frac{dn}{d\lambda}. \qquad \cdots \cdots \quad (11–6)$$

It will be seen that in order to resolve very close spectral lines a large prism is necessary.

In the above discussion it has been assumed that the width of the slit is infinitesimal. If this is not so, the widths of the spectral lines are increased and a larger difference in wavelength is necessary before neighbouring lines can be resolved. If $\Delta\lambda$ is the wavelength difference when two lines can be resolved with a certain slit width, $\lambda/\Delta\lambda$ is sometimes called the *purity*. As the slit width is decreased, $\Delta\lambda$ decreases and the purity increases. It reaches its maximum value (the chromatic resolving power) when the slit width is zero. For wide slits, the slit width is obviously the dominant factor governing the purity. With a continuous spectrum it is the purity which determines the range of wavelengths found at a given point in the spectrum.

11–6. Limit of Resolution with a Slit Aperture

A problem similar to the one discussed above arises when neighbouring object points are imaged by an optical system. In the image plane one has a Fraunhofer pattern centred at each geometrical image point, and it is necessary to know the separation of the object points when the images are just resolved. This is referred to as the *limit of resolution* of the instrument. Suppose that an optical system having a rectangular aperture images two independent (i.e. incoherent) point sources and that the line joining the sources is perpendicular to the edges of the aperture. Along the line joining the geometrical image points the variation in intensity is similar to that across a pair of spectral lines. Consequently, one can adopt the same criterion for resolution. That is, the objects are resolved if the separation of their geometrical images is equal to the distance from the centre of one pattern to the first minimum. Thus, from equation (11–1), the objects are resolved if the separation of the images is given by

$$h' = \frac{0\cdot5\lambda}{n'\sin U'}, \quad \cdots\cdots\cdots \quad (11-7)$$

where U' is the angular semi-aperture of the instrument in the image space and n' is the refractive index of that space.

Using this result one can find the value of the limit of resolution h, but the discussion would have very limited significance since optical instruments do not, in general, have rectangular apertures. The Fraunhofer pattern for a point source and a circular aperture is investigated in the next two sections and the limit of resolution of optical instruments is discussed in Chapter XIV.

11–7. Circular Aperture and Point Source. Qualitative Discussion

In Fig. 11–7, a circular aperture is placed between lenses L_1 and L_2. The point source S in the focal plane of L_1 causes a plane wave to be incident on the aperture, and the Fraunhofer pattern is formed in the focal plane of L_2 and is centred on S′, the geometrical image of S. In order to find the intensity at a point P′, divide the unobstructed part of the wavefront into strips of equal width perpendicular to S′P′. If the graphical method is used to sum the contributions of the strips, the vibration polygon will be equiangular since the phase difference between contributions from successive strips is constant (as for a rectangular aperture). However, the polygon is not equilateral because, as will be seen from the figure, the strips are not of equal length. When P′ is at S′, the polygon is, as before, a straight line [see Fig. 11–7(a)]. As P' moves away from S', the polygon takes the form shown in (b). When the difference between the optical paths from P' to the extreme edges of the aperture is λ/2, the extreme vectors are parallel but in opposite directions as in (c). When the path difference

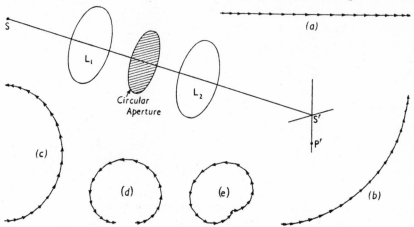

Fig. 11–7. Strip division for a circular aperture.

is λ they are parallel as in (d) but the polygon is not a closed figure as it was for a rectangular aperture. It can be shown that the polygon does not become a closed figure until the path difference is 1·22λ as in (e). Thus, for a circular aperture, the first minimum occurs at P' where the optical paths from P' to the extreme edges of the aperture differ by 1·22λ. The direction of the minimum is therefore given by

$$a \sin \theta = 1\cdot22\lambda$$

or

$$\theta = 1\cdot22 \frac{\lambda}{a} \text{ since } \theta \text{ is small.}$$

From the symmetry of the arrangement about the axis, it is obvious that the fringe system is circular so that, since $\theta = S'P'/f_2'$, there is a dark ring centred at S' of radius

$$S'P' = f_2' \cdot \frac{1\cdot22\lambda}{a}.$$

In order to deduce the exact nature of the pattern it is convenient to use an annular division of the wavefront as in the next section.

11–8. Derivation of the Airy Pattern

It has already been pointed out that when an optical system forms an image of a point source, one has, in the image space, diffraction of a converging spherical wave by the exit pupil.

In Fig. 11–8 ABCD is an annular zone, radius ϱ, of a spherical wave emerging from the circular exit pupil and converging to the geometrical image point G' on the optical axis. ds is an element of the annular zone in the azimuth ϕ referred to the plane containing the field point P' and the optical axis. AB and

CD are, respectively, perpendicular to and parallel to this plane. P'K is perpendicular to the line joining ds to G'. (ds)H is perpendicular to AB.

Fig. 11–8. Wave emerging from exit pupil.

If (ds)P'$=r$, the complex amplitude at P' due to the emergent wave is, from Kirchhoff's formula, given by

$$\psi_{P'}=\text{(constant)} \int_{\text{wave}} e^{-ikr}ds.$$

This may be written

$$\psi_{P'}=\text{(constant)} \int e^{-ik(r-R)}ds,$$

where R is the radius of curvature of the wave $[=$G'$(ds)]$. This is justified since R is a constant and one is interested in relative phases only.

From the figure,

$$(R-r)=\text{KG}'=h'\sin\theta=h'\frac{\varrho\cos\phi}{R},$$

$$\therefore\quad \psi_{P'}=\text{(constant)} \int_{\phi=0}^{\phi=2\pi}\int_{\varrho=0}^{\varrho=\varrho\,\text{max}} e^{i\left(\frac{kh'\varrho}{R}\right)\cos\phi}\varrho\,d\varrho\,d\phi,$$

which may be written

$$\psi_{P'}=\text{(constant)} \int_{\varrho=0}^{\varrho=\varrho\,\text{max}} \varrho\,d\varrho \cdot \frac{1}{2\pi}\int_{\phi=0}^{\phi=2\pi} e^{i\left(\frac{kh'\varrho}{R}\right)\cos\phi}\,d\phi,$$

$$=\text{(constant)} \int_{0}^{\varrho\,\text{max}} \varrho \cdot J_0\left(\frac{kh'\varrho}{R}\right)\,d\varrho.*$$

* $J_0(x)$ and $J_1(x)$ denote Bessel functions of order 0 and 1 respectively. Their properties are given in standard texts and their values have been tabulated for various values of x. Two standard results which are used here are: $\dfrac{1}{2\pi}\displaystyle\int_{0}^{2\pi} e^{ix\cos\phi}\,d\phi=J_0(x)$ and $\displaystyle\int_{0}^{z} xJ_0(x)dx=zJ_1(z)$.

It is convenient to put

$$x = \frac{kh'\varrho}{R} \quad \text{and} \quad z = \frac{kh'\varrho_{max}}{R}.$$

Since $\frac{k\varrho_{max}}{R}$ is constant, z can be used as a measure of the distance P'G'. Then

$$\varrho = \frac{R}{kh'} x, \quad \text{and} \quad d\varrho = \frac{R}{kh'} dx.$$

$$\therefore \quad \psi_{P'} = (\text{constant}) \left(\frac{R}{kh'}\right)^2 \int_{x=0}^{x=z} x J_0(x) dx$$

$$= (\text{constant}) \left(\frac{R}{kh'}\right)^2 z \cdot J_1(z)$$

$$= (\text{constant}) \varrho_{max}^2 \cdot \frac{J_1(z)}{z},$$

and the intensity is $|\psi_{P'}|^2$.

Now ϱ_{max} is constant, and $\frac{J_1(z)}{z} \to \frac{1}{2}$ as $z \to 0$. Hence, on normalizing the expression for the intensity distribution in the pattern to give unit intensity at the centre, one has

$$I = \left[\frac{2J_1(z)}{z}\right]^2. \qquad \cdots \cdots \quad (11\text{–}8)$$

This result, first derived by Airy in 1834, has an infinite number of zeros, and the variation of I along a line through G' is of the form shown in Fig. 11–9.

Fig. 11–9. Intensity distribution across Airy pattern.

The complete pattern is formed by rotating this about the central ordinate and obviously consists of a bright central disc (the so-called Airy disc) surrounded by rings of rapidly decreasing intensity. The first zero occurs at $z = 1.22\pi$. Now $z = (kh'\varrho_{max})/R = (2\pi/\lambda) h' \sin U'_{max}$ where U'_{max} is, as usual, the semi-angle of the emergent cone of light. Thus the first zero occurs at $h' = 0.61\lambda/(\sin U'_{max})$. In this expression λ is, of course, the wavelength in the medium of the image space. If one takes λ to be the wavelength in a vacuum, one has

$$\text{Radius of Airy disc} = \frac{0\cdot61\lambda}{n' \sin U'_{max}} \cdot \quad . \quad . \quad . \quad . \quad (11\text{–}9)$$

Further minima and maxima occur for the following values of the numerical factor in the numerator: minima for $1\cdot12$, $1\cdot62$, $2\cdot12 \ldots$ and maxima for $0\cdot82$, $1\cdot33$, $1\cdot85 \ldots$ If the central maximum has unit intensity, the intensities of the next three maxima are $0\cdot017$, $0\cdot004$ and $0\cdot0016$, i.e. the intensity falls off rapidly in the outer parts of the pattern; it can be shown that about 84 % of the energy falls within the first dark ring. The appearance of the pattern is shown in Plate IV(c).

11–9. Young's Eriometer

In Fig. 11–10 S is a monochromatic point source, L a lens, and AB a screen containing a large number of equal small circular apertures randomly distributed. Each aperture acting alone would give a broad Airy pattern centred at

Fig. 11–10. Screen with small holes.

S', the geometrical image of S. Now, since the apertures are the same size, the bright and dark rings have the same radii in every pattern. Consequently, the resultant pattern shows the same rings. Suppose the screen at AB is replaced by its complementary screen. Then, according to Babinet's principle, the two screens give the same pattern apart from the region of the geometrical image S'. By

Fig. 11–11. Young's eriometer.

measuring the ring diameters it is therefore possible to measure the diameters of small particles if a number of similar particles are scattered over a glass plate and held at AB. A convenient experimental arrangement is shown in Fig. 11–11. AB is a screen containing a small aperture 1–2 mm. in diameter at the centre of a ring of small pinholes. The actual radius r of this ring depends on the size of the particles to be measured. The screen is illuminated from the left by a monochromatic source. CD is a glass plate on which are scattered the particles whose mean diameter is required (e.g. lycopodium dust). This is held in front of the observer's eye E. The observer views the central hole in the screen AB and the Fraunhofer pattern as described above is formed on the retina since this is con-jugate to the screen AB. Thus a number of halos are seen. The angular diameter of the rings can easily be found by adjusting the distance x until one of the halos appears to fall on the ring of pinholes. (The pinholes do not transmit sufficient light for their own halos to be seen.) The angular radius of the first bright ring is $1·64\lambda/a$ where a is the diameter of each particle, and when this appears to coincide with the ring of pinholes one has

$$\frac{r}{x} = \frac{1·64\lambda}{a}$$

or

$$a = \frac{1·64\lambda x}{r}.$$

If the second bright ring is brought into coincidence with the ring of pinholes the numerical factor in the numerator becomes $2·66$; for the third bright ring it is $3·7$.

11–10. The Double Slit

In Fig. 11–12 the two equal slit apertures are illuminated by monochromatic light from a narrow slit source S located in the focal plane of L_1. Each aperture

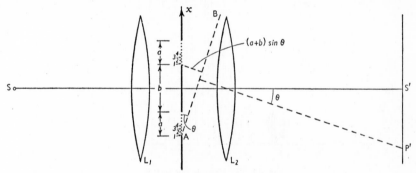

Fig. 11–12. The double slit.

acting alone would give rise to the usual Fraunhofer fringe system centred on S′, the geometrical image of S, in the focal plane of L_2. The complete pattern in this plane is therefore formed by the superposition of these two Fraunhofer single slit patterns which can interfere because the disturbances originate from the same source.

From the discussions of the earlier sections it will be seen that the variation in intensity along a line perpendicular to the direction of the slits may be found by discussing the case of a point source which causes a single plane wave to be incident on the slit apertures. Suppose that each aperture is of width a and that the opaque screen between them is of width b. At any point P′ the disturbance due to each aperture alone is given by equation (11–3). The effect of the super-position of the disturbances due to the two apertures may now be found if the phase difference between these disturbances can be found. It is convenient to divide the apertures into equal elementary strips and to number the strips from the lower edge of each aperture. It will be seen that since points on AB are optically equidistant from P', the optical path from P' to the first strip in th upper aperture is $(a+b) \sin \theta$ greater than the optical path from P' to the firs strip in the lower aperture. Hence the phase difference at P' between the dis turbances from these two strips is $(2\pi/\lambda)(a+b) \sin \theta$. This is also the phas difference between the disturbances from the second strips in the two aperture and so on, for all pairs of strips. Consequently, it must also be the phas difference at P' between the total disturbances due to the two separate sl apertures. It follows at once that, whatever the slit width, minima occur whe the path difference between disturbances passing through the middles of th slits is $(p+\tfrac{1}{2})\lambda$. In general, the disturbances to be added are each of amplitud $(\sin \alpha)/\alpha$ and the phase difference between them is $(2\pi/\lambda)(a+b) \sin \theta$.

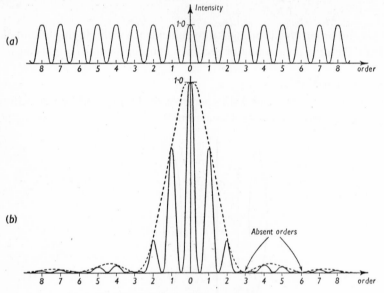

Fig. 11–13. Double slit pattern.

From equation (6–11) the resulting intensity is given by

$$I = \frac{4 \sin^2 \alpha}{\alpha^2} \cdot \cos^2 \left(\frac{\pi(a+b) \sin \theta}{\lambda} \right).$$

If this expression is normalized to give unit intensity at the centre of the pattern

$$I = \frac{\sin^2 \alpha}{\alpha^2} \cdot \cos^2 \left(\frac{\pi(a+b) \sin \theta}{\lambda} \right). \qquad \cdots \quad (11\text{–}10)$$

Fig. 11–13(b) shows the intensity variation across the pattern for the cas $b=2a$. The first term in equation (11–10) gives the intensity distribution in th Fraunhofer pattern for a single aperture and in the present problem gives th slowly varying envelope (shown dotted) within which lie the fringes given b the second term. The $\cos^2$ fringes are characteristic of the interference betwee two point or line sources $(a+b)$ apart, and the fringe separation does not depen on the width of the apertures. It is easily shown that the $\cos^2$ fringes do, in fact correspond to those observed in Young's experiment. [From § 10–9 it will be seen that in Young's experiment when D is large the interference pattern is, by definition, the Fraunhofer pattern for the narrow slits.] In Fig. 7–2 it is necessary to write, when θ is not small, $S_2A = d \sin \theta$, whence

$$I = 4a^2 \cos^2 \left(\frac{\pi d \sin \theta}{\lambda} \right), \quad \ldots \ldots \quad (11\text{--}11)$$

which, when normalized, is identical to equation (11–10) when the apertures are very narrow and the envelope term becomes unity.

The second term in (11–10) represents the effect of the *interference* between disturbances from the two apertures and the first term specifies the amount of light thrown, by *diffraction* at each aperture, into the part of the pattern considered. It should be borne in mind that, as pointed out in § 7–1, there is no real distinction between interference and diffraction. That is to say, when, in the present case, the pattern is said to be due to diffraction by the two wide apertures, this *means* that it is due to the interference between the secondary wavelets from the unobstructed parts of the wavefront. Fig. 11–13(a) shows the $\cos^2$ interference fringes for two narrow slits $3a$ apart (i.e. $b = 2a$); the dotted curve in (b) is the Fraunhofer pattern for an aperture of width a and the full curve is the combined effect for two apertures of width a whose centres are $3a$ apart. Plate II(d) shows a photograph of a double slit pattern for which $b = 3a$, i.e. for slits whose centres are $4a$ apart.

In the double slit pattern the intensity will fall to zero if either term in (11–10) is zero. One may say that the resultant is zero either if there is no light directed from each aperture to the field point concerned or if there is destructive interference between the disturbances from the two apertures. These two causes lead, respectively, to zeros at

$$\sin \theta = \frac{p\lambda}{a}, \quad \ldots \ldots \quad (11\text{--}12)$$

and

$$\sin \theta = (p + \tfrac{1}{2}) \frac{\lambda}{a + b}. \quad \ldots \ldots \quad (11\text{--}13)$$

The positions of the maxima are more difficult to calculate exactly, but at places where the variation due to the first term (i.e. the envelope) is small, the maxima are approximately at the interference maxima given by $(a + b) \sin \theta = p\lambda$. Following the usual notation, p may be called the order of interference. If the relation between a and b is such that an interference maximum occurs at a diffraction minimum, i.e. where the envelope to the fringes falls to zero, there will be no well defined maximum. In this way it is possible for interference maxima of certain orders to be missing from the pattern. (Actually each might

Fig. 11–14.
Appearance of "missing" orders.

be observed as a pair of weak maxima as indicated by Fig. 11–14.) Now, as stated above, interference maxima occur at $\sin \theta = p\lambda/(a + b)$ and diffraction minima at $\sin \theta = p\lambda/a$. It is possible for these conditions to be satisfied simultaneously when b is an integral multiple of a. Certain orders will then be missing. Thus in Fig. 11–13, for which $b=2a$, the missing orders are 3, 6, 9, etc., and in Plate II(d), for which $b=3a$, the missing orders are 4, 8, 12, etc.

If white light is used with a single or double slit, the central fringe is achromatic since this is the position of zero path difference for all wavelengths. In addition, a few coloured fringes can usually be observed where the path differences are small.

11–11. Derivation of the Double Slit Pattern from Kirchhoff's Integral

The analysis is identical to that of § 11–3 except that the integral must be taken over two apertures. If the intensity variation is required along a line perpendicular to the slits, the integration involving y may be omitted (i.e. included in the constant). It is again assumed that a disturbance from $x=y=0$ would have zero phase at P'. One has (see Fig. 11–12),

$$\psi_{P'} = (\text{constant}) \left[\int_{x=\frac{b}{2}}^{x=a+\frac{b}{2}} e^{-ikx \sin \theta} \, dx + \int_{x=-(a+\frac{b}{2})}^{x=-\frac{b}{2}} e^{-ikx \sin \theta} \, dx \right]$$

$$= \frac{(\text{constant})}{ik \sin \theta} \left[e^{-ik\frac{b}{2} \sin \theta} - e^{-ik(a+\frac{b}{2}) \sin \theta} + e^{ik(a+\frac{b}{2}) \sin \theta} - e^{ik\frac{b}{2} \sin \theta} \right]$$

$$= \frac{2 (\text{constant})}{k \sin \theta} \left[\sin \left\{ k \left(a + \frac{b}{2} \right) \sin \theta \right\} - \sin \left\{ k \frac{b}{2} \sin \theta \right\} \right]$$

$$= \frac{2 (\text{constant})}{k \sin \theta} \cdot 2 \sin \left(\frac{ka \sin \theta}{2} \right) \cos \left(\frac{k(a+b) \sin \theta}{2} \right).$$

That is, $$\text{Intensity} = \left[\frac{\sin \left(\frac{\pi a \sin \theta}{\lambda} \right)}{\left(\frac{\pi a \sin \theta}{\lambda} \right)} \right]^2 \cos^2 \left(\frac{\pi(a+b) \sin \theta}{\lambda} \right),$$

where, as before, the expression is normalized to make $I_{\max}=1$.

11–12. Double Source and Source of Finite Width

In Fig. 11–15 S_1 and S_2 are two independent point or line sources imaged geometrically at S_1' and S_2' by the lens L, and A_1 and A_2 are diffracting slits. Each source produces a Fraunhofer double slit pattern centred on its geometrical image and the total intensity at any point is simply the sum of the intensities due to the separate sources. If α, the angular separation of the sources, is very small the two patterns are nearly coincident and the brightness of the fringes is increased [Fig. 11–15(a)]. As α increases the resultant fringes become less distinct [Fig. 11–15(b)] until, when the first minimum of one pattern coincides with the central maximum of the other, the fringes disappear leaving a uniform intensity across the image plane [Fig. 11–15(c)]. A further increase in α causes the fringes to reappear. If A_1 and A_2 are narrow apertures, the superposed fringes are approximately $\cos^2$ fringes and they will again disappear when the central maximum of one pattern coincides with the second and any subsequent minimum of the other. If A_1 and A_2 are wide apertures, these subsequent disappearances of the fringes are incomplete, since the envelope to the $\cos^2$ fringes reduces the intensity of the outer maxima relative to the central maximum.

Fig. 11–15. Effect of double source.   *(a)*   *(b)*   *(c)*

According to equation (11–13), the minima of the interference fringes in the double slit pattern occur at angles given by (for small angles)

$$\theta = (p + \tfrac{1}{2}) \frac{\lambda}{(a+b)} \ (p \text{ integral}), \quad . \quad . \quad . \quad (11\text{--}14)$$

so that when α, the angular separation of the double source, has one of these values, the central maximum of one pattern falls on a minimum of the other and the fringes disappear. This is easily verified since the two sets of $\cos^2$ fringes will be of the form

$$\cos^2 \left(\frac{\pi(a+b)\theta}{\lambda} \right) + \cos^2 \left(\frac{\pi(a+b)(\theta+\alpha)}{\lambda} \right),$$

where θ is now measured from the centre of one of the patterns and α has one of the values given by (11–14). Therefore the total intensity is of the form

$$I = \cos^2 \delta + \cos^2 (\delta + (p+\tfrac{1}{2})\pi)$$
$$= \cos^2 \delta + \sin^2 \delta$$
$$= 1,$$

i.e. is independent of θ.

It will be seen that the fringes disappear when the disturbances from one source are π out of phase at the geometrical image of the other source, i.e. when the disturbances traverse paths which differ by $\lambda/2$ (or, in general, $(p+\tfrac{1}{2})\lambda$).

Consider now the cases where the source is a line $S_1 S_2$ or a slit of finite width $S_1 S_2$. In these two cases, respectively, each point or line element of the source gives the usual Fraunhofer pattern and the resultant intensity at any point is the sum of the separate intensities. The result will be a uniform intensity along the line $S_1'S_2'$ if, for every fringe system along that line, there is a complementary system. The point or line element at one edge of the source, and the first one past the middle, may be regarded as a pair of independent sources whose angular separation is half the angular width of the source. Equation (11–14) shows that if the angular separation of these source elements is $\lambda/2(a+b)$ they give complementary fringes. That is, they give complementary fringes when the angular width of the complete source (α) has twice this value. When this occurs, the second point or line element and the second one past the middle of the source also give complementary fringes, and so on, and the fringes disappear. The narrowest source for which this occurs is that whose angular width is $\alpha=\lambda/(a+b)$. When $\alpha=2\lambda/(a+b)$ the source can be divided into two halves and, *in each half*, the first element and the first past the middle give complementary fringes. By dividing the source into three parts it will be seen that the fringes again disappear when $\alpha=3\lambda/(a+b)$. Thus, in general, the fringes disappear for a single wide source when its angular width satisfies the equation

$$\alpha=\frac{p\lambda}{(a+b)}. \qquad \cdots \cdots \cdots \quad (11\text{--}15)$$

That is to say, the fringes disappear when the disturbances which travel from one edge of the source to the geometrical image of the other edge traverse optical paths which differ by $p\lambda$.

The above discussion is concerned with a simple form of extended source. In general, it follows from the discussion of partial coherence in §6–4 that when one has an extended source the disturbances emerging from A_1 and A_2 are partially coherent, and the fringes disappear as described above when the degree of coherence is zero. If A_1 and A_2 are equal small apertures, they give equal amplitudes in the image plane. If each gives amplitude a, it follows from equation (6–16) that the maximum and minimum intensities in the fringe pattern are given by

$$I_{\max}=2a^2(1+V_{12})$$
$$\text{and} \quad I_{\min}=2a^2(1-V_{12}).$$

Thus the fringe visibility is given by

$$\text{Visibility} = \frac{I_{\max}-I_{\min}}{I_{\max}+I_{\min}} = V_{12}. \qquad \cdots \cdots \quad (11\text{--}16)$$

It is now necessary to calculate the complex degree of coherence (γ_{12}) for the general case of light received from an extended source. In Fig. 11–16 the points P_1 and P_2 receive light from the self-luminous quasi-monochromatic source Σ which lies in a plane parallel to P_1P_2. The origin of (x,y) is at P_2 and the origin of (ξ,η) is at the foot of the perpendicular from P_2. Let $I(\xi,\eta)$ be the luminance of Σ (see §18–1). The luminous intensity of the source element $d\sigma$ is $I(\xi,\eta)d\sigma$ and the intensities at P_1 and P_2 are $I(\xi,\eta)d\sigma/r_1^2$ and $I(\xi,\eta)d\sigma/r_2^2$ respectively. Hence one may write, for the complex amplitudes at P_1 and P_2 due to $d\sigma$,

$$u_1\sqrt{d\sigma}=\frac{\sqrt{I(\xi,\eta)d\sigma}}{r_1}e^{-ikr_1},$$

$$u_2\sqrt{d\sigma}=\frac{\sqrt{I(\xi,\eta)d\sigma}}{r_2}e^{-ikr_2}.$$

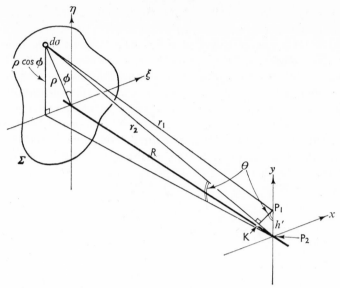

Fig. 11–16.

Hence the phase coherence factor γ_{12} for the disturbances at P_1 and P_2 is given by equation (6–14):

$$\gamma_{12} = \frac{1}{\sqrt{I_1 I_2}} \int\!\!\int_\Sigma u_1\, \bar{u}_2 d\sigma$$

$$= \frac{1}{\sqrt{I_1 I_2}} \int\!\!\int_\Sigma \frac{I(\xi,\eta)}{r_1 r_2}\, e^{ik(r_2 - r_1)}\, d\sigma,$$

where I_1 and I_2 are the total intensities at P_1 and P_2. It follows from Fig. 11–16 that

$$r_2 - r_1 = KP_2 = h'\sin\theta = \frac{h'\rho\cos\phi}{r_2}.$$

If $r_1,\, r_2 \gg \rho,\, h'$, the fractional variation in r_2 is small. Hence if one puts $r_2 = R$, the perpendicular separation of the (x,y) and (ξ,η) planes, one introduces only a small fractional error into $(r_2 - r_1)$. One then writes

$$\gamma_{12} = \frac{1}{R^2 \sqrt{I_1 I_2}} \int\!\!\int_\Sigma I(\xi,\eta) e^{i\left(\frac{kh'\rho}{R}\right)\cos\phi}\, d\sigma. \qquad . \quad . \quad (11\text{–}17)$$

On referring to §11–8, it will be seen that if one had a diffracting aperture whose boundaries were the same as those of the present source area Σ, and if one had a spherical wave emerging through the aperture and converging on to P_2, and if the *amplitude* across the wave were $I(\xi,\eta)$, then the complex amplitude at P_1 would be given by

$$\psi_{P_1} = (\text{constant}) \int\!\!\int_\Sigma I(\xi,\eta) e^{i\left(\frac{kh'\rho}{R}\right)\cos\phi}\, d\sigma.$$

This has the same form as (11–17) and can be normalized to make $|\psi_{P_1}| \to |$ $P_1 \to P_2$. (Equation (11–17) gives $|\gamma_{12}| \to 1$ as $P_1 \to P_2$, as it obviously should.) That is to say, *the phase coherence factor for two points on a plane illuminated by a parallel plane quasi-monochromatic self-luminous surface is equal to the normalized complex amplitude at one of the points in the Fraunhofer diffraction pattern associated with a spherical wave centred on the other point when the wave passes through an aperture whose boundary is the same as that of the source, the variation of amplitude across the wave being the same as the variation of luminance across the source.* This is referred to as the *van Cittert-Zernike theorem.* If the extended source is a uniform disc centred at $\xi = \eta = 0$ the related diffraction pattern is the Airy pattern and one has

$$\gamma_{12} = \frac{2J_1(z)}{z}, \quad \ldots \ldots \ldots \quad (11\text{–}18)$$

where $z = \dfrac{2\pi}{\lambda} \cdot P_1 P_2 \sin \alpha$, 2α being the angular diameter of the source seen from P_2. $|\gamma_{12}|$ falls to 0·88 when $z = 1$, i.e. when

$$P_1 P_2 = \frac{0 \cdot 16 \lambda}{\sin \alpha}. \quad \ldots \ldots \ldots \quad (11\text{–}19)$$

One can take 0·88 to be a convenient "tolerance" so that (11–19) gives the diameter of the *coherence patch* over which disturbances are coherent for many practical purposes. Frequently (11–19) is used to set a limit to the size of the source that can be used in an interference or diffraction experiment where a given area must be coherently illuminated.

11–13. Michelson's Stellar Interferometer

Suppose a double star is examined with a telescope and a double slit of variable slit separation is placed in front of the objective so that the slits are perpendicular to the line joining the stars. Then, in general, fringes will be observed in the focal plane of the telescope. If the separation of the slits is now increased from a very small initial value, the fringes will be seen to become narrower but less distinct until, when equation (11–14) is satisfied, i.e. (putting $p = 0$) when $(a+b) = \lambda/2\alpha$, the fringes disappear. The angular separation of the two stars can then be calculated from a measurement of $(a+b)$. This experiment can be performed provided the aperture of the telescope objective is sufficiently large. It will be seen that, for an objective of diameter d, the fringes disappear for a double star of angular separation $\lambda/2d$, but a decrease in the visibility of the fringes is detectable for somewhat closer stars. Thus the double nature of a star can be *inferred* from these observations even though it is not resolved by the telescope used in the normal way—when the limit of resolution is $1 \cdot 22 \lambda/d$ (see § 14–6). It must be remembered that the double star is not resolved by the present method although its double nature can be detected. In practice this method is not often used since more sensitive methods are available (see §6–13).

The use of the double slit arrangement is of more importance in determining the diameters of single stars. If the star radiates uniformly so that, viewed from the telescope, it can be regarded as equivalent to a uniform disc, then it follows from the discussion of §11–12 that the disturbances arriving at the two slits are partially coherent, the degree of coherence decreasing as the slit separation D is increased. The degree of coherence, and hence the fringe visibility, falls to zero when $z=1·22\pi$. One has

$$1·22\pi = \frac{2\pi}{\lambda} D \sin \alpha.$$

In practice α is small and when the fringes disappear the angular diameter of the star is given by

$$2\alpha = \frac{1·22\lambda}{D}. \qquad \cdots \cdots \quad (11\text{–}20)$$

It is worth noting that if D is increased beyond this value the fringes reappear and (11–18) gives a small negative value for γ_{12}. This corresponds to the reappearance of fringes of poor visibility and with reversed contrast, i.e. with maxima and minima interchanged. If one continues to increase D, the fringes repeatedly reappear and disappear, corresponding to the oscillating value of γ_{12} given by (11–18).

Fig. 11–17. Michelson's stellar interferometer.

In practice, stellar diameters are so small that the values of D corresponding to the first disappearance are more than 20 ft., i.e. larger than the diameter of the largest telescope objective. In addition, one would have very closely spaced fringes that would be difficult to observe. (Equation (11–13) shows that for a slit separation D the angular separation of the fringes is λ/D.) These difficulties are overcome in the Michelson stellar interferometer (Fig. 11–17). Light from the star falls on the outer mirrors M_1 and M_2 and is then directed via M_3 and M_4 to the slits A_1 and A_2. The degree of coherence between the interfering disturbances is determined by the distance D between M_1 and M_2, and the fringe spacing is determined by the slit separation A_1A_2. The separation of the outer mirrors is increased until the fringes disappear, when the angular diameter of the star is given by (11–20). It will be seen that when the fringes disappear there is a path difference of $1·22\lambda$ between disturbances travelling from one edge of the star disc to the point corresponding to the image of the other edge.

The use of the relatively small mirror and slit apertures helps to reduce the effect of atmospheric inhomogeneity which, in telescopes of large aperture, causes unsteadiness of the image.

9*

11-14. The Rayleigh Refractometer

Suppose that, in the double slit arrangement, a path difference is introduced between the disturbances that pass through one slit and those that pass through the other. There will be no change in the pattern produced by each aperture acting alone since this depends upon the relative phases of disturbances from various parts of the same aperture. Thus no change is produced in the slowly varying envelope in the fringe system. The $\cos^2$ interference fringes will, however, be affected since these are controlled by the phase differences between disturbances from corresponding elements of the two apertures. Very small

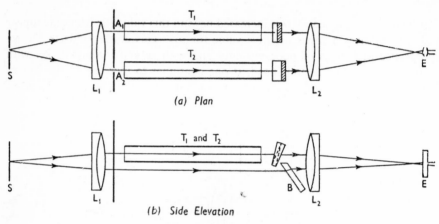

(a) Plan

(b) Side Elevation

Fig. 11-18. Rayleigh refractometer.

changes in optical path can be measured in this way. For example, if a path difference of only one wavelength is introduced between the disturbances passing through one slit and those passing through the other, the $\cos^2$ fringes move a distance equal to the fringe spacing. This fact is utilized in the Rayleigh refractometer which is used to measure the refractive indices of liquids and gases.

A plan of the optical system is shown in Fig. 11-18(a). Light from a slit source S in the focal plane of L_1 passes through the slit apertures A_1 and A_2 and along the tubes T_1 and T_2 which have glass ends. Since A_1 and A_2 are fairly wide, most of the light passes almost straight along the tubes. Hence the usual Fraunhofer double slit pattern is formed in the focal plane of L_2 if the optical paths through T_1 and T_2 are identical. Since the separation of A_1 and A_2 is fairly large, the fringes are very close together and a high magnification is required. The magnification is, however, only required in the direction perpendicular to the fringes so that a cylindrical lens can be used. In this way a considerable economy in light is effected, resulting in brighter fringes. However, it is essential for another reason to use a cylindrical lens (see below). In practice a glass rod is used as eyepiece at E.

If each tube is of length t and the liquids or gases contained in them differ in refractive index by δn, the optical path difference introduced is $t\delta n$. As in the Jamin refractometer, it is impracticable to observe the movement of the fringes but compensating plates of the same type can be used to return the fringes to their original positions. As before, monochromatic fringes cannot be distinguished from one another and white light fringes are employed. There is, however, one important difference between the two instruments in the method of setting. The fringes in the Rayleigh instrument are so fine that it is impossible to produce a sufficiently fine cross-wire. For this reason a separate stationary fringe system is used as a fiducial mark. It is also worth noting that a cylindrical eyepiece could not be used with cross-wires. The arrangement is shown in Fig. 11–18(b) which is a side elevation of the system. It will be seen that only the top half of the aperture is occupied by the tubes so that light that passes through the lower half of the aperture gives a fixed double slit pattern in the focal plane of L_2. The two sets of fringes are superposed in the focal plane of L_2, but if they are examined with a cylindrical lens the axis of whose cylinder is parallel to the fringes, the top half of the field of view contains the fringes formed by light which has passed through the tubes and the lower half of the field contains the fiduciary system. This is because the light forming the two fringe systems comes from different halves of the aperture of L_2 and passes on as

(a) Action of Cylindrical Lens   (b) Lifting action of Glass Plate

Fig. 11–19. Components of the Rayleigh refractometer.

indicated in Fig. 11–19(a). It will be seen that the cylindrical lens does not deviate the rays in the vertical plane. The plate B [Figs. 11–18(b) and 11–19(b)] raises the light forming the fiduciary pattern until the two pencils of light touch. In the field of view the upper edge of the fiduciary pattern then touches the lower edge of the other fringes and the setting is made easier.

After calibrating the compensators, the procedure is to introduce, into one of the tubes, the gas or liquid whose refractive index is required (the other being evacuated or containing air at known pressure). The compensator is then adjusted until the central white light fringe is returned to lie exactly above that of the fixed fringe system. It is found that many observers can make this setting more accurately than the setting of a fringe on a cross-wire. Displacements of about one-fortieth of a fringe width can be detected.

With a dispersive material it is obviously desirable to measure the refractive index for one wavelength rather than the mean value for white light. The procedure is to make an initial setting using white light in order to identify the central fringe. On changing to monochromatic light, the necessary fine adjustment can be made to bring the central fringes into exact coincidence. When a large tilt of the compensator is used, and the dispersive power of the material under test is very different from that of the material of the compensators, it may become difficult to identify the central fringe with white light (see §7–10). It is then necessary to make a preliminary measurement with a smaller concentration or with shorter tubes. This involves a smaller rotation of the compensator and enables the central fringe to be identified.

Rotation of the Jamin compensator causes the fringe systems to be slightly inclined to one another, and this is important in the present instrument which employs a cylindrical eye lens to view the fringes (which must be parallel to its axis). The defect is reduced to an unimportant magnitude by employing one fixed and one movable compensating plate which consequently has to be moved through a very small angle by means of a micrometer screw arrangement.

To obtain maximum sensitivity it is obviously desirable to employ long tubes since a given change in refractive index will produce a relatively large change in total optical path. However, the length of the tube that can be used is limited by the uniformity that can be achieved in the fluid contained therein. It is necessary to use relatively short tubes for liquids. The instrument has been used for checking the purity of a gas (e.g. of air in a coal mine) and is used in chemical analysis.

In the Rayleigh refractometer use is made of the Fraunhofer double slit diffraction pattern but the important fringes in that pattern are those associated with the interference between disturbances from the two slits. As pointed out in § 10–11, the purpose of the lenses is the concentration of the light into a single area so that the interference fringes are bright.

11–15. Further Discussion of Fraunhofer Patterns

Consider the arrangement shown in Fig. 11–20. If the lenses have very wide apertures and there is no diffracting screen at Σ, the plane wave W gives an approximate point focus on the axis. If a diffracting screen containing a slit aperture is interposed at Σ so as to limit the extent of the plane wave, a Fraunhofer pattern is formed on the receiving screen S. Now each point along the ξ' axis is the focus of a plane wave entering L_2. That is to say, when the incident plane wave W is limited by the slit Σ, it becomes equivalent to a continuous distribution of plane waves travelling in all directions (θ) through L_2, the relative amplitudes being given by the relative amplitudes on the receiving screen. The

Fig. 11–20. Analysis of Fraunhofer pattern.

complex amplitude at a point on the ξ' axis defined by the angle θ is given (from § 11–3) by

$$\psi(\theta) = \int_{\Sigma} a e^{ikx \sin \theta} \, dx.$$

If the disturbance passing through the slit aperture is not a uniform plane wave but is a function of x, then a is replaced by $f(x)$. Since $f(x)$ is zero outside the aperture of the slit, one can extend the limits of integration to $\pm\infty$. Now, since θ defines position in the diffraction pattern, one can put $(\sin\theta)/\lambda = u'$ and use u' in place of ξ' as "co-ordinate" in the image plane.

One can then write

$$\psi(u') = \int_{-\infty}^{+\infty} f(x)e^{2\pi i u' x}dx. \quad \ldots \ldots \quad (11\text{--}21a)$$

From §6–6 this implies

$$f(x) = \int_{-\infty}^{+\infty} \psi(u')e^{-2\pi i u' x}du'. \quad \ldots \ldots \quad (11\text{--}21b)$$

That is to say, for a Fraunhofer pattern the *pattern function* is the Fourier transform of the *aperture function* and vice versa. This means that if one thinks of $f(x)$ as being analysed into (synthesized from) simple harmonic Fourier components, the amplitude at u' in the image plane gives the amplitude of the component of $f(x)$ of spatial frequency u'. Alternatively, if $\psi(u')$, the distribution of light across the image plane, is analysed into spatial frequencies, $f(x)$ is the amplitude of the component of frequency x.

For a wave limited in two dimensions the results are

$$\psi(u',v') = \int\!\!\!\int_{-\infty}^{+\infty} f(x,y)e^{2\pi i(u'x+v'y)}dxdy, \quad \ldots \quad (11\text{--}22a)$$

$$f(x,y) = \int\!\!\!\int_{-\infty}^{+\infty} \psi(u',v')e^{-2\pi i(u'x+v'y)}du'dv'. \quad \ldots \quad (11\text{--}22b)$$

It was seen in Chapter VI that if one has a wave train of finite *length* it can be analysed into a continuous distribution of simple harmonic waves with all *frequencies* between $\pm\infty$. The above analysis shows that if a wave is limited in *width* it can be analysed into a continuous distribution of waves in all *directions*. In the former case the frequency distribution is narrower if the wave train is longer, and in the latter case the angular spread becomes smaller if the wave is wider.

In all the arrangements discussed so far there has been a uniform disturbance across the diffracting aperture, i.e. $f(x,y)$ has been a constant. $f(x,y)$ can be made to vary across the aperture by inserting a screen whose absorption and optical thickness varies from point to point. It is obvious that if this is done the diffraction pattern is altered. In particular, it is possible to decrease the intensities of the subsidiary maxima in the slit images formed by a spectroscope. The process is known as *apodization*. (See also pages 269, 308, and 332.)

CHAPTER XII

DIFFRACTION GRATINGS

ANY periodic arrangement of diffracting bodies may be referred to as a diffraction grating. One of the simplest types of grating consists of a number of identical equidistant slit apertures in an opaque screen. This is seldom reproduced in practice although the early gratings used by Fraunhofer were of this type. These consisted of a grid formed by winding fine wires on two parallel screw threads. Present-day gratings usually consist of equidistant diamond rulings on a plate or mirror or a replica of such a ruled grating. When the elements of the grating are narrow slits, they act as sources of disturbances and, since they are narrow, they radiate uniformly. When the grating elements are not narrow slits the elements can still be regarded as sources but in this case they do not radiate uniformly. The result is that maxima of almost exactly the same shape are formed in the same parts of the pattern as before but with different relative intensities. Thus many of the important properties of diffraction gratings (e.g. dispersion, resolving power, etc.) are associated with the interference effects between disturbances from corresponding parts of the separate elements. That is, they are concerned with the periodicity of the diffracting elements rather than the shape of the individual elements. Most of these results can be deduced without extensive mathematical analysis. For example, it is not necessary to find the complete form of the intensity distribution in the pattern. It is therefore useful to begin by discussing, in simple terms, a grating which consists of a number of equidistant very narrow slits.

12–1. Gratings with Narrow Apertures

Light from the monochromatic slit source S [Fig. 12–1(a)] is collimated by the lens L_1 and is incident normally on the grating G which consists of N very

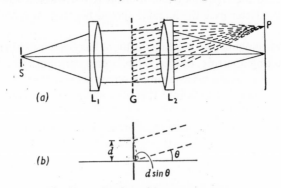

Fig. 12–1. Grating with narrow apertures.

narrow slits parallel to S and distance d apart. The Fraunhofer diffraction pattern is formed in the focal plane of the lens L_2. It will be seen from (b) that the phase difference at P between disturbances from adjacent slits is

$$\delta = \frac{2\pi}{\lambda}(d \sin \theta),$$

and when this is a multiple of 2π, the disturbances from all slits interfere constructively at P. There is therefore a maximum at P when

$$\frac{2\pi}{\lambda}(d \sin \theta) = p2\pi \text{ (p an integer)},$$

i.e. for a maximum

$$d \sin \theta = p\lambda. \quad . \quad . \quad . \quad . \quad . \quad . \quad . \quad (12\text{–}1)$$

For these and only these values of θ, the disturbances from all slits are exactly in phase at P. Hence there cannot be other maxima as strong as these; they are therefore called the *principal maxima*. Since the slits are narrow, the amplitude from each slit is independent of θ so that all the principal maxima have the same intensity. Now (12–1) does not contain N so that, *for a given slit separation*, the positions of the principal maxima are independent of the number of slits in the grating.

(a)

If the contributions of the slits are compounded by employing the usual graphical method, it is easy to show that the maxima become narrower as the number of slits is increased. At the centre of a principal maximum the vibration polygon is simply a straight line whereas a short distance away from the centre each vector is inclined to the previous one, the polygon being equiangular. In Fig. 12–2 (*a*) and (*b*) show the vibration polygons at a principal maximum and

(b)

Fig. 12–2. Vibration polygons near maxima.

at a short distance away for $N=5$ and $N=10$ respectively. The angle between successive vectors is δ, the phase difference between disturbances from adjacent slits. For a given movement away from the centre of a maximum, δ is the same in each case if the slit separations are the same. In the figure, the lengths of the vectors have been adjusted to give principal maxima of equal intensity. It will be seen that when one moves away from the maximum, the resultant R is smaller for $N=10$ than it is for $N=5$. The actual angular width of a principal maximum is easily found by locating the adjacent minima. The vibration polygon is a straight line when $\delta = p2\pi$. This corresponds to the principal maximum of order p and one has, at the centre of this principal maximum,

$$\frac{2\pi}{\lambda}(d \sin \theta) = p2\pi.$$

Now as one increases the angle between adjacent sides, a polygon of N sides first becomes a closed figure when the angle reaches $2\pi/N$. Therefore, at a minimum adjacent to a principal maximum

$$\delta = \frac{2\pi}{\lambda}(d \sin \theta') = p \cdot 2\pi + \frac{2\pi}{N}.$$

Thus the increment in sin θ in going from the centre of a principal maximum to the first minimum is given by

$$\sin \theta' - \sin \theta = \frac{\lambda}{Nd},$$

and the corresponding value of $d\theta$ is half the angular width of the maximum. Since $d(\sin \theta) = \cos \theta \, d\theta$ one has

$$d\theta = \frac{\lambda}{Nd \cos \theta} . \qquad \cdots \cdots \cdots \quad (12\text{--}2)$$

Fig. 12–3. Intensity distributions with narrow slits.

Minima also occur when the angle between successive vectors is $q.(2\pi/N)$ (q an integer) since, in this case, the vibration polygon executes q complete turns and is a closed figure. δ has the value $p.2\pi+q(2\pi/N)$, and when $q=N$ one has the principal maximum of the next order—given by $\delta=(p+1)2\pi$. $q=0$ represents the original maximum so that $(N-1)$ values of q represent minima between adjacent principal maxima.

Between these various minima lie the *secondary maxima*; they are obviously $(N-2)$ in number and their intensities will be calculated later (§ 12–7). The complete intensity distributions for various values of N are shown in Fig. 12–3, the scale being adjusted to make the intensities of the principal maxima equal. Photographs of the patterns are shown in Plate II(d–h). In the latter case slits of finite width were used and, as will be shown in § 12–8, the effect is to impose a slow variation of intensity across the pattern. That is to say, the intensity curves of Fig. 12–3 are contained within a slowly varying envelope as has already been proved in the case of two slits (see Chapter XI). As shown in § 12–8, the 4th, 8th, 12th, etc., orders are missing in Plate II because the opaque parts of the gratings were three times as wide as the transparent parts.

In Fig. 12–3 and Plate II, the separation of adjacent slits is the same in all cases and it is seen at once that, as pointed out above, the principal maxima occur in the same places for all values of N but become more narrow as N increases. Other results derived above and easily seen from the figure are that there are $(N-1)$ minima and $(N-2)$ secondary maxima between adjacent principal maxima. It can also be seen that as N increases most of the secondary maxima become much weaker (see § 12–7). In most gratings of practical importance N is very large and most of the secondary maxima are completely unobservable.

When N is large, the more interesting way of considering the effect on the patterns of increasing N is to make *the separation of the first and last slits constant*. This corresponds to taking a grating of fixed overall size and considering the effect of increasing the number of slits per centimetre. Equations (12–1) and (12–2) then show that as N increases the principal maxima become more widely spaced but retain the same width. It is important to realize that the *sharpness of the principal maxima depends only upon the total width of the grating* and not upon the number of lines per centimetre nor upon the shape of the individual diffracting elements.

12–2. Intensity Distribution near Principal Maxima

The separation of the first and last slits is $(N-1)d$ which, when N is large, approximates to Nd. It will be seen from equation (12–2) that for low orders when $\cos\theta \approx 1$, the angular width of each principal maximum approximates to that of the central maximum for a single slit aperture whose width is equal to the overall width of the grating. When N is large, the intensities of the nearby secondary maxima also approach those for a single aperture as wide as the complete grating. The reason for this is easily understood if one considers the vibration polygon for a large value of N. In the region of a principal maximum, this will approximate, in general shape, to the continuous vibration curve corresponding to the single aperture and will obviously yield similar maxima and minima. For example, at the centre of a principal maximum for a grating, and at the centre of the pattern for a single aperture, the vibration curve is a straight line, and in each case the polygon curls up as one moves away from the centre of the maximum. As one recedes from a principal maximum of a grating, one would therefore expect to get maxima and minima resembling those of the single aperture, but there is nothing in the latter case which corresponds to the subsequent increase in the intensities of the secondary maxima and the eventual appearance of another principal maximum. This is because, for a continuous vibration curve, there is nothing corresponding to the way in which discrete vectors become parallel when their phase difference is $p2\pi$. Consequently, the continuous vibration curve is never again a straight line. For large values of N, the various slits give contributions in a manner similar to the infinitesimal strips of the single aperture. For example, it was shown in § 11–1 that with a single aperture the first minimum occurs where the contributions from strips at the extreme edges of the aperture are 2π out of phase, i.e. when the optical paths from the edges of the aperture to the field point in the pattern differ by λ. Now when the first and last slits of the grating yield a path difference of λ, one has $(N-1)d \sin \theta = \lambda$. The discussion in § 12–1 shows that the minimum adjacent to the zero order principal maximum actually occurs when $Nd \sin \theta = \lambda$. The disagreement between these results is small when N is large, and the error in the present result is due to the fact that when N is odd the contribution of one slit goes unbalanced, whilst when N is even there is no slit exactly at the centre of the grating. When N is small, the analogy given above obviously breaks down, and when N is moderately large, the limited resemblance between the patterns referred to is due to the overlapping of the secondary maxima associated with neighbouring principal maxima.

12–3. Oblique Incidence. Minimum Deviation. Reflection Gratings

In § 12–1 it was assumed that the light was incident normally on the grating. Fig. 12–4 shows a collimated beam of light of wavelength λ incident at angle I on a grating with spacing d. It will be seen from the figure that the path difference introduced between disturbances passing through neighbouring slits is $d(\sin I + \sin \theta)$. But using, for θ and I, the same sign convention as that employed in geometrical optics for angles of incidence and refraction, I is negative in the figure. Therefore the angle of diffraction θ_p for the pth order principal maximum is given by

$d \sin I$ $d \sin \theta$

Fig. 12–4. Oblique incidence.

$$d(\sin \theta_p - \sin I) = p\lambda. \quad (12\text{--}3)$$

Equation (12–3) can be generalized to include the possibility of the refractive indices on the two sides of the grating being different. If these are n and n', the principal maxima are located by the equation

$$d(n' \sin \theta_p - n \sin I) = p\lambda. \quad \cdots \quad (12\text{–}4)$$

For the zero order maximum one has $p=0$ and $n' \sin \theta_0 = n \sin I$, which is Snell's law and defines the path of the direct or undiffracted light.

The light in the pth order maximum is deviated through an angle D where

$$D = \theta_p - I.$$

This reaches a maximum or minimum when $d(D) = 0$ or

$$d\theta_p - dI = 0.$$

From (12–4) one has

$$n' \cos \theta_p d\theta_p - n \cos I dI = 0,$$

so that at maximum or minimum deviation, when $n = n'$,

$$\cos I = \cos \theta_p$$

or, since both I and θ_p are acute,

$$\theta_p = \pm I.$$

The solution $\theta_p = I$ is trivial since it applies only to the zero order light where there is no diffraction. It is easily proved that for a given order, the result $\theta_p = -I$ does, in fact, correspond to a *minimum* value of D. Thus for minimum deviation the angles of incidence and diffraction must be numerically equal and

$$D_{\min} = 2\theta_p, \quad \cdots \quad \cdots \quad (12\text{–}5)$$

and, from (12–3),

$$2d \sin \left(\frac{D_{\min}}{2} \right) = p\lambda. \quad \cdots \quad (12\text{–}6)$$

Hitherto it has been assumed that the gratings are of the transmission type, i.e. light is transmitted through equally spaced slits and absorbed at all other points. The theory applies equally well to reflection gratings which reflect light from equally spaced line elements and absorb at all other points. For example, the positions of the principal maxima are given by equation (12–4) on putting $n' \equiv -n$, the usual method of converting a transmission or refraction result into one for reflection. One has,

$$d(\sin I + \sin \theta_p) = p\lambda.$$

In addition, it will be seen that for the zero order light $p=0$ and $\theta_p = -I$, which is the algebraic law of reflection with the present sign convention.

One important advantage of using reflection gratings is that they can be used for wavelengths that are absorbed by glass and other materials with which transmission gratings can be constructed.

12–4. Grating Spectra

Suppose that, in Fig. 12–5, the slit source S emits light of several discrete wavelengths. The collimated beam of light from the achromatic lens L_1 is incident on the grating G, and for each wavelength present in the source, the usual pattern is formed in the focal plane of the achromatic lens L_2. The central (zero order) maximum lies on the axis for every wavelength, but the first order maxima for the various wavelengths do not coincide. These are formed at angles defined by equation (12–3) if it is assumed that $n'=n$. In most cases of practical importance the total number of slits in the grating is sufficiently large to render the secondary maxima negligibly weak. Thus, on one side of the axis, each wavelength gives a single first order maximum, and the maxima of the several wavelengths fall alongside each other and constitute a line spectrum. It has been

Fig. 12–5. Grating spectra.

shown that each principal maximum for a diffraction grating resembles the central maximum in the Fraunhofer pattern of a single slit aperture. Therefore the lines in a diffraction grating spectrum resemble those obtained with a prism spectroscope having a rectangular aperture of width equal to the overall width of the grating. It will be seen later that prism and grating spectra differ in one important respect: they have significantly different dispersions. Each wavelength will also give a maximum in each of the higher orders so that several line spectra are formed. One refers to the first, second, third order spectra, etc.

12–5. Dispersion. Overlapping of Orders

Equation (12–3) defines the angles of diffraction for each wavelength, and on differentiating with respect to λ, the angular dispersion is at once found to be given by

$$\frac{d\theta}{d\lambda} = \frac{p}{d \cos \theta_p}. \qquad \cdot \quad \cdot \quad \cdot \quad \cdot \quad \cdot \quad \cdot \quad (12\text{--}7)$$

This gives the angular separation $\delta\theta$ of the spectral lines whose wavelengths are λ and $\lambda+\delta\lambda$.

For normal incidence higher orders correspond to larger angles of diffraction and for a given spectral region (12–7) shows that the dispersion increases with increasing order as indicated in Fig. 12–5. In a spectrum of given order θ_p increases as λ increases and (12–7) shows that the dispersion is greater in the red (longer wavelength) end of the spectrum. This contrasts with the prism spectrum where the dispersion is always greater at the blue (shorter wavelength) end (see §5–3).

In some cases one is interested in spectral lines lying sufficiently close to the axis to justify writing cos $\theta=1$. The dispersion is then constant throughout the relevant part of the spectrum. The linear dispersion in the focal plane of the lens L_2 is $dx/d\lambda$ where $x=f'\theta$ and, from equation (12–7), it follows that when θ is small

$$\frac{dx}{d\lambda} = \frac{pf'}{d},$$

or

$$x = \frac{pf'}{d}\lambda. \qquad \cdots \cdots \qquad (12\text{–}8)$$

Thus in a spectrum of any given order, the distance from the zero order image to the spectral line for wavelength λ is directly proportional to λ. A spectrum of this type, where there is a linear scale of wavelengths, is called a *normal spectrum*. A prism spectrum can be regarded as normal over only a very limited range of wavelengths.

Equation (12–7) indicates that *for a given order* the dispersion depends upon the grating interval d. However, if one wishes to compare the dispersions obtained with different gratings it is more realistic to assume that the same angles of incidence and diffraction are used and not that the same order is used. Using (12–3), equation (12–7) becomes

$$\frac{d\theta}{d\lambda} = \frac{\sin\theta_p \pm \sin I}{\lambda\cos\theta_p}, \qquad \cdots \cdots \qquad (12\text{–}7a)$$

the positive sign corresponding to a reflection grating. For the special case of a grating used in an arrangement of the Littrow type (see §§5–18 and 12–12), $I=\theta_p$ and one has

$$\frac{d\theta}{d\lambda} = \frac{2\tan I}{\lambda}. \qquad \cdots \cdots \qquad (12\text{–}7b)$$

If one wishes to use particular angles of incidence and diffraction with any particular wavelength one is restricted to certain values of d (i.e. those satisfying the equation $d(\sin\theta_p \pm \sin I)=p\lambda$), but it will be seen that the dispersion does not depend upon which of these gratings is chosen.

Within the range of wavelengths represented, the spectra of various orders are completely separated in Fig. 12–5. However, each spectrum does in fact commence on the axis for $\lambda=0$ so that, in general, the spectra of various orders overlap. For example, it will be seen at once from (12–8) that the p_1th order line

for λ_1 will coincide with the p_2th order line for λ_2 when $p_1\lambda_1=p_2\lambda_2$. The visib
spectrum extends from about 4000 angstroms to about 8000 angstroms so tha
as far as visible light is concerned, there is no overlapping of the first and secon
order grating spectra.

However, in general, one's interest is not confined to the visible region and on
may need to record the spectrum photographically or by using some othe
physical detector such as a photo-cell or thermopile. There is then no colou
discrimination and if two or more spectra overlap it may be difficult to identif
the various spectral lines. In a situation of this kind it is important to know th
free spectral range $\Delta\lambda$ lying between successive orders of any given spectra
line. If the source radiates over a wider spectral range one can employ auxiliar
apparatus (such as a filter, a prism, or a second grating) to prevent overlappin
by arranging that only the range of wavelengths $\Delta\lambda$ is incident on the gratin$
The spectral range is such that the $(p+1)$th order of λ coincides with the pt
order of $\lambda+\Delta\lambda$ so that one has

$$d(\sin\theta_p\pm\sin I)=(p+1)\lambda=p(\lambda+\Delta\lambda).$$

Hence

$$\Delta\lambda=\frac{\lambda}{p},$$

as for the Fabry-Perot instruments. In terms of wave numbers ($\nu=1/\lambda$) one ha

$$\Delta\nu=\frac{1}{\lambda}-\frac{1}{\lambda+\Delta\lambda}=\frac{\Delta\lambda}{\lambda(\lambda+\Delta\lambda)}.$$

(One cannot proceed as in §9–3 because the spectral range of a grating is no
small.) One has

$$\Delta\nu=\frac{1}{p(\lambda+\Delta\lambda)}=\frac{1}{d(\sin\theta_p\pm\sin I)},$$

or, with a Littrow system,

$$\Delta\nu=\frac{1}{2d\sin I}.$$

It will be shown in the next section that the resolving power is determined by
the total width of the grating and not by the interval d, so that an increase in the
resolving power (decrease in resolving limit) does not cause a decrease in the free
spectral range.

12–6. Resolving Power

As explained earlier, the chromatic resolving power of an instrument at wave
length λ is defined as $\lambda/\delta\lambda$ where $\delta\lambda$ is the wavelength difference between fringe$
or spectral lines when they are just resolved. Since, when N is large, the lines in
a grating spectrum closely resemble those of a prism spectrum, it is possible to
use the same criterion for resolution. The criterion is that due to Rayleigh and
states that two neighbouring lines will be just resolved when the centre of one
maximum falls on the first minimum of the adjacent line, i.e. when the centres

of the maxima are separated by half the width of the lines. From equation (12–2) it follows that at the limit of resolution the angular separation of the neighbouring lines is

$$\delta\theta = \frac{\lambda}{Nd\cos\theta}$$

and this is not restricted to the case of normal incidence. From (12–7) the corresponding increment in wavelength is given by

$$\delta\lambda = \frac{d\cos\theta}{p}\cdot\delta\theta.$$

Therefore the chromatic resolving power is given by

$$\frac{\lambda}{\delta\lambda} = pN. \quad . \quad . \quad . \quad . \quad . \quad . \quad . \quad (12\text{–}9)$$

Hence in a given order the resolving power is proportional to the total number of slits or, for gratings of the same overall width, proportional to the number of slits per centimetre. The resolving limit is given by

$$\delta\nu = \nu\cdot\frac{\delta\lambda}{\lambda} = \frac{1}{\lambda pN}.$$

Equation (12–3) shows that for a given wavelength and a given angle of incidence, the order corresponding to a particular angle of diffraction is given by

$$p = \frac{d\,(\sin\theta_p - \sin I)}{\lambda}$$

and (12–9) shows that the resolving power is then given by

$$\frac{\lambda}{\delta\lambda} = \frac{Nd\,(\sin\theta_p - \sin I)}{\lambda}.$$

Thus for a given wavelength the resolving power *for a given angle of incidence and diffraction* depends on Nd, the total overall width of the grating, but not upon the number of slits contained in that width. For coarser gratings a given angle of diffraction corresponds to a higher order and the overlapping of orders associated with the higher order spectra make such gratings less convenient for many purposes.

On putting $-I=\theta=90°$, it will be seen that the resolving power of a grating cannot exceed $2Nd/\lambda$, i.e. twice the width of the grating measured in wavelengths. In practice the intensity would be vanishingly small under such conditions.

For a reflection grating used in a Littrow mounting one has

$$\frac{\lambda}{\delta\lambda} = \frac{2Nd\sin I}{\lambda},$$

and if the grating is in a medium of index n this becomes

$$\frac{\lambda}{\delta\lambda} = \frac{2Ndn\sin I}{\lambda}.$$

That is, the resolving power is proportional to the index of the medium in which it is mounted.

12–7. Intensity Distribution in the Pattern for Narrow Slits

The positions and widths of the principal maxima have already been discussed in §§ 12–1 and 12–2. An expression will now be derived for the intensity distribution throughout the Fraunhofer pattern for a grating with narrow slit apertures. It will then be shown how it is possible to modify these results to allow for the finite width of the apertures. The theory will then be extended to cover gratings which do not consist simply of apertures in opaque screens.

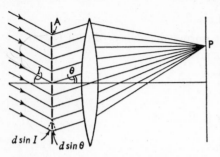

Fig. 12–6. Paths of superposed disturbances.

In Fig. 12–6 a collimated beam of light is incident at angle I on a grating consisting of very narrow slits which may be assumed to diffract equally in all directions. When the angle of diffraction is θ, the phase difference at P between disturbances from successive slits is (since I is negative in the figure)

$$\delta = \frac{2\pi}{\lambda} d(\sin\theta - \sin I).$$

If one takes the first slit, A, to give a disturbance of unit amplitude and zero phase at P, the complex amplitudes of the disturbances from the adjacent slits are $e^{-i\delta}$, $e^{-2i\delta}$, ... If there are N slits, the complex amplitude of the resultant is given by

$$z = 1 + e^{-i\delta} + e^{-2i\delta} + \ldots + e^{-(N-1)\delta}.$$

(See § 6–3.)

i.e.

$$z = \frac{1 - e^{-iN\delta}}{1 - e^{-i\delta}}$$

and the resultant intensity at p is given by

$$\begin{aligned}
\text{Intensity} &= z\bar{z} \\
&= \left(\frac{1 - e^{-iN\delta}}{1 - e^{-i\delta}}\right)\left(\frac{1 - e^{+iN\delta}}{1 - e^{+i\delta}}\right) \\
&= \frac{1 - e^{iN\delta} - e^{-iN\delta} + 1}{1 - e^{i\delta} - e^{-i\delta} + 1} \\
&= \frac{1 - \cos N\delta}{1 - \cos \delta} \\
&= \frac{\sin^2\left(\dfrac{N\delta}{2}\right)}{\sin^2\left(\dfrac{\delta}{2}\right)} \\
&= \frac{\sin^2\left(\dfrac{\pi N d(\sin\theta - \sin I)}{\lambda}\right)}{\sin^2\left(\dfrac{\pi d(\sin\theta - \sin I)}{\lambda}\right)} = \frac{\sin^2 N\beta}{\sin^2\beta}, \text{ (say)}, \quad (12\text{–}10)
\end{aligned}$$

where $\beta = \pi d(\sin\theta - \sin I)/\lambda$, or $(\pi d\sin\theta)/\lambda$ for normal incidence.

It has already been shown that for normal incidence the so-called principal maxima occur at values of θ given by $\sin \theta = p\lambda/d$. For these values of θ both numerator and denominator of (12–10) are zero so that the fraction is indeterminate. However, at points very close to the principal maxima the quantities $(\pi d \sin \theta)/\lambda$ and $(\pi N d \sin \theta)/\lambda$ are small.

$$\therefore \quad \text{Intensity} \rightarrow \left[\frac{(\pi N d \sin \theta)/\lambda}{(\pi d \sin \theta)/\lambda} \right]^2 = N^2 \text{ as } \sin \theta \rightarrow \frac{p\lambda}{d}.$$

Thus to normalize (12–10) to give unit intensity at the centre of the principal maxima, it is necessary to multiply by $1/N^2$.

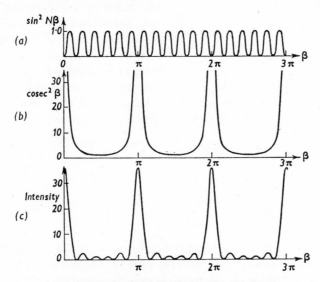

Fig. 12–7. Intensity distribution for six slits.

The numerator of (12–10) falls to zero more frequently than the denominator, giving minima between the principal maxima. Between these minima lie the secondary maxima. Fig. 12–7 gives an indication of the relative intensities of the various maxima for a grating having six slits. Fig. 12–7(a) shows the function $\sin^2 N\beta$ and (b) shows $1/(\sin^2 \beta)$ (i.e. $\operatorname{cosec}^2 \beta$). The intensity at any point is then given by the product of the corresponding ordinates. This resultant is shown in (c). (It is again seen that at the principal maxima the product is "zero $\times$ infinity" and is indeterminate.) Fig. 12–3 showed the intensity distribution in the pattern for a number of values of N, the intensities being adjusted to make those of the principal maxima equal.

12–8. Wide Slits and Other Diffracting Elements

In Fig. 12–8 G is a grating consisting of a number of apertures of finite width a in an opaque screen. Parallel light is again incident at angle I. To calculate the variation in intensity in the image plane along a line in the plane of the diagram, it is convenient to divide each aperture into a number of very narrow strips perpendicular to the plane of the diagram. For a given point P in the image plane, the phase difference between disturbances from *corresponding strips o* *adjacent apertures* is again $(2\pi/\lambda)d(\sin \theta - \sin I)$, where $d = a + b$ and b is th width of the opaque portion separating adjacent apertures. Consequently, thi

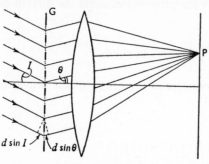

Fig. 12-8. Wide slits.

is also the phase difference between th *resultant* disturbances from adjacen apertures. Now it follows from the dis cussion of § 11-2 that at any point P i the image plane the resultant amplitud due to a single slit aperture of widt a is $(\sin\alpha)/\alpha$, where $\alpha = \pi a(\sin \theta - \sin I)/\lambda$ On summing the contributions of N such apertures, the resultant amplitud is $(\sin \alpha)/\alpha$ times the resultant for N very narrow slits (the resultant agai being normalized to give unit intensity a

the centre of the pattern). The resultant intensity for narrow slits must therefor be multiplied by $(\sin\alpha/\alpha)^2$ to give the intensity for slits of finite width. That is for a grating having N slits of width a separated by opaque elements of width b

$$\text{Normalized Intensity} = \frac{1}{N^2}\left(\frac{\sin \alpha}{\alpha}\right)^2 \left(\frac{\sin N\beta}{\beta}\right)^2, \quad . \quad (12\text{-}11)$$

where

$$\alpha = \frac{\pi a(\sin \theta - \sin I)}{\lambda}, \quad \beta = \frac{\pi(a+b)(\sin \theta - \sin I)}{\lambda}.$$

Fig. 12-9 shows the intensity distribution for $N=6$. It will be seen that, as with the double slit, the effect of the first term is the appearance of the slowly varying envelope beneath which the intensity curve is contained. As before, it may be said that the first term gives the amount of light from each aperture reaching any point in the pattern and that the second term gives the result of the interference between disturbances from N apertures.

If a principal maximum, as given by the second term, coincides with a mini mum of the envelope or first term then, as for the double slit, the principa maximum of that order is absent. If it is absent for one wavelength it will be absent for all wavelengths. For example, for normal incidence the principa maxima occur at angles θ defined by

$$\frac{\sin \theta}{\lambda} = \frac{p}{(a+b)}, \quad . \quad . \quad . \quad . \quad . \quad (12\text{-}12)$$

and the minima of the envelope term occur at angles θ defined by

$$\frac{\sin \theta}{\lambda} = \frac{q}{a}. \quad . \quad . \quad . \quad . \quad . \quad (12\text{-}13)$$

Therefore when

$$\frac{p}{a+b} = \frac{q}{a} \ (p \text{ and } q \text{ integers})$$

the principal maximum of order p is absent. Thus when $a=b$ the missing orders are given by $p=2q$. That is, all the even order spectra are absent from the pattern for a grating whose transparent and opaque elements have equal width.

Similarly, if $a=\frac{1}{2}b$, $p=3q$ defines the missing orders and every third order is missing; in Fig. 12–9 and Plate II(d–h) $a=\frac{1}{3}b$ and every fourth order is seen to be missing. It will be seen that an order is missing if the disturbances from corresponding parts of adjacent apertures are in phase when disturbances from the extreme edges of a single aperture are in phase. (See also § 11–10.)

The wire gratings used by Fraunhofer were transmission gratings, and consisted of apertures separated by opaque elements. Most present-day gratings are reflection gratings, and are aluminized plastic replicas of master gratings ruled on aluminium coatings on glass plates. For many of the older ruled gratings and replicas the ruled grooves are simply diffuse scattering elements and the intervals between them correspond respectively to the perfectly transparent or reflecting elements of a transmission or reflection grating. With a grating of this type a large proportion of the energy falls in the zero order maximum where there is no dispersion. It would obviously be an advantage if a larger proportion of the light was diffracted into orders other than zero since the spectra would become brighter and more easily examined. Now, as remarked above, the first term in (12–11) is characteristic of each separate element of the grating, and the second is associated with the interference between disturbances from different elements and is characteristic of the periodicity of the rulings. Whatever the nature of the separate elements, provided they are all the same, the phase difference between disturbances from corresponding parts of adjacent elements remains equal to $2\pi d(\sin\theta - \sin I)/\lambda$. As before, this will also be the phase difference between the *resultant* disturbances from adjacent elements. The third term in (12–11) gives the resultant of N such disturbances and will remain unchanged so that the positions of the principal maxima will be as before. The relative intensities of these maxima will be determined by the amount of light they receive from each element of the grating. Thus, if the elements diffract the incident light differently from a single slit aperture, the second (envelope) term of (12–11) will be changed since it gives the diffraction pattern for one element; the relative intensities of the spectra of different orders will then be altered. In Fig. 12–9 this corresponds to a displacement of the envelope so that its maximum occurs at an order other than zero. It would be an advantage if the central maximum of the envelope were made fairly sharp so that only one or two orders fell within it; this would maximize the brightness of the favoured orders. Gratings of this kind are referred to as *blazed* gratings and the possibilities of such gratings were first pointed out by Rayleigh. It should be noted that the dispersion and resolving power will not be affected by the structure of the grating elements since these quantities are determined by the third (interference) term. (The envelope is not sufficiently steep to make an appreciable difference to the shape of the individual principal maxima.)

It is important to realize that the periodic interruptions or distortions imposed across a wavefront by a grating are not present on the component wavefronts into which the transmitted light is resolved. The discussion of § 11–15 shows that the modulated wavefront emerging from the grating is equivalent to an angular

Fig. 12–9. Intensity distribution for grating with six wide slits ($a = \frac{1}{3}b$).

distribution of uniform wavefronts, each corresponding to a particular point in the pattern formed by the grating.

If, in Fig. 12–8, the grating is translated in its own plane the pattern in the focal plane of the lens remains stationary. The regular variations of refractive index in a medium through which an ultrasonic wave is passing constitute a moving grating of this kind, and a stationary pattern can be observed. (A stationary grating could be produced by setting up a standing wave pattern.) The acoustic grating is not confined to a plane such as G in Fig. 12–8 since the ultrasonic beam has finite width and, although it can be seen that the beam will act as a grating, an exact analysis of the intensity distribution in the pattern is difficult.

12–9. Blazed Gratings, Echelons, Echelettes, Echelles

The fundamental need for blazed gratings has been explained above. What is required is that each groove in the grating should direct as much light as possible into one of the grating spectra, and the space between the rulings should be as small as possible since this plane transmitting or reflecting surface contributes maximum intensity to the zero order image. It is now possible to rule a grating having a pre-determined groove form that concentrates most of the diffracted light within a narrow range of directions.

Fig. 12–10. Grating with wedge elements.

A grating having the form shown in Fig. 12–10 will be blazed with the maximum possible efficiency, maximum intensity occurring in the direction corresponding to specular reflection from the *face of each wedge*. (It is specular reflection from the plane of the unruled blank that gives a maximum intensity in the zero order.) One could, of course, utilize reflection from the shallow face of each wedge, corresponding to relatively small angles of incidence and diffraction and hence to a lower order, lower dispersion, and lower resolving power, but greater free spectral range. The angle of inclination of the face of the groove that is used is called the *blaze angle*; it is equal to the angle of incidence and diffraction when the grating is used in a Littrow mounting.

In the early years of grating spectroscopy it was impossible to produce a ruled grating with accurately spaced, identical, smooth, wedge-shaped grooves of this form, but in 1898 Michelson suggested that a coarse grating of this type could be produced by arranging a number of glass plates in step formation as shown in Fig. 12–11, the steps being silvered. It is convenient to use a *reflection echelon* grating of this type in a Littrow arrangement where the light is incident on each step nearly normally as shown. When the suggestion was originally made by Michelson in 1898, the manufacture of such a grating was held up by the difficulty of placing the plates in contact without unequal films of air between them. Such gaps would introduce unequal phase differences between the various adjacent disturbances. By using a *transmission echelon*, this difficulty was overcome although the order of interference was reduced. The arrangement is shown in Fig. 12–12. Collimated light passes normally through the echelon and each step acts as an aperture of width s and produces a single aperture pattern centred on the direction of normal transmission. In the focal plane of the lens L, this pattern provides the envelope beneath which there is formed the pattern resulting from the interference between disturbances passing through different steps. In

Fig. 12-11. Reflection echelon.

the direction of normal transmission, the path difference between the disturbances passing through adjacent steps is $(n_{glass}-n_{air})t$ whereas, for the reflection echelon, it would be $2n_{air}t$, or between 3 and 4 times greater. It will be seen that if, in the transmission echelon, there is an extra large air film between one pair of plates, an equal path is added to each disturbance so that the phase *differences* are unaffected. The width of the grating which the reflection echelon constitutes is the length of the dotted line in Fig. 12–11, and this will be somewhat longer

Fig. 12-12. Transmission echelon.

than Nt where N is the number of plates and t the thickness of each. (s is usually about 1 mm., and t about 1 cm.) Thus a grating of 40 plates has width over 40 cm.—wider than any ruled grating which has been produced. For normal incidence and diffraction from each step, the order is $2d/\lambda$ or roughly 40,000 for green light; with 40 plates the resolving power is $1 \cdot 6 \times 10^6$. Williams subsequently (1926) produced a satisfactory reflection echelon by wringing together quartz plates. With such high orders the overlapping of orders must be overcome by employing an auxiliary dispersion system to isolate a small range of wavelengths. The performance and use of the echelon will be discussed further below.

The blaze of an echelon is the most efficient possible and it is very difficult to produce ruled gratings with an efficiency approaching this. The first successful attempt to rule a blazed grating was by R. W. Wood in 1910. Initially, he produced gratings with between 2000 and 3600 lines per inch with a blaze angle of about 20° (see §12–13). With visible light these gave very little energy in the zero order but distributed most of the light in a group of orders—typically from the 12th to the 16th. These gratings were more suitable for the infra-red and, for a selected wavelength, could be blazed to give most of the energy in the first order. Wood called these gratings *echelettes* because their properties were intermediate between those of the classical unblazed ruled gratings and the echelons. Wood subsequently ruled gratings with up to 15,000 lines per inch blazed for the first order in the visible region.

It should be noted that a grating is blazed for particular angles of incidence and diffraction—for a single angle of incidence if it is assumed that a Littrow mounting is used. When, as in the echelon, there is no "space" between adjacent grooves, one has the sharpest possible envelope (maximum blaze efficiency). It is shown below that the central maximum of the envelope then contains either one or two orders for any given wavelength so that the blaze of the grating embraces the whole free spectral range, and hence all wavelengths, since successive ranges are superposed. (The blaze will, of course, be a maximum for those wavelengths falling at the centre of the envelope.)

In recent years there has been a very great improvement in the quality of ruled gratings—both in constancy of spacing and in groove form (see §12–13). In particular, it has proved possible to rule gratings that approach closely the ideal form of Fig. 12–10 where the steep side of the groove is utilized. These gratings, known as *echelles*, have the properties of an echelon with a large number of thin plates. Echelles have been ruled with from about one hundred to several thousand lines per inch. It is, perhaps, worth emphasizing that in principle echelles, echelettes, and echelons, are simply efficiently blazed gratings, echelons being the extreme form. The distinction between modern echelles and Wood's echelettes is that the echelles utilize the steep side of the wedge whereas the echelettes used the shallow side.

The echelon gratings are very difficult to manufacture and the transmission echelon must now be considered obsolescent since the Fabry-Perot etalon can give better resolution at a much smaller cost. Alternatively, the interferometer can do the work of several different transmission echelons—again with less expense. Both the reflection and transmission echelon require a high quality slit. On the other hand, the reflection echelon is the only existing high resolution instrument that can be used over the whole spectral range from infra-red to ultra-violet—it is not limited by the transmission of the material of the plate. In both echelons, the plates must be figured very accurately although for the reflection echelon the homogeneity of the material is unimportant. For the latter instrument, fused silica is usually employed for the plates. This has a comparatively high thermal conductivity and a low thermal expansion and can therefore be given a very good polish. In addition, these thermal properties facilitate the attainment of thermal equilibrium when the echelon is in use. As mentioned in the discussion above, the plates of a reflection echelon must be wrung together; the contact is improved by heating. A considerable saving in material is effected by employing identical plates which are aligned as indicated by Fig. 12–13. After mounting, the front surfaces of the plates are aluminized. In

Fig. 12-13.
Equal plates in echelon.

principle, the reflection echelon is similar to any other grating and the dispersion and resolving power are given by the usual formulae. In Fig. 12–14 the usual grating interval is d and the width and depth of each step is s and t respectively. For a collimated beam incident at angle I (defined in the usual way), the path difference between disturbances from corresponding points in adjacent steps for an angle of diffraction θ is seen from the figure to be given by the usual value

$$d(\sin \theta + \sin I).$$

Thus for a principal maximum

$$n_{\text{air}}\, d(\sin \theta_p + \sin I) = p\lambda, \quad \ldots \ldots \quad (12\text{–}14)$$

where p is an integer and λ is the wavelength in a vacuum. Since s is fairly large (e.g. 1 mm.), the light diffracted from such a grating is concentrated in the region

Fig. 12–14. Reflection echelon.

corresponding to specular reflection from each step. Thus for light incident normally on each step face, the angle ϕ will be small for all cases of practical importance. Now, from the figure, taking all the angles as positive for simplicity, one has

$$\theta = I - \phi,$$

$$\therefore \quad \sin \theta = \sin I \cos \phi - \cos I \sin \phi.$$

In addition, one has $\sin I = t/d$ and $\cos I = s/d$ and, putting $\cos \phi = 1$ and $\sin \phi = \phi$ since ϕ is small, (12–14) becomes

$$n_{\text{air}}\, (2t - \phi s) = p\lambda. \quad \ldots \ldots \quad (12\text{–}15)$$

Alternatively, it follows at once from the figure that the geometrical path difference is given by $t + AB = t + t \cos \phi - s \sin \phi = 2t - s\phi$ if ϕ is small. Ignoring the dispersion of air, the angular dispersion is given by

$$\frac{d\phi}{d\lambda} = \frac{p}{n_{\text{air}} s} = \frac{2t}{\lambda s} \text{ at } \phi = 0, \quad \ldots \ldots \quad (12\text{–}16)$$

which on putting $\cos \theta = \cos I = s/d$, follows at once from the usual value

$d\theta/d\lambda = (p/d\cos\theta)(1/n_{\text{air}})$ obtained from (12–14). Similarly, from either (12–14) or (12–15), one has

$$\frac{d\phi}{dp} = \frac{\lambda}{sn_{\text{air}}}$$

so that, putting $dp=1$, one has, for the angle between successive orders,

$$\delta\phi = \frac{\lambda}{sn_{\text{air}}}, \qquad \cdots \cdots \quad (12\text{–}17)$$

and from (12–16) the spectral range $\varDelta\lambda$ is given, as for Fabry-Perot instruments, by

$$\varDelta\lambda = \frac{\lambda}{p} = \frac{\lambda^2}{2tn_{\text{air}}}. \qquad \cdots \cdots \quad (12\text{–}18)$$

As in any other grating, the resolving power is given by the product of the order and the number of grating elements. While the latter is small (e.g. 40), the order is large (e.g. for a plate thickness of 7 mm. p is approximately 34,000 at $\phi=0$ for $\lambda4000$). Thus, as pointed out above, the resolving power is very large. The resolving limit is given by

$$dv = \frac{vd\lambda}{\lambda} = \frac{1}{\lambda pN} = \frac{1}{2tNn_{\text{air}}}, \qquad \cdots \cdots \quad (12\text{–}19)$$

and (ignoring the dispersion of the air) is therefore independent of the wavelength. It was shown in §9–3 that one has a similar result for Fabry-Perot instruments, the effective value of N being of the same order of magnitude as that used in echelons. Thus, for comparable resolution, the instruments have similar spectral ranges. When comparing results it must be remembered that in Chapter IX λ is the wavelength in air. In practice, the errors of figure of the echelon plates are larger fractions of a wavelength in the short wavelength region. That is, the resolution deteriorates (resolving limit increases) as the wavelength is decreased and does not remain constant as indicated by the above equation. For a transmission echelon $2tn_{\text{air}}$ is replaced by $t(n_{\text{glass}}-n_{\text{air}})$ so that the order is smaller and the dispersion and resolving power reduced. dv depends upon n_{glass} and therefore is no longer independent of λ.

As usual, the principal maxima as given by (12–14) and (12–15) are contained beneath the envelope corresponding to the diffraction pattern for one element of the grating. Here one has, by reflection, the pattern for a single aperture of width s, and for normal incidence the pattern will be centred on the normal to the step face. The first minima will therefore be given by the usual formula $\sin\phi=\pm\lambda/s$ or, in terms of the wavelength *in vacuo* (remembering that ϕ is small),

$$\phi = \pm\frac{\lambda}{n_{\text{air}}\,s}. \qquad \cdots \cdots \quad (12\text{–}20)$$

Now the angular separation of the principal maxima is $(\lambda/n_{\text{air}}s)$ so that there is room for only two principal maxima in the central maximum of the envelope. In general, these will fall in positions such as those indicated by Fig. 12–15(a).

When $2tn_{air}$ is an integral number (p) of wavelengths, the line of order p is central and is the only line observed since the adjacent lines coincide with minima of the envelope; one speaks of the *single-order position* [Fig. 12–15(b)]. When $2tn_{air}=(p+\frac{1}{2})\lambda$, one has the *symmetrical position*; two lines of equal intensity are observed at $\phi=\pm\lambda/2n_{air}\,s$ [Fig. 12–15(c)].

(a)   (b)   (c)

Fig. 12–15. Principal maxima with echelon.

With a transmission echelon one can change from the single order to the symmetrical position by a slight rotation of the echelon since this moves the lines but not the envelope. With a reflection instrument it is more convenient to effect the transformation by changing the air pressure in the chamber in which the echelon is mounted. This changes the optical path $2n_{air}t$ until it is $p\lambda$ or $(p+\frac{1}{2})\lambda$ as required.

Fig. 12–16. Mounting of reflection echelon.

The plan of a convenient arrangement for a reflection echelon is shown in Fig. 12–16. As shown, the high quality slit S_1 is vertical and the dispersion of the echelon either assists or opposes that of the auxiliary spectrograph whose slit S_2 is also vertical. The pressure is adjusted to give the symmetrical position of the lines and S_2 must be sufficiently wide to admit two orders. By changing the direction of the dispersion of the echelon, one can decide whether a satellite line is on the long or short wavelength side of the main line. For a spectrum rich in lines, it is necessary to make S_1 horizontal and to rotate the echelon so that its plates are horizontal and its dispersion is along the slit S_2 which can be made narrow. By adjusting the pressure one can then switch to the single-line position. If the echelon chamber is airtight, the density of the air is unaffected by temperature and, since the expansion of the fused silica echelon plates is negligible, the pattern will remain steady although the laboratory temperature may change. In this way long exposures may be given.

The use of an echelon with an auxiliary dispersion system is very similar to the use of a Fabry-Perot etalon. The auxiliary system isolates the very small spectral range to be examined in detail by the high resolution device. Owing to the large spectral range of an echelle, the combination of a coarse echelle with an auxiliary system has some special features and will be dealt with in §12–12.

12–10. The Concave Grating

By measuring the angle of incidence and diffraction for a given order, a grating ruled on a plane surface may be used to determine wavelengths if the grating spacing is known or measured with a travelling microscope. Small gratings can be used in this way if mounted on the prism table of a conventional prism spectrometer. If the wavelength of one line is known accurately, others may be determined by locating the position where the line of one order for the known wavelength falls on or near the line of another order for the unknown (e.g. the fourth order lines for wavelengths in the region of 4400 angstroms will fall near the third order sodium line, 5890 angstroms). It is possible to allow for the small separation of the lines compared in this way. In performing such an experiment, an important difficulty is encountered: the lens of the observing telescope (or camera) cannot have exactly the same focal length for all wavelengths, so that the lines to be examined cannot be exactly in focus simultaneously. This difficulty is overcome by using a concave grating. In 1882 Rowland discovered that gratings ruled on a concave spherical reflecting surface could form focused spectra without the use of lenses. There is then no chromatic aberration, and the lines of different wavelengths in overlapping orders are exactly in focus. In addition, it becomes possible to examine lines in the U.V. and I.R. regions beyond the limits of transmission of lenses. It is possible to secure a normal spectrum in which the linear separation of two lines is almost exactly proportional to the wavelength difference. Rowland's gratings were ruled on polished speculum metal but more recent reflection gratings have usually been ruled on aluminized glass plates. It is found very convenient to use concave gratings in the following manner. In Fig. 12–17 AB represents the concave spherical reflecting surface on which a grating is ruled with lines perpendicular to AB, *equidistant along the direction of the tangent at the mid-point* O. The circle whose centre is C touches the grating at O and has radius half that of the surface of the grating, i.e. the diameter of the circle is the radius of the grating. This is known as the *Rowland circle* and it is found that if the slit source is located at any point on this circle, the spectral lines of all wavelengths in all orders are in focus on the same circle. This fact is made use of in almost all methods of employing concave gratings. A brief account of the theory of the concave grating is given in the next section.

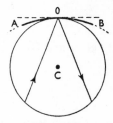

Fig. 12–17.
The Rowland circle.

In order to obtain adequate linear dispersion on the plate the radius of the grating must be large, and if it is pointed out that 21 feet has been a widely used value for the radius of curvature of the grating, it will be realized that the method of mounting the grating and auxiliary equipment is of considerable importance. Mountings for gratings are described in §12–12.

12–11. The Theory of the Concave Grating

A very extensive account of the properties of the concave grating has been given by Beutler (1945). In the simplified treatment given here the analysis is

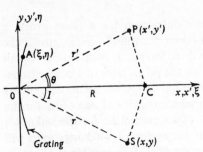

Fig. 12–18. The concave grating.

restricted to two dimensions and the aberrations will not be discussed in detail. In Fig. 12–18 O is the mid-point of the grating and is taken as the origin of co-ordinates. C is the centre of curvature of the grating and R is its radius. The point $P(x',y')$ receives light from the source $S(x,y)$ after diffraction at the grating. For light to and from O the angles of incidence and diffraction are I and θ respectively and, with the usual convention, I is negative in the figure. Consider a disturbance which is diffracted to P from the point $A(\xi,\eta)$ on the grating. Now it is assumed that the rulings of the grating are equidistant along the tangent at O (i.e. along the η axis) and that there is a diffracting element at O. Consequently, if there is a diffracting element at A, η must be an integral multiple of d, the grating interval. In other words, η/d is an integer and is the number of rulings from O to A. If there is a principal maximum at P, disturbances diffracted from adjacent elements of the grating traverse paths which differ by $p\lambda$ where p is an integer—the order. Thus disturbances via O and A have paths which differ by $(\eta/d)p\lambda$. Therefore the condition that a principal maximum is formed at P is

$$(\mathrm{SO}+\mathrm{OP})-(\mathrm{SA}+\mathrm{AP})=\left(\frac{\eta}{d}\right)p\lambda, \qquad \ldots \quad (12\text{–}21)$$

and it is now necessary to evaluate the left-hand side of this equation.

One has

$$\left. \begin{array}{l} \mathrm{SA}^2=(x-\xi)^2+(y-\eta)^2, \\ \mathrm{AP}^2=(x'-\xi)^2+(y'-\eta)^2. \end{array} \right\} \qquad \ldots \quad (12\text{–}22)$$

If $\mathrm{OS}=r$ and $\mathrm{OP}=r'$ one has

$$\left. \begin{array}{ll} x=r\cos I, & x'=r'\cos\theta, \\ y=r\sin I, & y'=r'\sin\theta. \end{array} \right\} \qquad \ldots \quad (12\text{–}23)$$

Since A lies on the circle, centre $(R,0)$, radius R, one has

$$(\xi-R)^2+\eta^2=R^2.$$

$$\therefore \quad \xi^2-2R\xi+\eta^2=0, \qquad \ldots \quad (12\text{–}24)$$

or

$$\xi=R\pm[R^2-\eta^2]^{\frac{1}{2}}$$

where only the negative sign is significant because the positive sign corresponds to points on the diametrically opposite side of the circle. On expanding the square root, one obtains

$$\xi=\frac{\eta^2}{2R}+\frac{\eta^4}{8R^3}. \qquad \ldots \quad (12\text{–}25)$$

Now (12–22) gives

$$SA^2 = x^2 + y^2 + \xi^2 + \eta^2 - 2x\xi - 2y\eta$$

or, using (12–23) and (12–24),

$$SA^2 = r^2 + 2R\xi - 2x\xi - 2y\eta.$$

Substituting for x, y, and ξ, from (12–23) and (12–25), one has

$$SA^2 = r^2 - 2r\eta \sin I + \left(1 - \frac{r \cos I}{R}\right)\left(\eta^2 + \frac{\eta^4}{4R^2} + \cdots\right)$$

$$= r^2 \left\{1 + \left[-\frac{2\eta \sin I}{r} + \frac{\eta^2}{r^2} - \frac{\eta^2 \cos I}{rR}\right]\right\} + \cdots,$$

$$\therefore \quad SA = r - \eta \sin I + \frac{\eta^2}{2r} - \frac{\eta^2 \cos I}{2R} - \frac{\eta^2 \sin^2 I}{2r}$$

$$+ \frac{\eta^3 \sin I}{2r^2} - \frac{\eta^3 \sin I \cos I}{2rR} - \frac{\eta^3 \sin^3 I}{2r^2} + \cdots,$$

where terms involving powers of η higher than the third are omitted.

$$\therefore \quad SA = r - \eta \sin I + \frac{\eta^2}{2}\left(\frac{\cos^2 I}{r} - \frac{\cos I}{R}\right) + \frac{\eta^3 \sin I}{2r}\left(\frac{\cos^2 I}{r} - \frac{\cos I}{R}\right) + \cdots.$$

Obviously AP is given by a similar expression involving r' and θ. The condition that disturbances via O and A arrive in phase at P (i.e. that there is a principal maximum at P) is obtained by substituting these values of SA and AP into equation (12–21). Remembering that SO$= r$ and OP$= r'$, one has

$$\eta(\sin I + \sin \theta) - \frac{\eta^2}{2}\left[\left(\frac{\cos^2 I}{r} - \frac{\cos I}{R}\right) + \left(\frac{\cos^2 \theta}{r'} - \frac{\cos \theta}{R}\right)\right]$$

$$- \frac{\eta^3}{2}\left[\frac{\sin I}{r}\left(\frac{\cos^2 I}{r} - \frac{\cos I}{R}\right) + \frac{\sin \theta}{r'}\left(\frac{\cos^2 \theta}{r'} - \frac{\cos \theta}{R}\right)\right] + \cdots = \left(\frac{\eta}{d}\right)p\lambda.$$

$$\cdots \quad (12\text{–}26)$$

This equation is satisfied if the first term on the left-hand side is equal to $(\eta/d)p\lambda$ and the other terms are zero. Since r, r', and R, are large compared with η, the terms on the left-hand side are in order of decreasing magnitude and, to a first order approximation, there is a maximum at P if $\eta(\sin I + \sin \theta) = (\eta/d)p\lambda$, i.e. if

$$d(\sin I + \sin \theta) = p\lambda. \quad \cdots \quad (12\text{–}27)$$

This is the usual grating equation which has already been seen to give the directions of the principal maxima for a plane reflection grating (see §12–3).

On putting $R=\infty$ in (12-26), it will be seen that the other terms become zero if $r=r'=\infty$. Thus for collimated light incident on a plane grating, the disturbances will arrive exactly in phase to give principal maxima at infinity (or in the focal plane of a lens) if (12-27) is satisfied.

For a concave grating, it will be seen that both the second and third terms of (12-26) become zero if

and
$$\left. \begin{array}{l} r=R \cos I \\ r'=R \cos \theta. \end{array} \right\} \quad \cdot \quad \cdot \quad \cdot \quad \cdot \quad \cdot \quad \cdot \quad (12\text{-}28)$$

Reference to Fig. 12-18 will show that if these equations are satisfied, angles OSC and OPC are right angles. Consequently S and P lie on the circle whose diameter is OC. As mentioned in the previous section, this is known as the Rowland circle, and for any position of a slit source S on this circle, the spectral lines of all orders are in focus on the circle. More detailed analysis shows that some of the higher order terms in (12-26) are also zero when the properties of the Rowland circle are utilized but that a large amount of astigmatism is present, the maxima being astigmatic focal lines. The presence of this astigmatism causes the light to be spread out in the direction of the lengths of the spectral lines with a consequent decrease in intensity (see § 16-7). The higher order terms in (12-26) cause a deterioration in the focus as the width of the grating is increased, and the optimum width of the grating can be shown to be larger for coarser gratings and smaller for higher order spectra. In the next section an account is given of a number of methods of utilizing the properties of the Rowland circle.

It can easily be verified that the second term in (12-26) becomes zero if

$$r=\infty$$

and
$$r'=\frac{R \cos^2 \theta}{\cos \theta + \cos I}. \quad \cdot \quad \cdot \quad \cdot \quad \cdot \quad \cdot \quad (12\text{-}29)$$

Thus if $r=\infty$, (12-29) defines the surface on which the maxima are most sharply focused for a given value of I. The residual path differences are given by the remaining terms in (12-26). If, in addition, one has $\theta=0$, the third term of (12-26) is zero and it can be shown that this also makes some of the higher terms, including the astigmatism, zero. That is to say, anastigmatic maxima of good definition are formed on the grating normal when the source is at infinity. However, it is obvious that for a given angle of incidence only one wavelength in each order can fall exactly on the normal. In the *Wadsworth* mounting, the incident light is collimated and the spectral lines are observed in the region of the grating normal, but it must be realized that as one moves away from the normal the definition deteriorates. The optimum width of the grating is again determined by the higher terms in (12-26) and decreases as θ increases. The wavelength range for which a satisfactory grating width can be used, and a satisfactory resolving power obtained, grows with increasing angle of incidence or, for θ constant, with increasing values of λ and of p. For this reason the Wadsworth mounting has been most widely used for the infra-red region. The arrangement is shown in the next section.

12–12. Mountings for Gratings

For visual observations small plane transmission and reflection gratings are conveniently mounted on the prism table of an ordinary prism spectrometer (Fig. 5–6). For spectral regions in which a lens can be used plane reflection

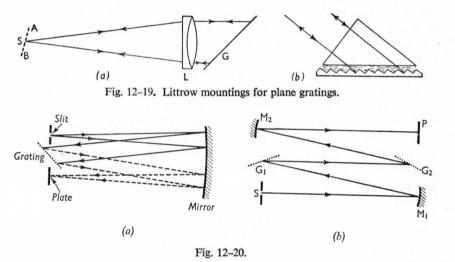

Fig. 12–19. Littrow mountings for plane gratings.

Fig. 12–20.

gratings can be mounted in spectrographs of the Littrow type shown in Fig. 12–19(a), the slits being mounted slightly above or below the plate AB. The grating G can be rotated to bring the required spectral region on to the plate.

As shown in §12–6, the resolving power of a grating is increased by increasing the index of the medium in which it is mounted. Hulthén and Neuhaus (1954) have achieved this improvement by placing a cover glass in immersion contact with the grating. If the grating is to be used at a large angle of incidence the cover glass is replaced by a prism as in Fig. 12–19(b). Fig. 12–20(a) shows a plan of the Ebert mounting first proposed in 1889. In 1930 Czerny and Turner used a modification of the Ebert mounting in which the collimating and focusing were performed by two separate mirrors instead of by the two halves of the large mirror, and Fastie (1952) replaced the plate by an exit slit to form a monochromator. It is worth noting that in the Ebert mounting the two mirrors (i.e. the two portions of the single mirror) are used off-axis by equal and opposite amounts. To a first approximation this symmetry eliminates the coma so that sharp spectral lines are formed. However, this correction applies only to the line that is the same distance off-axis as the entrance slit, so that only a small spectral range is sharp for any orientation of the grating. In consequence, the Ebert mounting is unsatisfactory for a spectrograph in which it is required to photograph a wide spectral range but is satisfactory for a monochromator if the exit slit is positioned correctly. The mirror does introduce some astigmatism and Fastie minimized its effect, and also compensated for spectral line curavture for all wavelengths, by using curved slits that formed arcs of the same circle. Fastie also used an "over-and-under" variation of the Ebert mounting in which the plate was mounted above, and the slit was mounted below, the level of the grating.

If two gratings are placed in series their dispersions add. Hence, if one wishes to double the resolving power of a grating system, one can double the width of the grating, or one can employ two identical gratings in series (or the same grating twice). When the grating width is doubled, the angular dispersion is unchanged while the doubled aperture halves the angular width of each line; when two gratings are used, the aperture is unchanged, so that the width of each line is unchanged, but the angular dispersion is doubled. A doubling of the aperture and a narrowing of each spectral line obviously leads to brighter lines. An improvement in the photometric efficiency also results from the use of two gratings in series since for a given *linear* dispersion the focal length of the focusing system can be halved. (See § 18–5.) The use of two gratings leads to the more compact system and, in any case, it may be impossible to produce a grating with twice the width of the original. (The required doubling of the aperture of the mirrors is not a trivial matter.) If there were no losses the use of two gratings in series, with a halved projection distance, would give a four-fold improvement in the photometric efficiency of the system. The best modern gratings are so good that, even after allowing for the losses of light at the second grating, the factor is between 2 and 3.

It is worth noting that if one uses the same grating twice, an extra mirror reflection is required to return the light to the gratings and the photometric efficiency of the system is reduced. Fig. 12–20(*b*) shows a double grating system due to Stroke (1958).

Fig. 12–21. Rowland mounting.

In connection with photometric efficiency it is important to note that while the resolving power of a grating in a Littrow mounting is proportional to sin I the angular dispersion is proportional to tan I. Thus, although there is no great improvement in resolution, an increase in obliquity from, say, $I=64°$ to $I=76°$ approximately doubles the angular dispersion, and for a given linear dispersion the projection distance is halved. The aperture of the system ($\propto \cos I$) is almost halved, but if the efficiency of blaze is retained the photometric efficiency of the system is approximately doubled.

Most of the mountings used for concave gratings make use of the properties of the Rowland circle. For photographic work the plate is curved to fit this circle of focus.

1. *Rowland Mounting.* The Rowland Mounting is illustrated in Fig. 12–21. The slit S remains stationary and the grating G and photographic plate P remain at opposite ends of the diameter of the Rowland circle. They are mounted on a rigid beam whose length is equal to the radius of curvature R of the grating. This beam is supported on swivel trucks which can slide along the arms SX and SY, which are rigid and at right angles. Since $\angle$XSY$=90°$, S will always lie on the Rowland circle (diameter R) as GP is moved. It will be seen that as the beam

GP slides round, the angle of incidence varies but the angle of diffraction remains close to zero. The pth order line of wavelength λ will be central on the plate when

$$d \sin I = p\lambda. \qquad \ldots \ldots \ldots \qquad (12\text{–}30)$$

Now
$$\sin I = \frac{PS}{GP}.$$

Thus as the beam is adjusted to bring successive wavelengths to a focus at P, one will have PS $\propto \lambda$. Also, for a given position of the beam, the angular dispersion is proportional to sec θ and in this arrangement θ, the angle of diffraction, is always very small. The dispersion is therefore almost constant and the spectrum on the plate is almost exactly normal.

From (12–30) it will be seen that $p\lambda/d$ cannot exceed unity, i.e. wavelengths greater than d/p cannot be examined. Using a grating with 20,000 lines to the inch, wavelengths exceeding 12,700, 6350, and 4233 angstroms cannot be examined in the 1st, 2nd, and 3rd orders respectively.

2. *Abney Mounting.* This resembles the Rowland mounting and has the same limitations of wavelength. The grating and plate have the same relative positions as before but are now fixed while the slit is carried on a beam pivoted at the centre of the Rowland circle. It is frequently more convenient to move the slit rather than the more cumbersome grating and plate mountings of the Rowland arrangement. This advantage is offset by the difficulty of moving the source and also by the fact that the slit must be rotated in its mount to keep the jaws perpendicular to the line from slit to grating.

3. *Paschen Mounting.* In this widely used arrangement, the slit and plate of the Abney mounting are interchanged. That is to say, the grating and slit are fixed and the plate is curved to fit any convenient portion of the Rowland circle. A typical arrangement is shown in Fig. 12–22. The approximate positions of the

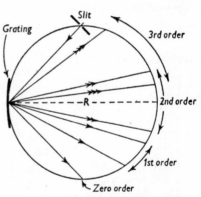

Fig. 12–22. Paschen mounting.

visible spectra are shown for a typical grating. Usually the slit and grating are mounted on separate piers while the plate mounting is extremely rigid. Again the spectra will be nearly normal where the angle of diffraction is small. It is frequently useful to provide facilities for mounting the slit in more than one position on the Rowland circle.

4. *Eagle Mounting.* A very compact and much used arrangement is that introduced in 1910 by Eagle (Fig. 12–23) and this may be regarded as a Littrow type of mounting. In principle the slit S is mounted alongside or just above or below the plate, and the properties of the Rowland circle are utilized as follows. Light from the slit S is reflected towards the grating G by the total reflection prism. S', the virtual image of the slit, is at the centre of the plate P which is

10*

curved to fit the Rowland circle. The grating can be moved to and from the plate and, as it is moved, both G and P are rotated so that P remains on the

Fig. 12–23. Eagle mounting.

Rowland circle. For example, when G is translated and rotated to G', P is rotated to P'. With this arrangement $\theta = I$ and, for a maximum,

$$2d \sin I = p\lambda \quad (p \text{ integral})$$

Fig. 12–24.
Wadsworth mounting.

so that wavelengths up to $2d/p$ can be examined. The working range is therefore double that of the Rowland mounting. The relative compactness of the Eagle mounting causes it to be widely used in vacuum spectrographs since a much smaller volume has to be evacuated. (Air absorbs wavelengths below about 2000 angstroms.) Temperature control is also easier with this smaller apparatus. (This is important since a variation of temperature causes a significant variation of the grating interval.)

5. *Wadsworth mounting.* The Wadsworth arrangement is the one important mounting which is not based on the Rowland circle; the optical system is shown in Fig. 12–24. Light from the slit S is collimated by the mirror M (originally Wadsworth used a lens) and falls on the concave grating G. The plate P is placed on the grating normal, and to investigate different spectral regions the angle of incidence must be varied to bring the middle of the range on to the normal. As was shown in § 12–11, the surface on which the spectral lines are in focus has a shape which depends upon the angle of incidence employed [equation (12–29)]. This means that the plate holder must be such that the curvature of the plate can be varied. The Wadsworth arrangement is confined within little more than half the area occupied by the Eagle mounting. (A similar

arrangement has been used with a plane grating placed in light rendered convergent by M.) Another important advantage of the Wadsworth arrangement is that the astigmatism is very much reduced (see § 12–11). In addition, the grating is used with a relatively large angular aperture and this, plus the absence of astigmatism, renders the lines more intense. For spectrochemical analysis the Wadsworth mounting is more convenient than the mountings due to Rowland and Paschen which were widely used in the earlier days when gratings were employed for the accurate measurement of wavelength. The Eagle mounting has been widely used in all branches of spectroscopy.

6. *The Seya and Johnson-Onaka Mountings.* The mechanical linkages used with the various Rowland circle mountings are impracticable for monochromators where the spectrum must be scanned across the exit slit. In the Seya mounting (1952) both slits are close to the Rowland circle for the zero order. The spectrum is then scanned across the exit slit by rotating the grating about its mid-point. The slits do not remain on the Rowland circle and there is some loss of focus. In the Johnson-Onaka mounting (1957–8) the grating is rotated about an axis some distance away from the centre of the grating in order to minimize the loss of focus.

Mountings for Echelles

The spectral range of an echelle in a Littrow-type mounting is $1/(2d \sin I)$ wave numbers. If this is less than the total range of the spectrum to be examined, the orders must be separated by means of an auxiliary dispersion system. Harrison and Bausch (1950) have described a system in which an echelle in an arrangement of the Ebert type is used to illuminate the slit of a large quartz prism Littrow spectrograph, the dispersion of the echelle being at right angles to that of the prism. If the dispersion of the echelle is in a vertical plane, that of the prism is in a horizontal plane, and the entrance slit for the echelle is horizontal (i.e. parallel to the rulings) while the prism spectrograph slit is vertical. To understand how the system works, first take the prism spectrograph alone and open the slit until its image on the plate extends over a range equal to the spectral range of the echelle. Now insert the echelle system in front of the prism slit. Successive echelle spectral ranges are superimposed on one another, each extending along the prism spectrograph slit, but on the plate these are spread out horizontally. The appearance of the pattern on the plate is represented by Fig. 12–25. AB represents a strip across part of a spectrum as formed by the prism spectrograph alone, using a narrow slit. The pattern below represents that photographed with the echelle in position. The echelle expands each spectral range vertically. In this way a very large spectral range can be photographed with high resolution on a single plate. The spectrograph is comparable with the best that can be produced with a very much more cumbersome concave grating installation using many more exposures. It will be appreciated that the particular arrangement described can be used only if the spectrograph slit can be made long enough to admit the dispersed spectral range of the echelle.

A simpler arrangement described by Harrison and Bausch for crossing an echelle with a prism substitutes the echelle for the mirror behind the prism in a Littrow system.

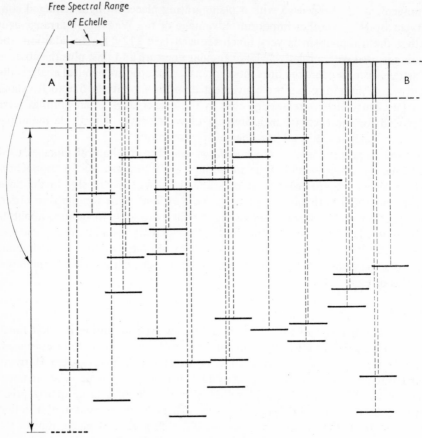

Fig. 12–25. Echelle spectrogram.

The auxiliary dispersion for an echelle can also be provided by a grating, and echelles, like any other gratings, can be used in series. For example, Harrison and Stroke (1960) have described a system using two echelles in series and in series with a concave grating which supplies the auxiliary dispersion. The layout resembles that shown in Fig. 12–20(b) which now represents a vertical section. The mirror M_2 is replaced by the concave grating with its lines vertical. The spectrogram again has the form illustrated by Fig. 12–25.

SISAM

This arrangement, due to Connes (1957), derives its name from: *s*pectromètre *i*nterferéntiel à *s*eléction par l'*a*mplitude de *m*odulation. It consists of a Twyman-Green interferometer (§8–12) in which the mirrors are replaced by dispersing elements such as diffraction gratings (see Fig. 12–26). Suppose the point source S emits light of wavelength λ and that the gratings are rotated into the Littrow position, i.e. $2d \sin I = p\lambda$. Then plane waves of wavelength λ enter lens L_2 to give coincident rectangular aperture diffraction patterns centred on S'. If the phase difference δ between the wavefronts is varied by displacing one of the

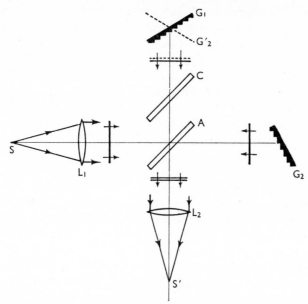

Fig. 12–26. SISAM.

gratings along the axis, or by rotating the compensator plate C, the flux received by the detector is given by

$$E = E_0(1 + \cos \delta)$$

i.e. the flux varies periodically and the depth of modulation is unity. Suppose, now, that the gratings are rotated through equal small angles so that G_1 and G_2' rotate in opposite directions. The plane waves enter L_2 obliquely and the diffraction images are displaced slightly in opposite directions from S'. It follows that the images overlap only partially so that interference occurs between only part of the light in the two patterns. In consequence, the variation of δ causes a variation of flux with a reduced depth of modulation M:

$$E = E_0(1 + M \cos \delta).$$

M falls to zero as the patterns for wavelength λ move away from S', and the next spectral line (λ') is detected by the increase in M as the gratings rotate to bring the corresponding images together at S'. It is important to note that it is the modulation depth in the total flux E and not the intensity at S' that is recorded. As the grating is rotated to scan a monochromatic spectral line in an ordinary single-beam Littrow system, the variation in intensity at a stationary scanning point is of the form $(\sin \alpha/\alpha)^2$ where α is proportional to the rotation of the grating. It can be shown that in the present method the variation of the modulation depth as the two gratings are rotated is of the form $(\sin \alpha/\alpha)$. It follows that the subsidiary peaks in M are proportionately much stronger than the subsidiary maxima in the intensity distribution in a single image (20% of the maximum instead of 4%—see Fig. 11–4). It can be shown that these subsidiary peaks can be suppressed if the aperture of the system is made diamond-shaped, the diamond being inscribed within the rectangular apertures of the dispersers, i.e. the system can be apodized (see §11–15). When apodized, SISAM gives a resolving power corresponding to the gratings used in an ordinary Littrow mounting with a slit of infinitesimal width. In practice one must use a finite source with SISAM, just as one must use finite slits in conventional systems. The advantage of SISAM is that for a given resolving power its photometric efficiency is superior to that of a conventional grating spectrometer; it is intended for use with weak sources in the infra-red region.

12–13. The Production of Ruled Gratings

The resolving power of a grating is given by

$$\frac{\lambda}{\delta\lambda}=pN=\frac{Nd(\sin\theta_p\pm\sin I)}{\lambda}.$$

Hence the requirement for maximum resolving power is that the total overall width of the grating should be as large as possible. If one rules few lines in this width a high order will be used and there will be serious overlapping of orders—the free spectral range will be small (see §12–5). To obtain maximum spectral range with maximum resolving power one must rule lines as closely as possible over the maximum width. The problem, then, is to rule thousands of parallel and equally-spaced grooves per inch over a width of several inches—using a Littrow mounting close to grazing incidence a perfect 10-inch grating is needed to achieve a resolving power of 10^6 at a wavelength of about 5000 angstroms.

Most gratings have been produced by ruling a glass or metal surface with a diamond tool. Speculum metal blanks were widely used in the past for the production of reflection gratings but most modern gratings are plastic replicas of master gratings ruled on aluminized glass blanks, reflection gratings being replicas with an evaporated metal film.

Rowland (1882) was the first to produce good-quality gratings of appreciable size. His machine moved the diamond across the stationary blank for each groove and moved the blank between rulings. This has been the most common method, although Strong has displaced the diamond between rulings and moved the blank past the stationary diamond when ruling each groove. Rowland's machine ruled 14,438 lines per inch. This gives $d=1\cdot6932\times10^{-4}$ cm., and equation (12–1) shows that with normal incidence the angle of diffraction becomes 90° when λ is 16,932, 8466, and 5644 angstroms in the first, second, and third orders respectively, so that the complete visible spectrum can be observed in only the first two orders. An idea of the dispersion can be obtained from the fact that in the first order the angles of diffraction are about 13·7° and 28·2° for wavelengths 4000 angstroms and 8000 angstroms, so that if the spectrum is formed in the focal plane of a lens of focal length 100 cm., the length of the visible spectrum is about 25 cm. If the grating were perfect the resolving power in the first order would be 14,438× (width of grating in inches), i.e. about 86,600 for a six-inch grating. Enormous numbers of copies have been made of gratings ruled on Rowland's machine. Rowland ruled concave gratings in addition to plane gratings.

Wood ruled his early blazed echelettes on gold-plated copper plates, using the natural edges of selected carborundum crystals. Collodion copies were mounted on glass and sputtered to give reflection gratings which were better than the originals because the glass mounts were flatter than the copper plates. Later, Wood replaced the carborundum tool by a diamond specially ground and polished to produce grooves of the desired form. Rulings were made on copper plates which were chromium plated after ruling. Subsequently, Wood ruled better echelettes on aluminized glass plates.

The groove depth, determined by the loading of the diamond, as well as the groove form, determined by its shape, is relevant to the efficiency of the grating. If the ruling is too light the grooves will be shallow, and therefore narrow, and there will be strips of the plane surface of the blank between grooves; these strips give light in the useless zero order. If the ruling is too heavy each groove spoils the shape of the previous one.

The resolution of a diffraction grating is reduced if the rulings are not exactly straight, parallel, and equally spaced, and if the blank is not accurately plane (or spherical). In consequence, a great deal of effort has been put into the design of ruling machines. Very great improvements have been made in recent years by checking the operation of the ruling machine interferometrically. For example, it is claimed that the machine at M.I.T. developed by Harrison and Stroke is producing gratings whose spectroscopic quality is almost 100 times that of Rowland's gratings, and efficiently blazed gratings are now available with resolving powers in the 1 to 2 million range in the visible and near ultra-violet. It was found that it was not satisfactory to apply interferometric control of a stop-start machine in which the blank was stationary during the ruling of each groove and was moved between rulings. The new procedure is to advance the blank uniformly and continuously so that it continues to advance slowly as the diamond moves uniformly across it. The motion of the blank carriage is watched continuously by employing a Twyman-Green interferometer system with one of the mirrors attached to the carriage. The output from the interferometer operates a servo-mechanism to advance or slow the carriage. In this way the movement of the grating blank is synchronized with the movement of the diamond to within about $\pm 0 \cdot 003 \mu$. In addition to controlling the translation of the blank carriage, an interferometric servo-mechanism is used to control the rotation of the blank about a vertical axis. In this way parallelism of the grooves is maintained to $\pm 1/200$ second of arc.

Since the diamond may be called upon to rule several hundred thousand grooves it is important to mount it with its axis orientated so that wear is reduced to a minimum. (Aluminized blanks are used because the metal is soft.) As remarked earlier, the loading of the diamond is also of great importance. Some idea of the magnitude of the problem of ruling a good grating can be obtained from the fact that it often takes more than a day to load and orientate the diamond; that the engine runs for about 18 hours to reach equilibrium before ruling starts; that the engine makes only about 10 strokes per minute; and that the temperature of the laboratory is controlled to within about $\pm 0 \cdot 02 °C$.

The interferometric control of the ruling machine is now so good that it is more difficult to obtain a sufficiently flat aluminium coating on the glass blank before ruling starts than to maintain a corresponding regularity of spacing. For the highest resolving powers the coated blank should be flat to less than $\lambda/10$, and it is particularly difficult to obtain the thick aluminium coatings (up to 30μ)

necessary to accommodate the deep grooves of coarse gratings. This, together with the heavy loading required on the diamond, makes it impracticable to rule efficiently blazed high resolution gratings on aluminized glass blanks with less than about 20 grooves per mm. Coarser gratings for use in the infra-red have been ruled on magnesium metal blanks.

The reflecting gratings supplied to users are not the masters actually produced by the ruling machine, but aluminized plastic replicas of these gratings mounted on flat (or concave) glass blanks. Transmission gratings simply consist of non-aluminized replicas. Bausch and Lomb have produced a transmission grating for use down to 2000 angstroms by employing a special resin for the replica and mounting it on a fused quartz blank. A step of major importance in the production of a replica grating is the clean separation of the replica from the master grating. It is claimed that a replica grating is actually more efficient than the master from which it is derived because in the replication process it is possible to eliminate the effect of the ridge thrown up by the diamond on the edge of each groove.

A novel method of producing plane gratings was devised by Merton (1950). There are three main operations:

1. Upon one half of a polished metal cylinder is cut a helix having a pitch equal to that of the required grating. The diamond tool is mounted on a suitably geared screw-cutting lathe. The helix as a whole must be free from progressive errors in pitch but periodic errors in the helix due to the gearing and lead-screw are corrected in the next stage.

2. A corrected helix is ruled by a diamond which is guided from the original helix by means of a nut lined with strips of soft elastic material such as cork. This *Merton Nut* effectively averages out the errors of the first helix.

3. The corrected helix is coated with a solution of a suitable plastic which, after hardening and annealing, forms a film which can be removed and opened out with rulings down on a moist gelatine-coated glass plate. When the gelatine is dry the original film can be removed, leaving the gelatine moulded into a plane grating which can be hardened and aluminized.

Up to the present the Merton process has not produced high resolution gratings equal to the best now available.

12–14. Irregularities in Gratings. Ghosts

In the foregoing theory it has always been assumed that all the rulings in a grating are identical and that the separation of adjacent rulings is constant. In practice this will never be true exactly, and errors in the grating spacing can cause troublesome effects. These errors are of three types:

1. *Random errors.* An error which is random in magnitude and direction gives a background illumination across the spectra and is relatively unimportant.

2. *Progressive errors.* An error in spacing which increases progressively across the grating can be shown to cause the spectral lines to be sharper in planes other than the focal plane of the optical system. Errors of this kind can occur over certain portions of the grating and they become very important in high resolution gratings.

3. *Periodic errors.* In the past these have been the most troublesome errors;

they cause the appearance of additional *ghost* lines in the grating spectra which, for a perfect grating, would indicate the presence of other wavelengths.

Frequently, periodic errors are caused by slight errors in the screw of the ruling engine or in its bearings. During a single rotation of the screw or spacing

$$A_1 \quad A_2 \quad A_3 \quad A_4 \quad A_5 \quad A_6 \qquad\qquad B$$

Fig. 12–27. Periodic errors.

head, a certain width of the grating is ruled. In this width there may occur slight and gradual variations of the grating spacing; these variations will then be repeated during the next turn of the screw, etc., so that the cycle of variations is repeated periodically across the width of the grating. It will now be shown that an error of this kind causes the appearance of satellite lines alongside the true principal maxima of the grating. The pattern then resembles that of a line with fine structure.

Suppose a grating with many lines is ruled between A_1 and B (Fig. 12–27). Suppose that if the grating is perfect a principal maximum lies in direction θ. The vector diagram is then a straight line. In a neighbouring direction there is a sufficient phase difference between disturbances from adjacent slits for the vector polygon to become a closed figure to give the first zero alongside the maximum. Successive zeros occur when the vector polygon makes an integral number of complete rotations. Suppose now that there are certain small variations of the grating interval in the region A_1A_2 and that these are repeated in the equal distances A_2A_3, A_3A_4, etc., across to B. It is convenient to assume that A_1B is an integral multiple of A_1A_2. (If it is not, no appreciable error is introduced by simply neglecting the effect of the small region of the grating between A_1 and B.) In the direction θ the vectors corresponding to A_1A_2 will not form an exact straight line but the resultants for the regions A_1A_2, A_2A_3, etc., will still do so and one still has a principal maximum at angle θ. Consider now what happens in the neighbouring direction which is such that the vectors corresponding to A_1A_2 form a closed figure for a perfect grating. That is, one is at a zero for the perfect grating. For the actual grating, the errors in the rulings between A_1 and A_2 cause the vector polygon for this region not to be closed. Now the resultants for this and successive regions A_2A_3, etc., will be identical so that, instead of zero intensity, one has a maximum. (The intensity reaches a maximum here because the resultants for a slightly different direction will be out of phase.) A similar spurious maximum will occur at the point where, for the ideal grating, the vectors for the region A_1A_2 execute two complete convolutions, and so on. The intensities of the ghosts are greater near the higher order parent lines. This is because the ruling errors cause a larger variation of phase difference between disturbances from adjacent rulings and therefore the vector polygon for A_1A_2 is less nearly closed in the direction of a minimum for a perfect grating, i.e. the resultant is larger.

Ghosts of the type described above are disposed symmetrically about the parent line and are fairly easily recognized. The theory of these false lines was very fully investigated by Rowland, who succeeded in reducing their intensity.

They are known as *Rowland Ghosts*. Certain kinds of periodic errors can give rise to ghosts which are very far removed from the parent line. These ghosts, discovered by Lyman and named after him, are weak; but under certain circumstances they may be confused with weak lines in a spectral region entirely different from that of the parent line.

Until recently there was little attempt to use gratings for high resolution spectroscopy requiring resolving powers in the region of those corresponding to perfect gratings working at high angles of incidence. In consequence, more attention was paid to the existence of ghosts that were separated from the parent line than to the existence of spurious lines—sometimes referred to as "satellites", sometimes as "grass"—affecting the sharpness or structure of the true spectral lines. Stroke (1960) has made a full investigation of the effect of grating imperfections on the spectral quality of gratings and has pointed out that since the ideal grating would give a plane diffracted wave, the grating defects are best thought of as sources of wavefront aberration causing loss of sharpness in the image (see §15–1). Stroke has pointed out that departures from flatness on the grating blank, as well as ruling errors, cause loss of resolution. A ruling defect of particular significance is a cumulative ruling error over a portion of the grating, the line interval increasing linearly across the defective region. This gives a wavefront error similar to that arising from a portion of the grating ruled perfectly on a region of the blank inclined to the main area. The wavefront from a grating can be examined in the usual way—with a Twyman-Green interferometer.

It is worth noting that, while the resolving power of a perfect grating in a Littrow mounting is proportional to $\sin I$, the quality of the grating needs to increase with $\sin^2 I$ in order to achieve the theoretical improvement resulting from an increased angle of incidence. The best modern gratings used in Littrow mounts at 64° or 76° have no satellites stronger than 1/100th of the intensity of the main line in the visible, and the Rowland ghosts are weaker than 1/2000th at those angles; resolving powers approaching 2×10^6 have been achieved.

12–15. Relative Merits of High Resolution Devices

Recent improvements in the production of ruled diffraction gratings have put them into the 10^6 resolving power class in the visible and ultra-violet regions. This is one of the most significant developments in high resolution spectroscopy since the invention of the Fabry-Perot interferometer, and has altered the classical concept of the need for an interferometer or echelon for work in this region. One of the great attractions of a grating or an echelle is the fact that one has a large free spectral range which is not reduced by using a wider grating to increase the resolving power. For example, a resolving power of 10^6 at 5000 angstroms (resolving limit 0·02 cm^{-1}) can be obtained with a 1-cm. etalon having a finesse of 25 and this has a free spectral range of 0·5 cm.$^{-1}$, which is insufficient to study the hyperfine structure of, for example, the λ 5461 mercury line without a pre-monochromator. The same resolving power can be obtained with a 10-inch grating or echelle in a Littrow mounting at 76°. A grating with 300 grooves/mm. would have a spectral range of 1500 cm.$^{-1}$, and an echelle with 30 grooves/mm. would have a spectral range of 150 cm.$^{-1}$. It is claimed by

Stroke that, when allowance is made for the pre-monochroma
used for most work with an etalon, there is often little to b
metrically by using such a system rather than a modern high re
Both SISAM and the Fourier transform method have hi
efficiency. A disadvantage of an etalon is that one often nee
parallelism of the plates. The etalon does have the advantage of ....
ghosts, and it remains true that an etalon can give a resolving power greater than
that obtainable with any other device. In normal circumstances in the middle of
the visible region the minimum resolving limits of the etalon, the reflection
echelon, the Lummer plate, and the ruled grating, are respectively about
0.0025 cm.$^{-1}$, 0.01 cm.$^{-1}$, 0.025 cm.$^{-1}$, and 0.02 cm.$^{-1}$. The Lummer plate is far
more expensive than the etalon and is now virtually obsolete, although it has
certain advantages over the etalon for short wavelengths; neither can be used
below 2000 angstroms, the transmission limit for quartz. The transmission
echelon is also virtually obsolete and the reflection echelon is extremely expensive
but usable in the far ultra-violet; only a few large echelons have ever been made.

The concave grating has the advantage of not requiring any additional optical
components, but the importance of this fact has decreased with the development
of aluminized mirrors. The need for auxiliary dispersion is eliminated by having
a large number of rulings and using a low order. The concave grating is still
widely used in the vacuum ultra-violet and in fixed-position spectrographs, but
in most applications calling for a grating a plane grating is preferable. Low
resolution concave gratings have been used to provide the auxiliary dispersion
for high resolution components. The advantage of an echelle crossed with a low
dispersion spectrograph over a classical large concave grating installation has
already been discussed in § 12–12. Attention has already been drawn to the
advantage of using a small grating interval, enabling a low order to be used.
However, it must be pointed out that if the groove aspect as "seen" by the light
is appreciably less than a wavelength, the grating will act as a plane mirror,
reflecting the light into the zero order. Thus one cannot use very low orders at
high angles of incidence.

For most scanning instruments of moderate resolution—spectrometers,
monochromators, and spectrophotometers—a plane grating is preferable to
a concave grating since no focus adjustment is required if the grating is rotated
to scan the spectrum. In addition, a plane grating is cheaper than a concave
grating.

The prism cannot be classified as a high resolution device—a dense flint prism
can give a resolving power in the visible of the order $1000 \times$ the length of the
prism base in cm. Prism instruments are, of course, widely used to provide
auxiliary dispersion for high resolution devices and also for many low resolving
power instruments (see §§ 5–16 to 5–18). However, owing to the recent improvements in the quality and availability of gratings it seems likely that gratings will
replace prisms in many applications. In the past one important photometric
advantage of a prism was that it gave only one spectrum; gratings are now blazed
so efficiently that this advantage is small.

In conclusion, it is worth noting here that the requirement for maximum
resolution with any instrument is that a displacement in the image should give

to the maximum possible phase difference between extreme disturbances in order that the intensity should decrease rapidly as one moves away from the centre of a spectral line or fringe. Thus the requirement is for a thick etalon with highly reflecting plates; for a long Lummer plate; for a wide grating or echelon; and for a large prism.

12–16. Two- and Three-dimensional Gratings

Suppose a collimated beam of light is incident on a series of equidistant diffracting point elements along the x-axis (Fig. 12–28). In the notation adopted hitherto, the direction of a maximum is given by

$$d_x (\sin \theta - \sin I) = p_1 \lambda, \quad \cdots \cdots \quad (12\text{–}31)$$

where d_x is the distance between elements. The figure indicates that the diffracted

Fig. 12–28. Diffracting elements along the x direction.

light lies in the xy plane but this is a special case and disturbances from these diffracting elements will be in phase in all directions which are inclined to the x-axis at the same angle $(\pi/2-\theta)$. Again, maxima are formed in these directions for incident light in any direction that is inclined to the x-axis at the same angle $(\pi/2-I)$. Consequently, it is better to write (12–31) as a relation between the angles which the incident and diffracted rays make with the x-axis. Writing α_o and α for the appropriate direction cosines of the incident and diffracted light, (12–31) becomes

$$d_x(\alpha - \alpha_o) = p_1 \lambda. \quad \cdots \cdots \quad (12\text{–}32)$$

It will be seen that for a given value of α_o the directions in which a maximum of given order is found form the generators of a cone whose axis is the x-axis and whose semi-vertical angle is $(\pi/2-\theta)$. Maxima are found in these directions for equally spaced diffracting elements along any line parallel to the x-axis.

For diffracting elements along the y-axis with spacing d_y, the directions of the maxima are given by

$$d_y(\beta - \beta_o) = p_2 \lambda, \quad \cdots \cdots \quad (12\text{–}33)$$

so that the directions in which a maximum of given order is found form the generators of a cone whose axis is the y-axis. (As before, maxima are found in parallel directions for similarly spaced elements along any parallel line.) Suppose, now, that both sets of diffracting elements are present together. One has a two-dimensional grating and maxima will be formed in directions which are specified by the values of the direction cosines α and β which satisfy (12–32) and (12–33) (remembering that $\alpha^2+\beta^2 \not> 1$). For given values of the integers p_1 and p_2, each of the direction cosines, α and β, determines a cone about the relevant axis so that for the two-dimensional grating the maxima are formed in directions given by generators which are common to those two cones. Obviously, a pair of values for p_1 and p_2 will not correspond to a maximum if the corresponding values of α and β define cones which have no common generators.

If one has, in addition, a set of equidistant diffracting elements along the z

direction, one has a three-dimensional grating. Maxima for a periodicity in the z-direction are defined by the relation

$$d_z(\gamma - \gamma_0) = p_3 \lambda, \quad \cdot \quad \cdot \quad \cdot \quad \cdot \quad \cdot \quad \cdot \quad (12\text{--}34)$$

and if (12–32), (12–33), and (12–34), can be satisfied simultaneously, the values of α, β, and γ, determine the direction of a maximum for the three-dimensional grating. Now since one must always have

$$\alpha^2 + \beta^2 + \gamma^2 = 1, \quad \cdot \quad \cdot \quad \cdot \quad \cdot \quad \cdot \quad \cdot \quad (12\text{--}35)$$

it follows that α and β completely determine a direction in space and, in general, the directions of the maxima for the two-dimensional grating will not be directions corresponding to maxima for the grating interval in the z-direction. That is to say, when values of α and β which satisfy (12–32) and (12–33) are substituted into (12–35), the resulting values of γ cannot, in general, satisfy (12–34) (i.e. do not give an integral value of p_3). It is only for particular values of α_0 and β_0 that it is possible for all the conditions to be fulfilled. That is, it is only for particular directions of the incident light that one gets any maxima with a three-dimensional grating. The necessary directions of incidence obviously depend upon the wavelength.

Fig. 12–29. Reflection planes.

Fig. 12–30. Reflection from parallel planes.

Three-dimensional gratings are very important since a crystal lattice constitutes a structure of this type. Since the grating intervals are very small, a crystal provides a grating suitable for use with waves of very short wavelength, i.e. X-rays. This opens up the vast subject of X-ray crystallography about which little more can be said here. One point of importance which should be mentioned is the interpretation, by Bragg, of the directions of the incident light which will give diffraction maxima.

According to Bragg, any plane in the crystal which contains a relatively large number of lattice points can be regarded as a reflecting plane. Fig. 12–30 indicates two such planes in a monoclinic crystal. Thus if a parallel beam of X-rays is incident on such a plane in a direction near to grazing incidence, a small fraction of the beam is reflected. In the lattice there will be a large number of equidistant parallel planes and reflections occur at these also (Fig. 12–30). The path difference between beams reflected from adjacent layers is $2d \sin \theta$ and there will be a "reflection maximum" if the reflected beams are exactly in phase. That is to say, there will be a maximum if the glancing angle of incidence θ satisfies the *Bragg equation*

$$2d \sin \theta = p \lambda. \quad \cdot \quad \cdot \quad \cdot \quad \cdot \quad \cdot \quad (12\text{--}36)$$

For a slightly different angle of incidence there will be a small phase difference between disturbances reflected from adjacent planes, but since there are a very large number of such planes, the resultant intensity is very small. That is, maxima can be observed only if the disturbances are incident at an angle which satisfies (12–36) exactly. Alternatively, for a given angle of incidence, maxima will be observed for certain wavelengths only. In the Laue method of observing X-ray diffraction spectra, the incident beam contains a wide range of wavelengths; in the Bragg method the angle of incidence is varied until the reflection condition is satisfied; and in the Debye-Scherrer-Hull method one employs a powder in which small crystals are orientated at random, thus giving all possible angles of incidence.

X-ray diffraction patterns are Fraunhofer patterns, and in the *optical diffractometer* they are simulated optically. In principle the arrangement is the same as that shown in Fig. 12–1, although in practice long focus (e.g. 150 cm.) lenses are used. One proceeds, by trial and error, to find an optical diffracting screen that gives a pattern resembling the X-ray diffraction pattern produced by the crystal whose structure is required. The atoms in the crystal are represented by small circular holes in an opaque screen, the array of holes representing a projection of the crystal on to a specific plane. When the optical pattern resembles the X-ray pattern the relative positions of the holes in the screen are similar to the relative positions of the atoms in the crystal.

12–17. Crossed Gratings—Moire Fringes

Suppose one has two identical transmission gratings, each of which consists of alternate opaque and transparent elements of equal width. Then, if these

gratings are placed face to face with their rulings inclined at a small angle, and viewed against a bright background, no light will be transmitted where the opaque parts of one grating fall on the transparent parts of the other. The appearance is of a set of dark fringes crossing the gratings as indicated by Fig. 12–31. These are known as *moire* fringes, and can be observed with various textiles by viewing through two layers. It will be seen that if D is the separation of the moire fringes and d is the grating interval of each grating, $D = d/\theta$, where θ is the angle between the rulings of the two gratings and is assumed to be small.

Fig. 12–31.
Formation of moire fringes.

Suppose, now, that one of the gratings is kept stationary and the other is moved in the direction perpendicular to its rulings. Reference to the figure will show that the moire fringes move in the direction perpendicular to the fringes themselves. They move a distance D as the grating moves a distance d. That is, one moire fringe crosses a point in the field of view each time the grating advances a distance d. Consequently, the movement of the moire fringes can be used to measure the movement of the grating and the magnification, $1/\theta$, can be made very large. This method of measuring linear displacements has found an application in the realm of automation. In operating an automatic lathe, for example, one grating is attached to the work and moves across a stationary grating. Light that has passed through the gratings is received by a photo-cell and varies in intensity as the movement of the work causes a moire fringe to cross the field. The output from the cell then controls the next displacement of the work in a predetermined manner.

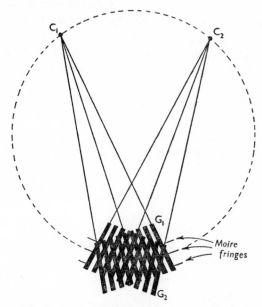

Fig. 12–32. Moire fringes with radial gratings.

By employing radial gratings, it is possible to employ moire fringes to measure rotations also. In Fig. 12–32, the rulings of the gratings G_1 and G_2 radiate from C_1 and C_2 respectively. Each moire fringe is now the arc of a circle which passes through C_1 and C_2, and if one grating is rotated, the fringe moves along the radius of the circle.

It is not essential to employ gratings of the opaque-transparent type, but not all gratings give moire fringes of good definition. It is beyond the scope of this book to investigate the conditions under which clear fringes are formed with ruled gratings.

FRESNEL DIFFRACTION PATTERNS

As stated in Chapter X, the Fresnel patterns most commonly investigated are those in which no lens system is involved. Such patterns are the subject of the present discussion. First there is given an elementary discussion of the division of a plane wavefront into annular half-period zones and the application to diffraction by screens having circular boundaries. This is followed by a discussion of the problem of diffraction by screens having linear boundaries: the straight edge, single slit, opaque strip, and double slit.

13–1. Elementary Discussion of the Division of a Plane Wavefront into Half-period Annular Zones

In Fig. 13–1 AB is a plane wavefront advancing to the right. In order to find the disturbance at P, the wavefront is divided into annular zones as follows: the

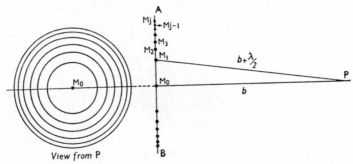

Fig. 13–1. Half-period zones on a plane wave.

central zone extends as far as M_1 where $M_1P=M_0P+\lambda/2$ and the second extends to M_2 where $M_2P=M_1P+\lambda/2=M_0P+\lambda$. Thus if $M_0P=b$ the jth zone extends from M_{j-1} to M_j where

$$M_{j-1}P=b+(j-1)\lambda/2$$

and
$$M_jP=b+j\lambda/2.$$

The area of the jth zone is obviously given by

$$\text{Area} =\pi M_jM_0{}^2-\pi M_{j-1}M_0{}^2$$
$$=\pi[(b+j\lambda/2)^2-b^2]-\pi[\{b+(j-1)\lambda/2\}^2-b^2]$$
$$=\pi[\lambda b+(\lambda^2/4)(2j-1)]\quad\cdot\quad\cdot\quad\cdot\quad\cdot\quad\cdot\quad\cdot\quad\cdot\quad(13\text{--}1)$$
$$\doteqdot\pi\lambda b$$

if the λ^2 term is neglected. That is, the areas of all the zones are approximately equal. Now, according to Fresnel, the contribution that any element of the wavefront makes to the disturbance at P has an amplitude which is proportional to the area of the element and to the amplitude at the element, and is inversely proportional to the distance from the element to P. In addition, the amplitude depends upon an obliquity factor. It is assumed that the obliquity factor varies slowly and that it may be regarded as constant over a single half-period zone. Now the amplitude of the primary disturbance is constant across the wavefront, and the distance from P varies only slightly across a single zone. Therefore, in a first approximation, a half-period zone can be taken as an element which gives, at P, an amplitude proportional to its area. Furthermore, the distances of successive zones from P are not widely different and, to a first approximation, the zones have equal areas. Consequently, it may be assumed that, apart from the obliquity factor, each zone gives a contribution at P of the same amplitude. Equation (13–1) shows that the areas of the zones actually increase slightly. In addition, the successive zones do get slightly farther away from P. Further analysis shows that these two factors exactly balance one another so that, apart from the obliquity factor, each zone does give a contribution at P of the same amplitude (see §10–3). Now since a given zone is $(\lambda/2)$ farther from P than the

Fig. 13–2. Contributions of half-period zones.

previous one, it gives a disturbance of opposite phase. The effect of the obliquity factor is simply to cause the amplitudes of successive zones to decrease gradually. Thus if a_1, a_2, a_3 . . . etc., are the amplitudes at P due to the half-period zones, $|a_1|>|a_2|>|a_3|$ . . ., and the resultant is given by

$$R=|a_1|-|a_2|+|a_3|-|a_4|+\ldots.$$

If one constructs zones over the complete wave and assumes that $a_n\rightarrow0$, this series sums to (see §10–3)

$$R=\frac{a_1}{2}. \qquad \ldots \ldots \ldots \quad (13\text{--}2)$$

The superposition of the contributions of the zones can be represented graphically in the usual way. The contribution of the central zone is represented by AB (Fig. 13–2). The contribution of the next zone has opposite phase and slightly smaller amplitude; it can be represented by BC. The next zone gives CD, and so on. The sequence of points ABCDE . . . converges on Z, the mid-point of AB, and the resultant=AZ=½AB.

13–2. Circular Obstacle and Circular Aperture

Suppose a spherical wave from a point source S (Fig. 13–3) is diffracted by a circular obstacle centred on the line SP joining S to the field point P. When S is at a large distance from the obstacle one has diffraction of a plane wave. In each case one may divide the exposed part of the wavefront into half-period zones commencing at the edge of the obstacle. The contributions of successive zones to the disturbance at P will again alternate in sign and decrease in amplitude, so that the effect at P is again half that of the first zone and is only slightly less than that found in the absence of the obstacle. As one moves away from P the intensity decreases rapidly. For larger obstacles the first zones become

increasingly narrow and any irregularities in the surface of the obstacle will cause
a serious reduction in the effect produced by the zones they partially obstruct.
In consequence, the bright spot at P can be observed only if the obstacle is
smooth and exactly circular.

For an accurately circular obstacle, point sources near S will give bright spots
near P, so that if a brightly illuminated object is placed at S, an image is formed
at P. The effect at P for a point source is shown in Plate III(a). The obstacle
was a small steel ball.

If the obstacle subtends an appreciable angle at P the maximum at P is very
narrow. For a source of finite area (even as small as most laboratory "point"
sources), neighbouring points of the source give neighbouring maxima at P so

Fig. 13–3. Circular obstacle.

that, although the area of the maximum is increased, its intensity is not. Outside
the area of the geometrical shadow the intensity increases as the area of the
source increases and, consequently, the intensity of the central maximum within
the shadow becomes a smaller fraction of that outside the shadow; it is therefore
more difficult to observe.

It has been pointed out in § 10–5 that if one places on SP a circular aperture
which obstructs all but the central zone, the whole of that zone is effective; the
amplitude is double that found when the whole wave is unobstructed [see (13–2)]
and the intensity at P is increased fourfold. If the aperture admits the first two
zones, the intensity at P is very small since these zones give disturbances of opposite phase and almost equal amplitude. Inclusion of the third zone will almost
cancel the effect of the second zone and the intensity at P is again approximately
that of the central zone, and so on. Now the dimensions of the zones depend
on the distance of P beyond the screen. Suppose P moves from a great distance
towards the circular aperture. The intensity at P gradually increases until the
central zone is sufficiently small to be admitted in its entirety. As P moves
nearer to the aperture, the zones become smaller and the intensity at P falls to a
minimum when the first two zones are admitted. It rises to a maximum again
when three zones are unobstructed and, as P continues to approach the aperture,
the intensity varies between a minimum and four times that due to the unobstructed wave. To find the intensity at intermediate positions along the axis
SP, it is necessary to calculate the effects of the zone partially admitted. It may
be shown that the off-axis pattern consists of a series of concentric rings [see
Plate III(b) and (c)].

13–3. The Zone Plate

As shown in §13–1, the jth zone on a plane wave approaching a point P extends from M_{j-1} to M_j (Fig. 13–1), where

$$M_0M_j = \sqrt{(b+j\lambda/2)^2-b^2}$$
$$= \sqrt{jb\lambda+j^2\lambda^2/4}.$$

If j is not large, the second term may be neglected, and it will be seen that for a particular position of P in front of the wavefront, the radii of successive zones are proportional to $\sqrt{j}$.

If a number of concentric circles are drawn whose radii increase in this way, and alternate spaces are made black and white, it is possible, by photographing the drawing, to construct a diffracting screen which obstructs alternate Fresnel zones for particular values of b and λ. Such a screen is known as a *zone plate* (Fig. 13–4). The intensity at P will be very large if such a screen is interposed between S and P at the appropriate distance b, since all the transmitted zones give contributions at P which are of the same sign. (A still greater intensity results at P from a so-called *phase reversal* zone plate in which alternate zones are phase-retarded by π instead of being obstructed.) Point sources near S give additional very bright spots near P so that the zone

Fig. 13–4. Zone plate.

plate acts as a lens in concentrating light to form an image.

When P is distance $\frac{1}{3}b$ from the zone plate, each transparent part of the plate transmits three zones, of which two give approximately equal and opposite contributions at P. It will be seen that the effect at P is the sum of the contributions of every sixth zone. These are of the same sign so that there is a maximum at P. Additional maxima occur at distances $b/5$, $b/7$, etc., from the zone plate, while at distances $b/2$, $b/4$, the disturbance is very small since each transparent area of the plate transmits an even number of zones.

Thus a zone plate has a primary focal length b, and a number of subsidiary focal lengths at which weaker maxima occur.

In the case of a lens, disturbances through every point of the aperture arrive at the focus in phase, but in the case of a zone plate, each point of a single zone is not equidistant from P. Thus, although the zones give appreciable disturbances at P, the zone plate is considerably less efficient than a lens in forming images.

13–4. Elementary Theory of Diffraction at a Straight Edge

In Fig. 13–5 S is a slit source which, in an elementary discussion, can be assumed to give a cylindrical wave. To find the disturbance at P, one divides the wavefront W into half-period strips; the jth strip extends from M_{j-1} to M_j, where $M_{j-1}=b+(j-1)\lambda/2$ and $M_j=b+j\lambda/2$. As with half-period zones, adjacent strips give disturbances at P which have opposite phases. Now when a plane or spherical wave is divided into annular half-period zones, the zones have approximately equal areas and give contributions whose amplitudes decrease owing to the obliquity factor only. In the present case, however, the half-period strips decrease in area as j increases so successive strips give contributions whose amplitudes decrease more rapidly as j increases. It should be noted that there are now two equal series of strips—one above and one below M_0.

Fig. 13–5. Cylindrical wave.

If a diffracting obstacle is placed between S and P, the disturbance at P is that due to the unobstructed strips.

In Fig. 13–6 S is a slit source parallel to the straight edge M_0 of an opaque screen which extends from M_0 to infinity. The cylindrical wave from S is diffracted at the straight edge and the Fresnel pattern is formed on the screen P'P''. To find the disturbance at P, on the edge of the geometrical shadow, one can divide the wavefront into half-period strips as above. It will be seen that all the strips on one side of M_0 are obstructed, and that all those on the other side are effective. Therefore the amplitude at P is half (and the intensity one quarter) that due to the unobstructed wave. This is indicated in the figure, the intensity due to an unobstructed wave being taken as unity.

Fig. 13–6. Diffraction at a straight edge.

For a point such as P', in the geometrical shadow, it is again the strips above M_0 which are effective, but the farther P' moves from P the greater is the obliquity. Consequently, each strip above M_0 gives a smaller contribution at P' than it gives at P and the resultant amplitude at P' is also smaller than at P. Thus as P' moves away from P the intensity decreases steadily as indicated in the figure.

For a point, such as P'', in the geometrically illuminated region, it is convenient to divide the wavefront into half-period strips commencing at M_0''. All the strips on one side of M_0'' are effective; they constitute half a wavefront and give a contribution at P″ equal to the total disturbance at P. In addition, the strips between M_0'' and M_0 give contributions. As P″ moves away from P it will reach a point such that $M_0''M_0$ contains one strip; its contribution must be added to that of the strips above M_0''. That is to say, its contribution must be added to the effect of half the wave and the resultant is somewhat greater than that at P. As P″ moves farther from P it reaches a point such that $M_0''M_0$ contains two strips; these give contributions of opposite phase and slightly different amplitude so that they give only a small total contribution. The intensity at P″ is then slightly larger than at P. When P″ moves to a point such that there are three strips between M_0'' and M_0, two of them almost cancel and the effect of the third must be added to the effect of half the wave. This suggests that as P″ moves away from P, the intensity passes through a series of maxima and minima as indicated in the figure. When P″ is far removed from P the obstructed zones below M_0 are only the relatively ineffective outer zones and the intensity approaches that of an unobstructed wave (unity on the scale adopted).

If it is assumed that one has a minimum at P″ when an even number of half-period strips is exposed between M_0'' and M_0, one has, for a minimum,

$$P''M_0 - P''M_0'' = p\lambda \text{ where } p \text{ is an integer.}$$

From the figure one has

$$P''M_0 = \sqrt{x^2 + b^2}$$

$$= b\left(1 + \frac{x^2}{b^2}\right)^{\frac{1}{2}}$$

$$= b + \frac{x^2}{2b} \quad \text{if } x \ll b.$$

Similarly,

$$P''S = \sqrt{x^2 + (r_o + b)^2}$$

$$= r_o + b + \frac{x^2}{2(r_o + b)},$$

$$\therefore \ P''M_0'' = b + \frac{x^2}{2(r_o + b)}.$$

Therefore, for a minimum at P″, one has

$$\left(b + \frac{x^2}{2b}\right) - \left(b + \frac{x^2}{2(r_o + b)}\right) = p\lambda,$$

$$\therefore \ x^2\left(\frac{r_o}{2b(r_o + b)}\right) = p\lambda,$$

or

$$x = \sqrt{\frac{b(r_o + b)2p\lambda}{r_o}}.$$

Similarly, for a maximum,

$$x = \sqrt{\frac{b(r_o + b)(2p - 1)\lambda}{r_o}}.$$

$$\quad \cdots \quad (13\text{–}3)$$

It must be realized that the above theory is only a first approximation. The half-period strips do not give contributions of equal amplitude so that the maxima and minima are not exactly at the points indicated by the above results. These approximations are valid for the first few fringes only and a more detailed analysis is given in the following sections. The Fresnel pattern for a straight edge and a slit source is shown in Plate III(g).

13–5. Rectangular Aperture. Cornu's Spiral and Fresnel's Integrals

As pointed out above, it is very often convenient, when investigating diffraction by a rectangular aperture, to employ a slit source parallel to one of the linear boundaries of the aperture. However, it is necessary, in a proper analysis, to commence with a discussion of the pattern formed with a point source. (See also Chapter XI.)

Fig. 13–7 illustrates the diffraction of a spherical wave from the point source S by a plane screen. To find the disturbance at P due to the secondary sources in the element ds of the wavefront, it is necessary to calculate the distance r from ds to P. In the present theory it is assumed that the apertures are not far removed from the axis SP, so that the obliquity factor is constant over the unobstructed parts of the wavefront and the variation in r is not large. As explained in §10–10, this means that the variations in r do not affect the amplitude factor, so that equal elements of area give disturbances at P which have equal amplitudes. However, the phase of the disturbance due to each element ds depends on r, and this distance must be found.

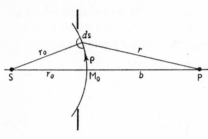

Fig. 13–7.
Lunar division of a spherical wave.

From the figure $r^2 = (r_o + b)^2 + r_o^2 - 2r_o(r_o + b)\cos(\varrho/r_o)$, where r_o, r, b, and ϱ, are as in the figure, ϱ being the length of the arc from M_0 to ds.

If ϱ is not large, powers of (ϱ/r_o) higher than the second may be neglected so that one may write

$$\cos\left(\frac{\varrho}{r_o}\right) = 1 - \frac{\varrho^2}{2r_o^2}.$$

Hence

$$r^2 = b^2 + \frac{r_o + b}{r_o}\varrho^2,$$

$$\therefore \quad r = b\left(1 + \frac{r_o + b}{r_o b^2}\varrho^2\right)^{\frac{1}{2}}$$

$$= b + \frac{r_o + b}{2br_o}\varrho^2, \quad \cdot \quad \cdot \quad \cdot \quad \cdot \quad \cdot \quad \cdot \quad (13-4)$$

if powers of ϱ higher than the second are neglected.

It is now necessary to sum the effects of the unobstructed elements of the wavefront. When discussing the diffraction of spherical waves by circular apertures and obstacles, it is convenient to divide the wavefront into annular zones because an elementary zone is either passed or obstructed in its entirety.

If, however, the diffracting aperture has linear boundaries, it will pass fractions of elementary zones and the effects of these fractions are not easily computed.

Fig. 13–8(a) illustrates the diffraction of a spherical wave by a slit or rectangular aperture whose edges are parallel to the axes of x and y. It is now convenient to divide the wavefront into lunes by means of great circles whose planes are perpendicular to the xz plane. Viewed from the direction of P, the wavefront appears as in Fig. 13–8(b). Suppose that, in this way, the wavefront is divided into a large number of equal lunes. In the present theory it is assumed that only the central part of the wave is unobstructed so that one is concerned with only relatively short sections of the lunes lying close to the axis SP. Suppose the arc

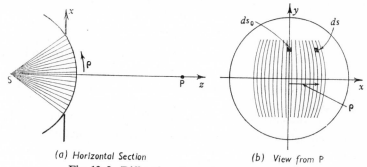

(a) Horizontal Section   (b) View from P

Fig. 13–8. Diffraction at a rectangular aperture.

length ϱ is measured along the wave in the xz plane. Consider equal lunes at the origin and at ϱ. The elements ds_0, ds [Fig. 13–8(b)] of these lunes, lying between planes y, $y+\delta y$, are equal and produce equal amplitudes at P. Equation (13–4) shows that the element ds in the lune at ϱ is $[(r_o+b)/2r_ob]\varrho^2$ farther from P than is the element ds_0 in the central lune. (The former is $[(r_o+b)/2r_ob](\varrho^2+y^2)$ and the latter $[(r_o+b)/2r_ob]y^2$ farther from P than is the pole of the wave.) It will be seen that each element in the lune at ϱ is $[(r_o+b)/2r_ob]\varrho^2$ farther from P than is the corresponding element in the central lune, so that if one takes the *total* contribution of the central lune to have zero phase at P, the phase of the total contribution of the lune at ϱ is $(2\pi/\lambda)[(r_o+b)/2r_ob]\varrho^2$, the two lunes giving equal amplitudes. For any lune, each element of area is proportional to the width of the lune so that the amplitude at P due to that lune is also proportional to the width. Consequently, if one divides the wavefront into lunes of equal width $d\varrho$, one may say that the lune at ϱ produces a disturbance at P whose amplitude is proportional to $d\varrho$ and whose phase is

$$\frac{\pi(r_o+b)}{\lambda r_ob}\varrho^2.$$

If one plots a vibration curve to represent the effects at P of these elementary lunes, the element of arc representing the amplitude of the lune at ϱ is of length ds (not to be confused with the area ds referred to above); it is proportional to $d\varrho$, and is inclined to the zero-phase line at angle $\psi=[\pi(r_o+b)/(\lambda r_ob)]\varrho^2$. Suppose the vibration curve is plotted in the XY plane with OX as the zero-phase line (Fig. 13–9) on such a scale that $ds=[\sqrt{2}(r_o+b)/(\lambda r_ob)]d\varrho$. If the vibration curve commences at the origin with the contribution of the central elementary lune, the element ds at distance $s=[\sqrt{2(r_o+b)/(\lambda r_o b)}]\varrho$ along the arc represents the contribution of the lune at ϱ and is inclined to the X-axis at angle $\psi=(\pi/2)s^2$. From the usual relations of differential geometry, i.e. $dX/ds=\cos \psi$, $dY/ds=\sin \psi$, one has, since $X=Y=0$ when $s=0$,

$$X= \int_0^s \cos \frac{\pi s^2}{2}\,ds, \qquad \ldots \ldots \quad (13\text{–}5(a))$$

$$Y= \int_0^s \sin \frac{\pi s^2}{2}\,ds. \qquad \ldots \ldots \quad (13\text{–}5(b))$$

These integrals are known as *Fresnel's integrals* and define a curve known as *Cornu's spiral*. The integrals have been evaluated in series form and have been tabulated for various values of the upper limit. The spiral is shown in Fig. 13–10; it has two branches and has asymptotic points J_1, J_2, at $X=Y=\pm\frac{1}{2}$. The values of s are indicated along the curve. For any point P, the upper and lower branches of the spiral are the vibration curves for the disturbances at P due to the lunes lying above and below the axis SP [Fig. 13–8(a)]. It was assumed initially that

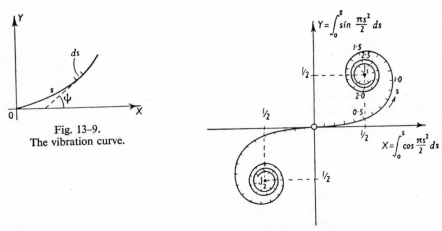

Fig. 13–9.
The vibration curve.

Fig. 13–10. Cornu's spiral.

only that part of the wave near the axis SP is unobstructed, so that Cornu's spiral is not accurately the vibration curve in the region of the asymptotic points. Within these limitations, the part of the spiral which lies between $s=s_1$ and $s=s_2$ is the vibration curve for lunes which lie between $\varrho=\varrho_1$ and $\varrho=\varrho_2$ where the relation between s and ϱ is as given above.

Consider the diffraction of a spherical wave from the point source S by a rectangular aperture in an opaque screen lying in the xy plane, the edges of the aperture being parallel to the axes of x and y. One is usually interested in the variation of intensity along the line AB parallel to the x-axis (see Fig. 13–11). The present theory can be applied only if P is not far removed from the z-axis

In this case, to the present accuracy, the vibration curve for the complete wave is the same complete Cornu spiral for all positions of P and a certain section of the spiral will be the vibration curve for the unobstructed lunes. Now one measures ϱ from the axis SP, so that for any position of P, the unobstructed lunes are those between $\varrho=\varrho_1$ and $\varrho=\varrho_2$, and the vibration curve is the corresponding arc of the Cornu spiral. As P moves along AB the values of ϱ_1 and ϱ_2 change, and different parts of the spiral become the vibration curve for the disturbance at P. Now the aperture always admits the same lunes although they are, effectively, different lunes for different positions of P. Hence the effective arc of the spiral will have the same length for all positions of P. Alternatively, one may simply say that $(\varrho_2-\varrho_1)$ is the same for all positions of P so that (s_2-s_1) is also constant. If one imagines a string of fixed length sliding along the spiral it will become the vibration curve for successive positions of P. This will be discussed in more detail later.

Fig. 13–11. Determination of effective part of spiral.

If, for a particular position of P, the values of ϱ at the edges of the aperture are ϱ_1 and ϱ_2, the corresponding values of s define the appropriate section of the spiral and the square of the distance between the ends of the arc gives the intensity at P. An approximate value for the intensity at P can be obtained by direct measurement if an accurate plot of the spiral is available. Alternatively, the tabulated values of Fresnel's integrals can be employed. If X_1, Y_1, and X_2, Y_2, are the values of the Fresnel integrals corresponding to s_1 and s_2 [from equation (13–5)], the intensity at P is given by

$$I=(X_2-X_1)^2+(Y_2-Y_1)^2. \quad . \quad . \quad . \quad . \quad (13\text{–}6)$$

The advantage of dividing the wavefront into lunes is that, in the case of diffraction by rectangular apertures, an elementary lune is either obstructed or passed in its entirety. Whereas in the case of annular division of the wavefront it was convenient to employ half-period zones, there is no particular advantage in using half-period lunes. If, however, this method of lunar division is employed, Cornu's spiral emerges as the limiting case of a vibration polygon which is equiangular but not equilateral. The advantage of employing the variable s is that the spiral is plotted on the same scale for all problems.

13–6. Derivation of Fresnel's Integrals from Kirchhoff's Formula

The above results follow at once from Kirchhoff's diffraction formula. As has already been pointed out, it may be assumed that the obliquity factor and the amplitude factor are constant so that, from equation (10–18),

$$\phi_p=(\text{constant})\int\!\!\int_\Sigma e^{ik[ct-(r_0+r)]+i\frac{\pi}{2}}\,ds.$$

Equation (13–4) gives the value of r for any element ds distance ϱ from the axis PS. If SP is always taken as the z-axis (Fig. 13–12), one may write $\varrho^2=x^2+y^2$

G. AND P.O.—11

and, since one is concerned with relative phases and relative intensities only,

$$\psi_p = \int\!\!\int_{\Sigma} e^{-ik\frac{r_0+b}{2r_0 b}(x^2+y^2)}\,dx\,dy.$$

This integral may be factorized into its x- and y-dependent parts. Now the integral with respect to y is the same for all points P along a line parallel to the x-axis. Hence, if one is interested only in the variations in intensity along such a line, the integral with respect to y is constant and one may write

Fig. 13–12. Use of rotating axes.

$$\psi_p = \int_{x_1}^{x_2} e^{-ik\frac{r_0+b}{2r_0 b}x^2}\,dx,$$

where x_1, x_2, are the values of x at the edges of the rectangular aperture. Or putting $s = [\sqrt{2(r_0+b)/(\lambda r_0 b)}]x$ and again omitting the constant term,

$$\psi_p = \int_{s_1}^{s_2} e^{-i\frac{\pi}{2}s^2}\,ds = X + iY \text{ (say)}.$$

The intensity at P is $\psi_p\bar{\psi}_p = X^2 + Y^2$, where

$$X = \int_{s_1}^{s_2} \cos\frac{\pi}{2}s^2\,ds,$$

$$Y = \int_{s_1}^{s_2} \sin\frac{\pi}{2}s^2\,ds.$$

Since $\int_{s_1}^{s_2} = \int_{0}^{s_2} - \int_{0}^{s_1}$, X and Y may be written in terms of the Fresnel integrals as defined above.

Ignoring the inaccuracy of the spiral in the region of the asymptotic points, the unobstructed wave gives an amplitude represented by the distance $J_1J_2 = \sqrt{2}$ since these points are at $X = Y = \pm\frac{1}{2}$. Thus if the intensity in the absence of diffracting screens is taken as unity, intensities calculated from Cornu's spiral must be halved.

13–7. The Use of a Slit Source

The above calculations give the variation in intensity along a line parallel to the x-axis. It will be seen that as far as relative intensities along a particular line are concerned, the result is independent of the y co-ordinate of the line for a given value of b provided all points of the diffracting aperture are fairly close to the axis SP. Thus the pattern consists of linear fringes parallel to the y-axis although there may be variations of intensity along the fringes themselves. If one employs a slit source through S parallel to the y-axis, an infinite number of these patterns are formed alongside one another in the y-direction and the intensity variations parallel to the y-axis disappear. Thus the above theory gives the relative intensity across the fringes in the case of a slit source parallel to one pair of edges of a rectangular diffracting aperture. Such an arrangement is common in practice since it greatly increases the amount of light in the pattern. It is obviously essential, in order to obtain clear fringes in such cases, for the slit to be accurately parallel to the edges of the aperture. If this is not so, different elements of the source slit will give fringes which are displaced laterally.

13–8. Diffraction at a Straight Edge

Suppose an opaque plane screen covers the region x negative of the xy plane [Fig. 13–13(a)]. S may be a point source or a slit source parallel to the y-axis.

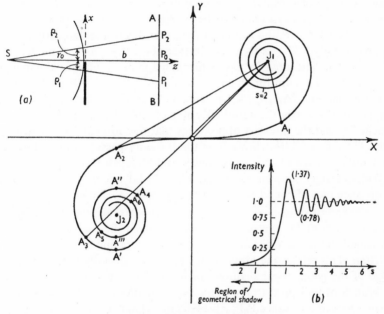

Fig. 13–13. Diffraction at a straight edge.

For any point P on the screen AB, one branch of the Cornu spiral corresponds to elements of the wave above SP, and the other to those below SP. (The inaccuracy of the spiral in the region of the asymptotic points will be neglected.)

The disturbance at P_0, on the z-axis, is due to exactly half the wave so that the amplitude at P_0 is half, or the intensity one quarter, of that due to the unobstructed wave (taken as unity). One complete branch of the spiral is effective and the intensity is represented by $(OJ_1)^2 = \frac{1}{4}(J_1J_2)^2 = \frac{1}{4}$ if the scale is adjusted to make $(J_1J_2)^2 = 1$.

When P moves below the z-axis to P_1, the part of the wave below SP_1 is completely obstructed so that the lower branch of the spiral is again ineffective. In addition, the elements of wavefront immediately above SP_1 are obstructed so that the portion near O of the upper branch of the spiral is ineffective also. The effective part of the spiral commences at A_1, a distance s_1 along the spiral from O where s_1 is determined by ϱ_1: $s_1 = [\sqrt{2(r_o+b)/(\lambda r_o b)}]\varrho_1$. Thus the effective part of the spiral is that between A_1 and J_1, and the intensity at P_1 is proportional to $(A_1J_1)^2$ [i.e. $\frac{1}{2}(A_1J_1)^2$]. As P_1 moves away from P_0, ϱ_1 (and therefore s_1) increases, and A_1 moves round the spiral so that $(A_1J_1)^2$ gradually decreases. That is to say, the intensity at P_1 gradually decreases as P_1 recedes from P_0. This is shown in Fig. 13–13(b). If P is above the z-axis at a point such as P_2, the whole of the upper part of the wave (that above SP_2) is unobstructed so that the whole of the upper branch of the spiral is effective. In addition, part of the wave below SP_2 is unobstructed. The corresponding part of the spiral is that between O and A_2 where A_2 is distance s_2 along the spiral, s_2 being determined, in the usual way, by ϱ_2. The total effective part of the spiral is, therefore, that between A_2 and J_1 so that the intensity at P_2 is $\frac{1}{2}(A_2J_1)^2$. As P_2 recedes from P_0, ϱ_2 (and therefore s_2) increases and A_2 moves round the lower branch of the spiral. It will be seen that the intensity at P_2 increases and reaches a maximum when A_2 reaches A_3. The intensity is then $\frac{1}{2}(A_3J_1)^2$ and is greater than that due to the unobstructed wave; it is approximately $1\cdot37$. As P_2 moves farther above the z-axis, A moves farther round the spiral. The intensity passes through a minimum (approximately $0\cdot78$) when P_2 reaches the point for which A reaches A_4. It passes through successive maxima and minima $(A_5J_1)^2$, $(A_6J_1)^2$, etc., as P_2 recedes from P_0. As P moves farther above the z-axis the terminal point of the effective part of the spiral approaches J_2 and the intensity approaches that due to the unobstructed wave, i.e. $\frac{1}{2}(J_1J_2)^2$. Fig. 13–13(b) shows how the intensity passes through a series of maxima and minima and approaches unity, and Plate III(g) shows a photograph of the fringes using a slit source. In Fig. 13–13(b) the intensity is plotted against s, the distance moved round the spiral by the point A. Now if $r_o = b = 100$ cm. and $\lambda = 5000$ angstroms, $\varrho = [\sqrt{(\lambda r_o b)/2(r_o+b)}]s = 0\cdot0354s$. For the point P_0 in the pattern, A is at O, and as P moves away from the z-axis a distance x, A moves round the spiral a distance s. From the figure one has $x = \varrho(r_o+b)/r_o$ or $x = 0\cdot0708s$. This relates the abscissa in Fig. 13–13(b) to distances moved from the edge of the geometrical shadow. In particular, when A_1 moves round the upper branch of the spiral to the point $s = 2$, the intensity falls to about $0\cdot025$. P has then moved a distance $P_0P_1 = 0\cdot1416$ cm. That is to say, the intensity falls to about $0\cdot025$ when one moves approximately $1\cdot4$ mm. inside the geometrical shadow.

In the preliminary discussion of § 13–4 it was assumed that maxima occur when the edge of the wave gives a disturbance at P_2 which is π out of phase with that from the pole of the wave. This corresponds to the occurrence of maxima when A is at A', $A''' \ldots$ and minima when A is at $A'' \ldots$ etc.

It was pointed out in § 10–13 that a diffraction pattern can be looked upon as the result of the superposition of (1) light propagated according to the laws of geometrical optics, and (2) light which can be considered to have come from the edges of the diffracting screen. When one is not very close to the diffracting edge, the pattern formed with a slit source and a single straight edge can be regarded as the result of the superposition of part of the original cylindrical wave envelope and a cylindrical wave envelope spreading out from the edge (Fig. 13–14). It must not be supposed that an exact cylindrical wave envelope actually

spreads out from the edge—that would give infinite amplitude at the line source along the axis of the cylinder, i.e. at the diffracting edge. However, when one is far removed from the edge, the *edge wave* behaves like a cylindrical envelope. The above discussion has shown that the intensity decreases as one passes into the geometrical shadow. In this region only the edge wave is effective and its

Fig. 13–14. The edge wave.

intensity must therefore decrease with increasing obliquity. In addition, the occurrence of the maxima and minima in the geometrically illuminated region is caused by the interference between the original wave and the edge wave. The amplitude of the latter must decrease as one passes into the geometrically bright region in order to explain the decreasing amplitude of the variations in intensity [Fig. 13–13(b)]. The existence of an edge wave of general cylindrical form can be demonstrated by viewing the diffracting edge with a low-power microscope placed just inside the region of geometrical shadow. A line of light will be observed along the edge of the screen and this is the effective source of the edge wave.

13–9. Single Slit

Fig. 13–15(a) represents diffraction by a slit or rectangular aperture whose length is considerably greater than its breadth. S is a point source or, more

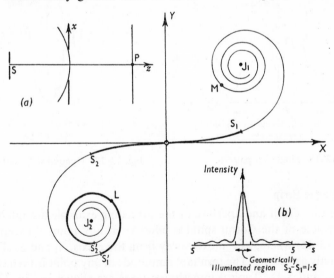

Fig. 13–15. Single slit.

usually, a slit source parallel to the diffracting slit. For any point P the effective section of Cornu's spiral is that which lies between $s=s_1$ and $s=s_2$, and is determined by ϱ_1 and ϱ_2, the values of ϱ at the edges of the slit. As remarked earlier, $(\varrho_2-\varrho_1)$ is constant for all positions of P so that (s_2-s_1) is constant, and the effective arc of the spiral is always of the same length. When P is on the z-axis, S_1 and S_2 are equal distances from O along the spiral. As P moves above or below the z-axis, S_1 and S_2 move along the lower or upper half of the spiral respectively, the arc length $S_1 S_2$ remaining constant. For each position of P, $(S_1 S_2)^2$ gives the intensity. In the figure the arc length $S_1 S_2$ is small and refers to a narrow slit. The greatest intensity obviously occurs when P is on the z-axis and the complete pattern is of the form shown in (b). The minima are not exactly zero but occur when S_1 and S_2 are opposite one another on successive rotations of the spiral, e.g. $S_1' S_2'$. The pattern for a narrow slit is shown in Plate III(d).

For certain slit widths, a minimum may occur on the z-axis. For example, if in that position S_1 and S_2 are at L and M, the intensity is at a minimum. This follows at once since, if one moves away from the z-axis so that M moves round towards J_1, L will move round towards O and LM will increase. The complete intensity pattern would then be of the form shown in Fig. 13–16. The relation between s and distance moved across the receiving screen is as given in § 13–8. That is, if $r_o=b=100$ cm., $x=0.0708s$. It will be seen that a minimum occurs in the middle of the geometrically illuminated region. Here the edge waves from the edges of the slit are out of phase with the "direct" light. A pattern of this type is shown in Plate III(e). For wider slits a number of maxima and minima occur in the geometrically illuminated region, and when the slit is very wide the pattern resembles two straight-edge patterns which meet in the middle of the bright region [see Plate III(f)].

Fig. 13–16. Single slit pattern.

Fig. 13–17. Opaque strip pattern.

13–10. Opaque Strip

Suppose the screen and aperture of the preceding example are interchanged. Then the whole of the Cornu spiral is effective at any point P except the arc $S_1 S_2$ (Fig. 13–15) where, as P moves away from the z-axis, S_1 and S_2 slide along the arc exactly as before. The resultant amplitude at any point is then the vector sum of $J_1 S_1$ and $S_2 J_2$. Typical intensity patterns are shown in Fig. 13–17 and Plate III(h). One fairly easily observed feature is the set of fringes within the geometrical shadow. These approximately equally spaced fringes can be regarded as being caused by the interference of the two edge waves. In effect, these spread into the geometrical shadow from the two edges of the opaque strip to form fringes as in Young's double slit interference experiment.

It is worth noting that the patterns for the single slit and the opaque strip are not the same—the conditions for Babinet's theorem do not obtain.

13–11. Double Slit

The effective portion of the Cornu spiral now consists of an arc corresponding to each slit, separated by a fixed arc length corresponding to the opaque screen between the slits. For any point P, if S_1S_2 and T_1T_2 represent the effective arcs of the spiral, the amplitude is the vector sum of the chords S_1S_2 and T_1T_2. As P moves across the receiving screen, S_1S_2 and T_1T_2 slide along the spiral, the arc lengths S_1S_2, S_2T_1, and T_1T_2, remaining constant. A double slit pattern for very narrow slits is shown in Plate III(i).

THE PHYSICAL THEORY OF IMAGE FORMATION IN OPTICAL INSTRUMENTS

14-1. Imagery by Perfect Optical Systems

IT has been remarked (p. 17) that in terms of geometrical optics a perfect optical system gives a point image of a point object. In terms of rays, the emergent rays in the image space pass exactly through the image point; in terms of waves, the emergent wave is exactly spherical. Thus the optical paths from object point to image point are independent of the zone of the aperture traversed and all the disturbances arrive in phase at the image point.

In terms of physical optics, it has been shown that one does not have an infinite concentration of energy at the image point, and that in the plane perpendicular to the axis the image formed by a perfect optical system is a Fraunhofer diffraction pattern. In particular, for an optical system having a circular aperture, the pattern corresponding to the image of a point source was found (§ 11-8). This pattern is centred on the image point indicated by geometrical optics and, if the angular aperture in the image space is not large, was seen to consist of a central maximum (the so-called Airy disc) surrounded by an infinite series of concentric bright rings. Although one must obviously not depend upon the rays to give the intensity distribution in the image, they are of interest because they are the wave normals and the condition for the formation of the Airy pattern is the condition for perfect geometrical imagery—concurrency of the rays. Moreover, away from a focus it is legitimate to think of the energy as travelling along the ray paths.

14-2. Optical Paths Along Neighbouring Rays

As stated in Chapter I, one may regard Fermat's theorem as the fundamental law of ray optics. It was seen that this theorem states that the ray path along which a disturbance travels is such that the optical path has a stationary value. Therefore, if one takes a fictitious ray path which everywhere lies close to an actual ray path, then the optical paths along the two paths are equal. In particular, if two actual ray paths lie close together everywhere, the optical paths along the neighbouring rays are equal. (The term "neighbouring rays" will be used to describe two rays which are everywhere close together so that at no point are they inclined to one another at a large angle.) It was shown in Chapter I that Snell's law of refraction follows from Fermat's principle, refractive indices being defined in terms of the speed of light. Adopting the alternative procedure of defining the refractive indices by means of Snell's law (a common practice), one can quickly prove the equality of optical paths along neighbouring rays in the case of refraction through a single surface.

In Fig. 14-1, $A_1B_1C_1$ and $A_2B_2C_2$ are neighbouring rays so that A_1A_2 and C_1C_2 may be regarded as perpendicular to either or both rays. B_2P and B_1Q are perpendiculars as shown so that $A_2Q=A_1B_1$ and $B_2C_2=PC_1$. Thus, using square brackets to denote optical paths, one may write

$$[A_2B_2C_2] - [A_1B_1C_1] = [QB_2] - [B_1P]$$
$$= nQB_2 - n'B_1P.$$

Fig. 14–1. Neighbouring rays.

Since the rays are neighbouring, B_1B_2 is small so that $\angle QB_1B_2$ and $\angle B_1B_2P$ may be equated to I and I', the angles of incidence and refraction respectively.

$$\therefore \quad QB_2 = B_1B_2 \sin I \quad \text{and} \quad B_1P = B_1B_2 \sin I',$$
$$\therefore \quad [A_2B_2C_2] - [A_1B_1C_1] = B_1B_2 (n \sin I - n' \sin I')$$
$$= 0.$$

Thus, along the neighbouring rays, the optical paths between A_1A_2 and C_1C_2 are equal.

14–3. The Sine Relation and the Sine Condition

The earlier discussions of optical systems commenced with the assumption that geometrically perfect imagery is possible and it was shown that, within the paraxial region, an optical system of spherical refracting surfaces satisfies the necessary conditions. That is, a system of infinitesimal aperture and field can give geometrically perfect imagery. The present section is concerned with the conditions under which small objects lying close to the optical axis, in a plane perpendicular to the axis, are imaged accurately by an optical system of *large* aperture. The discussion commences with the assumption that this is possible.

Fig. 14–2. Imagery of small object perpendicular to the axis.

In Fig. 14–2, A_1P_1 and A_KP_K represent the first and last surfaces of an optical system. BC is a small object of height h perpendicular to the optical axis BA_1 ... A_KB'. B'C' is its image, of height h'.

The ray BP_1 emerges along P_KB', the ray CA_1 along RC', and the ray CP_1 along QC'.

11*

Since B′ is the image of B, the optical path from B to B′ is independent of the zone of the aperture traversed, i.e.

$$[BA_1 \ldots A_K B'] = [BP_1 \ldots P_K B'],$$

or $\qquad nBA_1 + [A_1 \ldots A_K] + n'A_K B' = nBP_1 + [P_1 \ldots P_K] + n'P_K B', \quad (14\text{-}1)$

and since C′ is the image of C,

$$[CA_1 \ldots RC'] = [CP_1 \ldots QC'],$$

i.e. $\qquad nCA_1 + [A_1 \ldots R] + n'RC' = nCP_1 + [P_1 \ldots Q] + n'QC'. \quad (14\text{-}2)$

Now, since h is small, CA_1 and BA_1 are neighbouring rays. Therefore R, the point of emergence of ray CA_1, must be near A_K, and the optical path from A_1 to A_K for a disturbance from B must be equal to the optical path from A_1 to R for a disturbance from C.

Similarly, rays BP_1 and CP_1 are neighbouring rays and emerge from neighbouring points P_K and Q respectively, so that $[P_1 \ldots P_K]$ for a disturbance from B is equal to $[P_1 \ldots Q]$ for a disturbance from C.

Thus, on subtracting (14-2) from (14-1), the terms in the square brackets cancel and one has

$$n(BA_1 - CA_1) + n'(A_K B' - RC') = n(BP_1 - CP_1) + n'(P_K B' - QC'). \quad (14\text{-}3)$$

In addition, since h and h' are small,

$$BA_1 = CA_1 \quad \text{and} \quad A_K B' = RC'$$

and, dropping perpendiculars CD and B′E′ as in the figure,

$$CP_1 = DP_1 = BP_1 - BD \quad \text{and} \quad P_K B' = QE' = QC' - E'C'.$$

Thus, from (14-3),

$$0 = n(BD) + n'(-E'C').$$

Also, from the figure,

$$BD = h \sin U \quad \text{and} \quad E'C' = h' \sin U',$$

$$\therefore \quad nh \sin U = n'h' \sin U'. \qquad \ldots \ldots \quad (14\text{-}4)$$

This is known as the *Sine Relation*.

Now a geometrically perfect optical system is defined as one which gives geometrically perfect imagery for a wide aperture and a wide field for *all object positions*. It was pointed out in Chapter II that if one has perfect imagery for *two* pairs of conjugates, the system is perfect; and it was shown that for such a system the Helmholtz equation will be satisfied, i.e.

$$nh \tan U = n'h' \tan U'. \qquad \ldots \ldots \quad (14\text{-}5)$$

It will be seen that, except within the paraxial region where the sines and tangents may be equated, the Sine Relation and the Helmholtz equation are contradictory. As has just been proved, the Sine Relation must be satisfied in order to achieve imagery of a single small object with a wide aperture system. Therefore the Helmholtz equation cannot be satisfied and an optical system cannot be perfect in the sense defined above. That is to say, the most that can be hoped for in an optical system is geometrically perfect imagery for one pair of conjugates. In practice, it is seldom possible to achieve even this exactly; on the other hand, it can often be approached very closely. It must also be borne in mind that, although the imagery cannot be *perfect* for *two* pairs of conjugates, it might prove to be possible to make the imperfections small in each case. A further discussion of this problem is given in Chapters XV and XVI.

In deducing equation (14–4), the discussion was restricted to rays passing through a single zone of the system defined by the angles U and U'. Usually an optical system has a circular aperture centred on the axis and admits a solid cone of rays from each object point. Thus rays are admitted at all values of U up to the value for the so-called marginal ray which passes through the extreme zone of the aperture.

Now, for a given object, the size of the image formed by rays passing through any given zone of the aperture is given by

$$h' = h \cdot \frac{n \sin U}{n' \sin U'},$$

and, for a good image, this must be the same for each zone. In particular, an image of the same size must be formed by rays lying within the paraxial region. If u and u' refer to paraxial rays, the paraxial image height is

$$h' = h \cdot \frac{nu}{n'u'},$$

so that one may equate the values of h'.

$$\therefore \quad \frac{n \sin U}{n' \sin U'} = \frac{nu}{n'u'},$$

or
$$\frac{\sin U'}{u'} = \frac{\sin U}{u}. \qquad \ldots \ldots \quad (14\text{–}6)$$

This is known as the *Sine Condition* and must be satisfied for all zones of the aperture if the image is to be of the same size for rays traversing each of these zones. The significance of the Sine Condition is discussed further in Chapter XV.

14–4. Herschel's Condition

Suppose an optical system of large aperture forms an image of an axial point object B. Herschel's condition is the condition that must be satisfied if the system is to form, simultaneously, a good image of a neighbouring axial object point C.

In Fig. 14–3 A_1P_1, A_KP_K are the first and last surfaces of an optical system which is assumed to form a good image of both B and C—disturbances from B and C arrive in phase at B' and C' respectively.

Proceeding as in the previous paragraph, one has

$$nBA_1 + [A_1 \ldots A_K] + n'A_KB' = nBP_1 + [P_1 \ldots P_K] + n'P_KB' \quad (14\text{–}7)$$

and
$$nCA_1 + [A_1 \ldots A_K] + n'A_KC' = nCP_1 + [P_1 \ldots Q] + n'QC'. \quad (14\text{–}8)$$

Again $[P_1 \ldots P_K] = [P_1 \ldots Q]$ since these are optical paths along neighbouring rays. Hence, subtracting (14–8) from (14–7),

$$n(BA_1 - CA_1) + n'(A_KB' - A_KC') = n(BP_1 - CP_1) + n'(P_K'B' - Q'C').$$

Dropping perpendiculars CD and B'E' as in the figure, one has, as before,

$$DP_1 = CP_1, \quad \text{and} \quad QE' = P_K B'$$

$$\therefore \quad n(BC) + n'(-B'C') = n(BD) + n'(-E'C'),$$

i.e. $$n(BC - BD) = n'(B'C' - E'C').$$

But $$E'C' = B'C' \cos U' \quad \text{and} \quad BD = BC \cos U$$

$$\therefore \quad nBC(1 - \cos U) = n'B'C'(1 - \cos U'). \quad \dots \quad (14\text{--}9)$$

Fig. 14–3. Imagery of small axial object.

Now, since B' and C' are good images of B and C respectively, they must be the images as formed by paraxial rays in addition to rays traversing the zone defined by U, U'. If m is the paraxial transverse magnification for planes at B and B', the paraxial form of Helmholtz's equation (which has been shown to apply to a system of spherical refracting surfaces) gives [from equation (2–8)]

$$m = \frac{nu}{n'u'}, \quad \dots \dots \dots \quad (14\text{--}10)$$

where u and u' refer to paraxial rays through B and B'. Also, for imagery by paraxial rays, it has been found that, for conjugate increments dx and dx' along the axis [from equation (2–11)],

$$\frac{dx'}{dx} = m^2 \cdot \frac{n'}{n}.$$

In the present problem dx'/dx becomes B'C'/BC. Hence, from (14–10),

$$\frac{B'C'}{BC} = \frac{nu^2}{n'u'^2},$$

$$\therefore \quad nBCu^2 = n'B'C'u'^2, \quad \dots \dots \quad (14\text{--}11)$$

and, dividing (14–9) by (14–11), one has

$$\frac{1 - \cos U}{u^2} = \frac{1 - \cos U'}{u'^2},$$

or $$\frac{\sin^2 \dfrac{U}{2}}{u^2} = \frac{\sin^2 \dfrac{U'}{2}}{u'^2},$$

which is usually written in the form

$$\frac{\sin \dfrac{U}{2}}{\dfrac{u}{2}} = \frac{\sin \dfrac{U'}{2}}{\dfrac{u'}{2}}, \qquad \ldots \ldots \text{(14–12(a))}$$

or
$$n \sin \frac{U}{2} = n'm \sin \frac{U'}{2}, \qquad \ldots \ldots \text{(14–12(b))}$$

where m is the transverse linear magnification. This is *Herschel's condition* in the form given by Abbe, and cannot be satisfied if the Sine Condition is satisfied unless either $m = \pm 1$ or the system is telescopic. This confirms the fact that, in general, it is not possible to get good imagery for finite objects in adjacent object planes.

14–5. Limit of Resolution. The Rayleigh Criterion

In Fig. 14–4 P_1 and P_2 are neighbouring incoherent point sources of monochromatic light of wavelength λ. P_1P_2 is perpendicular to the axis. It is assumed

Fig. 14–4. Imagery of neighbouring points.

that disturbances from P_1 and P_2 arrive in phase at the geometrical image points P_1' and P_2' respectively, and that $P_1'P_2'$ is also perpendicular to the axis. On the image plane each point source will give rise to an Airy pattern centred on its geometrical image point. Since the sources are incoherent, the total intensity at any point on the image plane is simply the sum of the intensities associated with the separate patterns. If the distance $P_1'P_2'$ is large compared with the radius of the Airy disc, the separate patterns can be distinguished easily [Fig. 14–5(a)]. The images are said to be resolved. On the other hand, if $P_1'P_2'$ is very small the central maxima will overlap to such an extent that the total intensity shows no decrease at the mid-point and the resulting pattern will have roughly the same appearance as that for a single point source, i.e. the images are not resolved

Fig. 14–5. The Rayleigh criterion for resolution.

[Fig. 14–5(b)]. Obviously it is important to find the smallest separation of the images for which the resultant pattern can be seen to consist of two neighbouring patterns which are superposed.

The same problem arose in § 11–5 when discussing the chromatic resolving power of a prism spectroscope. In that case it was stated that, according to Rayleigh, two patterns with equal intensities may be said to be resolved when the central maximum of one pattern falls over the first minimum of the other. It is convenient to adopt the same criterion for the resolution of Airy patterns [Fig. 14–5(c)]. Thus the images are said to be just resolved if their centres (i.e. the geometrical images points) are separated by a distance equal to the radius of the first dark ring, i.e. $0.61\lambda/(n' \sin U')$, where λ is the wavelength of the light, U' is the semi-angle of the emergent cone of rays, and n' is the refractive index of the image space (see § 11–8). As pointed out in Chapter XI, the criterion is adopted largely because of its convenience and there is no doubt that detailed analysis of the intensity distribution would make it possible to decide whether the image was that of a single or double source for considerably smaller separations of the images. In using an optical instrument one is interested in the separation of the object points when the images are just resolved. This is referred to as the *limit of resolution* of the instrument and will be seen to be inversely proportional to the aperture of the system. Thus, to resolve finer detail in an object, an instrument must have a larger aperture and/or employ light of a shorter wavelength.

14–6. Limit of Resolution of a Telescope Objective

In the case of a telescope objective, the objects are usually at large distances so that the actual linear separation of the objects is very large when their images are just resolved. One consequently refers to α, their angular separation.

(a)   (b)

Fig. 14–6. Limit of resolution of a telescope objective.

In Fig. 14–6(a) and (b) L represents a telescope objective imaging two distant point sources whose angular separation, α, is small. (Since $n'=n=1$, the nodal points are at the principal points.) h' is the separation of the geometrical image points and therefore of the centres of their Airy patterns. Usually, u' is small so that one can say that the sources will be resolved when

$$h' = \frac{0.61\lambda}{u'}.$$

From Fig. 14–6(b) $\alpha = h'/f'$, so that the angular separation of the sources when the images are just resolved is

$$\alpha = \frac{0.61\lambda}{f'u'}.$$

But, from Fig. 14–6(a), $f'u'=a/2$

$$\therefore \quad \alpha = \frac{1\cdot 22\lambda}{a} \quad \cdots \cdots \cdots \cdots \quad (14\text{–}13)$$

Hence, for a given wavelength, the angular limit of resolution of a telescope objective depends only upon the linear diameter of the objective.

14–7. Limit of Resolution of a Microscope Objective. (Self-luminous Object)

In the case of a microscope, one needs to know the separation of the object points when the images are just resolved. In the present theory it is assumed that one is viewing two neighbouring non-coherent point sources whereas, in microscopy, one seldom has self-luminous objects. However, the conditions may be approached, at least for low powers, if a diffusing screen is placed behind the object and is illuminated from the rear. Again the angle u' is small, although U is usually large.

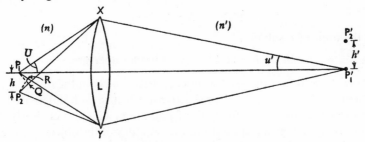

Fig. 14–7. Limit of resolution of a microscope objective.

In Fig. 14–7 P_1' and P_2' are the geometrical images of the point sources P_1 and P_2. If the objective L gives good images of both P_1 and P_2, the Sine Relation must be satisfied for all zones of the aperture. In particular, for the extreme marginal zone, one has

$$nh \sin U = n'h' \sin U'.$$

As before, the images are just resolved when $h'=(0\cdot 61\lambda)/(n' \sin U')$ so that, if h is the separation of the objects when the images are just resolved,

$$h = \frac{n'h' \sin U'}{n \sin U} = \frac{0\cdot 61\lambda}{n \sin U}.$$

The quantity $(n \sin U)$ is referred to as the *numerical aperture* of the objective and is written (N.A.), i.e.

$$\text{Limit of resolution} = \frac{0\cdot 61\lambda}{(\text{N.A.})}. \quad \cdots \cdots \quad (14\text{–}14)$$

The following discussion from first principles gives a useful alternative approach to the problem. It was shown in § 11–1 that, for a rectangular aperture, the first minimum in the Fraunhofer pattern for a slit or point source occurs at the point where the disturbances through the extreme edges of the aperture arrive after traversing paths which differ by λ. It was pointed out in § 11–7 that for a circular aperture and point source the path difference at the first minimum is $1 \cdot 22\lambda$. Thus the images of two point sources will be just resolved if disturbances which pass through the edges of the aperture from one source to the geometrical image of the other have a path difference of λ for a rectangular aperture (or $1 \cdot 22\lambda$ for a circular aperture). In Fig. 14–7 P_1 is on the axis so that $XP_1'=YP_1'$. Hence disturbances from P_2 to P_1' via the extreme edges of the aperture, X and Y, traverse paths which differ by (P_2X-P_2Y). From the figure one has

$$P_2X=QX+P_2Q=P_1X+P_2Q$$

and
$$P_2Y=RY=P_1Y-P_1R.$$

Now
$$P_1X=P_1Y,$$

$$\therefore \quad P_2X-P_2Y=P_2Q+P_1R.$$

If h is small

$$\angle P_2P_1Q= \angle P_1P_2R=U$$

and
$$P_1R=P_2Q=h \sin U,$$

i.e.
$$P_2X-P_2Y=2h \sin U,$$

and at the limit of resolution

$$2h \sin U=1 \cdot 22\lambda \quad \text{for a circular aperture.}$$

It will now be seen that this path difference arises solely in the object space and can be increased by increasing the refractive index. The path difference becomes $2nh \sin U$, giving (14–14) for the limit of resolution. This shows clearly that the limit of resolution depends upon the refractive index of the object space. Neither the size of the image patterns, nor the separation of the geometrical images at the limit of resolution, are affected by the index of the object space. However, the magnification is affected (as is shown by the Sine Relation) and the just resolved images correspond to the closer object points.

It follows from (14–13) and (14–14) that *for a given object distance* the limit of resolution of a lens (e.g. a camera lens) depends on its *linear* aperture. (At a given distance, the angle subtended by an object is proportional to its linear size, and the (N.A.) of the lens is determined by its linear aperture.)

14–8. Necessary Magnifying Power of a Microscope

For the standard observer, the near point is about 25 cm. from the eye, and for many purposes one can assume that at this distance the limit of resolution is about 0·01 cm. That is to say, objects can be resolved by the eye when they subtend an angle of about one minute. Thus for two optical images to be resolved by the observer, they must have an angular separation not less than this. If an optical instrument resolves two neighbouring object points in the sense of the previous section, the observer will be quite unable to appreciate the fact unless the magnifying power of the instrument is such that the physically resolved images subtend an angle of at least one minute at the observer's eye. Thus, for any visual instrument, there is a minimum magnifying power below which the eye will be unable to resolve the objects even though the images as formed by the instrument itself may be clearly resolved. This minimum magnifying power is usually called the *necessary magnifying power*. A magnifying power excessively greater than this is of no advantage since the eye will never be able to resolve images that the instrument does not resolve. Psychologically, this additional magnification is a disadvantage because it renders visible the diffuse nature of the separate Airy discs so that one gets an impression of poor image quality. Such additional magnification, greatly in excess of the necessary value, is called *empty magnification*.

The necessary magnifying power of a microscope is easily calculated from the results given above. The smallest resolvable separation of point objects, h, is given by (14–14) and the magnifying power must be such that the images subtend an angle of $0.01/D_v$.

$$M = \frac{\text{angle which images must subtend}}{\text{angle subtended at } D_v \text{ by just resolvable objects}}$$

$$= \frac{0.01/D_v}{h/D_v}$$

$$= \frac{0.01}{h}$$

$$= \frac{0.01 \times (\text{N.A.})}{0.61\lambda} . \qquad \ldots \ldots \ldots \ldots \ldots (14\text{–}15)$$

Now it has already been seen [equation (3–7)] that the magnifying power of a compound microscope is given by

$$M = \left(\frac{g}{f_O{}'}\right)\left(\frac{D_v}{f_E{}'}\right). \qquad \ldots \ldots \ldots (14\text{–}16)$$

Using a given objective, the numerical aperture is fixed. Hence the necessary magnifying power may be calculated from (14–15). In addition, g and $f_O{}'$ are given, so that, from (14–16), it is possible to calculate $D_v/f_E{}'$; this is the power of the eyepiece which must be employed with the given objective in order to give the necessary overall magnification.

It must be remembered that the value quoted above for the limit of resolution of the human eye is an average value. It is determined by a number of factors including the structure of the retina, the refractive condition of the eye, etc. Many authorities consider that for comfortable vision, especially during prolonged observation with a microscope, it is advisable to assume an angular limit of resolution of roughly 2' ($\frac{1}{5}$th mm. at the least distance of distinct vision).

Using equation (14–15), and assuming that the observations are carried out with sodium light ($\lambda = 0.000059$ cm.), one has, for the necessary magnifying power,

$$M = \frac{0.01 \times (\text{N.A.})}{0.61 \times 0.000059} \fallingdotseq 300 \, (\text{N.A.}), \qquad \ldots \ldots (14\text{–}17)$$

or 600 (N.A.) if one uses the more conservative estimate for the resolution of the eye.

The above discussion is an over-simplification since it has been assumed that the limit of resolution of the eye is constant at about one minute whereas it does, in fact, depend on the size of the eye pupil, and deteriorates considerably for pupil diameters below about 2 mm. (See §17–7.) If the exit pupil of the microscope is smaller than the actual eye pupil, the limit of resolution of the eye is determined by the area of the eye pupil that is filled with light, i.e. correspond to an eye pupil equal to the exit pupil. If the final image is at infinity the Sin Relation becomes

$$nh \sin U = -n'y'u'_{pr},$$

where $2y'$ is the exit pupil diameter and u'_{pr} is the angle (assumed to be small subtended by the image of h (see §2–10). Ignoring the sign and taking $n' = 1$, thi becomes

$$h(\text{N.A.}) = y'u'_{pr},$$

and one has

$$M = u'_{pr} \div h/D_v = \frac{D_v.(\text{N.A.})}{y'}.$$

If $M = 300$ (N.A.), $y' \risingdotseq 1$ mm., and the diameter of the exit pupil is approximatel 2 mm. This suggests that there would be no advantage in increasing M since th diameter of the exit pupil would decrease and the resolution of the eye woul deteriorate. One is led to the conclusion that for normal observers magnifyin powers below about 300 (N.A.) are usually too small, whilst values above abou 600 (N.A.) seldom reveal extra detail; within these limits the choice of magnifyin power is largely a matter of personal taste. The points of substance are:

1. It is necessary to employ an objective whose numerical aperture is suffi ciently large to give images which are physically resolved.

2. It is necessary to employ an eyepiece which will enable the physicall resolved primary images to be resolved by the observer's eye.

In practice, it is found that large values of the numerical aperture can b obtained only with objectives of short focal length, so that the primary magni fication increases rapidly as the numerical aperture increases. As a result, it i found that the necessary eyepiece power decreases for higher power objectives

14-9. Depth of Focus. The Rayleigh Quarter-wave Limit

If the image formed by an optical system is received on a screen placed som distance away from the actual image plane, the image received on the screen wil

Fig. 14–8. Depth of focus.

be of poor quality. It is said to be ou of focus, and the maximum movemen away from the ideal image plane whicl may be made without causing a seriou deterioration of the image is called th *depth of focus*.

In Fig. 14–8 A′P′ is a spherical wav converging to the geometrical imag point B′. An Airy pattern will be forme on the plane perpendicular to the axis at B′, and a slightly different pattern wil be formed on a screen at C′. For a screen at C′, points on A′P′ are no longe equidistant from the central point in the pattern so that the disturbances do no arrive in phase, and the intensity of the central maximum is therefore reduced

According to Rayleigh, there will be no appreciable deterioration of the image, i.e. no marked change from the Airy pattern, provided the maximum phase difference between disturbances arriving at the centre of the pattern doe not exceed $\pi/2$. It will be seen later that a very similar criterion exists concerning the presence of aberrations. Aberrations in a system also introduce phase differences between disturbances arriving at the Gaussian image point from various zones of the aperture, and again it is found that, provided the phase differences do not exceed $\pi/2$, the definition is not seriously impaired. Theory indicates that these tolerances correspond to a reduction in intensity at the centre of the pattern from unity to about 0·8. (In the Rayleigh criterion for resolution, a reduction of 26·4% occurs midway between the images with a circular aperture.)

If $\delta l'$ (Fig. 14–8) is the depth of focus, disturbances from A′ and P′ will arrive at C′ with a phase difference of $\pi/2$. Since A′P′ is a wavefront, the disturbances at A′ and P′ are in phase and the phase difference at C′ is caused by the in-equality of the optical paths A′C′ and P′C′. The optical path difference is obviously $\lambda/4$.

It is assumed that $\delta l' \ll A'B'$ so that each of the angles at B′ and C′ may be written as U'.

In the figure, let B′D′ be perpendicular to P′C′. Then, to the present order of accuracy,

$$P'D'=P'B'=A'B'.$$

The optical path difference $[A'C']-[P'C']$ is given by

$$n'(A'C'-P'C')=n'(B'C'-D'C')$$

$$=n'\delta l'(1-\cos U')$$

$$=2n'\delta l' \sin^2 \frac{U'}{2}$$

$$=\frac{\lambda}{4} \text{ when } \delta l' \text{ is the depth of focus.}$$

Hence the depth of focus is given by

$$\delta l'=\pm \frac{\lambda}{8n' \sin^2 \dfrac{U'}{2}}, \qquad \ldots \ldots \quad (14\text{--}18)$$

where "$\pm$" has been inserted because a movement towards A′ introduces the same optical path difference as an equal movement away from A′.

The deterioration of the image resulting from a movement of the receiving screen through the distance given by (14–18) will be noticeable only if the image is of good quality initially and if the image is examined very critically. In many instruments the state of correction is not good and a considerably greater deterioration can be tolerated. For large movements away from the best focus it is sufficiently accurate to rely on geometrical or ray optics. Thus, in Fig. 14–9, the image of a point source is assumed

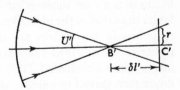

Fig. 14–9. Depth of focus.

to be formed in the region of B′. A movement of the receiving screen to C′ then causes the "image" to become an approximately circular patch of light and if one assumes that the image will be satisfactory for the purpose i question provided its radius does not exceed a certain value r, one obviousl gets, for the depth of focus,

$$\delta l' = \pm \frac{r}{\tan U'}. \qquad \cdots \cdots \quad (14\text{-}19)$$

The depth of focus is the permissible movement of the receiving screen for stationary object plane. If the receiving screen remains stationary and th object plane is moved, the conjugate image plane moves away from the receivin screen and the image on the screen is out of focus. The permissible movemen (δl) of the object plane is called the *depth of field*. It is given by an equation o the same form as (14-18) but involving undashed quantities. The depth of fiel is obviously the movement of the object plane which causes the image plane t move a distance equal to the depth of focus. That is, the depth of focus and th depth of field are conjugate axial distances. For small movements along the axi one has $\delta l = (\delta l'/m^2)(n/n')$ where m is the transverse magnification [see equatio (2-11)]. Frequently the object distance is large, m is small, and the depth of fiel is large; the above relation does not hold but δl remains conjugate to $\delta l'$.

It was pointed out in § 11-15 that it is possible to modify the image formed b an optical system by the introduction of a screen across the aperture. In similar manner it is possible to change the way in which the pattern varies as th receiving screen is moved along the axis. For example, it is possible to arrang that as the receiving screen is moved away from the ideal position the imag deteriorates more rapidly than it does with an ordinary lens system. That is, th depth of focus can be made much smaller by apodization. This can be a usefu method of improving the accuracy of longitudinal setting of a microscope.

14-10. Imagery by a Microscope of Non Self-luminous Objects

The foregoing theory assumes that the object is self-luminous and tha neighbouring points are independent sources emitting non-coherent disturbance which cannot interfere. This is justifiable for telescopes but not for microscopes With a low-power microscope, one may place an opal glass screen immediatel behind the object (assuming it to be a transparency) and, in this case, one doe get a close approximation to self-luminous objects emitting non-coherent light Usually, however, a cone of light emerges from the substage condenser, an neighbouring points of the object are not incoherently illuminated. In the pas it has been argued that if one images a diffuse source in the object plane b means of a perfect substage condenser whose numerical aperture is considerabl larger than that of the objective, the Airy discs in the object plane (correspondin to points in the source) are small and below the limit of resolution of th objective. It was then suggested that, in effect, neighbouring object points ar incoherently illuminated. This argument is unsound because the Airy pattern do, in fact, spread to infinity, and a portion of the light incident at one point o the object plane will always be coherent with a portion of the light falling on neighbouring point. Because of the above interpretation of the imagery by microscope, it became common practice to image a diffuse source in the plan of the object and, since this focusing of the source was thought to be critical

he arrangement was known as *critical illumination*. More recent analysis has
shown that there is nothing particularly critical about it and that, within limits,
any form of illumination will suffice provided the condenser supplies a wide cone
of light. That is, the numerical aperture of the condenser is important, but the
focusing and freedom from aberration are relatively unimportant. However,
the arrangement for critical illumination is a convenient one to use; it is shown
in Fig. 14–10. Usually the numerical aperture of the substage condenser can be
varied by means of the iris diaphragm I_1. In addition, since the source is imaged
in the plane of the object, a second iris I_2 immediately in front of the source can
be used to control the area of the object which is illuminated. It is always
advisable to illuminate only that part of the object which is to be examined since
in this way one reduces the amount of stray light entering the microscope.

Fig. 14–10. Critical illumination.

Another convenient form of illumination is that usually termed *Köhler
illumination*. The arrangement is shown in Fig. 14–11. The source S is imaged in
the back focal plane of the substage condenser by means of the auxiliary lens L.
Thus there emerges from the condenser an array of collimated pencils at various

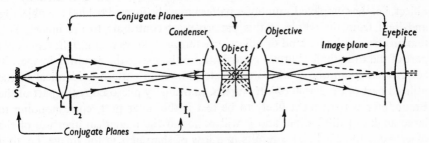

Fig. 14–11. Köhler illumination.

angles and there is no doubt that neighbouring object points are partly coherently
illuminated. It is frequently arranged so that the iris I_2 is imaged in the plane of
the object for the reason given above; the substage iris I_1 again controls the
obliquity of the illumination.

Whatever the nature of the illumination, there is obviously a two-fold diffraction of the light:

1. Incident light is diffracted by the object.
2. Light is further diffracted by the aperture of the objective.

Consequently, every point of the object, as well as every point of the aperture
of the objective, contributes to the disturbance at any point in the image plane.

14–11. Abbe Theory of the Microscope

One of the few cases that can be discussed in detail is the imagery of a regular grating of opaque and transparent elements. Initially, it is assumed that the illumination is restricted Köhler illumination where, in effect, a point source is located in the back focal plane of the condenser (Fig. 14–12). This gives rise to a single collimated beam of light incident parallel to the axis; the light strikes the grating G and is diffracted in the usual way. If the objective has a sufficiently large aperture, the diffracted beams are collected as indicated in the figure. The back focal surface of the objective is conjugate to the source so that the diffraction maxima are in focus in this surface and constitute a Fraunhofer pattern. The light passes on to interfere and give the image in the plane conjugate to the grating.

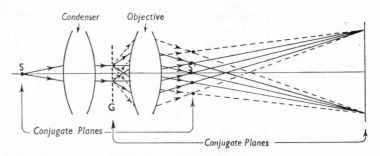

Fig. 14–12. Imagery of a grating.

Abbe was the first to realize that to obtain the best possible image the objective must have an aperture wide enough to admit all the light diffracted by the object, i.e. the complete Fraunhofer pattern must be formed behind the objective and light from the whole of this pattern must contribute to the image. This remains true with any kind of object structure. It follows that if light from only part of the Fraunhofer pattern contributes to the image the resulting image will correspond to an object whose complete diffraction pattern is identical to the utilized part of the actual object pattern. In ordinary microscopy the part of the Fraunhofer pattern most likely to be lost is the outer part, corresponding to large angles of diffraction, and it will be lost if the numerical aperture of the objective is too small. This results in a loss of sharpness in the image, i.e. to a deterioration of the resolution and a loss of the finer detail since it is the sharper boundaries and finer detail which diffract light at the larger angles.

Consider now how the image of a grating is built up. It follows from the discussion of §11–15 that an interrupted, distorted, or limited wavefront produced by any diffracting screen is equivalent to an angular distribution of uniform wavefronts. For an extended grating at G (Fig. 14–12) one has a uniform wavefront for each of the diffracted orders. It is important to realize that the interruptions imposed across the incident wavefront by the grating elements are not present on the component wavefronts into which the interrupted wavefront is resolved. Thus, in particular, the zero order beam is a uniform plane wave that proceeds to a focus S' at the second principal focus of the objective and then diverges to give uniform illumination across the image plane.

There will be two first order beams diffracted at equal angles above and below the axis and producing a pair of maxima behind the objective. These constitute two coherent sources from which disturbances travel to the image plane where they interfere to give the usual two-beam sinusoidal amplitude distribution (i.e. cos^2 fringes). Diffraction maxima of higher orders give effective sources of proportionally greater separation behind the objective and sinusoidal amplitude distributions with proportionally more cycles per unit distance across the image plane. The uniform amplitude produced by the zero order beam, and the sinusoidal amplitude distributions produced by the various pairs of diffracted beams, are superposed in the image plane to give the image. The synthesis of the image from these sinusoidal amplitude distributions occurs in exactly the same way as the synthesis of a square wave form from its Fourier components as described in §6–5. The student may be more familiar with the idea of analysing a complicated periodic motion into simple harmonic motions. In the present situation the Fourier components are simple harmonic variations of amplitude with distance across the image plane and not variations with time; in consequence, one speaks of *spatial frequencies*. Thus, the amplitude distribution across the image plane can be analysed into spatial frequencies in the same way as a complicated periodic motion or wave form can be analysed into simple harmonic oscillations or waves.

For example, in §6–5 the square wave has equally wide crests and troughs and, if a constant term a is added, this corresponds to the amplitude transmitted by a grating having equally wide opaque and transparent elements. In §6–5 the even Fourier components are zero and in §12–8 it is shown that for the corresponding grating the even orders are missing. It also follows from §12–8 that the relative amplitudes of the various odd orders diffracted by the grating are the same as the relative amplitudes of the odd Fourier components of the square wave form illustrated in §6–5. That is to say, the amplitude distribution transmitted by the grating object can be resolved into spatial frequencies, each of which gives a pair of maxima behind the objective and is reproduced in the image. (There will, of course, be a magnification factor between object and image.) In fact, this follows from the discussion of §11–15 where it is shown that, in general, for a Fraunhofer diffraction pattern the pattern function is the Fourier transform of the aperture function. In the present problem one has two stages: (1) the object diffracts to give a Fraunhofer pattern behind the objective, the pattern function being the transform of the aperture (i.e. object) function, and (2) the lens aperture can be said to diffract the light from the object (looked upon as the source) to give a Fraunhofer pattern in the image plane. In the second stage the pattern function describes the image and is the transform of the aperture function describing the distribution of light behind the objective. (Here it is implied that the lens pupil is in the back focal plane, but this is not a serious restriction.) The aperture function of stage (2) is the pattern function of stage (1) and it will be seen that if no light is lost the image is the transform of the transform (the synthesis of the analysis) of the object, and is identical to it. A grating object is periodic (strictly speaking, only if the grating is infinitely wide —see §6–7) and the analysis gives a Fourier series of discrete terms corresponding to integral orders in the diffraction pattern. A non-periodic or irregular object structure gives a Fourier transform corresponding to a diffraction pattern without discrete orders. A grating of finite width gives weak secondary maxima between principal maxima, i.e. contains the intermediate frequencies, but with small amplitudes.

It is now possible to understand the effect on the grating image of the limitations imposed by the aperture of the objective. The grating structure analyses into a discrete spectrum of spatial frequencies where each frequency corresponds to a diffracted beam of given order, and higher orders correspond to larger angles of diffraction. Diffracted beams above a certain order will fail to enter the lens, and the corresponding spatial frequencies in the object will not be reproduced in the image. The distribution of light in the image will be represented by the sum of the first p terms of the Fourier series, p being the number of diffracted orders entering the lens (see §6–5).

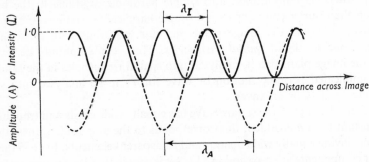

Fig. 14–13. Fourier component.

An irregular object structure analyses into a continuous distribution of spatial frequencies (referred to as a continuous Fourier spectrum) and, as before, the light diffracted at the larger angles corresponds to the higher frequencies. Again, if this light is not transmitted by the lens the corresponding frequencies will be missing from the image and this finer detail will not be observable.

One is now led to a new definition of limit of resolution: it is simply the highest spatial frequency in the object that is reproduced in the image. It is, of course, the reciprocal of this—the wavelength—that should be compared with the earlier definition in terms of resolved point objects. Attention must be drawn to a common source of confusion: in the above discussions the illumination across the object is coherent and in a theoretical treatment it is natural to discuss amplitudes in object and image. However, the eye detects intensities, and this can introduce a factor of 2 when discussing spatial frequencies in the image. This is illustrated in Fig. 14–13. The broken curve shows a simple harmonic variation of amplitude and the wavelength is λ_A; the square of the amplitude gives the intensity which is shown by the unbroken curve and the wavelength is λ_I. In what follows the limit of resolution is the smallest intensity wavelength that is imaged.

Return, now, to the simple grating object consisting of alternate opaque and transparent elements. At first sight, in view of what has been said in the earlier discussion, it might be thought that in order to be able to observe the periodicity of the grating the two first order beams must contribute to the image to reprouce the fundamental or lowest spatial frequency component in the amplitude distribution. However, one is, in fact, more interested in intensities, and it is easy to show that if the zero order and *one* of the first order beams enter the lens, giving two effective sources in the focal plane, the intensity distribution across the image plane exhibits maxima corresponding to the grating spaces, and the rulings of the grating are resolved. This need to transmit the zero order plus one of the first order beams is sometimes referred to as the *Abbe principle* and the limit of resolution is the grating interval of the finest grating that can be resolved in this way. Finer gratings give larger angles between the zero and first orders and so require lenses of larger numerical aperture in order to be resolved.

By interposing stops in the back focal plane of a microscope objective it is easy to vary the effective aperture of the lens, and Plate IV(*a*) and (*b*) shows the effect on the resolution of reducing the numerical aperture of the objective.

In addition to the possibility of some details in the object being absent from the image, there is also the danger that the image will show false detail, i.e. will indicate detail which is not, in fact, present in the object. As an extreme example, suppose that, with a grating as object, alternate maxima in the pattern are obstructed; the remaining maxima correspond to the pattern for a grating whose spacing is half that of the actual grating employed. Since the image is simply formed by the interference of light from the unobstructed maxima, it will have the appearance of an image of the finer grating instead of the real one. An obstruction of the Fraunhofer pattern such as that just described is, of course, extremely unlikely to occur accidentally. However, it must always be borne in mind that under certain conditions false detail may appear in the image. This is most likely to occur when extra stops and diaphragms, etc., are employed as in dark-ground and phase-contrast microscopy (see §14–14).

The above discussion of the mechanism of image formation with non self-luminous objects follows that given by Abbe (*c*. 1873). The same problem is approached rather differently in the following method due to Rayleigh. Light from the substage condenser falls on the object and, from each point of the latter, a certain resultant disturbance emerges. The light from each point in the object then gives an Airy pattern in the conjugate image plane. The final image is formed by the superposition of these Airy patterns, and the effect of the superposition can be calculated if the phase relations and degrees of coherence between the various disturbances are known. These are determined by the structure of the object and the form of the illumination. In this treatment of the problem, the Airy patterns result from diffraction by the objective and the structure of the object is taken into account by inserting the phase relations between the Airy patterns. In the Abbe theory, diffraction by the object gives the Fraunhofer pattern behind the objective and diffraction by the objective itself is taken account of by the way in which its aperture limits the extent of the Fraunhofer pattern. Thus in both methods of approach one takes account of diffraction by the object and by the objective.

It is natural that, associated with these two methods of approaching the problem, one has the two different definitions of the limit of resolution: the separation of two just resolvable points, and the spacing of a just resolvable grating structure (or a spatial frequency). The Abbe theory has been greatly

extended more recently and it is interesting to note that the results are of ve
great practical importance in considering the performance of almost all lens
except microscope objectives! This is because, as will be seen later, the resu
are relevant to the assessment of imperfect lenses, whereas for most purpos
microscope objectives can be considered to be aberration-free (see §14–15).

14–12. Derivation of Limit of Resolution from Abbe Principle

According to the Abbe principle given above, the minimum requirement f
any degree of resolution of a grating to be apparent is that the objective mu
collect the direct (zero order) beam and at least one of the first order beams.

Consider first the simple form of Köhler illumination where a single collimat
beam is incident along the axis [Fig. 14–14(a)]. The angle of diffraction for t
first order maximum is defined by

$$n'd \sin \theta_1 = \lambda,$$

where d is the grating interval and n' is the refractive index of the mediu
between the grating and the objective. Now, according to the Abbe princip
the limit of resolution of the objective is the value of d for which the first ord

Fig. 14–14. Limit of resolution from the Abbe principle.

beam can just enter the objective. It is the value of d when θ_1 is the semi-ang
of the largest cone of rays which the objective can admit, i.e. when $n' \sin \theta_1$ is t
numerical aperture of the objective. Hence the limit of resolution is given

$$d = \frac{\lambda}{(\text{N.A.})}. \qquad \cdots \cdots \quad (14\text{–}20)$$

Suppose now that the condenser is capable of illuminating the object by mea
of oblique beams. For the beam incident at angle I [Fig. 14–14(b)], the directi
of the pth order maximum is given by the usual grating formula

$$d(n' \sin \theta_p - n \sin I) = p\lambda. \qquad \cdots \cdots \quad (14\text{–}21)$$

For the zero order beam $d(n' \sin \theta_0 - n \sin I) = 0$, which simply gives Snell's la
of refraction. For the first order beam,

$$d(n' \sin \theta_1 - n \sin I) = \lambda,$$

or $$d(n' \sin \theta_1 - n' \sin \theta_0) = \lambda. \qquad \cdots \cdots \quad (14\text{–}22)$$

Now the Abbe principle is that the zero order beam and one first order bea
must enter the objective. For a given objective this can occur for the smalle
possible value of d (i.e. for the largest angle between the beams) when th

ncident light is so directed that the zero order and one of the first order beams nter diametrically opposite extremities of the objective aperture, i.e. when $\theta_0 = -\theta_1$. Putting $\theta_0 = -\theta_1$ in (14–22), one obtains

$$2dn' \sin \theta_1 = \lambda,$$

.e. the limit of resolution is given by

$$d = \frac{0 \cdot 5\lambda}{\text{(N.A.)}}. \quad \cdot \quad \cdot \quad \cdot \quad \cdot \quad \cdot \quad \cdot \quad (14–23)$$

This result indicates that the numerical aperture of the condenser is relevant o the limit of resolution of the objective since the ability of the condenser to lluminate the object with an oblique beam depends on its numerical aperture.

More detailed analysis of this and similar problems confirms that the aperture of the condenser is important, but indicates that, in general, its influence is ather less than that represented by the factor of two indicated by equations 14–20) and (14–23). It is interesting to compare the present results with that lerived on the assumption that the object is self-luminous. (See §14–7.)

It must be appreciated that the above discussion represents an approximate heory. For example, it is assumed that light associated with a given maximum s diffracted in a single direction and that all the light associated with a given rder is either accepted or rejected by the objective. That is, no account is taken f the possibility of part of the light in a given order being admitted, and no ccount is taken of the finite amount of light which is diffracted between the rincipal maxima.

4–13. Dark-Ground, Phase-Contrast, and Interference Microscopy

As the numerical aperture of the microscope objective is increased, more iffracted light contributes to the image and the distribution of amplitude and hase across the primary image plane of the nicroscope approaches that immediately be-ind the object. In the present discussion it will e assumed that the imagery is perfect in the ense that the distribution is exactly the same n these two planes. Although this condition an never be attained exactly, it provides a seful starting point in explaining the principles f the various methods of microscopy.

Fig. 14–15. Disturbances in image of phase object.

Suppose, now, that the object is completely ransparent but has an optical thickness which aries from point to point. Such an object is nown as a *phase object*—it introduces phase dif-erences between disturbances which pass through ifferent parts of it. Consequently, the disturbances immediately behind the bject, and in the conjugate image plane, have the same amplitude at all points ut will show variations in phase from point to point. Now the human eye is ensitive to intensity only and cannot detect changes of phase so that the field of iew appears uniformly bright. In Fig. 14–15 the lengths and directions of the

vectors shown as thick, full lines represent the amplitudes and phases of the dis
turbances at the various points A,B,C, . . . in the image plane; they will hav
equal lengths but different directions. Suppose that, in some way, a disturbanc
of constant amplitude and phase (represented by the dotted vectors) is added t
every point in the primary image plane, and that this disturbance is coheren
with the existing disturbances. At each point the two disturbances will interfer
and the resulting intensity (R^2) at any point will depend on the phase differenc
between them as indicated in the figure. The variations in optical thickness i
the object cause variations in intensity in the image so that the phase object i
rendered "visible". This method of converting differences in phase into dif
ferences in intensity is employed in some interference microscopes and als
forms the basis of the dark-ground and phase-contrast techniques. Thus, in on

(a)   (b)   (c)

Fig. 14–16. Amplitude object.

class of interference microscope a wavefront that has been modulated by havin
been passed through (or reflected by) the object structure interferes with a
unmodulated reference wavefront which constitutes the added constant "back
ground" disturbance. In the dark-ground method, a disturbance is *subtracte
from every point in the field of view, and in the phase-contrast method intro
duced by Zernike (*c*. 1935), part of the light at each point in the field is phase
shifted. Since phase-shifting the light is equivalent to removing it and the
adding light of different phase, this process also is equivalent to adding
constant background disturbance across the field. In a second class of inter
ference microscope the system resembles a wavefront shearing interferometer s
that light that has passed through one part of the object interferes with light tha
has passed through another part. The principle of the phase-contrast microscop
can be understood by comparing the imagery of a small absorbing particle wit
the imagery of a small phase object. Consider first a purely amplitude particle
i.e. one that does not introduce a phase change compared with its surroundings
In Fig. 14–16(*a*) the particle consists of a small, slightly absorbing region sur
rounded by non-absorbing material of the same refractive index. Suppose th
incident light from the substage condenser consists of a single plane wave W
The wave $\overline{W}$ that emerges from the object has a region of reduced amplitude
represented in the figure by the thinner line. The disturbance at 1 which has no
passed through the particle can be represented by the vector 1 in Fig. 14–16(*b*)

The disturbance at 2 which has passed through the particle has slightly reduced amplitude but has the same phase as 1; it is represented by vector 2. It will be seen that in (b) 2=1+3, which means that the disturbance in the region 2 is equivalent to the disturbance in region 1 plus a weak disturbance 3 having a phase lag of π. This out of phase disturbance corresponds to a wave travelling a distance $\lambda/2$ behind the wave 1. That is to say, the wave $\overline{W}$, which has the region of reduced intensity, is equivalent to a uniform wave W plus a small wave w following on $\lambda/2$ behind—Fig. 14–16 (c).

Consider these waves entering the microscope objective (Fig. 14–17). W passes through a region of focus at the principal focus F_0' and then spreads across the image plane. w, a wavefront of limited width (known as the diffracted wave), is equivalent to a broad angular distribution of disturbances that enters over the

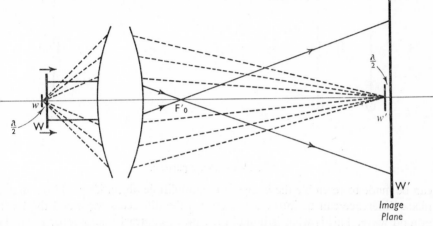

Fig. 14–17. Imaging a particle.

whole aperture of the lens. This is readily appreciated once it is realized that it is a wave such as w which would be transmitted by a very narrow slit, earlier discussion (§§11–1 and 11–2) having shown that light from such a slit is diffracted over a wide angle. (See also §11–15.) The transmission of this light through the lens is equivalent to the formation of the image of such a slit, and if the lens is well corrected and the aperture is wide enough to transmit most of the light involved, the image formation is almost perfect (§14–11). That is to say, a small wave w' will be found $\lambda/2$ behind the "background wave" W'. An argument that is the reverse of that given above referring to Fig. 14–16 then shows that across the image plane one has a wave of the form $\overline{W}$ [Fig. 14–16(a)]. On viewing this image plane the observer will detect the less bright region which is the image of the amplitude particle; the particle is seen.

Consider now the imagery of a phase object consisting of a small phase-retarding but non-absorbing particle [Fig. 14–18(a)]. If the particle introduces a small phase lag the transmitted wave $\overline{W}$ is of uniform amplitude but has a slightly retarded region (2). The disturbance (1) that has missed the particle is represented by vector 1 in (b) and the disturbance (2) that has passed through the particle is represented by vector 2, which is the same length as 1 but makes a small angle δ

with it, δ being the phase retardation introduced by the particle. Obviously 2=1+3. If δ is small, 3 is a weak disturbance approximately $\pi/2$ out of phase with 1. That is to say, $\overline{W}$ in (a) is equivalent to a uniform wave W plus a small wave w travelling $\lambda/4$ behind it—Fig. 14–18 (c). It will be seen at once that if these enter the microscope objective there will be found at the image plane a wave W' plus a small wave w' as in Fig. 14–17 except that one now has w' $\lambda/4$ behind W'. On inverting the argument referring to Fig. 14–18, one sees that across the image field one will have uniform intensity, and the particle will not be detectable. It will be seen that the conditions obtaining in the image plane with the phase particle closely resemble those with the amplitude object, except that with the phase object the diffracted wave lags in phase by $\pi/2$ whereas with the amplitude object it lags by π. Obviously, the appearance of the image of the phase object

(a)   (b)   (c)

Fig. 14–18. Phase particle.

can be made to resemble the image of the amplitude object if an additional $\pi/2$ phase difference can be introduced between the diffracted wave and the background wave. This is what is done in the phase-contrast microscope. It can be done by inserting into the back focal plane of the objective a *phase plate* of some transparent material that has a reduced thickness over a small region surrounding the principal focus. In this way the diffracted light, which is distributed widely over the aperture of the lens, is retarded by $\pi/2$ compared with the background light which is concentrated into the region of the focus (see Fig. 14–17). The total phase difference between the background light and the diffracted wave

becomes π and the particle is "seen".

Suppose now that the whole object plane is occupied by an extended phase object, the optical thickness varying from point to point. Following Zernicke, divide the object plane into a large number of equal small areas and suppose, as before, that the incident light is a plane wave. The disturbances emerging from the various elementary areas A, B, C, ... are represented in Fig. 14–19 by the

Fig. 14–19. Phase contrast.

ectors OA, OB, OC, . . . which, for convenience, are drawn from the common origin O so that for the pure phase object the points A, B, C, . . . lie on the circle centred at O. Since the phase-contrast method is chiefly of use when the variations of phase introduced by the object are small (less than about $\pi/4$), it is assumed that the points A, B, C, . . . lie on one side of O. In the figure, an anti-clockwise rotation of a vector about O corresponds to increased retardation of the disturbances. That is, the vector OD corresponds to the thickest, and OH to the thinnest part of the object. Each of the disturbances OA, OB, OC, . . . can be looked upon as the disturbance ON plus the disturbance NA, NB, NC,. . . . Hence, emerging from the object plane, one has, in effect, a uniform plane wave represented by ON plus diffracted waves represented by NA, NB, NC, . . . from the various object elements. As before, the broad plane wave is brought to a focus at F_0' and then spreads over the image plane. In addition, each of the diffracted waves NA, NB, NC, . . . gives a small contribution in the region of F_0', but if N is the centroid of the points A, B, C, . . . the resultant of all these small contributions is zero. Thus, since only *relative* amplitudes and *relative* phases are important, the total zero order contribution from F_0' to each point in the image plane can be represented by ON. As before, for a wide aperture well corrected objective, the vectors representing the disturbances at various parts of the object plane also represent those across the image, and the non-zero order light which does not pass through F_0' gives contributions represented by NA, NB, NC, . . . at the various image points, the resultant disturbances in the image being represented by OA, OB, OC, ... Absorbing elements in the object plane (amplitude objects) of average optical thickness would give vectors such as OX, OY, along the mean phase line.

In *central dark-ground* illumination the zero order light is removed without affecting the diffracted light. (With the arrangement shown in Fig. 14–17 this could be done by placing an obstruction at F_0'.) This corresponds to subtracting, from each point in the field of view, a disturbance represented by ON. In the figure, this corresponds to the addition of a vector NO to each vector OA, OB, etc., so that the resultants are OA', OB', OC', etc., where A', B', C', etc., lie a distance NO to the left of A,B,C, etc. The points A', B', C', etc., are not shown in the figure because the state of affairs can be represented equally well by moving the origin a distance ON to the right, i.e. to N. That is to say, with central dark-ground illumination the disturbances at the various points in the field of view are represented by NA, NB, NC, etc. Since these vectors are of different lengths, there will be variations in intensity across the field of view. However, a vector such as NC, which corresponds to a relatively thick part of the object, will have the same length as, say, NG, which corresponds to a relatively thin part, and since the intensity depends only upon the length of the vector, the two parts of the field appear equally bright. Furthermore, the more absorbing part of the object which corresponds to the point X, will now appear brighter than the more transparent part corresponding to Y; obviously this is a disadvantage.

In the phase-contrast method, the phase of the direct or zero order light is changed with respect to the diffracted light. As an example, suppose the phase of the direct light is advanced through $\pi/2$ with respect to the diffracted light.

Obviously this is equivalent to removing the direct light (which transfers the origin from O to N) and then adding a disturbance which is $\pi/2$ ahead of it. In the figure, ON_1 is a disturbance of the same amplitude as ON but $\pi/2$ ahead. When the origin is at N, the effect of adding ON_1 is to move the points A,B,C etc., a distance ON_1 downwards or to move the origin from N to O_1. The disturbances in the image plane are then represented by O_1D, O_1C, O_1B, etc., and it will be seen that the thicker parts of the object give smaller intensities than the thinner parts. This is known as *positive phase-contrast*. By retarding the phase of the zero order light with respect to the diffracted maxima, one obtains *negative phase-contrast* in which the thicker parts of the object appear brighter. If the retardation is $\pi/2$ the origin is at O_2.

By securing a progressive decrease (or increase) in intensity as the thickness of the object increases one overcomes the first disadvantage of central dark ground illumination mentioned above. On the other hand, one still has $O_1Y<O_1X$ so that the more absorbing part of the object (corresponding to X) appears brighter. This difficulty can be overcome for a fairly wide range of absorptions, while retaining the gradation of intensity with thickness, by advancing (or retarding) the phase of the direct light by something less than $\pi/2$. For example, ON_3 is less than $\pi/2$ ahead of ON, and if this is added when the origin is at N, the points A,B,C, etc., are moved "to the south-east" or the origin is moved to O_3. The disturbances in the image plane are then represented by O_3A, O_3B, etc., and the intensity decreases as the thickness of the object increases. In addition $O_3X<O_3Y$ so that the more absorbing part of the object appears less bright. It is, however, not possible to decide whether the reduction in intensity observed in a part of the field of view is due to absorption in the object or simply to increased retardation. This can be decided if one can examine the object under ordinary conditions of illumination since the only remaining reduction in intensity will be that caused by absorption. Plate IV(d) and (e) shows some flakes of mica immersed in glue with normal illumination and with phase-contrast. By absorbing some of the zero order light in addition to changing its phase, one can move the origin to any point on the lines NO_1, NO_2, NO_3, etc., thereby changing the ratio of, for example, O_1C/O_1B, and altering the contrast in the image. This is useful when the object shows only very small variations in thickness, but one must be careful to avoid placing the origin among the points A,B,C, . . . since this would reintroduce the unwanted reversal of contrast observed with central dark ground.

In the form of dark-ground illumination referred to above, the zero order light is removed but all the diffracted light contributes to the image. In addition the discussion really concerns the intensity over an elementary area of the image. For example, if the transparent object consists of a number of flakes of mica, the above discussion gives the intensity over the image of each flake. In the form of dark-ground illumination usually employed in practice (see next section), the illumination is oblique so that the zero order and all the diffracted orders on one side of it are ineffective. In addition, the most interesting effect is the appearance of the image of the actual boundary between adjacent elements of the object. In § 10–13 it was shown that after diffraction by an object the light can be analysed into two components: the direct light and the edge waves. In oblique dark ground illumination one collects only part of that portion of the edge wave which spreads to one side of the direct light. That is, the light entering the objective has the form of disturbances that have originated at the discontinuities in the object. These edge waves come to a focus in the image plane so that discontinuities in the object show up as bright lines in the image (see Plate IV(g)).

14–14. Experimental Arrangements

(a) *Bright-field, Dark-ground, and Phase-contrast*

In the previous section, dark-ground illumination is introduced as being the result of obstructing the zero order light. Normally it is only oblique dark-ground illumination that is used in practice and the simplest way of excluding the zero order light is to arrange that it does not enter the objective. This can be done if the object is illuminated by a hollow cone of light as indicated by Fig. 14–20. For low power objectives one can employ an ordinary condenser with an annular aperture in its back focal plane as indicated in the figure. For higher

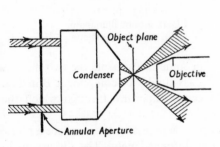

Fig. 14–20.
Low-power dark-ground illuminator.

Fig. 14–21.
Dark-ground illuminator.

powers (higher apertures) it is necessary to employ a reflecting condenser such as the Beck focusing dark-ground illuminator shown in Fig. 14–21. The upper component A is oiled to the slide and the lower component B can be moved to enable the illuminator to be used with slides of various thicknesses. In many fixed focus condensers a similar system is employed except that, in effect, A and B form a single block of glass.

An extreme example of oblique dark-ground illumination is the arrangement known as the *ultra-microscope*. Here an intense beam is incident at right angles to the optical axis of the microscope. Discontinuities in the object appear bright as usual and it is possible to detect the presence of particles that are considerably below the limit of resolution of the objective. The arrangement has been used to observe particles in colloidal suspensions. A small volume of the suspension is illuminated so that only particles in that region are observed.

The diagrams given in §14–10 illustrate critical and Köhler illumination of transmitting objects. Exactly similar arrangements are possible for the illumination of opaque specimens, the objective performing the function of the substage condenser as well as forming the image. This is achieved by inserting a semi-reflecting plate behind the objective as in Fig. 14–22. It will be seen that a plane mirror at the object plane, which is equivalent to a blank slide in transmission, reflects the light back through the objective so that the system gives ordinary bright-field illumination.

For opaque objects absorbing and phase-retarding structure correspond respectively to variations in reflectivity and departures from surface flatness. Oblique dark-ground illumination for opaque objects is achieved in a manner exactly analogous to that used for transmitting objects, the zero order light reflected from a plane mirror object falling outside the objective aperture.

Fig. 14-22. Illumination of opaque specimens.

Fig. 14-23. Dark-ground illuminator for opaque specimens.

Fig. 14-23 shows a suitable arrangement; in some instruments the two mirrors are the outer surfaces of a solid block of glass similar to component B in Fig. 14-21 except, of course, that there is a central aperture through which the objective passes.

As explained in §14-13, for phase-contrast it is necessary to introduce a phase difference between the zero order and the diffracted light. The discussion in §14-13 referred to a simple form of Köhler illumination with a point source whereas in practice one wishes to use a more extended source in order to obtain a brighter image. It can be shown that with an extended source each plane wave from the condenser gives the same effect so that the net result is that the extended

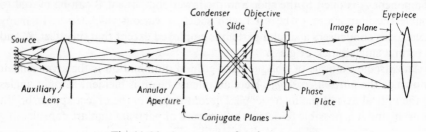

Fig. 14-24. Arrangement for phase contrast.

source simply raises the intensity level in the image without changing the relative intensities in different parts of it. This, of course, assumes that for each source point one can introduce the required phase difference between the zero order and diffracted light. Fig. 14-24 shows the arrangement usually employed for transmitting objects. An annular aperture is placed in the back focal plane of the substage condenser and the *phase plate* is conjugate to this, in the back focal plane of the objective. For positive phase-contrast, the phase plate has an annular depression as indicated, and this is exactly conjugate to the annular aperture. The figure shows the path of the zero order light and it will be seen that it passes through the thinner part of the phase plate. Consequently, its phase is advanced with respect to the diffracted light which passes through the thicker parts of the plate. There is no doubt that some of the diffracted light will also pass through the thinner annulus in the plate but this is unavoidable; it causes a slight reduction in image contrast. If t is the depth of the depression and n is the refractive index of the phase plate, the zero order light is advanced in phase by $(2\pi/\lambda)(n-1)t$ with respect to most of the diffracted light. It will be appreciated that, for maximum efficiency, all the direct light must pass through the thin annulus but that the latter must be as small as possible in order to reduce the amount of diffracted light transmitted. It is therefore important that the image of the annular aperture should coincide exactly with the annular depression in the phase plate. In practice this adjustment is checked by observation with a small auxiliary microscope inserted in the eyepiece tube. It is not essential to employ an annular aperture, and an aperture in the form of a cross has also been used. The relative merits of these arrangements cannot be discussed here. Since the back focal plane of a microscope objective frequently falls within the lens system, the phase plate must be "built in" as indicated by Fig. 14–25.

Fig. 14–25. Location of phase plate in a 4 mm. objective.

Before leaving the subject of phase contrast, mention must be made of a very simple method of rendering visible phase objects which show relatively large variations in thickness. When the direct and all the diffracted light is effective under ordinary illumination, the distribution of amplitude and phase in the image plane is an exact copy of that immediately behind the object. In the phase-contrast method this condition is upset, and the object rendered visible, by introducing a phase difference between the direct and diffracted beams. Now the direct and diffracted beams traverse different zones of the objective aperture and it was shown in §14–9 that disturbances traversing different zones of the aperture of an optical system are out of phase in planes slightly removed from the ideal image plane. That is to say, a phase difference between the direct and diffracted beams can be introduced simply by slightly defocusing the microscope. This is sufficient to render visible variations in optical thickness which are greater than about $\lambda/8$.

(b) Interference Microscopes

In an interference microscope one examines the form of the wavefront leaving a phase object. This is done by superposing a reference wavefront, coherent with the first, and observing the interference pattern. As has already been mentioned in §14–13, the second wavefront can be a wavefront that has not been modulated by the object structure, or it can be produced by a wavefront shearing interferometer. An example of the first class of instrument is the arrangement used by Linnik (1926) for opaque objects. The system resembles a Michelson or Twyman-Green interferometer. Identical microscope objectives are placed in the two arms, one being focused on a plane mirror at M_1 (Fig. 8–14) and the other on the specimen which replaces M_2. Equivalent systems for transmitting objects employ arrangements similar to the Jamin or to the Mach–Zehnder interferometer. For example, in Fig. 8–17, G and C can be replaced by (object and objective) and (blank slide and objective) respectively. This principle has been used in the Leitz microscope. A disadvantage of the systems referred to above is that each requires a pair of objectives that are optically identical. Alternative arrangements, such as that employed in the Watson interference

Fig. 14–26. Watson interference objective.

objective for opaque objects, avoid this difficulty by using a Michelson system with the beam splitter and reference mirror mounted between the object and the objective (see Fig. 14–26). One obvious difficulty in this system is the need for an objective with a long working distance in order to accommodate the beam splitter; the difficulty increases as the power and aperture are increased.

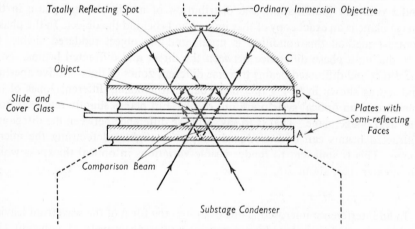

Fig. 14–27. Dyson's interference microscope.

Another system that produces an independent reference beam is that due to Dyson (Fig. 14–27). This is a unit magnification interferometer system added below an ordinary microscope objective. Light from the condenser is amplitude-divided at the upper surface of plate A so that the comparison beam is displaced sideways and misses the object. The other beam passes straight on, passes through the object, and is reflected in plate B to recombine with the comparison beam. The combined disturbances are then reflected at the spherical surface C and again at the upper surface of plate B before entering the objective. C is, in fact, the upper surface of a block of glass that is cemented to the plate B; contact between the other components is made with an immersion fluid as indicated. The totally reflecting spot on the upper surface of B obstructs the axial rays of both beams; this is necessary because both would have passed through the object. The ray paths shown in the figure indicate that, in effect, the objective is focused on both the object and the lower surface of plate A. That is to say, the interference occurs between light that has *passed through* the object and light that has been *reflected by* the lower surface of A acting as a reference surface—one is observing phase differences between disturbances in a beam that has passed through the object and those in an identical beam that has been reflected by a plane mirror occupying the position of the object. The plates A and B are slightly wedge-shaped (wedge angle 5 minutes) and one can vary the path difference between the two beams by displacing plate A laterally. If the path difference is made zero fine phase particles will appear dark on a bright background, and if the path difference is $\lambda/2$ they will appear bright on a dark background. It should be noted that if the lateral extent of the object is considerably larger than the field of view, the reference beam will traverse the outer region of the object structure and the system cannot be classified as one that produces an unmodulated reference beam.

It was stated earlier that there is a second class of interference microscope, which uses the principle of the wavefront shearing interferometer (see §8–15). There are two sub-classes: those that introduce a shear that is larger than the lateral extent of the object structure being examined, and those that introduce a very small shear comparable with the limit of resolution. Thus Françon refers to *image duplication* methods and *differential* methods.

(a)	(b)	(c)
Wavefront	*Image*	*Differential*
after Particle	*Doubling*	*Shear*

Fig. 14–28. Wavefront shearing.

Fig. 14–28(a) illustrates the form of a wavefront emerging from a phase particle. A shearing interferometer system giving image duplication will produce the effect shown in (*b*) and a differential system will give the effect shown in (*c*). $\triangle$ is the instrumental path difference.

It will be seen at once that if one is examining a single small particle with the duplication method the effect is the same as with the first class of interferometer where a completely independent reference wavefront is produced (except, of course, that two "images" of the particle will be seen). Obviously, the pattern is difficult to interpret when the object field contains other particles since the various images become superimposed. Referring now to the differential method, it will be seen from (*c*) that the path differences at positions (1) and (2) depend upon the slope of the wavefront and upon the extent of the shear and not upon the actual retardation introduced by the particle. That is to say, the differential method reveals optical path gradients in the object structure, and if the shear is smaller than the limit of resolution no double contours will be seen in the image. Differential systems are not restricted to the examination of isolated particles.

A large number of wavefront shearing interference microscopes have been produced employing birefringent double image prisms to introduce the shear. For example the image duplication system due to F. H. Smith and the differential system due to Nomarski employ double image prisms of the Wollaston type (see §22–7). In practice, it is usual to duplicate the wavefront and introduce a shear before passing through the object. The shear is then removed to give a net result equivalent to introducing a single shear after the object (see Fig. 14–29).

(c)
Shear
Removed

(a)
Sheared Wavefronts
before Object

(b)
Sheared Wavefronts
after Object

Fig. 14–29. Wavefront shearing.

The reason for this is as follows: a Wollaston prism introduces an optical path difference between the two emergent rays and this depends on the part of the aperture traversed, being zero at the mid-point where the thicknesses of the two component prisms are equal. Hence if there is only one shearing prism in the system the aperture must be made small. However, if one has a prism behind the condenser and a second one behind the objective, the optical path difference in the first can be balanced in the second, and a wide aperture can be used. If the limitation of aperture is accepted, one can simply insert a wavefront shearing interferometer system (an interference eyepiece) behind the objective of an ordinary microscope.

Another form of interference microscope that should be mentioned is the axial image duplication system due to Smith. A doubly refracting plate is added to the objective so that it has two planes of focus—the actual object plane and

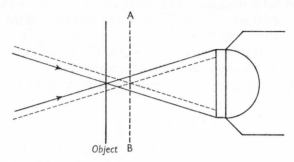

Fig. 14–30. Smith's axial duplication system.

the plane AB (Fig. 14–30). Thus these two planes are imaged into the same image plane and the reference "wavefront" is the distribution of light disturbances across the plane AB. This is equivalent to saying that interference occurs between an in-focus image and an out-of-focus or axially displaced image, instead of a laterally displaced image as before. As in the shearing systems a second image-doubling plate is added to the substage condenser, but again this does not affect the principle of the method.

In conclusion it should be pointed out that the phase-contrast microscope is not satisfactory if the lateral structure of the object is coarse. This is because the object structure will diffract only a small amount of light at an angle large enough for it to be well separated from the zero order light on reaching the phase plate. It will then be impossible for the phase plate to introduce a phase difference between the zero order and most of the diffracted light, and the contrast will be poor. Another disadvantage of the phase-contrast microscope is that images are often surrounded by halos caused by diffraction at the phase plate itself. Interference microscopes do not have these two disadvantages and, although they are often more complicated and difficult to adjust, they often have a variable path difference, giving the benefits of a variable phase plate and (since the path difference can be made zero) the possibility of using white light and colour contrast.

14–15. Further Discussion of Theory of Image Formation. The Optical Transfer Function

In the preceding sections there has been some discussion of the formation of an image by a microscope objective. In the present section the discussion is more appropriate to the formation of an image by a camera lens. Usually a camera lens has aberrations that are sufficiently large to make the overall performance of the lens significantly inferior to that of an aberration-free system. Hence one needs to be able to specify the image-forming properties of a lens so that it is possible to compare the performances of different lenses. From the designer's point of view, one needs to be able to specify the performance required from a particular lens and then to specify tolerances for its aberrations.

Suppose, then, that a lens with a circular aperture forms an image of an object plane, where it may be assumed that the disturbances from various parts of the object are completely incoherent. These conditions are approached very closely in most object fields presented to camera lenses. If the lens is aberration-free, each point in the object gives an Airy diffraction pattern and the image results from the superposition of these Airy patterns, the total intensity at any point being the sum of the separate intensities. The expression giving the intensity distribution in an Airy diffraction pattern (equation 11–8) is such that in general it is extremely difficult to find the intensity distribution in the image of an

(a)   (b)

Fig. 14–31. Imagery of sinusoidal component.

extended object. For a lens with aberration the diffraction image of a point is much more complicated than the Airy pattern and it becomes virtually impossible to calculate the form of an extended image. If one cannot find the effect of the aberration on the image it is impossible to specify an aberration tolerance appropriate to a given image quality. In fact, it is difficult even to specify the image quality or lens performance required if the problem is approached in the above manner. One thing that could be specified is the limit of resolution but it will be seen below that in general this is quite inadequate. Furthermore, it is usually not even possible to give an aberration tolerance corresponding to a stated limit of resolution, and the best that can be done is to state the magnitude of the aberration that causes the standard of image formation to become just noticeably inferior to that of an aberration-free system. That is to say, this method of approach to the problem is satisfactory only for very highly corrected systems such as microscope objectives. The reason for the failure of this approach for most camera lenses is that the object is thought of as being composed of a collection of points, each giving a complicated pattern. An alternative approach is suggested by the Abbe theory of image formation in a microscope. This leads one to think of the intensity distribution across the object as the superposition (the synthesis) of a number of sinusoidal distributions. The enormous advantage of this is that provided certain conditions are satisfied—and usually they are— the image of a sinusoidal intensity distribution also has a sinusoidal form that is independent of the presence of other sinusoidal components. That is to say, a lens is a linear filter of spatial frequencies, and this remains true, with certain limitations, when the lens has aberrations. The situation is as follows: if one has an object consisting of a line structure across which the intensity distribution is of the form

$$B(\xi)=a+\beta \cos 2\pi R\xi \quad \ldots \ldots \quad (14\text{–}24)$$

[see Fig. 14–31(a)], then the intensity distribution across the image is given by

$$B'(\xi')=a'+\beta' \cos (2\pi R'\xi'+\theta) \quad \ldots \ldots \quad (14\text{–}25)$$

[see Fig. 14–31(b)]. The contrast in the image is always lower than that in the object and, unless there is no asymmetrical (comatic) aberration, there is a spatial phase shift or a displacement of the image structure from the position corresponding to an aberration-free system. The ratio of the modulation or contrast in the image to that in the object $(=\beta'/a' \div \beta/a)$ is called the *modulation* (or *contrast*) *transfer factor* and is denoted by T; one then puts

$$D=Te^{i\theta}, \quad \ldots \ldots \ldots \quad (14\text{–}26)$$

where D is called the *optical transfer function* (or *frequency response*). D depends on the spatial frequency, R. It is convenient in this work to define "optical co-ordinates" (u, v), (u', v') in the object and image planes by the relations

$$u=\frac{n \sin U_{\max}}{\lambda}\xi, \quad v=\frac{n \sin U_{\max}}{\lambda}\eta, \quad \ldots \ldots \quad (14\text{–}27)$$

with similar expressions for u' and v', where (ξ, η) and (ξ', η') are the ordinary cartesian co-ordinates and the other symbols have their usual meanings. Corresponding to these new co-ordinates one has new spatial frequency variables in the object and image planes defined by

$$s=\frac{\lambda}{n \sin U_{\max}} R \text{ and } s' =\frac{\lambda}{n' \sin U'_{\max}} R'. \quad \ldots \quad (14\text{–}28)$$

It follows at once from the sine relation (equation 14–4) that the point at (u, v) is imaged at $u'=u$, $v'=v$, i.e. in these new co-ordinates all lenses have unit magnification and $s'=s$, i.e. the spatial frequency variable is the same for the object and the image. The performance of the lens is then specified by giving the

Fig. 14–32. $D(s)$ for abberation-free lens.

$T(s)$ and $\theta(s)$ curves. The limit of resolution is given by the value of s for which $T(s)$ falls to zero. For any aberration-free lens the limit of resolution corresponds to $s=2$, $\theta(s)=0$ and $D(s)$ $[=T(s)]$ has the form shown in Fig. 14–32. It should be noted that $s=2$ corresponds to different actual frequencies for different lenses

12*

—for $\lambda = 5 \times 10^{-4}$ mm. it corresponds to 182 lines per mm. in the image plane for an $f/11$ lens and 1000 lines per mm. for an $f/2$ lens. (It can be seen from the discussion of §14–11 that for an aberration-free lens with coherent illumination $D(s) = 1$ up to the limit of resolution when it falls suddenly to zero. This is because the diffraction maxima are either transmitted by the objective to reproduce the corresponding spatial frequency without loss, or they fall outside the objective aperture.) Always the effect of aberration is to cause a reduction in the value of the modulation transfer function below that for an aberration-free lens. Even for the lower spatial frequencies the presence of a small amount of aberration causes a significant reduction in the value of $T(s)$. This means that a lens may need to be highly corrected even if it is to be used solely to image relatively coarse detail—the fact that a lens can actually resolve 200 lines per mm. does not automatically mean that it is satisfactory for all purposes for a

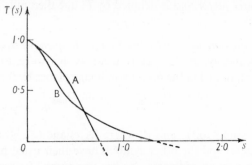

Fig. 14–33. Two imperfect lenses.

frequency of 100 lines per mm.! For example, in many TV cameras one is concerned only with frequencies up to 10 lines per mm. in the image plane but since one requires an extremely high performance over this range one must use a well corrected wide aperture lens over frequencies that are very low compared with the limit of resolution—with an $f/2$ lens $s \leqslant 0.02$.

The lens designer must be told the range of frequencies for which the lens is to be used and the value of $D(s)$ required. It is inevitable that a lens will have some aberrations; it is the task of the designer to reduce them as far as possible and to achieve the best balance between the unavoidable residuals (see Chapters XV and XVI). The aberrational balance that gives the best imagery of the finer detail and the best ultimate limit of resolution may be different from the compromise that gives the best performance for the lower frequencies. Consider, for example, two lenses A and B whose $T(s)$ curves have the forms shown in Fig. 14–33. Lens A will be better for imaging lower frequencies whilst lens B is better for imaging fine detail and has the better ultimate limit of resolution. By giving the $T(s)$ and $\theta(s)$ curves one gives a complete statement of the image-forming properties of the lens; stating the limit of resolution merely gives the value of s for which $T(s)$ falls to zero. Fig. 14–33 indicates that beyond the limit of resolution $T(s)$ becomes negative. This corresponds to a reversal of contrast—maxima occurring where there should be minima. The $T(s)$ curve can oscillate beyond the limit of resolution before finally falling to zero at $s = 2$. This explains the "spurious resolution" of detail below the limit of resolution of the lens.

It was stated above that provided certain conditions are satisfied a lens system is a linear filter of spatial frequencies. It will now be shown that the conditions are that over the relevant region of the field of view of the lens the aberrations must not vary rapidly, so that the movement of a point source within this region causes a corresponding movement of the diffraction image without significant change of structure. It is essential that the aberrations remain approximately constant over the area within which the diffraction image of a point source has appreciable intensity. A region in the field over which the aberration may be taken as constant is called an *isoplanatism patch*—the lens is *isoplanatic* over that region.

Now any two-dimensional distribution of intensity in the object plane can be represented as the superposition of line structures having various spatial frequencies and orientations. There is therefore no loss of generality in restricting the discussion to the imagery of line structures. In what follows the co-ordinates u, u' are those defined above. Let $G(u')\,du$ be the intensity distribution in the image plane when there is unit intensity along a strip of width du at $u=0$ in the object plane. $G(u')$ is often called the (line) *spread function*. If one remains in an isoplanatism patch a displacement of the line source merely gives a bodily displacement of the image so that unit intensity along a strip of width du at u in the object plane gives an intensity distribution $G(u'-u)du$ in the image. Suppose now that in the object plane there is, in fact, a one-dimensional variation of intensity (line structure) given by $B(u)$. Then the strip of width du at u produces (at u') in the image plane an intensity contribution $dB(u')=B(u)G(u'-u)du$. To obtain the total intensity at u' one adds the intensities due to neighbouring object strips. It is true that, strictly speaking, object strips far removed from u do give contributions, but only those close to the strip conjugate to u' (and hence within the isoplanatism patch) have spread functions with values at u' significantly different from zero. Hence one may write for the total intensity at u'

$$B'(u')=\int_{-\infty}^{+\infty} B(u)G(u'-u)du, \quad \ldots \quad (14\text{--}29)$$

the regions beyond the isoplanatism patch giving a negligible contribution. Now the object and image are looked upon as being synthesized from Fourier components, the amplitudes of the components of frequency s being given by

$$b(s)=\int_{-\infty}^{+\infty} B(u)e^{-2\pi ius}du \quad \ldots \quad (14\text{--}30)$$

$$\text{and } b'(s)=\int_{-\infty}^{+\infty} B'(u')e^{-2\pi iu's}du' \quad \ldots \quad (14\text{--}31)$$

(see §6–6).
Similarly, the transform of the spread function is given by

$$g(s)=\int_{-\infty}^{+\infty} G(u')e^{-2\pi iu's}du'. \quad \ldots \quad (14\text{--}32)$$

From equation 14–29 one has

$$b'(s) = \int\limits_{-\infty}^{+\infty}\left[\int\limits_{-\infty}^{+\infty} B(u)G(u'-u)du\right]e^{-2\pi i u's}du'$$

$$= \int\limits_{-\infty}^{+\infty} B(u)\left[\int\limits_{-\infty}^{+\infty} G(u'-u)e^{-2\pi i(u'-u)s}e^{2\pi i u s}du'\right]du$$

$$= \int\limits_{-\infty}^{+\infty} B(u)e^{2\pi i u s}\left[\int\limits_{-\infty}^{+\infty} G(u'-u)e^{-2\pi i(u'-u)s}d(u'-u)\right]du$$

$$= \int\limits_{-\infty}^{+\infty} B(u)e^{2\pi i u s}g(s)du$$

$$= g(s)b(s). \qquad \cdots \cdots \cdots \quad (14\text{–}33)$$

This shows that each spatial frequency in the object appears in the image modulated by $g(s)$, the transform of the line spread function. That is, provided the isoplanatism condition is satisfied a lens is a linear filter of spatial frequencies in the object, and the optical transfer function (frequency response) is given by the Fourier transform of the spread function. Since uniform illumination in the object gives uniform illumination in the image $D(s)$ is normalized to make $D(0)=1$, i.e. $D(s)=g(s)/g(0)$. Thus the optical transfer function can be found by measuring the intensity distribution in the image of a slit source and calculating the Fourier transform of the measured spread function. Alternatively, one can scan the image of a grating structure to obtain the transfer function directly. A square wave grating can be used and the result for a sine-wave structure obtained by selecting only the fundamental from the detector output.

It was pointed out in §11–15 that by means of the process of apodization one can change the aperture function and, therefore, the spread function. In other words, one can apodize an optical system in order to change the relative amplitudes and phases of the Fourier components from which an image is synthesized, i.e. one can change the optical transfer function.

In Fourier transform spectroscopy (§8–11) one can apodize by modifying the relative amplitudes of the Fourier components, either when the interferogram is recorded, or when the spectrum is obtained by calculation.

14–16. Wavefront Reconstruction (Holography)

In this section there will be given a brief account of a new method of image formation due to Gabor (1948). The principle is as follows. Suppose light from a point focus S (Fig. 14–34) is incident on the small object O located a short distance away. A small proportion of the light is diffracted by O, and on the plane AB the secondary disturbances from O are superposed on the strong coherent background provided by the primary wave from S. The diffraction pattern on the plane AB is called the *hologram*, and since the primary wave is uniform and much stronger than the secondary wave, the variations in intensity correspond to the variations in the phase of the secondary wave. If the hologram is recorded photographically and the plate is developed by reversal, or printed, the transmission at any point is determined by the phase of the secondary wave.

If the hologram is replaced at AB and illuminated by S alone, the disturbance transmitted by the hologram contains as a major component a reconstruction of the original wave. If one then looks through AB towards S, the object will appear to be in position at O. The reconstructed wave is only a component of the light transmitted by the hologram but Gabor has shown that the remainder

Fig. 14–34.
Production of a hologram.

gives an effect which can be removed almost completely. One then sees an accurate reconstruction of the object. Actually a given intensity in the hologram corresponds to a given phase *difference* between secondary disturbance and coherent background, and is unaffected by a change in the sign of that difference. That is, an object symmetrically placed behind S would give the same hologram as O. In consequence, this second object also appears to be in position on looking through the hologram. If the object O was originally three-dimensional, one plane after another can be viewed in the reconstruction simply by adjusting the focus of the observing lens.

(a) Electronic Analysis

(b) Optical Synthesis

Fig. 14–35. Arrangements for analysis and synthesis.

The proposed application of this technique depends on the fact that light of one wavelength can be used in the *analyser* to obtain the hologram and light of a longer wavelength used in the *synthesizer* to obtain the reconstruction. It is simply necessary for the dimensions of the synthesizer and analyser to be in the same ratio as the wavelengths employed. This, of course, involves a similar enlargement of the hologram. Thus the analysis can be carried out with electrons and the synthesis with light. This involves an enormous magnification factor

(10^5, say) and the necessary magnification of the hologram is obtained by the introduction of an additional lens into the synthesizer. This has a focal length equal to the distance from the object to the photographic plate in the analyser and is placed between the point focus and the hologram in the synthesizer so that the effective distance of the hologram is increased by a factor of 10^5 when viewed from the optical space of the point focus. The arrangements for electronic analysis and optical synthesis are shown in Fig. 14–35. It should be noted that the synthesizer must provide an exact imitation of the original (electron) wavefront in the plane of the hologram. Hence it is necessary for the spherical aberration of the electron lens to be copied in the optical system. The limit of resolution is determined by the angle U, being of the order $\lambda/\sin U$ where λ is the wavelength of the electrons.

(a)   (b)

Fig. 14–36. Reconstruction of a transparency.

In an ordinary electron microscope the difficulty of correcting the spherical aberration is an important factor limiting the resolution obtainable. The method of wavefront reconstruction described above enables one to circumvent this difficulty.

Although the method of wavefront reconstruction was originally proposed by Gabor with its application to electron microscopy in mind, it has never been applied seriously in this field—possibly because conventional electron microscopes were greatly improved before the problem of getting high-quality reconstructions was solved. However, during the past few years very great improvements have been achieved in the quality of the reconstructed images using new methods of optical analysis and synthesis. It was essential in Gabor's original arrangement to have a strong coherent background upon which the Fresnel diffraction pattern of the object was superposed to produce the hologram, and this severely limited the range of objects to which the method could be applied.

Fig. 14–36(a) illustrates the principle of a new method of producing a hologram which enables these difficulties to be avoided. The incident light consists of monochromatic plane waves. The object consists of a transparency at A, and the hologram at H results from the superposition of the Fresnel diffraction pattern of the object and the plane wave that has passed through the prism. (In practice, the prism is replaced by a mirror system.) With the object removed the pattern at H consists of linear fringes; with the object in position the amplitude variations in the Fresnel pattern cause an amplitude modulation of the fringes, and the phase variations in the Fresnel pattern cause a phase modulation (i.e. departures from linearity) of the fringes. The reconstruction system is shown in Fig. 14–36(b). The hologram H is illuminated by collimated monochromatic light and, due to its fine structure, acts as a grating. In the zero order there is a poor-quality real image formed at I_0 and a virtual image at I_0', but in the first order one obtains a reconstructed real image of high quality on one side of the zero (I_1) and a high-quality virtual image on the other side of zero (I_1'). By placing a photographic plate at I_1 one obtains an image of the object entirely without the use of lenses.

One can view the virtual image I_1' by looking through the hologram as though it were a window, but one sees the image as though one were viewing a transparency with a point source behind it, i.e. for any given eye position one sees

Fig. 14–37. Three-dimensional object.

only a very small part of the image. Suppose, now, that a diffusing screen is placed immediately before the object in Fig. 14–36(a). The reconstructed image then corresponds to a transparency backed by a diffusing screen, and the whole of the image can be seen from a single point of observation. With the diffuser in position there is virtually no correspondence between position in the hologram and position in the image, with the result that a dust particle or similar defect on the hologram does not give a localized defect on the reconstructed image as it does when no diffuser is used. In addition, since the whole image can be seen by viewing through any portion of the hologram, the remainder of the hologram can be removed. Similarly, the complete real image will be formed by a fragment of the hologram! Although no region of the image is lost by using only part of the hologram there will be an overall loss of detail as the utilized area is reduced.

The above discussion referred to an object consisting of a transparency. A hologram can be produced from a diffusely reflecting three-dimensional object by means of the arrangement shown in Fig. 14–37. The reconstructed image is also three-dimensional and exhibits perspective and parallax, depending upon the viewing position.

With the arrangements discussed above it is necessary to employ highly coherent illumination. There must be spatial coherence across the object and prism or mirror and the coherence length must be greater than the variations in depth of the object. With a non-laser source the necessary spatial coherence could be obtained by using a pinhole source, but the resulting intensity would be very low. A laser gives the necessary coherence length and also gives spatial coherence with high intensity.

If the original object is inserted at the image position in the synthesizer any differences between the object and the image will cause difference fringes to appear. In this way it is possible to detect any changes that have occurred in the object since the hologram was produced. There is also the possibility of applying the method to problems of pattern recognition.

The holograms described above are produced from the Fresnel pattern, but it is also possible to produce holograms from the Fraunhofer pattern. Finally, it is worth noting that arrangements have been devised whereby one can produce holograms from incoherent object fields.

14-17. The Foucault Test. Schlieren Systems

As mentioned in §4-8, the Foucault knife-edge test provides a method of examining the form of a mirror surface. In terms of geometrical (ray) optics, the reflected rays are not concurrent if the mirror surface is not a perfect sphere. It will be seen from Fig. 14-38 that when the knife edge is in the region of focus, rays reflected by some parts of the mirror are obstructed while those from other parts are not. Thus parts of the mirror such as A appear dark and parts such as B appear bright. The shadows on the mirror surface resemble those that would be obtained if a relief map of the mirror were illuminated at almost grazing incidence from the direction of the point X. This geometrical interpretation of the test is fairly satisfactory when the mirror exhibits gross errors of form but is unsatisfactory when the errors are very small.

Fig. 14-38. The Foucault knife-edge test.

In terms of wave optics, the incident wave is spherical but the reflected wave is a deformed sphere. It resembles the wave one obtains in the image space of the lens L_2 (Fig. 11-20, p. 236) if there is a phase structure across the diffracting aperture; that is, it resembles the wave emerging from the exit pupil of a microscope objective used to examine a phase object. It will be seen that the disturbances reflected from the imperfect mirror can be analysed into zero and higher order maxima in the plane of the knife edge—the disturbances in this plane (which is conjugate to the source) do, in fact, constitute a Fraunhofer pattern and the knife edge itself obstructs part of this pattern. If the knife edge obstructs the image of the source as formed by the ideal spherical mirror, the arrangement resembles that used in dark-ground microscopy with oblique illumination—the direct light and all orders on one side are obstructed. In this analogy the eye lens focused on the mirror surface plays the part of the microscope objective focused on the phase object. To increase the brightness of the field of view in the knife-edge test the pinhole can be replaced by a short slit source parallel to the knife edge. In the *phase-contrast test* the knife edge is removed and a small phase plate is placed in the position of the zero order maximum. This test bears the same relation to the phase-contrast method in microscopy as does the knife-edge test to the oblique dark-ground method.

The knife-edge method was applied by Toepler (1864) to the examination of variations in the refractive index of a medium. The principle of his method—

Fig. 14–39. Principle of the Toepler schlieren method.

known as the *schlieren method*—is as illustrated by Fig. 14–39. The slit source is imaged along the knife edge by the lens L. The medium whose variations in refractive index are to be investigated is located at S and the variations in optical path through S cause the emergent wavefronts to be distorted. These converging wavefronts then resemble those reflected from a mirror being examined by the knife-edge test and the shadows reveal the variations in refractive index in S. Since a shadow reveals an angular displacement of the rays, it indicates the rate of change of index across the region concerned.

Fig. 14–40. Schlieren systems employing mirrors.

To obtain a large field of view a large aperture lens L would be required. It is then more convenient to replace the lens by an appropriate mirror system. One then avoids chromatic errors and effects caused by striations in the lens itself. The mirrors must be used with oblique illumination in order to avoid double passage through the medium under investigation. Typical schlieren systems are shown in Fig. 14–40.

14–18. Fibre Optics

A fibre, or a bundle of fibres, provides a useful method of conveying light from one place to another. Each fibre consists of a long thin cylinder of a transparent material such as glass. If the diameter of the cylinder is large compared with the wavelength of the light, the passage of the light down the fibre can be discussed in terms of geometrical optics; if the diameter is comparable with the wavelength, the fibre acts as a waveguide and a geometrical optical treatment of the problem is inadequate. The former case will be discussed briefly by considering the path of a meridional ray down a fibre of refractive index n, situated in air (Fig. 14–41). The light is incident on the flat end at angle I, is refracted into the

Fig. 14-41. Ray path along a fibre.

fibre, and strikes the side wall at angle ϕ. The ray will be totally reflected if ϕ is greater than the criticual angle θ. Now the smallest possible value of ϕ will occur when there is the largest possible value of I'. Since $I'_{max}=\theta$ it follows from the figure that

$$\phi_{min} = \frac{\pi}{2} - \theta.$$

If $\phi_{min} \geqslant \theta$ all the light entering the fibre is totally reflected, and is then multiply reflected down the fibre. Hence the condition that all the light that enters the fibre should be conveyed down the fibre without loss is $2\theta \leqslant \pi/2$, i.e. $n = \text{cosec}$ $\theta \leqslant \sqrt{2}$. It is worth noting that the path length of a ray multiply reflected down a straight fibre is independent of the diameter of the fibre—it is $l \sec I'$ where l is the length of the fibre; for light incident at $40°$ on a fibre of index $1\cdot5$, it is only about 10% greater than the length of the fibre. It is important to note that it has

Fig. 14-42. Fibre bundles.

been assumed that the fibre is straight and homogeneous, with smooth clean walls. If the walls are dirty one does not have total internal reflection, and serious losses of light occur—for a 25μ diameter fibre of index $1\cdot5$ light entering at an angle of incidence of $10°$ suffers over 100 reflections per inch.

   If the fibre is bent the angles of incidence are changed and again there are losses. The simple discussion given above deals only with meridional rays and a complete analysis of the problem is far more complicated; in practice it is found that the losses become serious if a fibre is bent with a radius of curvature less than twenty times the fibre diameter. Since light can be conveyed efficiently from one end of a fibre to the other, a bundle of fibres can be used to convey a distribution of light from one surface to another—i.e. images can be conveyed. Fibre bundles are of two types: rigid bundles of relatively short fibres, and flexible bundles of long fibres (Fig. 14–42). Rigid bundles of large cross section have been used as field flatteners, conveying the image formed on a curved surface by a lens on to a plane, and also to convey an image from the screen of a cathode-ray tube on to a photographic film. Thin flexible bundles have been used in such instruments as cystoscopes where it is required to make observations in an enclosure that can be approached only by a curved path. In some flexible fibre-scopes the outer fibres in a bundle are used to convey light to illuminate the object, a lens is used to form an image, and the inner fibres are used to convey this image to the remote end. Bundles of both types have been used as light funnels to collect light from an aperture of one shape and convey it through an aperture of a different shape, e.g. to direct light through the slit of a spectroscope. Fibre bundles can be used also in coding devices—for example, by intertwining the fibres in a bundle an image can be "scrambled".

When an image is formed on one end of a fibre bundle and conveyed to the other end the limit of resolution is determined in an obvious way by the fibre diameters. One refers to *static scanning*. It is found that rapid random *dynamic scanning*, where the bundle is displaced 4 or 5 fibre diameters, effectively smooths out the fibre bundle structure from the final image and improves the resolution (the scanning period being small compared with the response time of the detector).

In a closely packed bundle one has frustrated total reflection (see §21–6), and light passes from one fibre to the next. This, and the difficulty of dirty fibres, can be overcome by employing high-index fibres with low-index coatings (or metal coatings).

One further application of fibres is in refractometry. For a given angular aperture of the light entering a fibre there will be a reduction in the flux reaching the far end as the index of the surround approaches that of the fibre, and this has been used to detect small changes in the index of the surround.

CHAPTER XV

THE MONOCHROMATIC ABERRATIONS

15–1. Introduction. Ray and Wavefront Aberration

FOR an optical system of finite aperture, the Gaussian image is defined as that which would be formed if, in terms of geometrical optics, the system gave perfect imagery and had the cardinal planes of its paraxial region. When defined in this way, the Gaussian image can be found for any object although both object and image may extend beyond the paraxial region. If, geometrically, the system does give perfect imagery, the rays from each point object intersect at the Gaussian image point and a spherical wave converges to the latter so that disturbances which have passed through different zones of the aperture arrive exactly in phase. However, it was proved in §§ 14–3 and 14–4 that, for a given optical system, such imagery is not possible for more than one position of the object plane. That is to say, outside the paraxial region a completely perfect optical system is impossible. In practice, for large aperture and field, it is usually impossible to secure *perfect* imagery for even one position of the object, although a close approach to perfection can be attained in many instances. Thus, in general, an image will show some defects caused by the aberrations of the optical system.

The defect of the image may be said to be caused by the failure of the rays from a point source to unite at the Gaussian image point, or by the failure of the emergent wavefront to be a sphere converging on this point and the consequent failure of the disturbances to arrive exactly in phase. The aberrations are frequently discussed in terms of their effect on the ray paths, but it has been pointed out that, near a focus, the rays do not give a good indication of the distribution of light in the image. To obtain information concerning the latter, it is necessary to consider diffraction by the aperture stop of the instrument, and it was found convenient to discuss this in the image space of the system. For a perfect instrument and a point source, one then has the diffraction of a converging spherical wave by the exit pupil of the system. In order to calculate the intensity at any point in the image plane, it was necessary to find the relative phases of the disturbances from each element of the wave. In the presence of aberration the emergent wave is no longer a sphere and these relative phases are changed. The new phase differences can be calculated if the shape of the wavefront is known, and it is convenient to specify this by means of the amount by which the wave differs from the ideal spherical shape. The deviation of the wave from the ideal spherical form, measured as an optical path length along the wave normal, is called the *wavefront aberration*; it is positive when the wave lies in front of the ideal position.

For regions which are not close to a focus it is possible to assume that the rays give a good indication of where the energy goes, and since there is no exact focus when the aberrations are large, it is possible in this case to get a fairly good idea of the distribution of light from the ray paths. In such cases it may be convenient to describe the aberrations by their effect on the rays, but since most optical systems are of little use unless the aberrations are small, it is usually better to discuss the shapes of the wavefronts.

The wavefront aberration in wavelengths gives the phase difference introduced in multiples of 2π, so that the importance of an aberration can be seen at once. On the other hand, the ray aberrations frequently give a very misleading idea of how significant the aberration is. In Fig. 15–1 B′ is the Gaussian image point at a large distance from the exit pupil E′. PQ is a wave with wavefront aberration W' at the edge of the aperture and, even when W' is small, the so-called marginal ray aberration $\delta l' = B'M'$ may be very large. This would give the impression that the image is very poor, whereas the small value of W' indicates that on the Gaussian plane at B′ the image is almost perfect. If the Gaussian image is at

Fig. 15–1. Ray and wavefront aberration.

infinity, the ray aberration must always be infinite which, in addition to the impression of seriousness, gives certain computational difficulties. Thus, except in special cases, the wavefront aberration gives a more reliable and useful measure of the imperfection of an optical instrument. Since the wavefront aberration is a measure of the retardation or advancement of the wave with respect to the ideal wave, the aberrations arising in different parts of a system are, for small errors, simply additive. On the other hand, the ray aberration after passage through one part of a system is not simply added to that which arises later.

15–2. Choice of Reference Surface

As defined above, the wavefront aberration is measured from a reference sphere centred on the Gaussian image point. Frequently it is convenient to choose an alternative spherical reference surface, and it is now necessary to find how the wavefront aberration is affected by a change in the reference surface. A change in the radius alone simply adds a constant to the aberration at all points on the wavefront, and is of little interest. A movement of the centre of the reference sphere is more significant. As originally defined, the wavefront aberration indicates the extent to which the intensity distribution in the region of the Gaussian image differs from that for a perfect instrument. If measured from a reference sphere that is not centred at the Gaussian image point, the aberration gives a measure of the phase differences between disturbances arriving at the centre of *that* sphere, i.e. it measures the perfection of the image in that region. In other words: a movement of the centre of the reference sphere corresponds to a change of mind concerning the region in which the wavefront is considered to be coming to a focus. For example, with one reference sphere the aberration may be large, whereas with another it is small. Instead of saying that the image in the region of the centre of the first reference sphere is poor, one may say that the image is at the centre of the second sphere and is good— the disturbances are more nearly in phase at the second point, which therefore comes closer to being a focus. Two special cases are important in practice: a movement of the reference sphere centre (a) along, and (b) perpendicular to, the principal ray of a pencil proceeding to a region of focus. (It must be noted that although the rays do not give a reliable indication of the distribution of energy in the region of focus, they are the wave normals, and their paths remain significant.)

15-3. Longitudinal Shift of Focus

A movement of the reference sphere centre along the principal ray corresponds to a longitudinal movement of the point which is regarded as the focus. In

Fig. 15-2.
Longitudinal shift of focus.

Fig. 15-2 $E'O_1'$ represents the principal ray of an image-forming pencil—it may, as a special case, be the optical axis of the system. $E'R_1'$ is a reference sphere centred at O_1', and W' is the wavefront aberration measured from this sphere. The curve shown in full represents the actual wave; the rays are not shown. Suppose the centre of the reference sphere is moved a distance $\delta l'$ to O_2' and that its radius is changed by the same amount so that the sphere is $E'R_2'$. The wavefront aberration is now $W' + \delta W_L'$, where $\delta W_L'$ is negative and equal to $-n'(R_1'R_2')$ where n' is the refractive index of the image space. It is assumed that $R_1'R_2'$ is small, so that $\angle O_2'R_2'O_1'$ is small and $\angle E'O_2'R_2' \fallingdotseq \angle E'O_1'R_1' = \theta$ where θ is also small.

From the figure
$$R_1'O_2' = R_1O_1' - \delta l' \cos \theta$$

and
$$R_2'O_2' = E'O_2' = E'O_1' - \delta l'.$$

Now $R_1O_1' = E'O_1'$ since $E'R_1'$ is a sphere centre O_1'.

$$\therefore \quad R_1'R_2' = (R_1'O_2' - R_2'O_2') = \delta l'(1 - \cos \theta)$$
$$= \tfrac{1}{2}\theta^2 \delta l' \text{ since } \theta \text{ is small,}$$
$$\therefore \quad \delta W_L' = -\tfrac{1}{2}n'\theta^2 \delta l'.$$

If the aberration is not large, θ may be replaced by the corresponding angle made by the ray. In terms of the linear aperture, ϱ, $\delta W_L' \propto \varrho^2$.

15-4. Transverse Shift of Focus

In Fig. 15-3 $E'O_1'$ again represents the principal ray. Suppose the centre of the reference sphere (radius $E'O_1' = R$) is moved from O_1' a distance $\delta h'$ to O_3'. At any point on the wave, the resulting change $\delta W_T'$ in the wavefront aberration will depend on the azimuth ϕ of that point with respect to the plane $E'O_1'O_3'$.

The figure shows the section of the wave and the old and new reference spheres in the plane of azimuth ϕ. $\delta W_T'$ is negative and is given by $-n'(R_1'R_3')$. One has

$$R_1'R_3' = R_1'O_3' - R_3'O_3'$$
$$= \frac{(R_1'O_3')^2 - (R_3'O_3')^2}{R_1'O_3' + R_3'O_3'}.$$

Now R_1' and O_3' are the points (x,y,z) and $(R,0,-\delta h')$ respectively, with axes as shown.

$$\therefore \quad (R_1'O_3')^2 = (x-R)^2 + y^2 + (z+\delta h')^2.$$

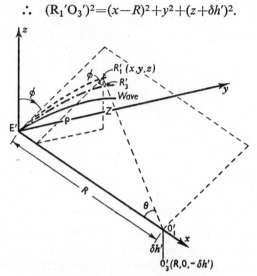

Fig. 15–3. Transverse shift of focus.

Since R_1' lies on the sphere, centre O_1' $(R,0,0)$, radius R, one has

$$(x-R)^2 + y^2 + z^2 = R^2,$$
$$\therefore \quad (R_1'O_3')^2 = R^2 + (\delta h')^2 + 2z\delta h'.$$

In addition, since $E'R_3'$ is the sphere whose centre is O_3',

$$(R_3'O_3')^2 = (E'O_3')^2 = R^2 + (\delta h')^2.$$

Hence $$(R_1'O_3')^2 - (R_3'O_3')^2 = 2z\delta h'.$$

It is sufficiently accurate to write $(R_1'O_3' + R_3'O_3') = 2R$.

$$\therefore \quad R_1'R_3' = \frac{z}{R}\delta h'.$$

Now $$z = \varrho \cos \phi,$$
$$\therefore \quad \delta W_T' = -\frac{n'}{R}\varrho\delta h' \cos \phi.$$

15–5. The Aberration Function

It will be assumed that each refracting surface in the optical system is a surface of revolution about a common axis of symmetry—the optical axis. It is not necessary to assume that the surfaces are spherical. When the object point lies on the optical axis, the emergent wavefront will also be a surface of rotation about the optical axis, and the wavefront aberration at any point P on the wave will depend only upon the aperture ϱ—i.e. its distance from the axis. For an off-axis object point, the aberration depends also upon the azimuth of P since the wave will not, in general, be a surface of rotation about the principal ray. It is the purpose of this section to deduce the form of the dependence of W' on the aperture and azimuth, and also the dependence of W' on the position of the object point. It is

Fig. 15–4. Sagittal and tangential planes.

convenient to define two planes as follows: (1) The *meridian* or *tangential plane*, from which the azimuth ϕ is measured, is the plane containing the optical axis and the off-axis object point (and Gaussian image point); throughout the system the principal ray lies in the meridian plane. (2) In the object, image, or any particular intermediate space, the *sagittal plane* is the plane which contains the principal ray and is perpendicular to the tangential plane. It will be seen that, whereas there is only one meridian plane for a given object point, the sagittal plane is different in different spaces through the system. Fig. 15–4 illustrates the passage of a principal ray through a system of three refracting surfaces; the tangential plane is shaded vertically and the sagittal planes are shaded "horizontally".

Fig. 15–5. Wave in image space.

Fig. 15–5 shows the reference sphere in the image space. E' is the centre of the exit pupil and O' is the Gaussian image point at height h' from the optical axis. The wavefront aberration of the element of wavefront associated with the ray through R' will depend on the aperture ϱ, and on the azimuth ϕ measured from the tangential plane E'B'O'. It is convenient to replace the variables ϱ and h' by their fractional values $r=\varrho/\varrho_{max}$, and $\sigma=h'/h'_{max}$; ϱ_{max} is the radius of the exit pupil and is therefore the maximum value of ϱ which can occur, and h'_{max} is the off-axis image height at the edge of the field of view of the instrument. For a particular ray in a pencil traversing the system, r remains constant whereas ϱ varies as the diameter of the pencil expands and contracts. In a similar way, σ is constant through the system for a particular extra-axial object point whereas, in intermediate image spaces within the system, h' has different values. Thus W' depends on σ, r, and ϕ, and $W'(\sigma,r,\phi)$ is referred to as the *aberration function*. Whilst it is very difficult to find $W'(\sigma,r,\phi)$ for any but the simplest systems, it is possible, from considerations of symmetry, to deduce the general form which the function can take. In those cases where the function does not contain ϕ, symmetry about the principal ray and about the optical axis require W' to be an even function of σ and r. That is, in the general form of the function the terms which do not contain ϕ must be functions of σ^2 and/or r^2. In addition, there is symmetry about the meridian plane, so that W' must remain unchanged if ϕ is replaced by $-\phi$. This condition is satisfied if terms involving ϕ are functions of $\cos \phi$. Again, when O' is an equal distance below the axis, the value of W' for the point corresponding to R' must be the same as for R' itself, i.e. W' is unchanged if r is constant and ϕ is changed to $\pi\pm\phi$ while the sign of σ is reversed. Alternatively, W' is unchanged if the sign of r and σ is changed, keeping ϕ constant. This means that terms which contain ϕ must also contain σ and r; the conditions are satisfied if these terms are functions of $(\sigma r \cos \phi)$. Thus the aberration function contains the variables in the forms σ^2, r^2, $\sigma r \cos \phi$, and can be written as the most general power series in these variables. One has

$$W'(\sigma,r,\phi) = {}_0C_{00} + ({}_0C_{20}r^2 + {}_1C_{11}\sigma r \cos \phi + {}_2C_{00}\sigma^2)$$
$$+ ({}_0C_{40}r^4 + {}_1C_{31}\sigma r^3 \cos \phi + {}_2C_{22}\sigma^2r^2 \cos^2\phi$$
$$+ {}_2C_{20}\sigma^2r^2 + {}_3C_{11}\sigma^3r \cos \phi + {}_4C_{00}\sigma^4) + \dots .$$

It is possible to show that some of these terms may be omitted.

It has already been pointed out that a change in the radius of the reference sphere adds a constant wavefront aberration to each part of the wave. If the radius of the reference sphere is always adjusted so that $W'=0$ along the principal ray, one has ${}_0C_{00} = {}_2C_{00} = {}_4C_{00} = \dots = 0$, since these are the only terms which remain on putting $r=0$. For an axial object, $h'=0$ and one has

$$W' = {}_0C_{20}r^2 + {}_0C_{40}r^4 + \dots .$$

Now it has been shown that a longitudinal shift of focus introduces a wavefront aberration proportional to the square of the aperture, so that such a shift can remove the first term. The movement required is the same for all points in the field of view, so that this term simply moves the image plane without changing the image quality; it corresponds to an error in the assumed position along the axis of the Gaussian image plane. In a similar way, the term ${}_1C_{11}\sigma r \cos \phi$ can be removed by a transverse shift of focus, since such a movement of the reference sphere centre introduces a term proportional to $(r \cos \phi)$. This term will be removed for all image heights simultaneously if one moves the centre of the reference sphere transversely by an amount proportional to σ; i.e. proportional to the existing height of the centre. Such a movement of the centre of the reference sphere for all object points therefore changes the size of the image but in no way affects the image quality. It corresponds to a change in the value of the Gaussian transverse magnification. Thus the terms $_0C_{20}\,r^2$ and $_1C_{11}\sigma r\cos\phi$ do not represent aberrations or defects of the image, but can be removed by changing the assumed values of the Gaussian constants of the system. There are other terms which correspond to longitudinal and transverse shifts of focus, but these do affect image quality (see below).

The remaining terms in the aberration function are as follows:

$$W'(\sigma,r,\phi)=_0C_{40}r^4+_1C_{31}\sigma r^3\cos\phi+_2C_{22}\sigma^2r^2\cos^2\phi$$
$$+_2C_{20}\sigma^2r^2+_3C_{11}\sigma^3r\cos\phi+\ldots\quad.\quad(15\text{--}1)$$

The terms given here are those in which the sum of the powers of σ and r does not exceed 4. They represent the so-called *primary aberrations*. When expressed as transverse ray aberrations, the aperture and field dependence leads to their being referred to as the *third order* aberrations. They are also called the *Seidel* aberrations since much early work on the evaluation of these errors was done by von Seidel.

The terms of (15–1) are, respectively, *primary spherical aberration, coma, astigmatism, field curvature,* and *distortion*; they will now be discussed in turn. When discussing each aberration it will be assumed that the others are absent.

15–6. Spherical Aberration

For an axial object point $\sigma=0$, and the aberration function reduces to

$$W'=_0C_{40}r^4+_0C_{60}r^6+_0C_{80}r^8+\ldots.$$

These terms represent the primary, secondary, tertiary, ... spherical aberration. The present discussion will be restricted to systems of moderate aperture so that only the primary aberration is important. Fig. 15–6 illustrates the shape of wavefront exhibiting positive primary spherical aberration. W' is proportional

Fig. 15–6. Spherical aberration.

Fig. 15–7. Ray and wavefront aberration.

to the fourth power of the aperture ϱ, and since the rays are simply the wave normals, the effect on the ray paths can also be seen. The rays in the paraxial region, where ϱ is vanishingly small, come to a focus at the Gaussian image point G′, and those from the marginal zone of the aperture intersect the axis at the so-called marginal focus M′. Rays from intermediate zones come to a focus between M′ and G′.

In Fig. 15–7 G′ is the Gaussian focus, and B′ is the point of intersection of the ray at aperture ϱ. $\delta l'$ is the longitudinal ray aberration, and $\delta u'$ the angular ray aberration. R is the radius of the reference sphere, and the wavefront aberrations at apertures ϱ and $\varrho + \delta\varrho$ are W' and $W' + \delta W'$. From the figure, remembering that W' is an optical path length, one has

$$\delta u' = \left(\frac{\delta W'}{n'}\right) \Big/ \frac{\delta\varrho}{\cos u'}$$

$$= \frac{\cos u'}{n'} \cdot \frac{\delta W'}{\delta\varrho}.$$

In addition, $\varrho = R \sin u'.$

$$\therefore \quad \delta u' = \frac{1}{n'R} \cdot \frac{\partial W'}{\partial u'}.$$

Now for primary spherical aberration one may write

$$W' = Cu'^4,$$

$$\therefore \quad \delta u' = \frac{4Cu'^3}{n'R}.$$

If the aperture is not large, one may write

$$B'D' = R\delta u' = u'\delta l',$$

$$\therefore \quad \delta l' = \left(\frac{4C}{n'}\right) u'^2.$$

That is, the longitudinal ray aberration is proportional to the square of the aperture.

It will be seen that in the presence of spherical aberration there is no real focus, i.e. no point where all the disturbances are in phase and all the rays intersect. In terms of rays, there will be a circular patch of light on any screen perpendicular to the axis. The size of this patch reaches a minimum when the screen is at Z' which divides M'G' in the ratio 1:3 (Fig. 15–6). This minimum patch is sometimes called the disc of least confusion and, in terms of geometrical optics, it is here that one has the closest approach to a focus. However, the disturbances from various zones of the aperture are most nearly in phase at the point P', midway between M' and G'. If the aberration is small, the best focus will certainly be at P' since this is the point where there is the least possible destructive interference. When the aberration is large, so that phase differences exceeding 2π are involved, there can be no simple discussion of the effect of the superposed disturbances, and it is likely that as the aberration increases the best focus moves towards Z'. This is in accordance with the general result that in the absence of a focus the energy travels approximately along the ray paths.

For the image of a point source, the effect of a small amount of spherical aberration is to cause the outer maxima to become more intense. In the absence of aberration, the patterns slightly inside and outside the focus consist of a series of rings, but with a small amount of positive spherical aberration, the pattern outside the focus quickly changes to a more diffuse distribution of light. This provides a useful test for the presence of aberration and a wavefront aberration of a quarter of a wavelength can be detected easily.

15–7. Coma

The term $_1C_{31}\sigma r^3 \cos\phi$ represents the aberration known as primary coma. Since it varies linearly with σ, it is the first aberration to appear as one goes off-axis. It is convenient to consider the shape of the wavefront in the sagittal and tangential planes. In the former, $\phi = \pi/2$ and $W' = 0$, so that the wavefront coincides with the reference sphere centred at the Gaussian image point. In the

Fig. 15–8. Coma.

tangential plane, $\phi = 0$ and, for a given extra-axial object point, W' is proportional to the cube of the aperture.

Fig. 15–8 shows, for positive coma, the shape of the wavefront in the tangential section and shows also the ray paths. It will be seen that the rays at a given aperture come to a focus below the principal ray, the error being a linear measure of the coma in the tangential section; it can be shown to be proportional to r^2. Although, in the sagittal section, $W' = 0$, the wavefront is tilted so that the rays do not intersect on the principal ray. This is illustrated by Fig. 15–9(a). For a given aperture, rays in the tangential section intersect at T′ and those in the sagittal section at S′. Rays from diametrically opposite elements of the wave in other azimuths come to a focus at other points on the circumference of the circle indicated. A similar coma circle gives the points of focus for rays from diametrically opposite elements of each annulus of the wave. The pattern of ray intersection points on the Gaussian plane is shown in Fig. 15–9(b), the

Principal ray

(b)

- - - - sections of sphere

——— sections of wave

(a)

Fig. 15–9. Coma.

radius of each coma circle being half the distance of its centre from the principal ray—G′T′ = 3G′S′; one may say that the linear tangential coma is three times the linear sagittal coma. Obviously the effect of coma is more easily discussed in terms of wavefront aberration! Again the pattern indicated by geometrical optics is observed only with very large aberrations—its comet-like appearance being the origin of the term coma. The appearance of the image in the presence of coma is shown in Plate IV; (f) is for about $\lambda/2$ and (h) is for about 5 wavelengths of aberration.

15–8. Astigmatism

As one proceeds farther off-axis, two more aberrations become significant. These are astigmatism and field curvature and the former, represented by the term $_2C_{22}\sigma^2r^2\cos^2\phi$, will be discussed first. As with coma, it is convenient to consider the sagittal and tangential sections of the wavefront, and again $W'=0$ in the sagittal plane where $\phi=\pi/2$. In the tangential plane, $\phi=0$ and, for a given object point, W' is proportional to the square of the aperture. Thus in this plane astigmatism corresponds to a shift of focus and, as indicated by Fig. 15–10, the

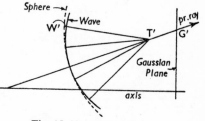

Fig. 15–10. Astigmatism.

rays intersect at a point T' somewhat removed along the principal ray from the Gaussian focus G'. In the sagittal plane the rays are focused exactly at G'. Usually field curvature accompanies astigmatism and the rays in the sagittal section are then focused at a point S' which is also removed from G'. That is, in the presence of both field curvature and astigmatism, the wavefront is a circle in both sagittal and tangential sections. The circles differ from each other and differ from the circular section of the reference sphere. The shape of the wavefront in the presence of astigmatism and field curvature is shown in Fig. 15–11. In terms of geometrical optics, one obtains line foci at T' and S', the lines being perpendicular to the tangential and sagittal planes respectively and centred on

Fig. 15–11. Effect of field curvature and astigmatism.

the principal ray. To visualize the paths of the rays, it is convenient to divide the cone of light entering the optical system into fans of rays as follows. In Fig. 15–12 G is the object point. E and E' are the entrance and exit pupils. The cone of light from G which enters E can be divided into fans of rays which intersect E along lines parallel to the tangential plane; these are known as tangential fans of rays. A typical tangential fan of rays is shaded vertically. It emerges from E′ and proceeds to a focus as shown. In the same way the cone of light from G could be divided into sagittal fans which enter E along lines parallel to the sagittal plane. A typical sagittal fan is shaded "horizontally". It is found that each tangential fan comes to a focus at a point on the so-called *tangential focal line* and each sagittal fan is focused at a point on the *sagittal*

Fig. 15–12. Astigmatic pencil of rays.

focal line. The general appearance of an astigmatic pencil of rays is therefore as illustrated. The maximum cross-section of the pencil is least midway between the focal lines; here the cross section is a circle. Since the point on the principal ray midway between the focal lines is also the point where the disturbances from all elements of the emergent wave are most nearly in phase, there is little doubt that this is the position of the best focus. The appearance of the focal line in the presence of about λ and $2\frac{1}{2}\lambda$ of astigmatism is shown in Plate IV (*i*) and (*j*). (*k*) and (*l*) show the appearance of the image midway between the focal lines for $2\frac{1}{2}$ and $6\frac{1}{2}$ wavelengths of astigmatism.

15–9. Field Curvature

Since it is proportional to the square of the aperture, the term $_2C_{20}\sigma^2 r^2$ corresponds to a longitudinal shift of focus. The wavefront is therefore spherical,

Fig. 15–13. Effect of field curvature and astigmatism.

but focused on a point removed along the principal ray from the Gaussian image plane. Since the term is also proportional to σ^2, the shift of focus is proportional to the square of the image height. Therefore, to a first approximation, if one has a series of point objects such as G in a plane perpendicular to the axis (Fig. 15–13), the emergent wavefronts are focused on points such as

P' lying on a spherical surface which touches the Gaussian image plane; i.e. the image field is curved. In practice, the various constant coefficients in the aberration function are not completely independent; e.g. $_2C_{20}$ and $_2C_{22}$ are related. The curvature of the image in the absence of astigmation is called the Petzval field curvature, and is positive when as shown in the diagram. As far as the image quality on the Gaussian plane is concerned, one has a simple out of focus effect corresponding to the distance P'G'. If astigmatism and Petzval field curvature are present together, the coefficient $_2C_{20}$ is changed, and in the sagittal section the wavefront is not focused on P'. For positive astigmatism one has focal lines at S' and T'. It can be shown that P'T'=3P'S', where P' is defined by the value of $_2C_{20}$ when $_2C_{22}=0$. Thus, as the astigmatism decreases, S' and T' approach P', and for negative astigmatism T' and S' lie to the right of P', the three to one relationship being maintained.

15–10. Distortion

The first three aberrations affect the quality of the image of a point source, and the fourth affects its position. However, since the latter introduces an out of

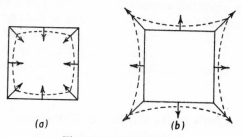

(a)   (b)

Fig. 15–14. Distortion.

focus effect, all four may be said to affect the quality of the image on the Gaussian plane. The fifth primary aberration is defined by the term $_3C_{11}\, \sigma^3 r \cos \phi$ and, for a point source, causes a displacement of the image in the Gaussian plane without loss of image quality. This can be seen at once, since any term proportional to $r \cos \phi$ corresponds to a transverse shift of focus. The displacement is proportional to σ^3 and causes a distortion of the shape of the image without loss of definition. The aberration is known simply as distortion and is the one aberration which is best thought of in terms of geometrical optics. (For a point object there is little sense in saying that the image at G' is poor if a perfect image is, in fact, formed a short distance away.) The nature of distortion is best illustrated by its effect on the image of a square in a plane perpendicular to the axis. For positive distortion, each point in the image is moved towards the optical axis by an amount which is proportional to the cube of its distance as indicated by Gaussian optics. For negative distortion, the displacement of each image point is away from the axis. The effects are shown in Fig. 15–14(a) and (b) for positive and negative distortion respectively; the figures shown dotted are the distorted images of the squares whose Gaussian images are as shown. For obvious reasons, positive and negative distortions are referred to as barrel and pin-cushion respectively.

15–11. Coma and the Sine Condition

It was shown in Chapter XIV that in the absence of spherical aberration an optical system of large aperture will give good imagery of points near the axis for one pair of conjugates if the Sine Condition is satisfied for all zones of the aperture. Now for points near the axis one can neglect the aberrations which depend on powers of σ higher than the first, and, for the inner zones of the aperture, primary coma is the only significant aberration if spherical aberration is absent. That is to say, by satisfying the Sine Condition for the inner zones, one ensures elimination of primary coma. For a somewhat larger aperture there will be the possibility of an aberration $_1C_{51}\sigma r^5 \cos\phi$, and for a still larger aperture $_1C_{71}\sigma r^7 \cos\phi$ may become important. If the Sine Condition is satisfied for all zones of a wide aperture system, there can be no significant aberration for small values of σ, and all these coma type aberrations must be absent. Thus the satisfaction of the Sine Condition provides a more highly corrected system than the elimination of primary coma.

In deducing the Sine Condition, it was assumed that the magnification was the same for all zones of the system. Reference to Fig. 15–8 will show that this must eliminate the coma, since this aberration causes a variation with aperture of the height above the axis of the point of intersection of the rays. It is possible to formulate a Sine Condition of much wider significance than that given above. In particular, it is useful to investigate the significance of the condition in the presence of spherical aberration. Such analysis is beyond the scope of the present discussion.

15–12. Tangent Condition for the Elimination of Distortion

In Fig. 15–15 it is assumed that the plane at B′ is the Gaussian image of the plane at B. The entrance and exit pupils are at E and E′ and it is assumed that

Fig. 15–15. The tangent condition.

there is no spherical aberration of the principal rays from object points in the plane at B.

Referring to the figure, one has

$$\frac{h_1}{h_2} = \frac{\tan u_{pr1}}{\tan u_{pr2}}$$

and

$$\frac{h_1'}{h_2'} = \frac{\tan u'_{pr1}}{\tan u'_{pr2}}.$$

if
$$\frac{h_1}{h_2} = \frac{h_1'}{h_2'}$$

one has
$$\frac{\tan u_{\text{pr1}}}{\tan u'_{\text{pr1}}} = \frac{\tan u_{\text{pr2}}}{\tan u'_{\text{pr2}}},$$

i.e. there is no distortion if
$$\frac{\tan u_{\text{pr}}}{\tan u'_{\text{pr}}} = \text{a constant.}$$

This result is frequently quoted but is of limited application since it is true only if there is no aberration of the pupil points E and E'. In practice, the spherical aberration is corrected for the object and image planes and not for the pupil planes.

15–13. Astigmatic Correction in the Presence of Petzval Field Curvature

Most simple optical systems of positive power have positive Petzval field curvature. It follows that in the absence of astigmatism the image of a point

Fig. 15–16. Positive Petzval field curvature and negative astigmatism.

object is at a point such as P' [see Fig. 15–16(a)], and the image is out of focus on the Gaussian plane. If negative astigmatism is introduced into the system, the focal lines S' and T' will lie on the principal ray in positions such as those indicated. As more negative astigmatism is introduced, the best focus, which lies midway between the focal lines, moves towards the Gaussian plane. As it does so, however, the best focus itself deteriorates since its quality depends on the magnitude of the astigmatism alone. Thus, whilst the out of focus effect associated with the Petzval field curvature is reduced, the astigmatic effect is increased. It can be shown that the disturbances are most nearly in phase on the Gaussian plane when the tangential focus lies on that surface. Since both field curvature and astigmatism are proportional to σ^2, it follows that the whole tangential field is then flat and, for a plane object, the image on the Gaussian plane is as good as possible. This would be the correction for maximum resolving power; it is not always the state of correction actually required (see §14–15).

In the absence of spherical aberration, the axial image will be perfect and the image quality on the Gaussian plane will deteriorate as one moves towards the

G. AND P.O.—13

edge of the field. It may be desirable to sacrifice the image quality in the cen
of the field in order to improve it farther out and it is then desirable to introdu
rather less negative astigmatism and to move the receiving plane to the positi
indicated in Fig. 15–16(b).

15–14. Permissible Aberration

It has been seen that for each point in the object the effect of aberration is
distort the emergent wavefront from its ideal spherical shape. This means th
there is no longer an image point at which all the disturbances arrive in pha
and, in consequence, there is a deterioration of the image quality. The appea
ance of the image of a point source in the presence of aberration was discuss
in §15–6 to §15–8. If the aberration is small the phase differences betwe
disburbances arriving at the centre of the point source image are small, and t
image retains the general form of a strong central maximum surrounded by we
secondary maxima. The intensity at the centre of the pattern is slightly lov
than that at the centre of the ideal Airy pattern and in general there is a slig
broadening of the central maximum and a slight increase in the intensities
some of the outer maxima. A similar effect results from the introduction of pha
differences by a small shift of focus, and in discussing depth of focus for
aberration-free system it was stated that, according to Rayleigh, there is
appreciable deterioration of the image if the phase differences do not exce
$\pi/2$. It seems reasonable to take the same criterion in the present problem. Th
one may say that the image quality will not be seriously impaired provided t
wavefront aberration does not exceed $\lambda/4$, it being assumed that the maximu
aberration of the wave is reduced as far as possible by appropriate choice of r
reference sphere—it is at the centre of this sphere that the image may be said
be located. An alternative approach is to assume that provided the general for
of the point source image remains unchanged the intensity at the centre of t
pattern—known as the Strehl intensity—provides a measure of the state
correction of the lens. It is then assumed that the image quality will not
noticeably inferior to that for an aberration-free lens provided the Str
intensity does not fall below $0.8 \times$ the intensity at the centre of an ideal A
pattern.

The Rayleigh quarter-wave limit and the limit of 0.8 on the Strehl intens
ratio give very similar aberration tolerances. These tolerances correspond to ve
highly corrected systems and, provided they are not exceeded, the image qual
for any kind of object will not be appreciably inferior to that for an aberratic
free system. It is found that if the aberrations exceed these tolerances there
usually a rapid deterioration of the image quality. Whereas it is necessary fo
microscope objective to be highly corrected and to give near-ideal imagery
all spatial frequencies up to the limit of resolution, there are other systems wh
are required to be near-perfect over a more limited frequency range. One cou
for example, require that over the frequency range concerned the modulat
transfer factor should not fall below $0.8 \times$ the value for an aberration-f
system. It is worth noting that for frequencies in the range $s = 0.2$ to $s = 1.4$ (
§14–15) this criterion gives tolerances similar to those given by the Str
criterion, and for frequencies outside this range the aberration tolerances

larger. For lower standards of image formation one can set more liberal tolerances on the frequency response over the range of interest.

For systems of relatively low quality it may be satisfactory to discuss the imagery in terms of geometrical optics and to define the permissible aberration by placing a limit on the size of the light patch formed by the intersection of the pencil of rays with the image plane.

THE OCCURRENCE AND CONTROL OF
ABERRATIONS IN OPTICAL SYSTEMS

16–1. Factors Influencing the Monochromatic Aberrations

ABERRATIONS appear immediately one goes outside the paraxial region of an optical system, i.e. whenever one has a finite aperture, or finite field, or both. In terms of geometrical optics, the appearance of the defects is associated with the occurrence of large angles of incidence, and large angles of inclination between rays and the optical axis. When one has a finite angle of incidence at a refracting

Fig. 16–1. Refraction at a single surface.

surface, the path of the refracted ray is determined by Snell's law ($n \sin I = n' \sin I'$), and the deviation of the ray given by this equation is greater than that which would be given by the paraxial form ($ni = n'i'$). Thus for a single refracting surface as in Fig. 16–1, the ray BP, incident at the large angle I, is refracted along PM' instead of along PB' as it would be if the paraxial form of Snell's law was applicable. In this way spherical aberration is introduced, and one may say that there is a general tendency for large angles of incidence to cause large aberration. There are exceptions to this [see, for example, §16–4(d)]. For any system of refracting surfaces, the angles of incidence obviously depend upon the orientation of the initial incident ray, so that the aberrations of a system depend upon the position of the object.

Fig. 16–2. Refraction through a lens.

The purpose of a lens is to deviate the rays and, as indicated in Chapter II, the deviation produced is proportional to the power of the lens. Now there are an infinite number of possible shapes for a lens of given power and refractive index, and, in giving the desired deviation to the ray, the angles of incidence involved depend upon the lens shape as indicated in Fig. 16–2. Thus, in general, the aberration introduced by a lens system depends upon the shapes of the components. Moreover, for a given deviation of a ray at a refracting surface, the necessary angle of incidence depends on the change of refractive index. One may generalize again and say that the aberrations of a system will depend upon the refractive indices of the components. The angles of incidence at the various surfaces of a system depend also upon the separations of the surfaces, so that this is another factor which influences the aberrations. One of the most important factors which influences the aberrations of extra-axial images is the position of the aperture stop. As indicated in Fig. 16–3, this controls the part of a lens through which the oblique pencils pass. It does not, of course, affect the spherical aberration of an axial pencil of rays. Although an exact analysis of the effects

Fig. 16–3. Influence of stop position.

of a shift of stop cannot be given here, it is possible to give a simple summary of the results. One tabulates the primary aberrations as follows:

> Spherical Aberration
> Coma
> Astigmatism
> Petzval Field Curvature
> Distortion.

(It should be noted that this is the order in which they appear as one increases the field.) It can be shown that, in general, a particular aberration is affected by a movement of the stop if one or more of those present above it in the list is present in the system. The exception is field curvature, which is never affected by a stop shift; it is included in the list because distortion will be affected if field curvature is present. In many simple and inexpensive systems (e.g. cheap camera lenses of low aperture), it is customary to leave some spherical aberration in the system in order to be able to remove the coma by a suitable positioning of the stop. A system which is free from spherical aberration and coma is said to be *aplanatic*; it will be seen that the astigmatism of an aplanat cannot be controlled by moving the stop. Again, if a system has a flat field free from astigmatism it is said to be *anastigmatic*; if it is also aplanatic the distortion is independent of the stop position. The variation of coma and distortion is illustrated in the next two sections.

For a given position of the object, the factors which influence the aberrations of a system may be summarized as follows:

> The distribution of the power between the components
> Shapes, thicknesses, and separations, of the components
> Stop position
> Glass types employed.

16–2. Variation of Coma with Stop Position

It was stated in the last section that if a system has spherical aberration the coma depends upon the position of the aperture stop. This fact is demonstrated by Fig. 16–4(a). With the stop in the first position, E_1' is the centre of the exit pupil and $E_1'P'$ is the principal ray. The other rays belong to the pencil of rays from an off-axis object point, it being assumed that there is spherical aberration

Fig. 16–4. Variation of coma with stop position.

but no coma. If the stop is moved so that E_2' is the centre of the exit pupil, $E_2'P'$ is the new principal ray, and the rays adjacent to it (i.e. those from E_1' and X) are now the rays at about half aperture. Their point of intersection, M', does not lie on the principal ray $E_2'P'$, and negative coma is now present. Fig. 16–4(b) shows that if there is no spherical aberration, coma is not introduced by such a movement of the stop.

16–3. Variation of Distortion with Stop Position

In Fig. 16–5 it is assumed that the point B is imaged without spherical aberration or coma by the wide aperture thin lens L which has astigmatism and field curvature. The tangential focus is B'. If one introduces the aperture stop (1) in contact with the lens, ray (1) is the principal ray and, since it passes undeviated through the thin lens, P_1' is the Gaussian image point and there is no distortion. When the stop is moved to position (2), the ray marked (2) is the principal ray and obviously there is barrel distortion since P_2' lies closer to the axis than the Gaussian image P_1'. Similarly, there is pincushion distortion when the stop is

Fig. 16–5. Variation of distortion with stop position.

at (3). This diagram represents a special case but shows the manner in which the distortion is affected by the stop position. It will be seen that the effect is dependent upon the position of the tangential focus B'. For example, if B' is to the right of the Gaussian plane, stop (2) gives pincushion, and stop (3) barrel distortion. One particularly important result emerges: the distortion is not affected by a stop shift if the system is an aplanat with a flat tangential field.

16–4. The Aberrations of a Single Spherical Refracting Surface. The Aplanatic Points

For a surface of given power separating two given media, the angles of incidence (and therefore the aberrations) can depend only upon the positions of the object and the aperture stop. There are fewer variables than there are with a lens since, with the latter, one is free to choose the refractive index of its material, and its shape and thickness. There are, however, a number of cases of special interest.

(*a*) *Stop at the Centre of Curvature*

If the stop is at the centre of curvature, every principal ray is a radius of the surface (see Fig. 16–6) and all pencils are effectively axial pencils so that coma,

Fig. 16–6. Field curvature.

astigmatism, and distortion, are absent. Spherical aberration is still present, since this does not depend upon the stop position, and there is also Petzval field curvature. The fact that the field is curved is shown by Fig. 16–6(a). $B_o{}'$ is the image of the axial object B_o, formed by a surface of radius r separating media n and n'. (The spherical aberration is removed by using a small aperture at C.) If B_o is moved round a circle (centre C) to B, the image will move round a concentric circle to B' since this corresponds to an unchanged object and image distance measured from the refracting surface. If B is moved back to $\bar{\text{B}}$ where $B_o\bar{\text{B}}$ is perpendicular to the axis, the increased object distance must result in a decreased image distance, and the image will move from B' to a position such as $\bar{\text{B}}'$. Thus, corresponding to the plane object $B_o\bar{\text{B}}$, one has the curved image $B_o{}'\bar{\text{B}}'$.

In general, the refracting surface will be part of a system of surfaces and the object field will be curved. In order to deduce a relationship between the object and image field curvatures, it is convenient to change to an all-positive diagram as in Fig. 16–6(b). It is assumed that the stop at C is small and that B'D' is the image of BD; BE and B'E' are arcs centred on C. Thus E and E' are also conjugate points, and the elements ED and E′D′ are conjugate distances along the auxiliary axis CD. They are therefore related by equation (2–11) so that one has

$$\frac{E'D'}{ED} = \left(\frac{h'}{h}\right)^2 \frac{n'}{n},$$

or

$$\frac{h^2 E'D'}{n'} = \frac{h'^2 ED}{n}. \qquad \ldots \ldots \ldots (16\text{--}1)$$

Now if h and h' are small, one may write ED and E′D′ in terms of the sags in the circular arcs BD, BE, B′D′, and B′E′. One has

$$ED = \frac{h^2}{2(l-r)} + \frac{h^2}{2R}$$

and

$$E'D' = \frac{h'^2}{2(l'-r)} + \frac{h'^2}{2R'},$$

where R and R' are the radii of curvature of the object and image fields. Therefore, from (16–1),

$$\frac{1}{n'(l'-r)} + \frac{1}{n'R'} = \frac{1}{n(l-r)} + \frac{1}{nR}. \qquad \ldots \ldots (16\text{--}2)$$

Now l, l', and r, are related by the usual paraxial equation

$$\frac{n'}{l'} - \frac{n}{l} = \frac{n'-n}{r}.$$

This gives

$$l' = \frac{n'lr}{nr + (n'-n)l},$$

i.e.

$$l' - r = \frac{nr(l-r)}{nr + (n'-n)l}.$$

On substituting this into equation (16–2), one obtains

$$\frac{1}{n'R'} - \frac{1}{nR} = \frac{1}{n(l-r)} - \frac{nr + (n'-n)l}{n'nr(l-r)},$$

whence

$$\frac{1}{n'R'} - \frac{1}{nR} = -\left(\frac{n'-n}{nn'r}\right).$$

To conform to the sign convention for aberrations used in the previous chapter, it is necessary to regard R and R' in this example as negative. One then has

$$\frac{1}{n'R'} - \frac{1}{nR} = \frac{n'-n}{nn'r}. \qquad \ldots \ldots (16\text{--}3)$$

Thus for a given object curvature, the image curvature is independent of the object and image distances. It can be shown that it is also independent of the position of the aperture stop. When one has a system of refracting surfaces, equation (16–3) can be applied to each in turn. Consequently, for the complete system one obtains

$$\frac{1}{n'R'} - \frac{1}{nR} = \sum \left(\frac{n'-n}{nn'r}\right),$$

where this so-called *Petzval sum* extends over every surface in the system.

(b) Object at the Centre of Curvature

If the axial point of the object is at the centre of curvature, all the rays of the axial pencil are normal to the surface, and the axial object and image points coincide—there is obviously no spherical aberration. If the stop coincides with the surface, it can be seen from Fig. 16–7 that for a small object h, the angle i_{pr} is small, so that $ni_{pr}=n'i'_{pr}$ and $h'/h=i'_{pr}/i_{pr}=n/n'$. Since $u'=u$, the Sine Condition is satisfied, so that there is no coma for this position of the stop, and since there is no spherical aberration, there will be no coma for other stop positions. There will, however, be astigmatism, field curvature, and distortion, the astigmatism and field curvature being independent of the stop position.

Fig. 16–7.
Object at centre of curvature.

(c) Object Coincident with Surface

When the axial point of the object coincides with the pole of the refracting surface, the Gaussian image coincides with the object. Each object point lies close to the refracting surface so that, approximately, the wavefronts diverge from points on that surface, and its presence cannot alter the shapes of the wavefronts. Consequently, there is no spherical aberration, coma, or astigmatism. In effect, the fact that these conditions do not hold exactly gives rise to field curvature. (As stated above, this is the same for all object positions.) Associated with the deviation imposed on the principal rays, there is distortion. An approach to these conditions occurs in field lenses.

(d) The Aplanatic Points

In addition to the above, there is one position of the object for which there is no spherical aberration, and for which the Sine Condition is satisfied for a large aperture. This, and the corresponding image point, are called the aplanatic points, and one is said to have aplanatic refraction—there is no spherical aberration or coma. One of the aplanatic points is virtual, and the points are defined by

$$\left.\begin{aligned} l &= \left(\frac{n'+n}{n}\right)r, \\ l' &= \left(\frac{n'+n}{n'}\right)r. \end{aligned}\right\} \qquad \cdots \cdots \quad (16\text{-}4)$$

Fig. 16–8(a) shows the aplanatic points B and B′, assuming B is a real object and B′ a virtual image; a reversal of the arrows gives a virtual object B′ and real image B. The positions of B and B′ can be more easily described and remembered for the case when $n'=1$ and one has a sphere of material of index n. (The more general case follows at once on putting n/n' for n since this is the index of the first medium with respect to the second.)

13*

If one has a sphere of glass, centre C, radius r, of index n, as in Fig. 16–8(b), the positions of the aplanatic points B and B′ can be specified by drawing concentric circles centre C with radii r/n and rn. B and B′ are then as shown, it being assumed that refraction occurs at the right-hand side of the sphere. To prove that B is imaged without spherical aberration at B′ and that the Sine Condition

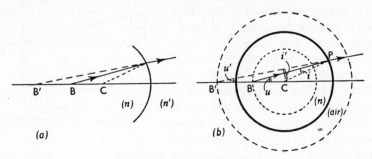

Fig. 16–8. The aplanatic points.

is satisfied, one proceeds as follows. Take any point P on the refracting surface and join CP, BP, B′P. The angles i, i', u, and u', are as shown. If it can be proved that $n \sin i = \sin i'$, then a ray BP is refracted along B′P produced; if this is true for any point P, B′ is the image of B, and if $(\sin u/\sin u')$ is constant, the Sine Condition is satisfied.

Now in △'s BPC, B′PC one has

$$\frac{BC}{PC} = \frac{PC}{B'C} \quad \text{(by construction)}$$

and $\angle BCP$ is common.

Therefore the triangles are similar.

$$\left.\begin{array}{l} \therefore \quad u = i', \\ u' = i. \end{array}\right\} \quad \dotsc \dotsc \dotsc \quad (16\text{–}5)$$

and

Now from △ BPC,

$$\frac{BC}{\sin i} = \frac{PC}{\sin u},$$

or, from (16–5),

$$\frac{\sin i'}{\sin i} = \frac{PC}{BC} = n.$$

Since P was chosen at random, it follows that B is imaged at B′ without aberration. Further, from (16–5) one has

$$\frac{\sin u}{\sin u'} = n.$$

That is, the Sine Condition is satisfied. Therefore, for object and image planes at B and B′, spherical aberration and coma are absent. This will be true for all stop positions. When the stop is at C, there can be no astigmatism, and since the system is aplanatic, it is anastigmatic for all positions of the stop. There will, as always, be field curvature, and there will also be distortion. Since no restriction was placed on the size of u, it follows that all orders of spherical aberration are absent, and from the Sine Condition, all the terms linearly dependent on σ are absent.

One frequently finds that one or more surfaces in a system can be positioned so that one or more of the conditions (a)–(d) can be approached, if not reached exactly. For example, the properties of the aplanatic points described in (d) are frequently utilized for at least one surface in a microscope objective; condition (c) is approached in field lenses; and condition (a) in certain wide-angle lenses. These points will be discussed further in §§ 16–8 to 16–12.

16–5. The Aberrations of a Single Thin Lens

(a) Spherical Aberration

For a thin lens of given power, one is free to choose the refractive index and the shape of the lens, and for a given position of the object, both these factors will affect the spherical aberration since they affect the angles of incidence involved. It is necessary to introduce a parameter to specify the shape of the lens; it is convenient to introduce a second parameter to specify the relative positions of object and image. The shape and object position parameters are defined respectively by the relations

$$X = \frac{r_2 + r_1}{r_2 - r_1},$$

$$Y = \frac{l + l'}{l - l'},$$

r_1 and r_2 being the radii of curvature of the lens, and l and l' the conjugate distances. It will be seen that these parameters are dimensionless—their values are independent of the units in which lengths are measured. (There are, in fact, certain advantages to be gained by defining X and Y in terms of the angles α_1, α_2, u_1, u_2', where these have their usual meanings. For example, $X = (\alpha_1 + \alpha_2)/(\alpha_1 - \alpha_2)$ and $Y = (u_2' + u_1)/(u_2' - u_1)$ are more convenient if a conjugate is infinite or a surface is plane.) Figs. 16–9 and 16–10 show the lens shapes and object positions corresponding to various values of X and Y respectively. In Fig. 16–10 a reversal of the arrows does not change Y.

Fig. 16–9. The shape parameter.

Fig. 16–10. The conjugate distance parameter.

For any given object position, and for a lens of given aperture and refractive index, the variation of the spherical aberration with X follows a parabolic curve. The curves in Fig. 16–11 show the spherical aberration parabolae for $Y=0$ for thin convex lenses of refractive index 1·5 and 1·7 (in air), the lenses having unit power. The figure shows that the aberration is reduced to a minimum by distributing the bending of the rays equally between the surfaces of the lens, and

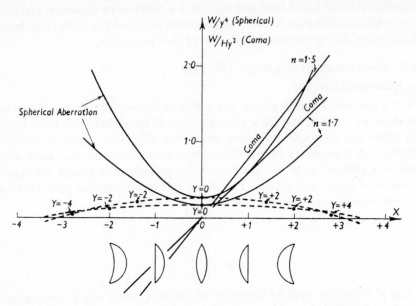

Fig. 16–11. Spherical aberration and central coma for thin lens.

is also reduced by increasing the refractive index. For other values of Y, each parabola retains the same shape but moves bodily, its vertex following the inverted parabola shown as a broken curve. In each case, the position of the vertex is indicated for various values of Y. The corresponding curves for a concave lens are obtained by changing the sign of the ordinates. It will be seen that, except for heavily meniscus shapes and one real and one virtual conjugate

Fig. 16–12. Use of the aplanatic points.

so that $|Y|$ is fairly large, the spherical aberration has the same sign as the power of the lens. That is, it is positive for converging lenses and negative for diverging. It is easy to show from the results of § 16–4 that, for a virtual object or image, it is possible to have zero spherical aberration for a particular meniscus shape lens. Thus if the object point B (Fig. 16–12) is at the centre of curvature of surface (1) and at the aplanatic point of surface (2), there will be no spherical aberration or coma.

(b) Coma

If the stop coincides with the lens, the so-called central coma for a given aperture and field is a linear function of both X and Y. The coma lines for a lens of unit power are shown in Fig. 16–11 for refractive indices 1·5 and 1·7 for $Y=0$. It will be seen that the coma is zero for the same value of $X(X=0)$ as the spherical aberration is a minimum. This is exactly true only when $Y=0$, but for small values of $|Y|$, the central coma is small when the lens shape is adjusted to give minimum spherical aberration.

It has been stated that when spherical aberration is present, the coma depends upon the position of the aperture stop; this fact is frequently used to correct the coma of a single lens (see §16–11).

(c) Astigmatism

Astigmatism is caused by the fact that the lens has different powers in the sagittal and tangential sections, and it is easily shown that when the stop coincides with the lens, this difference in power depends only on the angle of field; that is, it is independent of the lens shape and refractive index for a lens of given power.

Suppose a collimated beam of light is incident centrally at angle U_{pr} on a thin lens of focal length f'. Figs. 16–13(a) and (b) show the sections in the tangential

Fig. 16–13. Astigmatism of a thin lens at the stop.

and sagittal planes respectively. The incident wave is plane, and if there is no spherical aberration or coma, the emergent wave has a circular section in each of these planes; the radius in each case is the focal length in that section. The curvature of the emergent wave is caused by the fact that the optical path through the centre is greater than that through the edge of the aperture; this introduces a retardation of the centre of the wave and causes the sags (x) in the circular sections of the wavefront. The sags in the sagittal and tangential sections are obviously equal, but they correspond to chords of different lengths. Thus, if a is the linear aperture of the lens, this may be taken as the length of the chord in the sagittal section, but in the tangential plane the chord is of length $a \cos U_{pr}$. Now if x is the sag of a circular arc of radius r, for a chord of length $2c$, one may write $r=c^2/2x$ if x is small. Thus for circular arcs having equal sags, r is proportional to the square of the length of the chord. If f_S' and f_T' are the focal lengths in the sagittal and tangential sections, they are the radii of the circular sections of the wavefront, and one has

$$\frac{f_S'}{f_T'} = \frac{a^2}{a^2 \cos^2 U_{pr}}, \quad \cdot \quad \cdot \quad \cdot \quad \cdot \quad \cdot \quad (16\text{–}6)$$

$$\therefore \quad f_T' = f_S'(1-\sin^2 U_{pr}).$$

Hence one may write

$$\delta f' = f' \sin^2 U_{pr},$$

where $\delta f' = f_S' - f_T'$, and is the separation of the focal lines.

In terms of powers, one has, from (16–6),

$$\frac{F_T}{F_S} = \frac{1}{\cos^2 U_{pr}},$$

whence

$$F_T - F_S = F \sin^2 U_{pr}, \quad \dots \dots \quad (16-7)$$

so that the astigmatic difference of power depends only upon the paraxial power F and the angle of field. That is, as pointed out above, it does not depend on the lens shape or refractive index.

(d) Field Curvature

On applying equation (16–3) to each surface of the lens in turn, one has, for a lens of index n in air,

$$\frac{1}{R'} - \frac{1}{R} = \frac{n-1}{nr_1} + \frac{1-n}{nr_2}$$

$$= \frac{(n-1)}{n}\left(\frac{1}{r_1} - \frac{1}{r_2}\right)$$

$$= \frac{1}{nf'} = \frac{F}{n}, \quad \dots \dots \dots \quad (16-8)$$

so that the field curvature is dependent only upon the power of the lens and the refractive index of its material; that is to say, it does not depend on the object position, stop position, or lens shape. It will be seen that the Petzval field curvature of a thin lens is reduced if the refractive index is increased. Now, in order to reduce the chromatic aberration, it is desirable to use a glass having a small dispersion. These two factors indicate the desirability of having glasses with high indices and low dispersions, and considerable advances have been made in recent years in the production of such glass types.

Fig. 16–14. Central passage of a principal ray.

(e) Distortion

To a first approximation the principal rays emerge parallel to their original directions when a thin lens is coincident with the stop. The lens acts as a plane parallel plate and, in this case, there is no distortion (see Fig. 16–14). For other positions of the stop there will, in general, be distortion present.

16–6. The Achromatic Doublet

(a) Residual Chromatic Aberration

It was shown in Chapter III (§ 3–9) that a combination of two thin lenses in contact has the same power for two different colours R and B if the powers of the component lenses for an intermediate colour Y are given by

$$F_{1Y}=F_Y\left(\frac{V_1}{V_1-V_2}\right),$$
$$F_{2Y}=-F_Y\left(\frac{V_2}{V_1-V_2}\right),$$

$$\left.\right\} \quad \cdots \cdots \quad (16\text{–}9)$$

where V_1 and V_2 are the values of $V=(n_Y-1)/(n_B-n_R)$ for the materials of the lenses.

If R_1 and R_2 are the total curvatures of each lens $[R=(1/r_a-1/r_b)]$, $F=(n-1)R$ and the above equations give

$$R_1=\frac{1}{f_Y{}'(V_1-V_2)(n_{1B}-n_{1R})},$$
$$R_2=\frac{-1}{f_Y{}'(V_1-V_2)(n_{2B}-n_{2R})}.$$

$$\left.\right\} \quad \cdots \cdots \quad (16\text{–}10)$$

It was pointed out in Chapter III that a combination of two lenses which satisfies these equations is not completely free from chromatic aberration, and

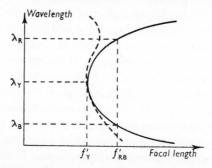

Fig. 16–15. Achromatic and apochromatic correction.

for a doublet employing hard crown and dense flint glass, the variation of focal length with wavelength is as indicated by the full curve in Fig. 16–15. The vertex of the curve lies in the region of the wavelength Y and a good indication of the magnitude of the residual aberration (*secondary spectrum*) is obtained if the difference between $f_Y{}'$ and $f_{RB}{}'$ is found. One has

$$\frac{1}{f_Y{}'}=(n_{1Y}-1)R_1+(n_{2Y}-1)R_2,$$

and

$$\frac{1}{f_{RB}{}'}=(n_{1B}-1)R_1+(n_{2B}-1)R_2,$$

$$\therefore \quad \frac{1}{f_{RB}{}'}-\frac{1}{f_Y{}'}=\frac{f_Y{}'-f_{RB}{}'}{f_Y{}'f_{RB}{}'}$$

$$=(n_{1B}-n_{1Y})R_1+(n_{2B}-n_{2Y})R_2,$$

$$\therefore \quad \frac{f_Y{}'-f_{RB}{}'}{f_{RB}{}'}=(n_{1B}-n_{1Y})R_1f_Y{}'+(n_{2B}-n_{Y2})R_2f_Y{}'.$$

Substituting for R_1 and R_2 from (16–10), one has

$$\frac{f_Y' - f_{RB}'}{f_{RB}'} = \frac{\left(\dfrac{n_{1B} - n_{1Y}}{n_{1B} - n_{1R}}\right)}{V_1 - V_2} - \frac{\left(\dfrac{n_{2B} - n_{2Y}}{n_{2B} - n_{2R}}\right)}{V_1 - V_2}$$

$$= \frac{\beta_1 - \beta_2}{V_1 - V_2}\,(\text{say}). \qquad \cdots \cdots \quad (16\text{–}11)$$

This equation gives the fractional difference in focal length for wavelength Y and the wavelengths R and B for which achromatism was effected. It will be seen that in the region of the wavelength Y, approximately midway between B and R, the variation of focal length with wavelength is small. For visual instruments this should occur in the middle of the visible spectrum where the eye is most sensitive. In consequence, it is convenient to use the C (λ 6563) and F (λ 4861) lines of hydrogen for R and B respectively, and the helium d (λ 5876) line for Y. For visual observations, f_d' is then the effective focal length of the lens and equation (16–11) gives, approximately, the maximum focusing error in the visible range. $(n_F - n_C)$ is usually called the *mean dispersion* and $(n_F - n_d)$ is a *partial dispersion*. (For any other wavelength λ, $(n_F - n_\lambda)$ is the corresponding partial dispersion.) The quantities β_1 and β_2 are called the *relative partial dispersions* and, in glass catalogues, are tabulated for certain wavelengths. Considerable effort has been made to produce crown and flint glasses whose relative partial dispersions are not widely different. It has proved possible to reduce the secondary spectrum considerably and the broken curve in Fig. 16–15 indicates the state of correction attainable. In such cases, where the focal length has the same value for three wavelengths, the lens is said to be *apochromatic*. An apochromatic system is frequently achieved by the use of a triplet with three different glasses.

In the early days of photography, the plates were sensitive over a relatively small spectral range at the blue end of the spectrum. In consequence, the lenses were achromatized for the sodium D (5893) and hydrogen G' (4341) lines so that the visual and photographic foci were the same. With present day emulsions that are sensitive over a wide range, the achromatic correction must be improved; an apochromatic correction is even more desirable here than with visual instruments.

(b) Monochromatic Aberrations

The most obvious advantage of a doublet over a single thin lens is the fact that the former can be achromatic; an equally important advantage is that it is possible to exercise a far greater control over the monochromatic aberrations. For any position of the object, it is possible to make a doublet achromatic and aplanatic. Achromatism is achieved by adjustment of the relative powers of the components, and aplanatism by adjustment of the lens shapes. The spherical aberration and central coma of each component vary with shape in the manner described in the previous section, and the aberrations of one component can be balanced by those of the other. For example, it was seen that for most object positions a converging lens gives positive, and a diverging lens negative, spherical aberration.

If the lens is to be a cemented doublet, one has fewer degrees of freedom since the shapes of the components cannot be adjusted independently. However, by a suitable choice of glasses, it is possible for a cemented doublet to be achromatic and aplanatic. When suitable glasses are used, the variation of spherical aberration and coma with lens shape is of the form indicated by Fig. 16–16. The curves relate to a ten-inch telescope objective covering a 6° field at $f/5$; they show the spherical aberration at the edge of the aperture and the coma in the tangential section at the edge of the aperture and field, and indicate that an aplanat is possible. Such an achromatic aplanat may be possible with several pairs of

Fig. 16–16. Spherical aberration and coma for a cemented doublet.

glasses, and the final choice will be influenced by consideration of the secondary spectrum and the steepness of the lens surfaces. For example, a doublet which contains steeply curved surfaces should be rejected because there will be a tendency for higher order aberrations to be introduced at those surfaces. If the components are not cemented together, one has a much greater choice of glasses since the lens shapes can be varied independently. With uncemented doublets, there are more air-glass surfaces and therefore greater losses of light and, in addition, the lens is less easily mounted and handled. For systems of moderate aperture, cemented combinations are usually employed.

If the doublet is thin, the central astigmatism will be given by equation (16–7) and will again be independent of the choice of glasses and lens shapes. It will also be independent of the stop position if the doublet is an aplanat. The Petzval sum of the doublet will be given [from equation (16–8)] by

$$P = \frac{F_1}{n_1} + \frac{F_2}{n_2}.$$

∴ from equation (16–9)

$$P = \frac{F}{(V_1 - V_2)}\left[\frac{V_1}{n_1} - \frac{V_2}{n_2}\right]. \qquad \ldots \quad (16\text{–}12)$$

In order to reduce the magnitude of the term in square brackets, it is necessary that the glass with the higher V-number should have the higher refractive index.

The original crown and flint glasses were very unsatisfactory in this respect, since the more dispersive flints also had the higher indices. The position has been improved by the production of additional glasses although, in many cases, the resulting doublet has rather steep curves. A considerable advance in the production of glass types was made by Abbe and Schott in Jena (*c.* 1886). They pointed the way to the production of glasses with a high index and low dispersion (e.g. Dense Barium Crowns), and with a low index and high dispersion

Fig. 16–17. Astigmatism of a concave mirror.

(Light Flints). However, the Petzval sum of a doublet is still usually positive so that it is desirable to introduce some negative astigmatism. This cannot be done if the doublet is a thin aplanat since it will always have the astigmatism given by (16–7). If spherical aberration is not corrected, it is possible to choose a lens shape and stop position to give zero coma and negative astigmatism, and this will be a more desirable state of correction if the lens is to cover a wide field.

The uses of an achromatic doublet are discussed further in §§ 16–8, 16–9, and 16–11.

16–7. The Astigmatism of a Concave Mirror

In Fig. 16–17 M_1M_2 is a concave mirror of small aperture, forming part of the spherical surface AB, radius r, centre C. P is an off-axis object point. As far as the larger surface AB is concerned, P may be taken as a point on the axis AC and, from this point of view, the rays PM_1S_1, PM_2S_2 may be taken as rays which exhibit the small difference in longitudinal spherical aberration S_1S_2. If the diagram is rotated about ACP through small angles in both directions, the rays PM_1 and PM_2 trace out sagittal fans of rays incident on the mirror M_1M_2, and since S_1 and S_2 remain stationary during this rotation, S_1S_2 is the sagittal focal line. PM_1M_2 is obviously a tangential fan of rays, incident on M_1M_2, and T is the focus which, during the rotation mentioned, traces out the tangential focal line.

Let s' and t' be the distances measured along the principal ray from O to the sagittal and tangential focal lines. Since the object is free from astigmatism, s

and t are the same and are conveniently denoted by a (not by l since this is always measured along the axis—in this case along OC).

From the figure,

$$\triangle POS = \triangle POC + \triangle COS,$$

$$\therefore \quad \tfrac{1}{2}as' \sin 2I_{pr} = \tfrac{1}{2}ar \sin I_{pr} + \tfrac{1}{2}rs' \sin I_{pr},$$

where I_{pr} is, with the usual notation, the angle of incidence of the principal ray,

i.e. $$2as' \sin I_{pr} \cos I_{pr} = ar \sin I_{pr} + rs' \sin I_{pr},$$

whence, on dividing throughout by $ars' \sin I_{pr}$, one obtains,

$$\frac{1}{a} + \frac{1}{s'} = \frac{2 \cos I_{pr}}{r}. \quad \ldots \ldots \quad (16\text{–}13)$$

If I_1 and I_2 are the angles of incidence at M_1 and M_2, and angles α, β, γ, θ, and ϕ, are as shown in the figure, one has

$$(\pi - \theta) = \alpha + I_1 = \beta + I_2, \quad \text{i.e. } I_1 - I_2 = \beta - \alpha,$$

$$(\pi - \phi) = \gamma + I_2 = \beta + I_1, \quad \text{i.e. } I_1 - I_2 = \gamma - \beta,$$

$$\therefore \quad \alpha + \gamma = 2\beta. \quad \ldots \ldots \ldots \quad (16\text{–}14)$$

Now $$\beta = \frac{M_1 M_2}{r}$$

and, since $M_1 M_2$ is small, one may write

$$\alpha = \frac{M_1 M_2 \cos I_{pr}}{a}$$

and $$\gamma = \frac{M_1 M_2 \cos I_{pr}}{t'}.$$

Hence, from (16–14), one obtains

$$\frac{1}{a} + \frac{1}{t'} = \frac{2}{r \cos I_{pr}}. \quad \ldots \ldots \quad (16\text{–}15)$$

With a concave grating, one has rulings on $M_1 M_2$ and a slit at P perpendicular to the plane of the diagram; it will be seen that each point of the slit gives a focal line at T. If the slit is twisted, the focal lines for each point are not collinear, and the width of the spectral line is increased.

16–8. The Design of Small Objectives

The lenses considered in this section are the small aperture objectives such as those used in most prismatic binocular telescopes, in low-power microscopes, and in the telescopes and collimators of spectrometers, etc. In systems of this kind, the aperture rarely exceeds $f/5$ and the field of view is very small. Consequently, the most important aberrations are primary spherical, coma, and the chromatic errors. The lens is usually a cemented achromatic aplanatic doublet and the lens holder itself is usually the aperture stop. There is little point in providing a separate diaphragm since its position will not affect the astigmatism if the system is aplanatic. The astigmatism will have the large positive value given in § 16–5 and the Petzval sum will also be positive, so that the image quality rapidly deteriorates as one moves away from the axis; little can be done to improve it. One can place either the crown or the flint component on the long conjugate side. The former is known as the Fraunhofer, and the latter as the Steinheil type (see Fig. 16–18). The Fraunhofer type usually has shallower surfaces and is therefore easier to produce, and, for a telescope objective, it has the more stable crown glass on the exposed side. The Steinheil type can sometimes give better correction. A third form of doublet is shown in Fig. 16–18; it is known as the Gauss type. With these uncemented meniscus lenses, one can achieve better correction for spherical aberration at the expense of coma. (The spherical aberration can be corrected for two different wavelengths.)

It should be noted that in a system such as a visual telescope containing an objective and an eyepiece, the lens system should be designed as a whole. For

(a) Fraunhofer (b) Steinheil (c) Gauss

Fig. 16–18. Achromatic doublets.

example, the objective and eyepiece need not be corrected separately for, say, spherical aberration, provided that the aberration of the eyepiece is corrected by the objective. This fact is often overlooked. For measuring instruments which include a graticule in an intermediate image plane, it is obviously necessary to correct separately those parts of the system which precede and follow the graticule. The apertures of these simple systems are ultimately limited by the appearance of higher order aberrations.

16–9. Microscope Objectives

Microscope objectives have a large aperture and a small field, so that spherical aberration, coma, and the chromatic aberrations, are again the most important. A doublet is satisfactory for many of the low power ($f'=2$ inches or 1 inch) smaller aperture objectives found in measuring microscopes. If a somewhat better state of correction is required, a cemented triplet lens may be used. This has less residual chromatic aberration, and since it has less steeply curved surfaces, a larger aperture can be used before higher order aberrations begin to appear. It was pointed out in Chapter XIV that the limit of resolution of a microscope objective depends on the numerical aperture, $n \sin U$. That is to say, the objective must admit the largest possible cone of light. In order to collect a wide cone, it is necessary to employ objectives of short focal length—high power. Lenses commonly used in microscopy have nominal focal lengths of (a) $\frac{2}{3}$ inch or 16 mm., (b) $\frac{1}{6}$ inch or 4 mm., (c) $\frac{1}{12}$ inch or 2 mm. Many 16 mm. objectives consist of two cemented doublets as shown in Fig. 16–19(a). It was discovered in 1830 by Lister that a doublet having a plano-convex outer form can have two pairs of conjugates for which there is no spherical aberration. For one pair, one conjugate is virtual, and for the other, both are real. It will be seen that the objective shown in Fig. 16–19(*a*) employs a doublet working under each of these conditions. It was found that the coma was of opposite sign in the two cases and it has proved possible to employ a system of this type to give an achromatic aplanatic objective having a numerical aperture of about 0·28. In practice, some deviation from the plano-convex outer form of each component may be an advantage. Since the aperture is now fairly large, secondary spherical aberration is likely to appear, and this must be examined by finding the exact paths of the rays in the axial pencil. In addition, it is desirable to ensure that the Sine Condition is satisfied for all zones of the aperture rather than examine the primary coma alone (see § 15–11).

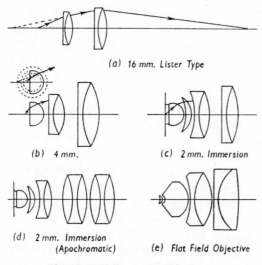

(*a*) 16 mm. Lister Type

(*b*) 4 mm.   (*c*) 2 mm. Immersion

(*d*) 2 mm. Immersion
(Apochromatic)   (*e*) Flat Field Objective

Fig. 16–19. Microscope objectives.

Fig. 16–19(*b*) illustrates the optical system of many 4 mm. objectives. The use of the hyperhemispherical front component followed the work of Amici (*c*. 1850) and, at the rear surface, one has approximately aplanatic refraction [see § 16–4(*d*)]. The front component has large power and gives considerable chromatic aberration which must be removed in the lenses that follow. One of the most troublesome surfaces in this system is the plane front surface, and it is largely the appearance of higher order aberration at this surface which limits the numerical aperture to about 0·8. (The small size of the front component makes it very undesirable to deviate from the plano form.)

The chromatic aberration can be reduced, and the general state of correction improved, by employing more complex systems. By using fluorite as a crown glass in these more complicated systems *apochromats* can be produced—the image distance is the same for three, or even four, wavelengths and therefore shows little variation over a wide range. With the simpler achromatic objectives the balance between the primary and higher order spherical aberrations is such that the total aberration is very small at the edge of the aperture. For an intermediate zone, however, there is some residual aberration. In the apochromatic objectives this zonal aberration can be reduced considerably. Furthermore, with a system such as a microscope objective, in which it is important to secure a very high degree of correction, it becomes desirable to consider the chromatic variation of the monochromatic aberrations. For example, the spherical aberration may be different for different wavelengths, and usually it is only corrected for one. In the apochromatic objectives the spherical aberration is corrected for two wavelengths (and is consequently small over a wide range) in addition to the improved longitudinal chromatic correction. It is found that many apochromatic objectives (especially those of higher power) give a chromatic difference of magnification; this can be corrected by using a *compensating eyepiece* (see §16–12). By employing fluorite as the crown component of a doublet, the secondary spectrum and the zonal aberration can be reduced. It is then possible to improve the performance of the achromatic type of objective; the correction is inferior to that of an apochromat but the lens is less complicated.

A further factor must be considered when seeking very good correction: many specimens to be examined with a microscope are contained beneath a cover glass. Now it can be shown that a parallel-sided glass plate introduces negative spherical aberration. This can be balanced by the positive aberration introduced if the objective is used at a slightly shorter tube length than that for which it is designed to be corrected. (Usually objectives are designed for a tube length of 160 mm.) Many objectives are specially designed for a standard cover glass thickness of 0·18 mm.

Now the numerical aperture is $n \sin U$ so that by filling the space between the object and the objective with a material medium, the numerical aperture may be increased without increasing the obliquity of the rays entering the objective. It will be seen below that by interposing a suitable material medium, it is also possible for the objective to collect a wider cone of rays without increasing the aberration, so that the numerical aperture can be increased in two ways.

Although the use of an immersion fluid was first suggested much earlier by Brewster, high power immersion objectives were not produced until about 1877, when prominent workers in the field were French, Abbe, and Tolles. The system shown in Fig. 16–19(c) represents an achromat of 2 mm. focal length and numerical aperture about 1·25. The space between the cover glass of the slide and the front lens is filled with a liquid of refractive index approximately equal to that of the cover glass; usually cedar oil, index 1·517, is employed. The refractive index of the front component is not very different from this so that the rays pass almost undeviated from the object to the rear surface of the first lens where there is, as before, approximately aplanatic refraction. The rays are then incident normally on the first surface of the meniscus lens and therefore pass undeviated to the rear surface where there is again aplanatic refraction. Thus the first two components impart a considerable deviation to the rays with the introduction of little spherical aberration or coma. Since these two components are non-achromatic and of large power, considerable chromatic aberration is introduced, and this must be removed in the rear lenses. In order to obtain a large amount of negative chromatic aberration from the rear components, it is necessary to employ rather steeply curved surfaces and this renders difficult the avoidance of high-order aberration. As stated above, there is approximately aplanatic refraction at the second and fourth surfaces, and normal incidence at the third. However, it must always be remembered that, in practice, there is some slight deviation from exact aplanatism and exactly normal incidence.

As with the 4 mm. objective, it is possible to increase the numerical aperture and obtain an apochromatic lens of better all-round correction by employing more complicated systems. An example is shown in Fig. 16–19(d) which illustrates an objective of about 2 mm. focal length, the numerical aperture being about 1·35. It is not possible to discuss these objectives further in simple terms.

Frequently it is desirable to examine objects under water and, for this purpose, water immersion objectives are designed in addition to the more usual oil immersion systems.

As stated at the beginning of this section, it is the spherical aberration and coma which are the most important monochromatic aberrations in microscope objectives. Usually these systems have a large Petzval sum and positive astigmatism. For microscopes that are to be used for plotting the tracks of atomic particles in photographic emulsions, and similar work, it is desirable to have an objective with a flat field. These are very much more difficult to design and manufacture. An example is shown in Fig. 16–19(e); it has a numerical aperture of 0·85 and gives a primary magnification of 30.

16–10. Substage Condensers

It was seen in § 14–12 that it is necessary for the substage condenser to supply a wide cone of light. However, it is not necessary for the condenser to be as highly corrected as an objective, and a popular system is the Abbe condenser shown in Fig. 16–20. If oiled to the slide, a numerical aperture of 1·2 is attainable. As indicated, this system has very large spherical aberration (especially when used "dry") and is unachromatic. Frequently it is desirable to employ a more highly corrected system; the condenser then resembles an achromatic objective used in reverse.

Fig. 16–20.
The Abbe condenser.

If an annular aperture is placed behind the condenser, a hollow cone of light emerges and this is suitable for dark-ground illumination with objectives of moderate power (see § 14–14). For higher powers, reflecting condensers are available (see § 14–14).

16–11. Photographic Lenses

(a) Simple Meniscus

If it is intended to use a single thin lens as a photographic objective, it is obviously impossible to correct its spherical aberration, chromatic aberration, or Petzval field curvature. Since the lens must cover a fairly wide field, it is necessary to concentrate on reducing the effect of the off-axis aberrations. The presence of spherical aberration enables the coma to be varied by moving the aperture stop, and it is usual to choose the stop position for zero coma. It has been shown (§ 15–13) that the effect of positive Petzval field curvature is reduced by the introduction of negative astigmatism. For a system with positive spherical aberration, it can be shown that the astigmatism reaches a minimum value for the stop position that removes the coma. The exact value of this minimum astigmatism depends upon the shape of the lens. Fig. 16–21 shows the form of the astigmatic fields for three meniscus lens shapes employing the stop position for zero coma. In order to show the effect more clearly, the deviations from the Gaussian plane are increased by a factor of about 2·5. The astigmatism is

Fig. 16–21. Astigmatic fields for coma-free meniscus lenses.

negative and therefore reaches a maximum numerical value. It will be seen that as the lens is made more heavily meniscus, more negative astigmatism is introduced, and one chooses the shape which gives an approximately flat tangential field with zero coma [i.e. shape between (a) and (b)]. It will be seen that no attempt is made to choose a lens shape for minimum spherical aberration, and the effect of this defect must be reduced by employing a rather small aperture. Meniscus lenses of this type usually have an aperture of about $f/12$ or less. It is possible to employ a meniscus convex to the object with the stop behind the lens, and this has less spherical aberration.

(b) The Achromatic Doublet

The most obvious development from the simple meniscus is the use of an achromatic doublet. As pointed out in § 16–6, it is possible to control the astigmatism and coma if the spherical aberration is not corrected. Now, as with the simple meniscus, the Petzval field curvature is positive, and again it is usual to choose the lens shape and stop position to give zero coma and a flat tangential field. For obvious reasons this system is frequently referred to as a landscape lens; it can take either of the forms shown in Fig. 16–22. In the Grubb type, considerable negative secondary spherical aberration is introduced at the contact surface, and this to some extent reduces the effect of the residual positive primary aberration. Originally these lenses used hard crown and dense flint glasses, but when further glass types were evolved, these were employed also. The chief advantage of these newer glasses is that the Petzval sum is reduced (see § 16–6) so that less negative astigmatism is required. The correction in the outer parts of the field is therefore improved, although the spherical aberration

(a) Grubb Type   (b) Chevalier Type

Fig. 16–22. Landscape lenses.

is often worse than with the older glasses. The general appearance of the lens is similar to that of the Chevalier type. Before describing the modern photographic lens types, it must be pointed out that it is much easier to design a satisfactory lens of short focal length than it is to produce a long focus system. A design for a short focal length will not produce a long focus lens simply by being scaled up, because its aberrations will be scaled up also. Thus a wavefront aberration which was a small fraction of a wavelength (and therefore unimportant) becomes a larger fraction and more harmful.

(c) Symmetrical Lenses

If a lens system is completely symmetrical about the aperture stop, there can be no coma, distortion, or chromatic difference of magnification. This, however, implies that the object and image distances are equal. In a photographic lens

(a) Double   (b) Rapid   (c) Protar
    Meniscus   Rectilinear

Fig. 16–23. Developments from the double meniscus.

the object distance is usually much larger than the image distance; nevertheless, it is found that the control of the above aberrations is facilitated by employing a system of approximately symmetrical construction. It must be remembered, however, that small deviations from exact symmetry may be advantageous.

The simplest system of this type employs two non-achromatic meniscus lenses as in Fig. 16–23(a). The design of this lens proceeds along lines similar to those for a single meniscus. Frequently the power of the double meniscus can be varied for focusing purposes by changing the separation of the components. The obvious development from the double meniscus is the use of two achromatic doublets. (As was proved in § 3–10, a system of two separated thin lenses can, in general, be free from both chromatic aberrations only if the lenses are separately achromatic.) Fig. 16–23(b) shows an early lens of this type, employing hard crown and dense flint components; it is known as the *Rapid Rectilinear* lens, and was produced by Dallmeyer in 1866. The symmetry of the system automatically reduces the coma, distortion, and transverse chromatic aberration. The spherical aberration for each component is reduced but each has coma which is used to control the astigmatism by varying the distance of the component from the stop. Since each component has a large positive Petzval sum, it is necessary to introduce negative astigmatism. The lens covered a 25° semi-field with an aperture of about $f/8$ and marked a great advance in the performance of photographic objectives.

When the newer glasses were produced at Jena, they were at once substituted into lenses of the Rapid Rectilinear type, the order of the convex and concave components being reversed. The reduced Petzval sum enabled the correction to be improved in the outer part of the field, but the spherical aberration was increased and the overall performance was not markedly improved.

The next major advance was made by Rudolph in 1890 with the lens shown in Fig. 16–23(c). The front component was an old glass achromat of small or even negative power, and the rear component employed the newer glasses. This enabled the Petzval sum to be reduced considerably. (As shown by equation (16–12), the Petzval sum of an old glass achromatic doublet can be small only if the power is small, and negative only if the power is negative.) The contact surface in the front component gave an important contribution of negative spherical aberration, and the rear cemented surface was important in the control of the astigmatism. A number of versions of this lens have been produced and it has been made to cover a semi-field of 30° at f/8. It must be pointed out that it was now becoming possible to exercise some control over more than just the

(a) Dagor   (b) Celor   (c) Cine Anastigmat

Fig. 16–24. Developments from the symmetrical type.

primary aberrations. For example, the secondary spherical aberration was made to balance the primary in the outer zones of the aperture, and the higher order astigmatism caused the astigmatic fields to bend back towards the focal plane after deviating from it in the usual way [see Fig. 16–23(c)]. This lens was, in fact, the first *anastigmat* and was known by that name originally. However, when the term came to be used to describe any lens which has a substantially flat field free from astigmatism, the name *Protar* was adopted for the original lens.

It will be appreciated that in designing a lens the desirability of exercising greater control over the several aberrations calls for more degrees of freedom. Thus the doublets of the Protar lens become triplets, as in the *Dagor* designed by von Höegh [Fig. 16–24(a)]. For a focal length of about 10 cm., this lens covered a field of 50°–60° at f/6·8. There have been a number of similar types— some having four cemented components on each side of the stop, and some having each half of the system corrected separately. With the latter type, one can use one half alone to give a lens of half power.

Another type of lens of approximately symmetrical construction is the *Celor* designed by von Höegh in about 1897 [Fig. 16–24(b)]. For a focal length o 10 cm. this had an aperture of about f/5 and covered a field of 50°–60°. A few years later a modified Celor lens was produced; this was not exactly symmetrica and had rather larger separations between the positive and negative components It had an aperture of f/3·5. A large number of similar lenses have been designed some for small field and large aperture, and some for large field and smal aperture. The f/1·9 *Cine Anastigmat* (8 or 16 mm. cameras) can be regarded as an extreme example of the former kind, although it is probably better regarde as a development of the Petzval type (see below). It is interesting to compare the general appearance of these lenses [Fig. 16–24(b) and (c)] with the wide-angle type shown in Fig. 16–28(b).

A further important advance in symmetrical lenses was made by Lee in 1920 with the *Cooke Opic* lens shown in Fig. 16–25. This covered a field of about 48° at the very large aperture of $f/2$. The Opic resembles the Celor in so far as it consists of two diverging components (now doublet menisci) between two converging components. This construction is also responsible for the Opic and its many derivatives being referred to as *double-Gauss* type lenses; they can be said to resemble two Gauss-type objectives [Fig. 16–18(c)] with the stop between them. The resemblance is not always obvious at first sight because the components are sometimes complex. Wynne (1944) has described a double-Gauss lens of relative aperture $f/1·0$ in which the rear diverging meniscus is reduced to a single thick component. Most modern wide-aperture lenses covering a reason-

Fig. 16–25.
The Opic lens.

ably large field are of the double-Gauss form; there are also double-Gauss or Celor type lenses that cover a very much wider field of view with somewhat smaller apertures.

(d) *The Cooke Triplet and its Derivatives*

It was pointed out in §3–10 that a system of three separated, thin, un-achromatic lenses can be free from longitudinal chromatic aberration and chromatic difference of magnification. The *Cooke Triplet* designed by H. D. Taylor (*c.* 1895) is corrected in this way [Fig. 16–26(a)]. In addition to the relative simplicity of the chromatic correction, the use of a diverging lens between two converging lenses has another important aspect. When a ray is incident at height y on a thin lens of power F, the ray is deviated through an angle Fy. It will be seen that the height of incidence of a ray in an axial pencil is relatively small at the second component, so that the lens can have a relatively high negative power. This gives a relatively large negative contribution to the Petzval field curvature, with a corresponding improvement in the off-axis correction. Triplet lenses are still widely used. They can have apertures of about $f/4·5$ for a field of about 50° for a 10 cm. lens. For longer focal lengths or wider fields, the aperture is smaller, and for smaller fields the aperture can be increased to $f/3·5$. For shorter focal lengths, the aperture can be increased still further

(a) Cooke Triplet   (b) Tessar   (c) Pentac

Fig. 16–26. Triplet lenses.

and, as an extreme example, a triplet has recently been used in an 8 mm. cine camera with an aperture of $f/1·9$ and a 26° field. The triplet is one of the few lenses which was originally designed analytically rather than empirically. It will be seen that the Celor lens can be regarded as a derivative of the triplet.

The *Tessar* [Fig. 16–26(b)], introduced by Rudolph in 1902, may be considered as a development of the triplet. It can also be regarded as a development of the

Protar, the front component becoming uncemented. The state of correction of a Tessar is rather better than that of a triplet; it has a flatter field and the spherical aberration is smaller. Almost every manufacturer produces Tessars and, for apertures of $f/2\cdot8$ or $f/3\cdot5$, they may be regarded as the standard lenses for the better grade cameras.

Another lens which may be regarded as a derivative of the triplet or of the symmetrical types is the *Pentac*, designed by Booth in 1919 [Fig. 16–26(c)]. Apertures of $f/2\cdot9$ have been achieved with fields of about 50° and the lens has been widely used for aerial cameras. Pentacs with focal lengths of 12 inches or more, have been produced.

Further developments of the symmetrical and Triplet types are very numerous and very complicated; a discussion of these lenses is beyond the scope of the present book.

(e) Lenses of the Petzval Type

There are several applications for which one can sacrifice the size of the field in order to obtain a lens of wide aperture. In such cases the spherical aberration,

(a) Petzval Portrait   (b) Projection Ektar

Fig. 16–27. Portrait and projection lenses.

coma, and chromatic aberrations, are the most important aberrations to consider. Lenses for portrait photography and certain projection systems and cine cameras are of this type. In the original *Petzval Portrait* lens [Fig. 16–27(a)], designed by Petzval in 1840, one cemented and one uncemented doublet were used. This had large aperture ($f/3\cdot4$ with a 20° field) in order to reduce the exposure required with the rather slow plates available. In many cases, no special aperture stop was provided and the field of view was limited by the lens holder as indicated. More recent lenses have employed two uncemented components, and the lens shown in Fig. 16–24(c) can be regarded as one of this type.

It was pointed out by Piazzi-Smyth (1874) that a concave component close to the focal plane will introduce negative Petzval field curvature and help to flatten the field without upsetting the other corrections; it is a field lens [see § 16–4(c)]. A field flattener of this type was used in a projection lens by von Rohr (1911). Fairly recently, a 16 mm. projection lens (the Projection Ektar) employing a field flattener has been described by Schade. This is shown in Fig. 16–27(b); it has a focal length of $2\frac{1}{4}$ inches and, with an aperture of $f/1\cdot5$, gives extremely good definition over a 14° field—it will resolve 90 lines per mm. over the entire flat 16 mm. gate.

(f) Wide-angle Lenses

The main consideration in the design of wide-angle lenses is the reduction of the angles of incidence in the oblique pencils. Consequently, there is a tendency for the components to be heavily meniscus around the stop. A simple example is the *Hypergon* designed by von Höegh [Fig. 16–28(*a*)]. For a focal length of 10 cm. this lens covered a field of 140° at $f/22$ or less. It has a very flat field free from distortion.

Many lenses of the Celor type have been designed to cover a wide field. As they are made more meniscus, they cover a larger field at a smaller aperture. An extreme example is the *Topogon* shown in Fig. 16–28(*b*). For a 15 cm. lens, this

(*a*) Hypergon   (*b*) Topogon   (*c*) Ross

Fig. 16–28. Wide-angle lenses.

covers a 90° field at $f/8$–$f/11$. It has been widely used as an aerial survey lens. Another wide-angle lens is shown in Fig. 16–28(*c*). This is made by Ross and covers a field of 70° at about $f/4\cdot5$.

(g) Telephoto Lenses

The principle of the telephoto lens was described in § 3–4. If the system consists of two separated, fairly thin components it is necessary, as usual, to achromatize each component separately. One would expect the simplest telephoto lenses to consist of two separated achromatic doublets, the first of positive, and the second of negative power. The *Dallon* lens designed by Booth is of this type [Fig. 16–29(*a*)]. It has an aperture of $f/5\cdot6$. In order to secure a large aperture, the telephoto magnification is now usually restricted to 2–3.

(*a*) Dallon   (*b*) Distortionless

Fig. 16–29. Telephoto lenses.

A simple positive lens placed before the aperture stop gives pincushion distortion; so, also, does a negative lens placed after the stop, and, for many years, designers were unable to produce distortionless telephoto lenses. The problem was first solved by Lee, who produced the system shown in Fig. 16–29(*b*). The broken contact surface in the rear component enables one to introduce barrel distortion and positive astigmatism which are balanced in the front component. This lens had an aperture of $f/5$ and had a telephoto magnification of 2·3.

16–12. Eyepieces

It has already been pointed out (§ 3–12) that the Huygens eyepiece gives less chromatic difference of magnification than the Ramsden, but that the latter must be used if a graticule is employed. Since each system consists of two single converging lenses, each has considerable positive Petzval field curvature. It is therefore desirable to introduce negative astigmatism. (As far as the complete instrument—objective and eyepiece—is concerned, the negative astigmatism is also desirable since the objective gives astigmatism of positive sign.) It is found that the Ramsden eyepiece has better astigmatic correction and is also better corrected for spherical and the other monochromatic aberrations. Little advantage is to be gained by deviating from the simple plano-convex form of the Huygens or Ramsden eyepieces. The chromatic correction of the Ramsden eyepiece can be improved considerably, and the general usefulness of the system

(a) Kellner   (b) Compensating   (c) Orthoscopic

Fig. 16-30. Eyepieces.

greatly extended, by employing a doublet eye lens. This *achromatized Ramsden* or *Kellner* eyepiece is shown in Fig. 16-30(*a*), the field stop and eye point being as indicated. This system covers a rather wider field of view than the simple eyepieces. The Huygens eyepiece is widely used in microscopy where the relative aperture and field of view are small. It has already been remarked that some microscope objectives give chromatic difference of magnification. This can be removed by a *compensating* eyepiece in which each lens of the Huygens system is a doublet [Fig. 16-30(*b*)]. With this eyepiece, it is possible to introduce negative transverse chromatic aberration.

Fig. 16-30(*c*) shows the system frequently referred to as an *orthoscopic* eyepiece. This system, due to Abbe, is widely used in systems whose aperture and field are beyond the capabilities of a Kellner system. It can now cover a visual field of up to 70°, and gives a very good eye clearance. There are many other

Fig. 16-31. Effect of spherical aberration of principal rays.

forms of eyepiece but these cannot be described in simple terms and will not be discussed here.

A defect whose importance is not always appreciated is spherical aberration of the principal rays. This is often severe in eyepieces of the Ramsden and Kellner types and arises chiefly at the curved surface of the field lens. The beams emerging at large angles are displaced, and in some cases enter the eye in part only (see Fig. 16-31). This results in a decrease in the apparent image brightness and, for certain eye positions, can cause isolated shadows to appear in the field of view.

16-13. Reflecting Systems

Apart from the complete absence of chromatic aberration, a mirror has certain advantages over a lens. It has been pointed out several times that a formula describing refraction at a single surface can be converted into the corresponding formula for reflection by putting $n' = -n$. A reflecting surface therefore corresponds to a change in refractive index of 2 compared with 0·5–0·7 for most refracting surfaces. Consequently, one would expect some of the aberrations of a reflecting surface to be less than those of a refracting surface under similar conditions. Thus it is found that a concave spherical mirror has considerably less spherical aberration than a thin converging lens of the same focal length. Now if the aperture stop is located at the centre of curvature of the mirror (Fig. 16–32), all principal rays are incident normally and, in each pencil of rays, there is symmetry about the principal ray in the same way as there is about the axis for an axial pencil. Consequently, there can be no coma or astigmatism. There is field curvature as illustrated, but the image surface is convex to the oncoming light, as opposed to concave as it is for a convex lens. This is obviously an advantage if a concave mirror and a convex lens are combined, since the combination will have a reduced Petzval sum. The obvious

Fig. 16–32. Concave mirror with stop at centre of curvature.

difficulty associated with reflecting systems is the obstruction of the incident light by the image surface or by subsequent components. The image-forming pencils consequently consist of hollow cones of rays and this can upset the image quality although it seldom does so to a serious extent. The loss of light is usually of the same order of magnitude as the loss by absorption in a purely refracting system of comparable aperture.

For a concave mirror with the stop at the centre of curvature, spherical aberration is the only outstanding defect apart from field curvature. Now with positive spherical aberration the wavefront lies in front of the reference sphere in the outer zones of the aperture. The wave can be rendered spherical if the outer parts can be retarded, and this was done very effectively in the *Schmidt*

Fig. 16–33. Schmidt systems.

system by placing a corrector plate at the aperture stop as in Fig. 16–33(a). Disturbances in the outer zones of the aperture are retarded by an amount proportional to ϱ^4 so that the spherical aberration of the mirror is corrected. In terms of rays, the latter are deviated by the plate so that, after reflection, they pass through the paraxial focus P. It will be seen that the corrector has the general form of a diverging lens (although the second surface is not spherical) so that chromatic aberration is introduced. This dispersive effect is reduced to a minimum if the maximum ray deviation introduced by the plate is as small as possible. In the system shown in Fig. 16–33(b), the rays at the centre and marginal zones of the aperture are made to pass through a point between the marginal and paraxial foci of the mirror. This point is chosen to be the place where the maximum transverse ray aberration is as small as possible and is at the disc of least confusion—one quarter of the way from the marginal to the paraxial focus. It can be shown that the oblique aberrations introduced by the corrector plate are smaller for the second system. By introducing a suitable corrector plate, it is obviously possible to correct the secondary as well as the primary spherical aberration.

(a)   (b)

Fig. 16–34.
Development of the concentric system.

Now a diverging lens with spherical surfaces introduces negative primary spherical aberration, so that this aberration can be removed from the system shown in Fig. 16–34(a). The amount of spherical aberration introduced by the lens depends on its shape, and it is found that by employing a meniscus lens its power (and therefore its chromatic aberration) can be reduced. Proceeding in this way, one finds that it is possible to employ a lens for which the centre of curvature of each surface coincides with that of the mirror. This *concentric system* is shown in Fig. 16–34(b) and has an important advantage over the Schmidt system: since each surface is centred at C each principal ray is incident normally at all surfaces if the stop is also at C. Thus there is again no coma or

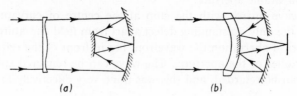

(a)   (b)

Fig. 16–35. Cameras of the Cassegrain type.

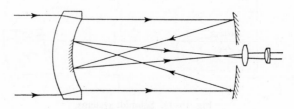

Fig. 16–36. Gregorian telescope.

astigmatism. For small systems such as cameras and terrestrial telescopes, the meniscus system is very useful, but for large astronomical telescopes the meniscus is more difficult to make than the Schmidt plate.

The optical systems of the classical reflecting telescopes were shown in Fig. 3–18. The Herschellian type has the disadvantage of employing the mirror off-axis. For terrestrial instruments, it is undesirable for the observer to look at right angles to the direction observed as in the Newtonian instrument. In recent years, several systems resembling the Gregorian and Cassegrainian instruments have appeared, some using one or more non-spherical mirrors, and some incorporating correctors of the Schmidt or meniscus type. Figs 16–35(*a*) and (*b*) show cameras suggested by Baker and by Bouwers and Maksutov; Fig. 16–36 shows a Gregorian telescope described by Bouwers.

When an attempt is made to design a purely refracting microscope objective for use in the ultra-violet, it is found that it is impossible to secure a satisfactory

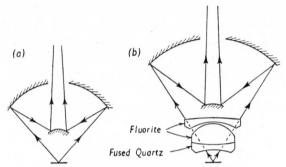

Fig. 16–37. Reflecting microscope objectives.

correction of the chromatic aberration with the transparent media available at present. This difficulty can be overcome by employing a reflecting or a catadioptric objective. Fig. 16–37(*a*) shows a simple reflecting objective, and (*b*) shows a catadioptric objective described by Grey; in the latter the second mirror obstructs a relatively small proportion of the aperture.

CHAPTER XVII

VISUAL OPTICS

17–1. General Structure of the Eye

FIG. 17–1 represents an approximately full size horizontal section through a human right eye. The greater part of the eyeball is bounded by a tough, opaque, white membrane known as the *sclera*. At the front, this merges into a transparent, rather horny layer known as the *cornea*. The cornea has a thickness of about 0·5 mm. and the radius of curvature of its front surface is about 7·8 mm. The general spherical shape of the eyeball is maintained by the internal excess pressure which is some two or three cm. of mercury. Behind the cornea is the

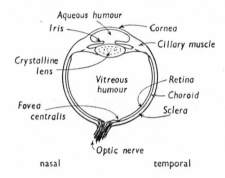

Fig. 17–1. Horizontal section of a right eye.

so-called *anterior chamber* which has an axial thickness of about 1·3 mm. and is filled with a watery, slightly saline fluid of index 1·336, known as the *aqueous humour*. At the rear of the anterior chamber is the *crystalline lens* whose aperture, usually referred to as the *pupil*, is controlled by the *iris* which is strongly coloured and almost opaque. The pupil size is varied by the iris from about 2 mm. diameter in very bright light, to about 8 mm. diameter in darkness. The crystalline lens has a bi-convex outer form, the front and back surfaces having normal radii of about 10 mm. and 6 mm. respectively, and the axial thickness being about 3·6 mm. The lens is not homogeneous but is built up of successive fibrous layers whose refractive indices vary from about 1·37 in the outer parts to about 1·42 in the middle. The *posterior chamber* behind the crystalline lens contains a transparent jelly-like substance known as the *vitreous humour* (index about 1·336). The inner surface of the rear part of the eyeball contains the receiving screen known as the *retina*. This consists effectively of a mosaic of light-sensitive elements upon which the image is formed when the eye is in use. The retina lies on the *choroid*, a layer which is dark brown in colour and richly supplied with blood vessels. Nerve impulses from the retinal receptors are communicated to the brain through the *optic nerve*.

There are no receptors where the optic nerve leaves the eyeball and that region is the so-called *blind spot*. This renders invisible a field measuring about 6° horizontally and 8° vertically. This fact often passes unnoticed—partly because the dark spot of one eye lies in the field of view of the other, and partly because the eyes are constantly rotating to explore the field of view. The existence of the blind spot can be observed as follows. Using only the right eye, look at A (Fig. 17–1). On varying the distance from eye to figure, a position will be found at which B disappears from view. Its image is now falling on the blind spot.

The resolving power of the retina reaches a sharp maximum in the region of a small depression known as the *fovea centralis*. When it "looks at" an object the eye is rotated until the image falls on the fovea. When a "normal" eye is at rest the optical system brings parallel rays to a focus on the retina, i.e. distant objects are clearly seen. In order to view nearer objects the power of the optical system of the eye is increased—a process known as *accommodation*. Although most of the power of the optical system of the eye is derived from refraction at the cornea, the *changes* in power during accommodation are effected by means of a change in the shape of the crystalline lens. The greatest observable change is in the curvature of the front surface of the lens and is controlled, in a way not fully understood, by the *ciliary muscle*. Some observers state that the shape of the eyeball changes also, the curvature of the cornea increasing.

17–2. The Optical System of a Normal Unaccommodated Eye

The optical system of the eye is complicated by the non-homogeneous nature of the crystalline lens. Gullstrand suggested a "schematic" eye which employed a lens of only two parts—an outer layer of index 1·386 and a core of index 1·406. This would give properties very similar to those of a real eye. He suggested, also, a simpler schematic eye in which the cornea was replaced by a simple refracting surface separating air and the aqueous humour. In addition, the lens was replaced by a simple one (see Fig. 17–2). The specification is:

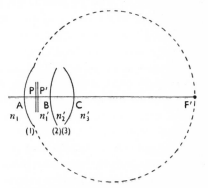

Fig. 17–2. Optical system of the eye.

$$(n_1 = 1·000\text{—air})$$

(cornea) $r_1 = +0·78$ cm.

$\qquad\qquad d_1' = 0·36$ cm. $(n_1' = 1·336\text{—aqueous humour})$

(lens) $\begin{cases} r_2 = +1·00 \text{ cm.} \\ \qquad\qquad d_2' = 0·36 \text{ cm.} \\ r_3 = -0·60 \text{ cm.} \end{cases}$ $(n_2' = 1·413\text{—crystalline lens})$

$$(n_3' = 1·336\text{—vitreous humour})$$

The positions of the cardinal points are best found using the deviation method (§ 2–22). One obtains:

$$f = -1.678 \text{ cm.}$$
$$f' = +2.242 \text{ cm.}$$
$$F = 59.59 \text{ dioptres.}$$
$$AP = +0.147 \text{ cm.}$$
$$CP' = -0.545 \text{ cm.}$$
$$AN = +0.711 \text{ cm.}$$
$$CN' = +0.019 \text{ cm.}$$

The separation of the principal points (and therefore of the nodal points) is only 0·028 cm. so that, for many purposes, one can assume that the principal points coincide and that the nodal points also coincide.

The above results are for a normal eye with relaxed accommodation but, as pointed out in the previous section, the power of the eye is changed in order to view objects at finite distances. The maximum change in power which the eye can effect is called the *amplitude of accommodation* and, for the "average person", this varies from about 14 dioptres at the age of 10 years to about 4 dioptres at the age of 40, falling almost to zero at age 75. The object point for which the image is in focus when the optical system has minimum power is called the *far point*, and the *near point* is focused when the eye has maximum power. For the average observer, the far point is at infinity until the age of about 50. Thus, at age 40 the near point is 25 cm. in front of the eye and this has come to be taken as the standard *least distance of distinct vision* and is written "D_v". Beyond the age of about 50 the power of the optical system of the eye tends to decrease so that, when the accommodation is relaxed, light entering the eye must be convergent in order to be focused on the retina; the far point is then virtual. The associated loss of the ability to accommodate causes the near point to recede from the observer until it, too, becomes virtual.

As pointed out above, the eye rotates to bring the image on to the fovea for critical examination, and the line joining the fovea, the nodal point, and the so-called fixation point, may be called the *visual axis*. The optical system of the eye does not constitute an exactly centred system but for most purposes one may assume that it does. The axis approximating most closely to a true optical axis does not coincide with the visual axis but is inclined to it at an angle, α, of 5°–6° in the approximate direction of the figure 4 when the fixation point is the centre of the clock face. The centre of rotation of the eyeball is about 14 mm. from the front surface of the cornea.

The iris obviously constitutes the aperture stop, but there is no field stop. Although the retina can give good resolution near the fovea only, the complete field of view of the eye is very large. It extends laterally beyond even 90° on the temporal side and over 60° on the nasal side; it extends vertically about 50° upwards and 70° downwards. The retina cannot give good resolution in the outer parts of the field and the oblique aberrations are unimportant. The eye has the usual axial aberrations—chromatic and spherical—but the effect of the former is reduced by the fact that the eye is mainly sensitive to a relatively small range of colours. For many purposes, the aberrations of the "average" eye can be neglected. (See §§ 17–6 and 17–7.)

17–3. Defects in the Optical System. Spectacles

If, with a normal amplitude of accommodation, the power of the optical system is too great, the far point is at a finite distance and the near point is abnormally close to the eye. This condition is referred to as *myopia* or *short sight* and can be corrected by placing a concave lens in front of the eye in order to balance its excess positive power. If the power of the optical system is too small—a condition known as *hypermetropia* or *long sight*—the correction is effected by the use of a convex lens. With simple myopia and hypermetropia the effect of the spectacle lens is simply to shift the range of powers covered by the accommodation of the eye so that it covers the usual region. A reduction of the power of accommodation below about 4 dioptres is referred to as *presbyopia.*

If the far point remains at infinity or at a fairly large distance, the effect of presbyopia is a rather remote near point and this causes a difficulty with reading and other close work; it can be overcome by the use of a convex lens. As pointed out above, the lack of accommodation over the age of about 50 years is usually associated with an all-round reduction in the power of the optical system and it is then necessary to use a pair of spectacles with convex lenses to see distant objects, and a second pair with stronger convex lenses to see near objects. Frequently a spectacle lens of conventional appearance

Fig. 17–3.
Vision through a
spectacle lens.

has the upper part of its aperture of one power and the lower half of a higher power since it is chiefly when reading that the eyes are directed downwards.

During use the eyes are rotated in their sockets and, as indicated by Fig. 17–3, the light entering the eye will pass obliquely through the spectacle lens. In order to reduce the effect of this oblique passage it is obviously desirable to employ a meniscus lens as indicated. This need is less marked when using spectacles for reading since the eye rotates through relatively small angles only.

In addition to the above defects many eyes exhibit axial astigmatism. The power of the optical system is then different in different azimuths, even when the object is on the axis. The variation of power with azimuthal angle is not always similar to the $\cos^2 \phi$ variation associated with primary oblique astigmatism in a system which has axial symmetry, but the defect can be reduced considerably by using a cylindrical lens which does introduce astigmatism of the conventional type. For example, if the astigmatism is such that the eye has the correct power in one azimuth and maximum incorrect power in an azimuth roughly at right angles, the defect is reduced considerably by the use of a cylindrical lens whose maximum power lies in the direction of the maximum error of the eye. Simultaneous myopia or hypermetropia can be corrected by using a lens of which one surface is spherical and one cylindrical. If a meniscus lens is desired, it is necessary for one surface to have a variation of curvature with azimuthal angle which may be described as a superposition of sphere and cylinder —a *toric* or *toroidal* surface.

In recent years *contact lenses* have been used to correct the refractive errors of the eye. These are small lenses which are placed in direct contact with the eyeball.

17-4. The Retina

The structure of the retina is extremely complex and it is sufficient for the present purpose to regard it simply as a mosaic of light-sensitive elements. The receptors are of two main types: *rods* and *cones*. These terms came into use because microscopic examination of the retina revealed the presence of bundles of rod-like and narrow conical elements, the light being incident end-on. The cones are responsible for so-called *photopic* vision, under ordinary bright conditions such as daylight, and the rods are responsible for vision in dim light such as moonlight (*scotopic* vision). There are no rods in the centre of the fovea where one has the maximum resolving power under conditions of photopic vision. The fact that there are no scotopic receptors in the fovea is easily demonstrated by attempting to look fixedly at a luminous figure on the dial of a watch in a dark room. It is found that as one tries to fixate on the figure it disappears from view. The sensation of colour is entirely dependent upon the cones so that one cannot distinguish colours in very dim light. The greatly increased resolving power of the fovea is associated with the fact that in that region the cones are very tightly packed. As one moves away from the fovea, the number of cones decreases as they intermingle with an increasing number of rods. Moreover, in the extra-foveal regions it is found that several receptors appear to be connected to a common nerve fibre; presumably this reduces the resolving power.

The first effect when light falls on a receptor is probably a photo-chemical reaction. Thus the rods are found to secrete a purple fluid known as *visual purple* which is bleached by light and is assumed to play the leading part in the scotopic visual process. One cause of night-blindness (inability to see in dim light) is known to be vitamin A deficiency and this is also known to affect the secretion of visual purple. No substance analogous to visual purple has yet been found in the cones.

17-5. Adaptation

A given stimulus does not always produce the same visual response. For example, the brightness level in a moderately well lit room appears very high if one enters from a dark room, but appears relatively dim if one enters from a considerably brighter room. After a time the impression of excessive brightness or excessive dullness disappears—one's eyes have become *adapted* to the level of illumination. The effect is particularly noticeable (although rather slow in action) when one leaves a well lit house on a dark night. At first one can see almost nothing, but after a few minutes a few outlines can dimly be seen, and one's vision continues to improve over a period of more than half an hour. One speaks, broadly, of light and dark adaptation when referring to the two extremes, although there are an infinite number of states of adaptation. The changes in the sensitivity of the eye are to a small extent due to changes in the size of the pupil which is increased involuntarily by the iris in dim light. By far the greater part of the process of adaptation is associated with a variation in the sensitivity of the retinal receptors. The process of dark adaptation can be explained readily if it is assumed that the sensitivity of the rods depends on the magnitude of the photo-chemical effect which occurs when light falls on the visual purple. In bright light the visual purple is quickly decomposed and, if the regeneration process is slow, the concentration is kept at such a low level that the photo-chemical effect is negligible and the rods are inactive. On entering a dark place, the relatively insensitive cones are not stimulated and the initial low concentration of visual purple causes the rods also to be insensitive. After a time, more visual purple is generated and the increased concentration gives a greater photo-chemical effect with the feeble stimulus; the visual response therefore increases. This increase in sensitivity continues until a balance is achieved between the processes of regeneration and photo-chemical decomposition. There are therefore an infinite number of degrees of dark adaptation, each corresponding to different magnitudes of the stimulus. Similarly, there are many states of adaptation corresponding to different levels of bright light when the cones alone are active. The eye becomes adapted to a decrease in stimulus in the region of photopic vision far more quickly than in scotopic vision. Whilst the photo-chemical substance in the cones is unknown, measurements of the adaptation times in relatively bright light indicate that the regeneration process is complete in a few minutes. As the stimulus is reduced from a very large value the cones become dark adapted, i.e. more sensitive. When the stimulus is reduced below the so-called *threshold* for the cones they can no longer respond and the rods alone are active. Further reduction in the stimulus allows the rods to become dark adapted and more sensitive until, when the stimulus is reduced below the threshold of visibility, even the rods cannot be sufficiently sensitive and nothing can be seen. Between the true photopic and scotopic regions both rods and cones are active and one may say that the cones are dark adapted and the rods light adapted. Light adaptation is obviously caused by a reduction in concentration of the photo-chemical substances resulting from rapid decomposition and causing reduced sensitivity. It occurs much more quickly than dark adaptation. When a steady stimulus is suddenly applied to the dark adapted eye, the sensation rises to a peak and then falls to a fairly steady value within less than a fifth of a second. In addition, when the stimulus is removed suddenly, the sensation takes a finite time to disappear. This latter *persistence of vision* is responsible for the effectiveness of the stroboscope and cine film; it makes possible the removal of the flicker which would otherwise result from the repeated cessation of the stimulus. (See also the flicker photometer, § 18–13.)

The so-called *after-image* which is "seen" when a stimulus is suddenly removed takes a form which varies considerably with the conditions of adaptation, and the strength and duration of the stimulus, etc. If, for example, a strong white light is observed for about a second by a moderately dark adapted eye, the after-image often changes colour through red, green, and blue, becoming less definite in form. Again, if one looks at a strong source of one colour and then suddenly looks at a weakly illuminated white screen, an after-image is seen whose colour is complementary to the original stimulus. (For the meaning of the term "complementary colour", see § 17–9.) This corresponds to a light adaptation (i.e. a reduced sensitivity) for the colour originally observed. Again, if the eye is adapted to red light and then receives light which under normal conditions appears yellow, it appears green.

17–6. Spectral Sensitivity of the Eye

For the average observer, a visual sensation is produced by electromagnetic waves whose wavelengths lie between about 0.4μ and 0.75μ. Different wavelengths produce different sensations of colour, and this subject is discussed later. In addition, the sensitivity of the eye varies with wavelength and equal amounts of energy of different wavelengths will, in general, produce different sensations of brightness. Thus, if a spectrum is viewed and the energy received per second is the same for all wavelengths, the middle of the visible region appears brighter than the red and blue ends. When the intensity is high (i.e. for photopic vision) the maximum brightness occurs at about $\lambda 0.555\mu$.

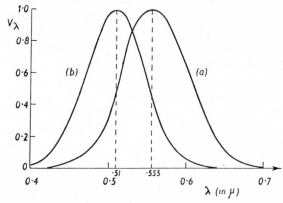

Fig. 17–4. Relative luminous efficiency curves. (a) Photopic. (b) Scotopic.

Under ordinary conditions of observation, the brightness of a source of a given wavelength (due to light emitted, reflected, refracted, or scattered) depends upon the energy per second received per unit area of the retina, and upon the state of adaptation of the eye. It also depends upon the size of the illuminated field of view and upon the psychological state of the observer. Thus in order to measure the spectral sensitivity of the eye it is necessary to consider the energy flux received per unit area of the retina, to maintain a constant state of adaptation, and to employ a constant field size.

Suppose one observes two luminous elements of equal area of which one (known as the *standard patch*) gives light of a standard wavelength λ_0, and the other (the *test patch*) gives light of any other wavelength λ. Suppose the standard patch is maintained unchanged while, for a number of values of λ, one finds the energy per second which the eye must receive in order to make the brightness of the test patch equal to that of the standard patch. If this energy flux is e_λ, $1/e_\lambda$ is a measure of the sensitivity of the eye to the wavelength λ. That is, $1/e_\lambda$ measures the effectiveness of light of wavelength λ in producing a visual response. This is usually plotted on a scale such that e_λ is unity at the wavelength of maximum sensitivity. $1/e_\lambda$ is then known as the *relative luminous efficiency* of light of wavelength λ and is denoted by V_λ. This was formerly called the *visibility* or *relative luminosity* (see below). The variation of V_λ throughout the visible spectrum is shown for photopic vision in Fig. 17–4(a). It should be noted that when the wavelengths of the standard and test patches are widely different, the colour difference makes it difficult to judge equality of brightness, and it may be desirable to proceed through the spectrum step by step comparing λ_1 with λ_2, λ_2 with λ_3, etc. The curve (a) applies to photopic vision, and for observations under rather lower levels of illumination it is found that the maximum of the relative luminous efficiency curve moves towards the region of shorter wavelength. For observation under true scotopic conditions one obtains curve (b), having a maximum at about 0.51μ. This shift of the maximum is known as the *Purkinje effect*. Obviously curves (a) and (b) can be associated with the cone and rod mechanisms respectively and are associated with the foveal and peripheral regions of the retina. The Purkinje effect is responsible for the relatively dark appearance of red objects under low levels of illumination since it causes a decrease in the value of V_λ in the long wavelength region.

Referring to Fig. 17–4(a) it will be seen that $V_\lambda = 0.5$ when λ is about 0.51μ. This does not mean that a test patch giving light of wavelength 0.555μ appears twice as bright as a patch giving the same amount of energy of light of wavelength 0.51μ. (Sensations such as brightness cannot easily be measured in this way.) What it does mean is that it is necessary to have twice as much energy of wavelength 0.51μ in order to make the patches appear equally bright. Thus if one has energy e_λ of light of wavelength λ entering the eye per second, it is the weighted energy flux $e_\lambda V_\lambda$ which determines the magnitude of the visual response in the sense that equal values of $e_\lambda V_\lambda$ give equal responses. When an amount of energy is weighted in this way one speaks of the quantity of light. The weighted flux $e_\lambda V_\lambda$ is the light flux or *luminous flux* and is sometimes referred to as the *luminosity* of the energy flux e_λ. (It will be seen that if one has a spectrum giving the same energy flux for all wavelengths, V_λ measures the relative luminosity of wavelength λ.) If one has light of wavelengths λ_1, λ_2, λ_3, etc., entering the eye, and the energy fluxes are e_{λ_1}, e_{λ_2}, e_{λ_3}, etc., respectively, one would expect that the brightness experienced would depend upon $\Sigma e_\lambda V_\lambda$ in the sense that equal values of the sum give equal sensations (and *not* that different values of Σ give sensations proportional to Σ). The fact that luminosities are additive in this way is confirmed in practice although a given value of $\Sigma e_\lambda V_\lambda$ corresponds to different colours if the relative values of e_{λ_1}, e_{λ_2}, etc., are changed.

In photometry one is concerned with the measurement of the total light flux (see Chapter XVIII). In this work one usually assumes that the conditions of photopic vision obtain.

17–7. Visual Acuity

Assuming that the eye is stationary, the following conditions must be satisfied if two neighbouring independent point sources are to be resolved by the observer: firstly, the optical system of the eye must give physically resolved images, and secondly, the mosaic of retinal receptors must have a structure sufficiently fine to record the resolved images. With regard to the first requirement, taking an average value of 4 mm. for the pupil diameter (assumed circular), one finds that the angular limit of resolution of the optical system is about half a minute. With regard to the second requirement, it is reasonable to assume that if the eye is to resolve two neighbouring retinal images, there must be an unstimulated

14*

receptor between them. In the fovea it is estimated that a cone subtends an angle of about half a minute at the nodal point, i.e. has just the order of magnitude necessary to take advantage of the resolving power of the optical system. These estimates of the limit of resolution which an eye might be expected to have are

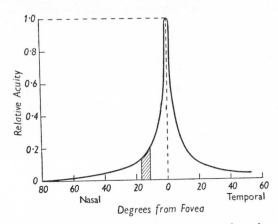

Fig. 17–5. Variation of visual acuity across the retina.

in good agreement with the observed value for an eye pupil of about 4 mm. diameter, and confirm the long accepted rough estimate of one minute of arc (corresponding roughly to a linear distance of about a tenth of a millimetre at the least distance of distinct vision—D_v=25 cm.). It seems that for pupil diameters of about 4 mm. the full theoretical resolution is attained so that the effect of the aberrations of the eye is practically negligible. The deterioration in acuity to more than one minute for pupils below about 2 mm. is explained by the increased size of the Airy pattern on the retina, and the poorer resolution for larger pupils is probably caused by the increased aberrations.

As one moves away from the fovea, the visual acuity for photopic vision decreases rapidly as indicated by Fig. 17–5. This is caused by the decreased resolving ability of the retina and also by the oblique aberrations of the optical system. For scotopic vision the fovea is inactive and the region just beyond it gives the maximum sensitivity and also maximum acuity.

The simple discussion given above is certainly not adequate to explain all the phenomena associated with the resolving power of the eye. One is not justified in assuming that the eye is stationary since, in practice, it is constantly executing small movements. This ceaseless scanning of the object may be an important factor contributing to the very good *vernier* or *contour* acuity which is observed. This is concerned with the extraordinary ability of the eye to line up two straight lines as indicated by Fig. 17–6. It is found that the lines may be adjusted to be collinear to an accuracy corresponding to less than 10 seconds of arc. It is interesting to note that this implies that one can confidently use a simple vernier scale to measure linear movement as small as 1/50th mm. using the naked eye but that it is necessary to employ an observing lens for smaller distances. It is also

Fig. 17–6.
Vernier acuity.

found that the eye is able to detect very small movements of an object, and this ability does not decrease as rapidly as the simple limit of resolution as one moves away from the fovea. The detection of movement is associated with the sensitivity of the retinal receptors to small changes in stimulus, and it is found that the sensitivity to an intensity flicker is greater in the peripheral regions.

17–8. The Stiles-Crawford Effect

It was found by Stiles and Crawford that light entering the eye near the centre of the pupil is usually more effective in producing a visual response than that entering near the periphery. In scotopic vision the effect is found only with wavelengths greater than 0.58μ, but under conditions of photopic vision the effect is found throughout the visible region and is the same in the foveal and extra-foveal regions; it has been attributed to a directional property of the retinal receptors. It is obvious, from Fig. 17–7(a), that rays passing through the marginal zones of the eye pupil are

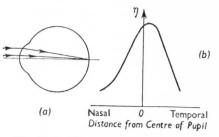

Fig. 17–7. The Stiles-Crawford effect.

incident on the retina more obliquely than rays lying close to the axis. Fig. 17–7(b) shows how the relative luminous efficiency, η, varies across the aperture of the eye pupil.

Suppose the eye receives a beam of light and that the energy is evenly distributed across the eye pupil. As far as the effective flux reaching the retina is concerned, an eye pupil of area a in the presence of the Stiles-Crawford effect is equivalent to an area Sa with the effect absent. For an eye pupil of diameter 2 mm. the *Stiles factor* S is 0.95, but it falls to 0.82 when the diameter of the eye pupil is 4 mm., and 0.66 when the diameter is 6 mm.

17–9. Colour Vision. Additive Mixtures

As pointed out in §17–6, radiations of different wavelength produce different sensations of colour. For a normal eye the hues corresponding to the various regions of the visible spectrum are approximately as follows: 0.40μ to 0.45μ violet, 0.45μ to 0.48μ blue, 0.48μ to 0.51μ blue-green, 0.51μ to 0.55μ green, 0.55μ to 0.57μ yellow-green, 0.57μ to 0.59μ yellow, 0.59μ to 0.63μ orange, above 0.63μ red. A stimulus which does not contain a marked excess of any one group of wavelengths produces a sensation of white light. A fairly wide range of sources of this kind are referred to loosely as white (e.g. a tungsten filament lamp, sunlight, etc.). For many purposes it is convenient to define white as the colour of a source emitting an equal energy spectrum. If one wavelength is slightly dominant the sensation is of a pale or *desaturated* colour. As the proportion of the dominant wavelength is increased the colour is said to become more saturated until, for monochromatic light, complete saturation is reached. Thus, by adding white light to a saturated colour, a desaturated or pale colour is produced.

No attempt will be made to give an account of the various theories concerning the mechanism of colour vision, but it should be pointed out that colour cannot be distinguished under conditions of scotopic vision; it is therefore concluded that the cones are responsible for colour vision. Since the distribution of rods and cones varies across the retina, it became usual, in work on colour vision, to employ a field of view of not more than 2° so that only the foveal region is employed. This is also made desirable by the fact that in the region surrounding the fovea the retina is covered by a yellow pigment which probably influences the perception of colour. However, with a small field there is poor sensitivity to colour differences, and recent workers have used a 10° field.

It is found that a wide range of colours can be produced by an additive mixture of red, green, and blue light. It must be emphasized that this mixture is the superposition of red, green, and blue *light*, and must not be confused with the mixing of pigments which is discussed later. Convenient stimuli are monochromatic radiation with wavelengths 0.70μ, 0.5461μ, 0.4358μ. Using these it is possible to secure a perfect match between the additive mixture and many colours which are not highly saturated. It is found that a mixture of red and green light gives a fairly saturated orange, yellow, or yellow-green, according to the proportion of red and green employed; a mixture of blue and green gives various blue greens; and red plus blue gives various purples. A certain mixture of red, green, and blue, matches the colour of an equal energy source. If the proportion of one of the three components is increased, one obtains a desaturated red, green, or blue. If the proportion of any two of the three is greater than that which gives white, the result is a desaturated yellow, blue-green, or purple.

It is found that an additive mixture of red, green, and blue, as described above, cannot match very saturated colours. This is most noticeable in the blue-green region. In order to secure a match involving a saturated (e.g. monochromatic) blue-green, it is found that it is necessary to add some red light to it and to match this combination with a mixture of blue and green. One can look upon the saturated blue-green as being matched by a mixture of blue, green, and a negative quantity of red.

It is not essential to use the red, green, and blue radiations as given above although it is found that these enable a wide range of colours to be matched by a positive mixture. It is found that if negative quantities are allowed a colour C can be matched by a mixture of *any* three colours, which need not be monochromatic but which must be independent in the sense that it must be impossible to match one by mixing the other two. Thus, apart from the pure spectral colours, a given colour does not correspond to a unique spectral distribution (distribution of energy through the spectrum) of light entering the eye. A given spectral distribution can, however, give only one colour. The latter is simply the result of the additive mixture of the spectral colours concerned, although it could have been produced by other spectral distributions.

It may happen that an additive mixture of light of two colours produces white. The colours are then said to be *complementary*. From what has already been said, it will be seen that the fact that two colours are complementary does not necessarily mean that the superposition of their constituent radiations gives an equal energy spectrum. For example, it has been pointed out that a certain mixture of monochromatic red, green, and blue, can match the colour of an equal energy white. If the blue is omitted from this mixture, the remaining combination of red and green gives a yellow. Now this latter, when mixed with the blue, gives white; hence the blue and the yellow are complementary.

Fig. 17–8 illustrates a simple arrangement for demonstrating complementary colours. S is a slit illuminated by a filament lamp and, by means of the lens L_1 and the prism P, a spectrum is produced at A. Except for the edges, the patch of light B produced by lens L_2 contains a mixture of the spectral colours and appears white. If a region of the spectrum is obstructed, the patch at B becomes

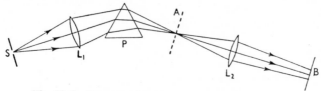

Fig. 17–8. Demonstration of complementary colours.

coloured, and its colour is complementary to that of the radiation obstructed. In this way it is easy to observe the colour which is complementary to an approximately monochromatic colour.

17–10. The Trichromatic System of Colour Measurement

As stated in the previous section, it is possible for a mixture of red, green, and blue stimuli (or any other three) to match white or any other colour. If three standard stimuli are chosen it is possible to specify a colour by stating the amount of each standard required to produce a match. It is convenient to choose, as standards, the red, green, and blue stimuli described above, but it is now necessary to define the units in which amounts of red, green, and blue light are to be measured. The units are chosen so that equal amounts of red, green, and blue, are required to match the white colour of an equal energy source.

Suppose a light flux (i.e. weighted energy flux or luminosity—see §17–6) L_W' of white light is matched by the superposition of light fluxes L_R of red, L_G of green, and L_B of blue. Then one may write:

$$L_W'W = L_R R + L_G G + L_B B.$$

Now it was shown in §17–6 that light fluxes are additive so that

$$L_W' = L_R + L_G + L_B.$$

In order to measure W in the new so-called *trichromatic units* it is obviously necessary to multiply the measure of red light by $1/L_R$, that of green light by $1/L_G$, and that of blue by $1/L_B$. Thus, in all similar measurements, the quantities of R, G, and B, must be modified in this way. Suppose that a light flux L_C' of colour C is matched by L_R' of R, L_G' of G, and L_B' of B. Then the equation in terms of light fluxes is

$$L_C'C = L_R'R + L_G'G + L_B'B,$$

where

$$L_C' = L_R' + L_G' + L_B'.$$

In terms of the trichromatic units, the amounts of R, G, and B, necessary to match a light flux L_C' of C, will therefore be r', g', and b', respectively, where

$$r' = \frac{L_R'}{L_R}, \qquad g' = \frac{L_G'}{L_G}, \qquad b' = \frac{L_B'}{L_B}.$$

The colour, as opposed to the intensity, of C determines the relative amounts of R, G, and B, the absolute values of r', g', and b', being determined by the *amount* of C concerned. One now defines a unit amount of C as the amount matched in intensity and colour by the additive mixture of R, G, and B, when their quantities in trichromatic units have been scaled down to make their sum unity.

Thus, $1 \cdot 0C = rR + gG + bB$ . . . . . .   (17–1)

where one must have $r + g + b = 1$, i.e.

$$r = \frac{r'}{r' + g' + b'}, \qquad g = \frac{g'}{r' + g' + b'}, \qquad b = \frac{b'}{r' + g' + b'}.$$

Equation (17–1) is known as the *unit trichromatic equation* and r, g, and b, are the *trichromatic coefficients* or co-ordinates. The amount of the colour C represented by equation (17–1) is known as one *trichromatic or T. unit*.

If, in a unit trichromatic equation, two of the coefficients are known, the third can be calculated since $r + g + b = 1$. The expression for C is therefore a function of only two variables and can be represented on a plane diagram such as Fig. 17–9. This is known as the *Chromaticity diagram*. The red radiation R is represented by the point (1,0), G by (0,1), and B by (0,0). The white colour of an equal energy source is the point W (1/3, 1/3). BG, BR, and GR, are the loci of colours which contain no R, G, and B, respectively. Thus, along BG one has blue-green (B–G); along BR purples (P); and along GR yellow-green (Y–G), yellow (Y), and orange (O). It is found that spectral colours cannot be matched exactly by positive mixtures of the R, G, and B, standard stimuli, but, if negative values of r, g, and b, have the significance explained in the previous section, one can plot the locus of the spectral colours on Fig. 17–9, as shown. An indication of the wavelength of the monochromatic radiation represented is shown at various points along the locus. It will be seen that all the saturated blue-greens correspond to negative values of r.

Fig. 17–9. The spectral locus on the RGB chromaticity diagram.

Suppose p T. units of colour C_1 and q T. units of colour C_2 are mixed additively to give colour C_3. For p units of C_1, one has $pC_1 = pr_1R + pg_1G + pb_1B$ and, for q units of C_2, $qC_2 = qr_2R + qg_2G + qb_2B$ where r_1, g_1, b_1, and r_2, g_2, b_2, are the unit trichromatic coefficients, i.e.

$$r_1 + g_1 + b_1 = 1 = r_2 + g_2 + b_2.$$

On adding these two colours the sum of the coefficients is $(p+q)$ so that the mixture gives $(p+q)$T. units of C_3. The unit equation for C_3 is therefore given by

$$1 \cdot 0C_3 = \frac{pr_1+qr_2}{p+q} \cdot R + \frac{pg_1+qg_2}{p+q} \cdot G + \frac{pb_1+qb_2}{p+q} \cdot B.$$

From the geometry of the chromaticity diagram, the point representing C_3 must lie on the line C_1C_2 such that it divides C_1C_2 in the ratio $q:p$.

Thus, if one imagines masses p and q at the points representing C_1 and C_2, the point representing C_3 is at the centre of gravity. This can be extended to the mixture of any number of colours. It will be seen that W is at the centre of gravity of equal weights at R, G, and B. For any colour it is also easy to find the complementary colour. For example, various blues and yellows form complementary pairs.

It will be seen from Fig. 17–9 that the spectral locus is always concave inwards. Now all colours must be mixtures of the spectral colours, so that only points which lie in the area bounded by the spectral locus and the line joining its extremities correspond to colours with physical significance. Points outside this area do not correspond to colours of actual physical stimuli. As far as the geometry of the figure is concerned, there is no reason why the position of the point corresponding to a given colour should not be referred to three reference points lying outside this area. In the system introduced by the Commission Internationale de l'Éclairage (the so-called C.I.E. system), three such reference points are chosen. These do not correspond to three physical stimuli, but in terms of these "theoretical" stimuli all colours are matched by positive mixtures.

The colour matches which have been referred to throughout the above discussions are those accepted as corresponding to a normal observer. Thus, the location of the spectral locus in the RGB chromaticity diagram will be slightly different for different observers and internationally agreed results have now been adopted.

Apart from the small variations in the matching of colours by different observers with more or less "normal" colour vision, it is found that some so-called *colour-blind* persons have distinctly defective colour vision. In some cases the observer is able to match all the colours he can see by mixing only two standard stimuli; he may, for example, be quite unable to distinguish between red and green.

The fact that a normal eye can match almost any colour by an additive mixture of saturated red, green, and blue, has led to the suggestion that the average observer has three primary mechanisms for the perception of colour. This theory, associated with Young, Helmholtz, and Maxwell, has not yet been proved or satisfactorily replaced.

17–11. The Colour of Non Self-luminous Objects

If a source emitting an approximately equal energy spectrum illuminates an object which reflects equally at all wavelengths, the object will appear white or grey according to its reflectivity. If the object absorbs some wavelengths and reflects others it will appear coloured. For example, a pigment which reflects only wavelengths above about $0 \cdot 60\mu$ will appear red. If it is highly reflecting for all wavelengths above about 0.5μ while for shorter wavelengths its reflectivity is low, it will appear yellow. Blue-green pigments reflect well in the short wavelength region but their reflectivity falls off above about 0.5μ. Thus a mixture of these yellow and blue-green pigments does not reflect a mixture of yellow and blue light, but only those wavelengths which are reflected by both constituents. In practice, the region 0.5μ to 0.55μ is partially reflected by both, so that a mixture of blue-green and yellow pigments produces a green pigment. This will be true if the illuminating source emits all wavelengths; for other cases it must be remembered that the colour which an object appears to have is determined by the wavelengths which it reflects to the eye. The following is an example: a surface whose spectral reflectivity curve shows a broad peak centred at the middle of the visible spectrum would appear as a desaturated green when illuminated by an equal energy white source, but could appear red, yellow, or blue, if illuminated by monochromatic sources of these colours respectively. Again, by referring to Fig. 17–9 one can see that a surface whose reflectivity curve shows a broad peak stretching from about 0.51μ to about 0.70μ could appear yellow-green when illuminated by an approximately equal energy source such as daylight. If this surface is illuminated by a source which emits narrow bands of wavelengths in the regions of 0.49μ and 0.65μ, it will appear red although the source itself may appear white. It will be seen that one must be careful to distinguish between the colour of a source and its colour rendering properties. The source just referred to is white but has poor colour rendering properties in the sense that an object illuminated by it may have a colour which is different from its colour in daylight. The colour rendering properties of a source can be completely satisfactory only if it emits fairly uniformly throughout the visible spectrum.

17–12. Subtractive Colour Mixture

It was pointed out above that a mixture of yellow and blue-green pigments gives a green pigment. It is interesting to consider the possibility of producing a wide range of colours from, say, three "primary" pigments. In order to produce a wide range of colours one needs to be able to control the amounts of red, green, and blue light which enter the eye, and in additive mixing one has direct independent control of these three stimuli. Now a pigment of a certain colour reflects some wavelengths and absorbs the rest. By varying the proportion of this pigment in a mixture, one can vary the intensity of the wavelengths it absorbs but not those which it reflects since these will remain at maximum intensity. Consequently, one obtains control of the red, green, and blue light which enters the eye by varying the proportions of those pigments which absorb the spectral region corresponding to these three colours. Thus in additive mixing one starts with no light and *adds* chosen amounts of red, green, and blue; in the case of pigments one starts with light of all wavelengths and *subtracts* chosen amounts of red, green, and blue. One speaks of a *subtractive mixture* and the primary pigments may be referred to as minus red, minus green, and minus blue. The colours of these pigments are blue-green, magenta, and yellow, respectively. (Loosely referred to as blue, red, and yellow.) The control which one can exercise in a subtractive mixture is less complete than in an additive mixture since the wavelengths nominally reflected by a pigment are actually partially absorbed and the absorption bands of the various pigments overlap to some extent.

17–13. Stereoscopic Effect

When viewing a scene with one eye there are a number of factors which help one to decide the relative distances of various objects in the field of view. Firstly, one finds that different degrees of accommodation are necessary to view the various objects clearly; secondly, one draws on one's experience concerning the relative sizes of familiar objects; thirdly, one can interpret the variations of light and shade. However, these factors alone do not enable one to get an impression of three dimensional "solidity" when viewing an object. For this *stereoscopic* effect, binocular vision is essential.

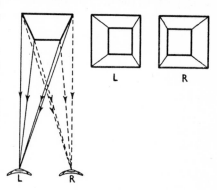

When using both eyes to view a scene, two slightly different perspective retinal images are formed, the perspective centre of each eye being its first nodal point. When the brain "fuses" the two images an impression of depth or relief is obtained. For example, Fig. 17–10 shows how an observer's two eyes obtain slightly different views of a truncated pyramid.

Fig. 17–10.
Perspective views for left and right eyes.

When one "looks at" a given point with both eyes they are rotated in their sockets until, in each eye, the image point falls in focus on the fovea. It is therefore necessary to adjust the accommodation of the eyes and the convergence of their visual axes. These adjustments are, of course, made unconsciously.

The fact that it is necessary to have two different perspective retinal images to produce a stereoscopic effect explains why this effect must necessarily be absent from a simple photograph. However, as was originally pointed out by Wheatstone, if one has two photographs taken by identical cameras from positions representing those of an observer's eyes, a stereoscopic effect is produced if each eye views the appropriate photograph. The effect will be precisely the same as that obtained by binocular observation of the original scene if the camera lenses were separated by the correct interocular distance (approximately 65 mm.) and the photographs are viewed at the correct viewing distance (see §3–4). The method of viewing the photographs is of some importance. For example, it is possible to place them side by side and to view one with each eye directly, a screen being positioned so that each eye can see only the correct photograph. The necessary accommodation and convergence are obviously determined by the positions of the two photographs. However, many observers find it difficult to employ combinations of accommodation and convergence which are very different from those employed in normal vision, and they would have considerable difficulty in fusing the images. This difficulty can be reduced by employing viewing lenses as shown in Fig. 17–11. An arrangement such as this is called a *stereoscope*. Suppose the photographs are in the focal planes of the lenses so that the accommodation is relaxed. For a given separation of the photographs there will be, in the stereoscopic view obtained by the observer, a certain apparent object distance for which the convergence of the eyes is also relaxed. When the observer fixates on points which appear to be at other distances there will be some convergence without accommodation. However, it is found that the combinations of accommodation and convergence which occur with this arrangement can be made less objectionable than when the lenses are omitted.

Another way of producing a stereoscopic picture is as follows: one of the photographs, printed in red, is superimposed (with very small displacement) on the other, printed in blue. If the combination is viewed through a red filter, the dark parts of the red photograph still reflect red light and are indistinguishable from the bright parts. The dark parts of the photograph printed in blue do not

Fig. 17–11.   Fig. 17–12.
Simple stereoscope.   The grid system for stereoscopic pictures.

reflect red, and they appear dark; the contrast in the photograph is seen. Similarly, when viewing through a blue filter, only the red photograph can be seen. Thus, by placing a red filter in front of one eye, and a blue filter in front of the other, one can ensure that each eye sees only the correct perspective view. On fusing the two images, a stereoscopic picture is seen.

A further method is to print parts of the two photographs on alternate narrow strips of the screen and to view this through a grid in such a way that each eye sees alternate strips and, therefore, only the correct image (see Fig. 17–12). A similar effect can be obtained by placing, immediately in front of similarly prepared photographs, a lenticular grid whose linear elements are actually long and very narrow cylindrical lenses. Refraction by these elements causes each eye to see only the correct perspective image.

A stereoscopic effect is produced in cinemas by projecting two images on to the screen. Each image is formed by plane polarized light (see Chapter VI), the planes of vibration being mutually perpendicular and inclined at 45° to the vertical. Each member of the audience wears spectacles which place a polaroid analyser in front of each eye so that only the correct image is seen.

It must be pointed out that projections on an extra-wide screen do not give a true stereoscopic picture. Their chief advantage is that the eye is presented with a wide field of view as in normal vision.

It will be seen that binocular vision involves a co-ordination of convergence and accommodation. Normally the visual axes of the eye are parallel when the muscles are at rest. If they are not parallel when the muscles are relaxed (a condition known as *heterophoria*), it may be difficult to fuse the images properly.

Frequently this defect can be overcome by decentring the spectacle lenses to obtain a slight prismatic effect. If the muscle imbalance is very marked, it may be impossible to make the visual axes converge on the point to be viewed. This is known as *strabismus* or *squint*. The images cannot be fused but, usually, one of them is suppressed so that, in effect, one has monocular vision.

17-14. Stereoscopic Range. Binocular Telescopes

Suppose an observer views points P and Q which are at distances r and $r+\delta r$ and lie close to the perpendicular bisector of the line joining N_L and N_R, the first nodal points of the left and right eyes (see Fig. 17–13). It is assumed that the ability to detect the difference δr depends upon the difference in size between the retinal images of PQ. This is proportional to the difference, $\delta\theta$, between the angles subtended by PQ at N_L and at N_R. From the figure one has

$$\angle PN_RQ - \angle PN_LQ = \angle N_LPN_R - \angle N_LQN_R.$$

Thus, if $N_LN_R = b$, one has

$$\delta\theta = \frac{b}{r} - \frac{b}{r+\delta r} \qquad (17\text{--}2)$$

$$= \frac{b\delta r}{r^2} \text{ if } \delta r \text{ is small.}$$

Fig. 17–13.
Binocular
parallax.

Alternatively,

$$\delta r = \frac{r^2\delta\theta}{b}.$$

Hence the minimum detectable difference δr is determined by the minimum detectable difference $\delta\theta$. This latter is found to be about $\frac{1}{2}$ minute.

If r is large equation (17–2) shows that δr is large and, when $r = b/\delta\theta$, δr becomes infinite. This means that for objects situated at distances greater than $r_{max} = b/\delta\theta$ (i.e. about 450 metres) it is impossible to decide, from the stereoscopic effect alone, which of the points—P or Q—is nearer. A knowledge of the actual, and observation of the apparent, size does, in practice, play a more important part in such cases.

The distance r_{max} is called the *stereoscopic range*, and if one places mirrors in

front of the eyes as in Fig. 17–14, the difference between the perspective images is increased and the range is increased to $B/\delta\theta$. In many binocular instruments (e.g. prismatic binocular telescopes) this effect is accompanied by a magnification of the retinal images. If M is the magnifying power of the telescopes the difference ($\angle PN_RQ - \angle PN_LQ$) is magnified M-fold. Thus if $\delta\theta$ is again the minimum

Fig. 17–14. Mirror system for enhanced stereoscopic effect.

value detectable by the observer, the range is extended to

$$r_{max} = \frac{MB}{\delta\theta},$$

where B is the separation of the centres of the telescope objectives. Similarly, for nearer objects the minimum detectable distance δr is decreased to

$$\delta r = \frac{r^2}{MB}\delta\theta \cdot$$

17–15. Binocular Microscopes

It must be pointed out at once that not all binocular microscopes give stereoscopic vision. Non-stereoscopic binocular microscopes are widely used and have a distinct advantage over monocular instruments when it is necessary to employ a microscope for long periods. It is found that a binocular instrument is more comfortable and less tiring.

Fig. 17–15. Beam-splitting systems for binocular microscopes.

For low powers it is possible to combine two complete monocular instruments. Now a normal microscope gives an inverted image, and if two instruments are combined, one has an inverse stereoscopic effect. This difficulty can be overcome if each instrument incorporates an erecting system; in the Greenough microscope, prism erectors are used. The erect image and stereoscopic effect are very useful if the microscope is used in dissecting, etc.

For high powers it is impossible to position two objectives alongside one another and sufficiently close to the object. Consequently a single objective must be used in conjunction with a beam splitting device and two eyepieces. Typical systems, for non-stereoscopic instruments, are shown in Fig. 17–15(a) and (b). In the first, due to Beck, the beam splitter is placed behind the objective. It is necessary to employ a convergence of the eyes and it is therefore convenient to bring the image to the near point. One eyepiece is co-axial with the objective and, by removing the prism system, the instrument is easily converted into a monocular microscope. In the second system the optical axes of the eyepieces are parallel and the images are viewed with relaxed accommodation.

To obtain a stereoscopic effect, the two eyes must have slightly different views of the object, and this must be achieved by employing one half of the objective aperture for each eye. No erecting system is necessary if both eyes look through a single inverting objective-eyepiece system. As will be seen from Fig. 17–16, the effective positions of the eyes is reversed and this, plus the inversion of the image, gives a normal stereoscopic effect. When one employs a beam splitter and two eyepieces, one has, in effect, two simple objective-eyepiece systems; the left eye must use the left half of one exit pupil aperture, and the right eye must use the right-hand side of the other exit pupil. The right eye then uses the left side of the entrance pupil, and vice versa, as in Fig. 17–16. This can be ensured

Fig. 17–16. Binocular observation with a single inverting system.

if suitable screens are positioned in the exit pupils. It will be seen that with high powers and stereoscopic vision only half the objective aperture is used by each eye, with a consequent loss of resolving power. The usefulness of high power stereoscopic microscopes is, in any case, open to question since the depth of focus is very small.

PHOTOMETRY

18–1. Fundamental Photometric Quantities

(a) *Luminous flux.* Luminous flux was defined in §17–6 as the energy flux weighted according to its efficiency in producing a visual response. It was seen that if one has energy flux e_λ of wavelength λ, the luminous flux may be defined as $e_\lambda V_\lambda$, where V_λ is the relative luminous efficiency of light of wavelength λ, and that if one has light of several wavelengths, the luminous flux is $\Sigma e_\lambda V_\lambda$. Since one never has light of a number of discrete wavelengths one should say that, for a spectrum giving energy flux $E_\lambda \delta \lambda$ in the range $\lambda–\lambda+\delta\lambda$, the luminous flux is $\int V_\lambda E_\lambda d\lambda$. The idea of luminous flux is convenient because, under identical conditions, equal luminous fluxes produce equal sensations of brightness, but it must be remembered that it is not implied that different fluxes produce sensations of brightness in direct proportion. It must be remembered also that a flux is a rate of flow so that if one says the energy flux entering the eye is E_λ, this represents the energy entering per second; it can be measured in ergs per second or joules per second (watts). Employing any convenient units of power such as these, $\int V_\lambda E_\lambda d\lambda$ can, without modification, be used as the measure of luminous flux. Although in theory it is not essential to do so, an independent system of units is employed in Photometry. This is described in §18–8.

Fig. 18–1. Radiation from an elementary source.

(b) *Luminous Intensity.* In Fig. 18–1 ds is a small source, or element of a source, which does not necessarily radiate equally in all directions. The luminous flux emitted per unit solid angle in any given direction is called the *luminous intensity* in that direction. That is, if in any direction the source emits flux dF into the elementary solid angle $d\omega$, the luminous intensity in that direction is given by

$$I = \frac{dF}{d\omega}. \qquad \ldots \ldots \quad (18\text{–}1)$$

In the past the luminous intensity has frequently been called the *candle power.* This is unfortunate since the term candle power was also used for the unit itself. Many sources can, for practical purposes, be regarded as point sources. One speaks of a uniform point source if the luminous intensity is the same in all directions. The total flux emitted is then given by

$$F = \int I d\omega = I \int d\omega = 4\pi I,$$

i.e.
$$I = \frac{F}{4\pi}. \qquad \ldots \ldots \quad (18\text{–}2)$$

For a non-uniform point source which emits a total flux F, $F/4\pi$ is called the *mean spherical candle power*; it is obviously the average value of the luminous intensity in all directions.

(c) *Illumination.* If a luminous flux is incident upon a surface, it is said to be illuminated and the flux received per unit area at any point on the surface is called the *illumination* (or intensity of illumination or *illuminance*). That is, if an element of area ds at the point concerned receives a flux dF, the illumination E is given by

$$E = \frac{dF}{ds}. \qquad \cdots \cdots \cdots (18\text{–}3)$$

In Fig. 18–2 the elementary area ds receives light from the point source P. The distance from P to ds is r and the normal to ds is inclined at angle θ to the direction

Fig. 18–2. Illumination of a surface element.   Fig. 18–3. Illumination of a plane.

ds—P. The solid angle subtended at P by the element ds is $d\omega = (ds \cos \theta)/r^2$ so that, if the luminous intensity of P in the direction of ds is I, the flux radiated into the solid angle $d\omega$ is

$$dF = I d\omega = \frac{I ds \cos \theta}{r^2},$$

and the illumination at ds is given by

$$E = \frac{dF}{ds} = \frac{I \cos \theta}{r^2}. \qquad \cdots \cdots (18\text{–}4)$$

This equation may be said to embody the two fundamental laws of photometry: the *inverse-square law* and the *cosine law of illumination.* Frequently the luminous intensities of two sources are compared by assuming the inverse-square law and comparing the distances at which the sources produce equal illuminations on a screen (see § 18–9). In Fig. 18–3 S is a uniform point source distance r from a plane AB. The illumination at the point P distance d from the foot of the perpendicular from S to AB is given by

$$E = \frac{I \cos \theta}{PS^2} = \frac{I \cos \theta}{r^2 + d^2},$$

but

$$\cos \theta = \frac{r}{\sqrt{(r^2 + d^2)}},$$

$$\therefore \quad E = \frac{I \cos^3 \theta}{r^2}. \qquad \cdots \cdots (18\text{–}5)$$

If S is not a uniform point source but has luminous intensity I_θ in direction θ,

$$E = \frac{I_\theta \cos^3 \theta}{r^2} \, .$$

(*d*) *Luminance.* In general, a surface will reflect some of the light that is incident upon it and, unless the surface is highly polished, the reflected light will be distributed over a wide range of directions. Thus a reflecting surface of this type resembles a self-luminous surface, and each element of such a surface will have a certain luminous intensity in each direction. At any point on a surface the luminous intensity per unit projected area in a given direction is called the *luminance* at that point in the direction concerned. That is, if an elementary area *ds* of a surface has a luminous intensity *dI* in a direction inclined to the normal at angle θ, the projected area in direction θ is *ds* cos θ and the luminance is given by

$$L = \frac{dI}{ds \cos \theta} \qquad \cdots \cdots \cdots \quad (18\text{--}6)$$

(see Fig. 18–4).

It is important to distinguish clearly between illumination and luminance. The former measures the flux received by the surface, and the latter measures the flux emitted in a given direction.

Fig. 18–4. Luminance of an elementary source.

When one looks at a surface which reflects or emits light it is the luminance which, for a given state of adaptation, determines the subjective brightness of the surface. Thus, under identical conditions, surfaces of equal luminance appear equally bright. However, if the luminance of one surface is double that of another, this does not mean that it appears twice as bright. Consequently, it is necessary to distinguish between luminance and *subjective brightness* although, until recently, the term brightness was used for both. The luminance is a measure of the luminous flux emitted, the latter being defined, as above, in terms of the standardized values of the relative luminous efficiency and the physical energy radiated. The subjective brightness describes the actual sensation experienced and cannot be measured quantitatively. For a surface of given luminance the subjective brightness will depend upon the observer's state of adaptation, etc. Although subjective brightness certainly cannot be measured quantitatively with accuracy, it is usually assumed that for a constant state of adaptation it is roughly proportional to the logarithm of the physical stimulus. This logarithmic law seems to apply to other sensations, e.g. the loudness of a sound.

18–2. Uniformly Diffusing Surfaces

Observation of self-luminous and diffusely reflecting surfaces indicates that in many cases the brightness of the surface is almost independent of its angle of inclination to the direction of observation. It will be shown in the next section that this will occur if the luminance of the surface is the same in all directions. Equation (18–6) shows that this requires *dI*, the luminous intensity of any element, to be proportional to cos θ. This is known as Lambert's *cosine law of emission.*

A surface which obeys this law is called a *uniformly diffusing surface* (or *uniform diffuser*). Although no surfaces are completely uniform diffusers a large number of so-called "matt" surfaces ("good" diffusers) approach this condition.

A reflecting surface which obeys the cosine law of emission for all directions of the incident light is called a *uniformly diffuse reflector*, and if such a surface reflects all the incident light it is said to be a *perfect diffuser*. A surface which is coated with a thick layer of freshly prepared magnesium oxide is an almost perfect diffuser. Some translucent surfaces such as opal glass provide almost uniformly diffuse transmission, i.e. the transmitted light is radiated approximately according to the cosine law.

In Fig. 18–5 ds_1 is an element of a uniformly diffusing surface whose luminance in all directions is L. ds_2 is an elementary area illuminated by ds_1. Now the luminous intensity of ds_1 in the direction of ds_2 is $Lds_1 \cos \theta_1$, and this is the flux emitted per unit solid angle in direction θ_1. Now ds_2 subtends a solid angle $(ds_2 \cos \theta_2)/r^2$ at ds_1, so that the total flux received by ds_2 from ds_1 is

$$dF = \frac{Lds_1 ds_2 \cos \theta_1 \cos \theta_2}{r^2} \quad \ldots \ldots \quad (18\text{--}7)$$

and the illumination of ds_2 is

$$dE = \frac{dF}{ds_2} = \frac{Lds_1 \cos \theta_1 \cos \theta_2}{r^2}.$$

Fig. 18–5. Radiation from one surface element to another.

Fig. 18–6. Observation of a surface element.

18–3. Brightness of a Diffuse Radiator

Under given conditions of observation the brightness is determined by the luminous flux received by each retinal receptor, i.e. by the retinal illumination. In Fig. 18–6 ds_1 is an element of a uniformly diffusing surface of luminance L, and ds_2 is the pupil of an eye viewing ds_1. From equation (18–7) it will be seen that the flux from ds_1 entering the eye is given by

$$dF = \frac{Lds_1 ds_2 \cos \theta_1}{r^2},$$

since $\theta_2 = 0$. The flux reaching the retina is kdF where k is the transmission factor of the eye, and this flux is spread over the area ds_1' which is the retinal image of ds_1. The retinal illumination is therefore dF/ds_1'. Now the projected area of ds_1, normal to the visual axis, is $ds_1 \cos \theta_1$. Consequently, if l' is the distance of the retina from the second nodal point of the eye, the area of the retinal image is given by

$$ds_1' = (ds_1 \cos \theta_1) \frac{l'^2}{r^2},$$

$$\therefore \quad \text{Retinal Illumination} = \frac{kLds_2}{l'^2}. \quad \ldots \ldots \quad (18\text{--}8)$$

It will be seen that the retinal illumination, and therefore the subjective bright-ness of the element, ds_1, is independent of θ_1 and of r. Thus a uniformly diffus-ing surface appears equally bright for all distances and directions of observation. The Stiles-Crawford effect need not be considered here because the conditions of observation, including the diameter of the eye pupil, remain constant.

18-4. Total Flux Radiated by a Uniformly Diffusing Surface Element

In Fig. 18-7 ds is an element of a uniformly diffusing surface of luminance L.

The luminous intensity of the element in direction θ is therefore $Lds \cos \theta$. The flux radiated from ds between the cones of semi-angles θ and $\theta+d\theta$ is given by the product of the luminous intensity and the solid angle involved. This is the solid angle subtended at ds by the annular strip of area $2\pi r \sin \theta . r d\theta$ on the hemisphere (radius r) described above ds. Hence the solid angle is $2\pi \sin \theta d\theta$ and the flux radiated into it is given by

Fig. 18-7. Total radiation from a surface element.

$$dF = 2\pi Lds \sin \theta \cos \theta d\theta. \quad \ldots \ldots \quad (18\text{--}9)$$

The flux radiated into the cone of semi-angle θ is then given by

$$F = \int_0^\theta 2\pi Lds \sin \theta \cos \theta d\theta,$$

$$\therefore \quad F = \pi Lds \sin^2 \theta \quad \ldots \ldots \ldots \quad (18\text{--}10)$$

and the total flux radiated from ds is found by putting $\theta = \pi/2$,

i.e.   Total Flux $= \pi Lds$. $\ldots \ldots \ldots$ (18–11)

18-5. The Luminance and Illumination of the Image Formed by an Optical System

In Fig. 18-8 EP and EP' are the entrance and exit pupils of an optical system forming an image ds' of a uniformly diffusing surface element ds of luminance

Fig. 18-8. Luminance of an image.

L held perpendicular to the optical axis. From equation (18–9), the flux entering the system in the annular zone of the aperture between U and $U+dU$ is given by

$$dF = 2\pi Lds \sin U \cos U dU \quad \ldots \ldots \quad (18\text{--}12)$$

and flux kdF emerges between U' and $U'+dU'$, where k is the transmission factor of the instrument. Now, for good imagery of linear object elements perpendicular to the axis, the Sine Relation must be satisfied for all zones of the aperture.

$$\therefore \quad nh \sin U = n'h' \sin U',$$

where n and n' are the refractive indices of the object and image spaces. It will be seen that for conjugate elements of area ds and ds' one has

$$n^2 ds \sin^2 U = n'^2 ds' \sin^2 U' \quad . \quad . \quad . \quad . \quad (18\text{–}13)$$

and, differentiating, one obtains

$$n^2 ds . 2 \sin U \cos U \, dU = n'^2 ds' . 2 \sin U' \cos U' dU'.$$

Therefore, from equation (18–12), it follows that the flux kdF emerging from the system between U' and $U'+dU'$ is given by

$$dF' = kdF = kL\left(\frac{n'}{n}\right)^2 ds' 2\pi \sin U' \cos U' dU'. \quad . \quad (18\text{–}14)$$

This flux passes beyond ds' between U' and $U'+dU'$ and is exactly the flux which ds' would give if it radiated according to the cosine law and had luminance $L' = kL(n'/n)^2$. Obviously no light emerges from the system at an angle greater than U'_{max} but, within this cone, the image ds' behaves as a uniformly diffusing surface element. Thus, for an eye placed beyond ds' and entirely within the cone of light emerging from the system, the brightness of the image will correspond to that of a uniform diffuser of luminance $kL(n'/n)^2$. Obviously, if the eye is outside this cone the image will not be seen, and if the eye pupil is partly within the cone it will see an image whose brightness depends on the fraction of the eye pupil which receives light.

It should be noted that in the above discussion the value of k was assumed to be the same for all zones of the aperture of the optical system. In practice, k is not exactly constant so that the image does not obey the cosine law of emission exactly. Now k must be less than unity and, except for cases where $(n'/n)^2$ is greater than $1/k$, the luminance of the image must be less than that of the object.

As indicated by the above discussion, it is the luminance of the image which is important in visual instruments. If, however, the image is received on a screen as with a photographic lens, it is the illumination of the image rather than its luminance which is important.

From equation (18–10), the total flux entering the instrument is

$$F = \pi L ds \sin^2 U_{max}$$

and the flux leaving the instrument is $F' = kF$. Using equation (18–13) one has

$$F' = k\pi L\left(\frac{n'}{n}\right)^2 ds' \sin^2 U'_{max} \quad . \quad . \quad . \quad (18\text{–}15)$$

and the illumination of the image is given by

$$E = F'/ds',$$

i.e.

$$E \propto \sin^2 U'_{max}.$$

Hence it is important for a system such as a camera lens to have a large angular aperture. The linear aperture of a camera lens is usually given as a fraction of its focal length, e.g. f/n. The *f-number*, n, obviously gives U'_{max}.

Suppose a photographic lens images an evenly illuminated and perfectly diffusing object plane perpendicular to the axis. The flux dF received by the entrance pupil from an extra-axial surface element in a direction inclined to the axis at angle θ is given by equation (18–7) (p. 373), where ds_2 is now the entrance pupil, $\theta_1 = \theta_2 = \theta$, and $(1/r^2) \propto \cos^2 \theta$. It will be seen that $dF \propto \cos^4 \theta$. If k is the transmission factor of the lens, flux kdF reaches the image element. Now for a perfect lens equal elements in different parts of the object plane give equal image elements. It follows that the illumination across the image plane is proportional to $\cos^4 \theta$. This factor causes an appreciable reduction in illumination at the edge of the field of a wide-angle lens.

In 1941 Slussareff pointed out that the $\cos^4 \theta$ law applies only to a perfect lens, and that if the aperture stop is imaged to the entrance pupil with a large amount of coma, the effective area of the entrance pupil can be increased for oblique pencils. This can be done without upsetting the image quality. In this way it is possible to reduce the falling-off of the illumination away from the centre of the field. The illumination across the image plane can also be varied by introducing distortion of the image since this will cause the magnification to vary across the field of view.

18–6. Observation with Visual Instruments

(a) *Extended objects.* It was pointed out in the previous section that, when an observer views an object with the aid of an optical instrument the eye pupil may be only partially filled with light. In addition, the Stiles-Crawford effect will reduce the effectiveness of the light which enters through the outer zones of the eye pupil. Consequently, the subjective brightness of any part of the field of view does not depend solely upon the luminance of the image formed by the instrument. The *apparent luminance* of any object or image is now defined as the luminance of a uniformly diffusing surface which, when the Stiles-Crawford effect is absent and the eye pupil is unobstructed, would give the same brightness as the object or image under identical conditions of adaptation, etc. The apparent luminance will be proportional to the retinal illumination produced by the object or image viewed, and to the appropriate Stiles factor (see §17–8), assuming that the beam of light which enters the eye is symmetrical about the axis. From equation (18–8) it will be seen that the apparent luminance is propor-

tional to the luminance of the object or image viewed, the area of the eye pupil which receives light, and the Stiles factor.

Consider now the observation of an extended object of luminance L with a telescope whose magnifying power is M, whose transmission factor is k, and whose objective has area A. The area of the exit

EP
(Area A)

EP'
(Area A/M²)

Fig. 18–9. Vision with a telescope.

pupil is A/M^2, and if this is larger than ds, the area of the eye pupil, the latter is filled with light (see Fig. 18–9). From above, the apparent luminance of the object using the telescope is then proportional to k, L, ds, and S_0, where S_0 is the Stiles factor for an eye pupil (assumed circular) of area ds. The apparent luminance of the object viewed without the telescope is proportional to L, ds, and S_0, assuming that the size of the eye pupil and the state of adaptation are unchanged.

$$\therefore \quad \frac{\text{Apparent luminance of object using telescope}}{\text{Apparent luminance of object viewed directly}} = k. \quad (18\text{–}16)$$

If the exit pupil of the telescope is smaller than the eye pupil, an area A/M^2 of the latter is effective and the apparent luminance of the object using the telescope is now proportional to k, L, A/M^2, and S_1, where S_1 corresponds to a circular eye pupil of area A/M^2.

$$\therefore \quad \frac{\text{Apparent luminance of object using telescope}}{\text{Apparent luminance of object viewed directly}} = \frac{kAS_1}{dsM^2S_0}.$$

$$\quad \quad \quad \quad \quad \quad \quad \quad \quad \quad \quad \quad \cdot \quad \cdot \quad \cdot \quad (18\text{–}17)$$

When an object is observed with a microscope it is easily shown that the apparent luminance is proportional to $[(\text{N.A.})/M]^2$. The magnification which makes the apparent luminance of the object the same with and without the instrument is sometimes called the *normal magnification*. This has little significance since, in microscopy, the illumination can be adjusted to any desired value, and the desirable magnification is determined by the limit of resolution.

(b) *Point sources.* An object such as a star is effectively a point source and the retinal image is the Airy diffraction pattern. No finite magnification can increase the size of the geometrical point image so that the same Airy pattern is formed on the retina when a telescope is used. Consequently, when viewing the star the subjective brightness depends upon the total flux which enters the eye. For any telescope, all the light which enters the objective will enter the eye if the exit pupil of the telescope is not larger than the eye pupil. It will be seen that it is desirable to increase the magnifying power of the telescope until the exit pupil is reduced to the size of the eye pupil. When this stage is reached,

$$\frac{\text{Apparent luminous intensity of star viewed through telescope}}{\text{Apparent luminous intensity of star viewed with naked eye}}$$

$$= \frac{\text{Flux entering eye with telescope}}{\text{Flux entering eye without telescope}}$$

$$= k \times \frac{\text{area of telescope objective}}{\text{area of eye pupil}}, \quad \cdot \quad \cdot \quad \cdot \quad (18\text{–}18)$$

where k is the transmission factor of the telescope, and the *apparent luminous intensity* for a point source is defined in the same way as apparent luminance for extended objects. The Stiles-Crawford effect can be neglected here since the size of the eye pupil is assumed to be constant. If the Stiles-Crawford effect is present and the exit pupil is made smaller than the eye pupil, the light enters the latter closer to the axis and produces a larger visual response. That is, the apparent luminous intensity is increased.

By using a telescope objective of large linear aperture the brightness of the image of a star is increased and, for example, stars which are invisible to the naked eye can be seen with the aid of a telescope using a sufficiently large objective. The way in which the range of a telescope depends upon the size of its objective is easily seen. Suppose that in order to see a star a certain flux F

must enter the eye. For an eye pupil of radius p, the solid angle subtended at a star at distance d_1 is $\pi p^2/d_1^2$ and if the luminous intensity of the star is I the flux entering the eye is $I\pi p^2/d_1^2$. The star can be seen when $I\pi p^2/d_1^2 = F$. Suppose a star of the same intensity is viewed at distance d_2 by means of a telescope whose objective has diameter $2a$. Then the solid angle subtended at the star by the telescope objective is $\pi a^2/d_2^2$ and, if the transmission factor of the telescope is k and the magnifying power is such that the exit pupil is not larger than the eye pupil, the flux which enters the eye is $kI\pi a^2/d_2^2$, and the star will be just observable when

$$\frac{kI\pi a^2}{d_2^2} = F.$$

The distances d_1 and d_2 at which the star can be seen without and with the telescope are therefore related by the expression

$$d_2 = \frac{ad_1\sqrt{k}}{p}. \qquad \ldots \ldots \quad (18\text{-}19)$$

That is to say, the range of an astronomical telescope is directly proportional to the diameter of its objective. It is interesting to note that a telescope enables many stars to be observed during the day. As shown by the above discussions, the telescope increases the brightness of the star but not that of the continuous background.

18-7. The Maxwellian View

If an optical system forms an image of a small source at the pupil of an observer's eye, the whole aperture of the system appears to have a uniform

Fig. 18-10. Maxwellian view.

luminance proportional to the luminous intensity of the source in the direction of view. This arrangement is frequently useful in photometry and elsewhere. It is a convenient way of obtaining an extended field of view of uniform luminance, and is useful in the photometry of weak sources because the luminance of the field is much greater than that of the diffuse reflector which the optical system replaces.

A simple arrangement for *Maxwellian view* is shown in Fig. 18-10. S is a source of luminous intensity I at distance l from the lens O. The eye pupil P is placed at the conjugate distance l' and the eye is looking at O so that the image of O falls on the retina R. It is assumed that S and the aperture of O are small compared with l, and that the image of S is smaller than the eye pupil. The flux reaching an element (area a) of the lens aperture at A is Ia/l^2, and if k is the transmission factor of the lens the flux reaching P from S via A is kIa/l^2. If O were replaced by a uniformly diffusing surface of luminance L, the flux reaching P from A would be paL/l'^2 where p is the area of the eye pupil. Equating this to the flux actually reaching P from A one obtains

$$L = \frac{kIl'^2}{pl^2}.$$

This is the same for all elements of the lens aperture if l is large, so that the aperture of the lens appears as a uniform diffuser having this luminance.

The figure shows that the neighbouring source S′ illuminates the same element of R via the same element of aperture at A but via a different part of the eye pupil P. It will be seen that if S is very small any one part of P is transversed by light from one point in the field of view. Consequently the uniformity of the field of view is marred by any imperfections in P. For use in photometry it is important to ensure that the eye pupil cannot act as a stop of variable aperture. One can either make the image of S very small so that the eye pupil never obstructs light or one can employ a diffuse source whose image is considerably larger than P, thereby ensuring that the eye pupil is always filled. The existence of the Stiles-Crawford effect makes the latter preferable.

18–8. Photometric Units. Standard Source

It was pointed out in §18–1 that one may define luminous flux as $\int E_\lambda V_\lambda d\lambda$, where E_λ is in ergs or joules per second and the values of V_λ are those for a standard observer. However, it is convenient to define a separate system of units based not upon a fundamental unit of flux but upon the luminous intensity of a standard source. The two systems of units can then be related. For many years the standard source was a candle of standard composition. The luminous intensity or candle power of a source was then given by comparison with that of the standard candle. A number of attempts were made to replace this rather unsatisfactory standard by more easily controlled flame standards. Foremost among them were the Vernon-Harcourt pentane lamp which burnt a mixture of pentane vapour and air from a wickless burner under controlled conditions, and the Heffner lamp which burnt amyl acetate. The horizontal luminous intensity of the pentane lamp was about ten times that of a standard candle. The *international candle* was a standard of luminous intensity corresponding roughly to that of a standard candle but was maintained by carbon filament lamps of special construction. None of these standards gave satisfactory precision and the standard source is now a black-body radiator working at the freezing point of platinum. This has the advantage that its radiation, which is independent of small variations in construction, closely follows definite and well established laws concerning the total energy emitted and the spectral distribution. The major difficulty is the need for very precise temperature control. (At 2000° K a change of 10° produces a change of 5–6 % in the luminous intensity of a black body.) The construction of a suitable black-body radiator is shown in Fig. 18–11. The source is a small hollow cylinder of pure fused thoria about 45 mm. long with internal diameter about 2·5 mm. and wall thickness 2–3 mm. The bottom of this cylinder is packed with powdered fused thoria to a depth of 10–15 mm. and it is supported vertically in a fused-thoria crucible of about

20 mm. internal diameter nearly filled with pure platinum. This crucible has a lid with a small hole in the centre about 1·5 mm. in diameter, which acts as the source of light. The crucible is embedded in powdered fused thoria and the

platinum is heated by a high-frequency induction furnace. The power necessary to melt the platinum is about 7 kilowatts at about 1 megacycle per second. The temperature can be controlled so closely that it takes over 20 minutes for the platinum to solidify. When the standard is in use a reflecting prism and cemented doublet lens are positioned as indicated in the figure.

Platinum

Fused
Thoria

Unfused
Thoria

Fig. 18–11.
Black-body primary source.

When a satisfactory black body was produced a new unit of luminous intensity was introduced. This was called the *candela* and the luminous intensity per square cm. of a black body at the temperature of solidification of platinum was defined as 60 candelas. This unit was introduced on 1st January 1948, and the numerical factor 60 was chosen because it is the nearest convenient whole number which will make the candela and the old international candle approximately equal. (For precise equality the numerical factor would have been about 58·9.) Units for the other photometric quantities can now be defined in terms of the above primary unit.

The unit of luminous flux is the *lumen* and is defined as the flux emitted into unit solid angle by a uniform point source whose luminous intensity in all directions is one candela. It will be seen that the total flux emitted by such a uniform point source is 4π lumens. It was pointed out above that the luminous flux can be defined as $\int V_\lambda E_\lambda d\lambda$. It is found that if the luminous flux is calculated in this way (measuring E_λ in watts) it corresponds to a unit of flux equal to about 682 lumens. In particular, if one has monochromatic radiation at the wavelength of maximum visibility, $V_\lambda = 1$ and it will be seen that an energy flux of 1 watt gives a luminous flux of 682 lumens. At other wavelengths the luminous efficiency of the radiation is less and the same energy flux gives a smaller luminous flux.

There are several units of illumination. The usual metric unit is the *lux* and the illumination is 1 lux when the surface receives 1 lumen per square metre. The lux has been called a *metre-candle* and defined as the illumination on the surface of a sphere of radius 1 metre due to a uniform point source of 1 candle placed at its centre. The equivalence of the two definitions is easily seen since the total area of the sphere is 4π and the total flux from the source is 4π lumens so that each square metre receives 1 lumen. An alternative metric unit is the *phot* or lumen per square cm. but this unit is inconveniently large. On the British system the illumination is expressed in lumens per square foot or *foot-candles*. These two are synonymous since the latter is defined in the same way as the metre-candle.

Luminance is luminous intensity per unit projected area and is expressed in candelas per square cm. (known as *stilbs*) or candelas per square metre (known as *nits*). It will be seen that the primary standard is, in reality, a standard of luminance. On the British system luminance is expressed in candelas per square foot or per square inch and these units have (mercifully perhaps) no other names.

In illumination engineering the luminance of any surface in any direction is measured by comparing it with the luminance of a uniform diffuser which emits a total flux of 1 lumen per unit area. Thus a uniform diffuser which emits a total flux of 1 lumen per square cm. is said to have a luminance of 1 *lambert* (1000 millilamberts). One which emits a total of 1 lumen per square foot has a luminance of 1 *foot-lambert*, and a total emission of 1 lumen per square metre corresponds to a luminance of 1 *apostilb*.

Now equation (18–11) shows that a uniform diffuser of luminance L emits a total flux πL per unit area. Hence if it emits a total flux of 1 lumen per unit area, its luminance in all directions is $1/\pi$. Thus a lambert is equivalent to $1/\pi$ candelas per square cm. (i.e. $1/\pi$ stilb), a foot-lambert is equivalent to $1/\pi$ candelas per square foot, and an apostilb corresponds to $1/\pi$ candelas per square metre.

18–9. The Visual Photometer Head and Bench

A convenient method of comparing the luminous intensities of two sources is to compare the distances at which they produce equal illuminations. From the inverse square law it then follows that the ratio of the luminous intensities is equal to the inverse ratio of the squares of the distances. The usual method involves the use of an optical bench at opposite ends of which the sources are mounted. Between the sources is a so-called *photometer head* which includes two identical screens each of which is illuminated by one of the sources. The distances of the sources are varied (by moving the sources and/or the photometer head) until the screens are equally illuminated. If the screens are identical and are viewed under identical conditions, this will be when they appear equally bright to the observer. Various photometer heads have been designed in order to facilitate the comparison of the illuminated surfaces. In order to obtain accurate results, the fields of view whose brightnesses are compared must have a sharp demarcation line, care being taken to ensure that there is neither a gap between them nor a region of overlap. To avoid errors caused by deviations from the cosine law of emission, the illuminated surfaces should be viewed at the same angle. The luminance of these surfaces depends on their illumination and if the light is not incident on each at exactly the same angle, an error is introduced since the illumination is proportional to cos θ. Now cos θ has a stationary value at $\theta=0$, so that the possibility of this error is reduced if, nominally, the light is incident normally on each surface. It is also found desirable for the field of view to be not smaller than about 10°.

18–10. Equality-of-Brightness Photometer Heads

One of the earliest arrangements for comparing the intensities of two sources was Rumford's *shadow photometer*. In its original form this employed two opaque rods as in Fig. 18–12(*a*), but one can use a single rod as in (*b*). Shadows of the rods are cast on a white surface. In each case, the parts of the screen falling in the shadows are illuminated by one source only, and when the two shadows appear equally bright, one can assume that the illuminations are equal. The ratio of the intensities of the sources is then inversely as the ratio of the squares of their distances from the screen if the light is incident at equal angles.

Fig. 18–12. Rumford's shadow photometer.   Fig. 18–13. The Ritchie wedge.

A simple photometer head suitable for use with an optical bench is the *Ritchie wedge* (Fig. 18–13). The white diffusing surfaces AB and AC are illuminated by the sources S_1 and S_2 and viewed by the eye at E. It will be seen that one has equal angles of incidence and equal angles of view although the former do not approach zero. In the modification due to Trotter [Fig. 18–14(a)] one surface is seen through the middle of the other which facilitates comparison, and in the arrangement due to Yvon one has normal incidence [Fig. 18–14(b)].

Fig. 18–14. Modifications of the Ritchie wedge.   Fig. 18–15. The Joly wax block.

Another simple photometer head is that due to Joly. This consists of two identical thin blocks of some transparent material (often paraffin wax) separated by a thin sheet of tin foil (see Fig. 18–15). The distances of the sources are adjusted until the sides of the blocks appear equally bright. It is difficult to decide from where the distances of the sources should be measured.

The most satisfactory equality-of-brightness photometer head is that usually ascribed to Lummer and Brodhun. This is shown in Fig. 18–16 and will be seen to satisfy the requirements enunciated above. Light from the sources S_1 and S_2 is incident normally on the two sides of A which are good diffusers. (Frequently A is a thick disc of plaster of Paris.) The diffusely reflected light from each side of A is reflected by the mirrors M_1 and M_2 to the prism system PQ. In this system, originally due to Swan, Q is an ordinary 45°–45°–90° prism but the hypotenuse face of P is replaced by a ground spherical surface having a polished flat central region which makes good contact with Q. The observer views the contact surface by means of the eyepiece system L and it will be seen that the outer part of the field of view is illuminated by light from S_2 while the central part is illuminated by light from S_1. When the sources are adjusted to give equal

Fig. 18–16. The Lummer-Brodhun head.

illumination at A the inner and outer parts of the field of view are equally bright and the demarcation line practically disappears. With this arrangement one has normal incidence at A, the two surfaces at A are viewed under similar conditions, and a sharp demarcation line can be obtained.

18–11. The Bunsen Grease Spot Photometer

This was the first photometer head capable of good accuracy. It consists of a piece of opaque, unglazed white paper in the middle of which a small area has been rendered translucent by applying a little grease or oil. Alternatively, one can cut a hole in the opaque paper and fit a piece of translucent paper. If the illuminations on the left- and right-hand sides of the paper are E_L and E_R, then on the left-hand side the luminance of the opaque portion is rE_L/π and that of the translucent portion is $(r'E_L+t'E_R)/\pi$, where r, r', and t', are respectively the reflection factor of the opaque part, and the reflection and transmission factors of the grease spot.

There are three methods of using this simple photometer head:

(a) E_R is kept constant by means of a subsidiary source additional to the two whose luminous intensities are to be compared. The left-hand side is then illuminated by one of the latter sources and the distance of this source is varied until, when viewed from the left, the grease spot and the opaque part appear equally bright. It will be seen from above that this will occur when $rE_L = r'E_L+t'E_R$. If the same adjustment is performed with the second of the two sources to be compared, the grease spot will obviously disappear when the second source produces the same illumination E_L as was produced by the first. The ratio of the luminous intensities of the sources is then given by the inverse ratio of their distances from the photometer. Since the two portions of the photometer screen may not be uniform diffusers, all observations should be made from the same direction. This applies to all three methods of using the instrument.

(b) One of the sources to be compared is placed on each side of the photometer and, viewing the left-hand side of the photometer, the distances d_L and d_R of the lamps on the left- and right-hand sides are found for which the grease spot disappears, i.e. for which $rE_L = r'E_L + t'E_R$. One then views the right-hand side of the photometer and the distances d_L' and d_R' found to make the grease spot disappear. *If r and r' are the same for the two sides of the photometer head,* the second disappearance occurs when $rE_R' = r'E_R' + t'E_L'$. These equations give

$$\frac{E_L}{E_R} = \frac{t'}{r - r'} = \frac{E_R'}{E_L'}.$$

Now, for normal incidence, $E_L = I_L/d_L{}^2$, $E_L' = I_L/d_L'^2$, $E_R = I_R/d_R{}^2$, and $E_R' = I_R/d_R'^2$, where I_L and I_R are the luminous intensities of the sources on the left- and right-hand sides respectively. Substitution of these values in the last equation gives

$$\frac{I_L}{I_R} = \frac{d_L d_L'}{d_R d_R'}.$$

If the photometer head is not

Fig. 18-17. The Bunsen grease spot.

symmetrical it should be reversed and the measurements repeated. The true value of I_L/I_R is then the geometric mean of the two values obtained.

(c) In the third method one does not adjust for equality of brightness between the opaque and translucent portion, but for equality, on the two sides, of the contrast between the grease spot and its surroundings. This requires the two sides of the photometer head to be viewed simultaneously, and a simple arrangement for doing this is shown in Fig. 18-17. When there is equality of contrast the ratio of the luminances of the opaque and translucent portions must be the same on the left- and right-hand sides, i.e.

$$\frac{rE_L}{r'E_L + t'E_R} = \frac{rE_R}{r'E_R + t'E_L}$$

whence
$$E_L = E_R,$$

$$\therefore \quad \frac{I_L}{I_R} = \frac{d_R{}^2}{d_L{}^2}.$$

If the photometer head is not symmetrical it must be reversed (or the lamps interchanged) and the adjustments repeated. Again the geometrical mean of the two values for I_L/I_R is taken.

The third method of using the Bunsen grease spot photometer marks an important advance in visual photometry since it is found that in favourable circumstances the eye is capable of judging equality of contrast even more accurately than equality of brightness.

The Bunsen photometer head suffers from one major defect: the luminance of the translucent portion is due partly to light from one lamp and partly to light from the other. It is easily shown that this leads to a decrease in sensitivity. This difficulty is overcome in the widely used photometer head described below.

18–12. The Lummer-Brodhun Contrast Head

The Lummer-Brodhun photometer can be converted into a *contrast head* by a suitable modification of the prism system PQ (Fig. 18–16). The new prism system is shown in Fig. 18–18. Contact between the hypotenuse faces is broken, at the places indicated, by etching prism P. Light incident from the right is then totally reflected at those parts of Q where contact is broken, and light entering P from the left is transmitted through Q at points where contact between the prisms is good. The shape of the etched portions is such that, if the beams are

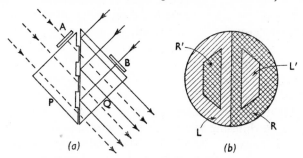

Fig. 18–18. The Lummer-Brodhun contrast head.

not equally intense, the appearance of the field of view is as in (b). Patch R' and background R are illuminated by light entering the prisms from the right and appear equally bright. Similarly L and L' have the same brightness. The field of view would be of uniform brightness if the beams entering from left and right were equally intense.

Two glass plates A and B are now added in the positions shown in (a). Owing to the additional air-glass surface, A causes the luminance of the patch L' to be about 8% below that of the background L, and B causes an equal reduction in the luminance of the patch R' below that of the background R. At the position of balance the backgrounds L and R still appear equally bright but the patches L' and R' appear somewhat less bright. In each half of the field the contrast between the patch and background is the same and this condition can be judged more accurately than the equality of the brightnesses of the backgrounds. According to Lummer and Brodhun, maximum sensitivity would be obtained if the luminance of each patch was about 4% below that of its background.

18–13. Flicker Photometers

The intensities of sources of slightly different colour can be compared fairly accurately by using a Lummer-Brodhun contrast head. However, none of the photometers described above is really suitable for comparing sources of widely different colours since it is difficult for an observer to judge brightness when there are colour differences.

Now if two fields of view of different colour and slightly different luminance are presented alternately to an observer's eye, and the frequency of alternation gradually increased, it is found that a stage is reached where the colour difference is not observed. By adjusting the luminances of the two fields to be equal, the flicker can then be made to disappear completely. In this way one can adjust the illuminations of the two screens of a suitable photometer head to be equal, and the luminous intensities of two sources can be compared in the usual way.

Fig. 18–19.
The Abney flicker photometer.

The flicker caused by a difference in brightness between the two fields of view can be removed also by increasing the frequency of alternation, and the smaller the brightness difference the lower is the required frequency. In order to make the adjustment of luminance as accurate as possible, it is necessary to be able to detect the smallest possible brightness difference. Consequently, it is necessary to employ the lowest possible frequency of alternation and one increases the frequency from a low value until it is just possible to remove the flicker completely by an adjustment of luminance.

The simplest of the early flicker photometers is that due to Abney (see Fig. 18–19). Light from the source S_1 falls on the diffusing surface A, and light from S_2 falls on the diffusing surfaces of the sector disc B which can be rotated about the horizontal axis C. As the disc is rotated the eye receives, alternately, light from A and from a sector of B. In the Simmance-Abady flicker photometer, light from the sources is directed to the observer by means of the disc D which rotates about the axis A [Fig. 18–20(a)]. The form of the disc can be described as follows. In Fig. 18–20(b) P and Q are two truncated cones of a material such as plaster of Paris. If the shaded portions are taken and their adjacent faces in the figure connected together, one obtains a disc of the form used.

It will be seen that in these photometers the light is not incident normally on the diffusing surfaces as is desirable. It has been found that in a flicker photometer the following additional conditions should be fulfilled:

(a)

(b)

D

A

P   Q

Fig. 18–20. The Simmance-Abady
flicker photometer.

1. The illumination of the comparison surfaces should be at least 25 lux.

2. The photometric field should be about 2° in angular diameter and surrounded by a field of about 25° diameter maintained at approximately the same luminance as the photometric field, there being no dark demarcation line separating them.

3. When the moving parts of the flicker head are rotated slowly no shadows should be seen in the field.

4. The two halves of the field should be visible for equal lengths of time during each rotation, i.e. uniform speed of rotation is essential.

It is found that observers cannot use a flicker photometer for periods exceeding about an hour without undue fatigue and loss of accuracy.

Several flicker photometers have been designed which fulfil the conditions described above. That due to Guild is illustrated in Fig. 18–21. Light from the source S_1 passes through the prism P and is incident normally on the diffusing surface A. The sector disc B which rotates about the axis C has 90° sectors which have diffusing surfaces. When a sector is suitably positioned, light from the source S_2 is incident normally upon it. The illuminated surfaces of A and B are viewed alternately from E through the aperture D which gives a 2° field. The inner surface of the tube F is a diffusing surface which is illuminated by the source G. It will be seen that the photometric comparison surfaces A and B are

Fig. 18–21. Guild's flicker photometer.

both viewed at 45°. These surfaces and the inside of F (which provides the necessary bright surround) are coated with magnesium oxide. The aperture D has a sharp edge to avoid a discontinuity in the field of view. The necessity of finding the transmission of the prism P can be avoided by using the substitution method, i.e. by keeping S_1 unchanged and placing the sources to be compared at S_2 in turn.

It is obvious that the results obtained in the visual comparison of sources of different colour depend upon the spectral sensitivity of the observer's eye, and some check must be made to ensure that this does not deviate markedly from that of a "standard observer". This difficulty is overcome by using a physical receptor such as a photo-cell in place of the eye.

18–14. Physical Photometry

Radiant energy can be measured by any device which gives a physically measurable response which varies in a known manner with the energy received. In photometry one measures the radiant energy weighted according to its ability to produce a visual response. Consequently, in comparing the luminous intensities of sources emitting different wavelengths, the correct result will be obtained only if the receiver has the same spectral sensitivity as the eye of the standard observer. Once it has been found how the output from such a receiver varies with the flux received, it can be used to measure luminous fluxes of any magnitude and colour. It is, for example, not limited to detecting the equality of two fluxes as is the eye. To use a receiver such as a photo-cell it is simply necessary to insert before it a filter which will make the overall spectral sensitivity close to that of the eye. For the measurement of fairly large fluxes a barrier layer (photo-voltaic) cell is very convenient since its output can be measured directly on a micro-ammeter. However, such a cell has rather low sensitivity and shows fatigue when exposed to steady illumination. For greater sensitivity a photo-emission cell is better since the output can be amplified conveniently. Such a system is generally more reliable. An alternative method of securing high sensitivity is to use a photo-multiplier cell. A physical receptor is very useful at low levels of illumination. In this region the Purkinje effect renders the eye unsatisfactory as a receptor since its spectral sensitivity is not constant.

18-15. Directional Properties of Sources

As has already been pointed out the luminous intensity of a source is the flux emitted per unit solid angle in the direction considered. In general, sources are not uniform, and it is frequently necessary to examine the variations of luminous intensity with direction. If the source can be used in any orientation, the ordinary visual optical bench can be used to measure the intensity for various positions of the source. Actually very few sources are unaffected by orientation (a vacuum filament lamp is one of the few) and if a visual photometer bench is used, it is necessary to employ a system of mirrors to collect light radiated in directions out of the horizontal plane.

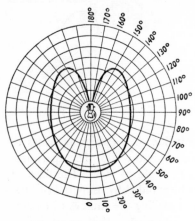

Fig. 18–22. Polar curve for a gas-filled filament lamp.

If a physical receiver such as a photo-cell is employed, it can be moved round the source and this is frequently a more convenient method. It should be remembered, however, that it is necessary for the photo-cell to be positioned sufficiently far from the source for the latter to be regarded as a point source.

Using the above method, it is possible to measure the luminous intensity of a source in any direction. The results of a number of such measurements on a source are most conveniently shown on a polar diagram in which the source is origin and the length of the radius vector in any direction represents the luminous intensity in that direction. Fig. 18–22 shows a diagram of this type for the vertical section through a gas-filled electric lamp. Sometimes the length of a radius vector at a given angle to the vertical represents the mean luminous intensity for all azimuths measured from a vertical plane.

If the source does not radiate approximately symmetrically about an axis it is better to construct a so-called *isocandela diagram*. A sphere is imagined surrounding the source and on this sphere are drawn loci of points from which the source appears to have the same luminous intensity. This diagram is then projected on to a plane by one of the projections used in ordinary map making. An equal area projection is desirable so that by comparing two diagrams one may obtain an approximate idea of the relative values of the total fluxes emitted by the two sources.

18-16. The Integrating Sphere

It is possible to find an approximate value of the total flux radiated from a source by finding the mean spherical candle power from measurements of the luminous intensity in a number of directions. It is much easier to use an *integrating sphere*, the theory of which will now be given. In Fig. 18–23 ds_1 and ds_2 are elementary areas of the surface of a sphere, centre C, radius r, the inner surface of the sphere being a uniformly diffuse reflector. Suppose there is a source of light inside the sphere so that the luminance of ds_1 is L. Then it follows from equation (18–7) that the flux dF received by ds_2 from ds_1 is $L ds_1 ds_2 \cos^2 \theta / d^2$. Now $\cos \theta = d/2r$

$$\therefore\ dF = \frac{L ds_1 ds_2}{4r^2}. \qquad \cdots \cdots \quad (18\text{–}20)$$

Hence, for a given element ds_1, the flux received by ds_2 is independent of its position on the sphere, i.e. the flux reflected from each part of the sphere is equally distributed over the other parts, or the flux received by an element *after reflection at other points* is everywhere the same. For a given sphere it can therefore depend only upon the total flux radiated by the enclosed source. The exact relation between the two is easily found as follows. Suppose that the total flux radiated by the enclosed source is F. The illumination at any point on the surface of the sphere is due to direct and reflected light. Let ϱ be the reflection factor of the surface of the sphere, and let L be the luminance of any point due to light received directly from the source. Then an element ds emits a total flux $\pi L ds$ and must have received a total flux $\pi L ds / \varrho$ directly from the source.

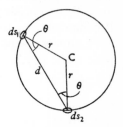

Fig. 18–23.
Integrating sphere.

$$\therefore\ \frac{\pi}{\varrho} \int L ds = F, \qquad \cdots \cdots \quad (18\text{–}21)$$

where the summation is taken over the whole surface of the sphere. Now the total flux received by an element ds' due to a single reflection from every point of the sphere is, from equation (18–20), given by $(ds'/4r^2)\int L ds$ or, from (18–21), $ds' F \varrho / 4\pi r^2$. This flux will give the element ds' a luminance $\varrho^2 F / 4\pi^2 r^2$. Thus the luminance of any point of the sphere due to the direct light and light which has undergone one previous reflection is $L + \varrho^2 F / 4\pi^2 r^2$. Consequently, the flux received by any element of area ds' due to light which has undergone the first two reflections is

$$\frac{ds'}{4r^2} \int \left(L + \frac{\varrho^2 F}{4\pi^2 r^2} \right) ds = \frac{ds'}{4r^2} \int L ds + \frac{ds' F \varrho^2}{16\pi^2 r^4} \int ds$$

$$= \frac{ds' F}{4\pi r^2} (\varrho + \varrho^2).$$

Similarly, when further reflections are considered, it may be shown that the total flux, due to reflected light, which reaches any elementary area ds' is

$$\frac{ds' F}{4\pi r^2} (\varrho + \varrho^2 + \varrho^3 + \varrho^4 + \ldots) = \frac{ds' F}{4\pi r^2} \cdot \frac{\varrho}{1-\varrho}. \quad \cdots \quad (18\text{–}22)$$

This is independent of the position and directional properties of the source. It assumes that the source causes no obstruction of the reflected light and that the

15*

surface of the sphere is a uniformly diffuse reflector. In order to measure the illumination at any point due to reflected light it is necessary to introduce a screen to obstruct the direct light and this will also obstruct the reflected light. Nevertheless an integrating sphere which is large compared with the source of light does provide an accurate method of comparing the total fluxes radiated by two sources. In practice a uniformly diffusing translucent window is built into the side of the sphere and a screen positioned to prevent light from the source falling directly on the window (see Fig. 18–24). The luminance of the window viewed from outside the sphere is then measured. It will be seen that this is directly proportional to the total flux emitted by the source inside the sphere. The luminance of the window can be measured by means of a photo-cell placed immediately outside it or one can adapt a photometer head such as the Lummer-Brodhun as indicated in Fig. 18–24. If the luminance of the window is high, the luminous intensity can be measured in the usual way, using an ordinary photometer bench.

Fig. 18–24. Visual photometry with an integrating sphere.   Fig. 18–25. Measurement of reflection factor.

18–17. Transmission and Reflection Factors

The visible specular reflection factor of a plane mirror, and the transmission factor of a plane parallel filter, can be measured by using the visual photometer head. The method is illustrated by Fig. 18–25 and needs no further explanation.

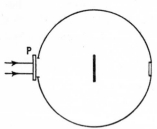

Fig. 18–26. Measurement of transmission factor.

The reflection factor is simply the ratio of the "apparent" luminous intensity of S_1' to the luminous intensity of S_1 measured directly.

If the mirror is not plane or the filter to be measured is not homogeneous and deviates or scatters some light, the above method is obviously of little use. This difficulty can be overcome by using an integrating sphere. For example, Fig. 18–26 shows the arrangement for measuring the transmission factor of a translucent plate P. The cross section of the incident beam must be less than the entrance aperture in the sphere. The transmission factor is the ratio of the illuminations of the window with and without the plate in position. A similar method can be used to find the transmission factor of an optical instrument. This is placed at P and the measurements made as before. Care must be taken that interposing the instrument does not cause the light to be obstructed by the edge of the sphere aperture. For example, when measuring the transmission factor of a small terrestrial telescope the eyepiece should be placed nearer the sphere, so that the beam which emerges has a smaller diameter than that which enters.

18–18. Illumination Photometers

The measurement of the illumination on a surface is frequently of considerable practical importance. For example, it is necessary to know whether there is adequate illumination on a desk or in a street at night. In many cases it is necessary for the apparatus to be portable. One of the simplest methods employs a barrier layer photo-cell provided with the usual correcting filter. This is simply placed face upwards on the surface where the illumination is required. The only auxiliary apparatus required is a micro-ammeter, and this can be calibrated to read the illumination directly. The chief disadvantage of this method is that the output for a given illumination falls off rapidly when the light is incident at an

Fig. 18–27. The Benjamin foot-candle meter.

angle exceeding about 50°. This is mainly due to the directional properties of the cell itself and is made worse by the presence of the filter whose transmission decreases with increased obliquity. The *exposure meters* used in photography are of this type.

The simplest visual illumination photometer is the Benjamin *foot-candle meter*. The construction of this meter is illustrated by Fig. 18–27. A screen S of opaque white paper has a row of grease spots, and these are illuminated from inside the meter by direct and reflected light from the lamp L and mirror M so that their luminance gradually decreases from one end to the other. The apparatus is simply placed on the surface whose illumination is required and the grease spot found which most nearly disappears. An empirical scale along S then indicates the illumination directly.

In more accurate illumination photometers a portable diffusing screen is placed on the surface under test and the brightness of this screen measured by the usual photometric comparison methods. It is necessary for the observer and photometer to cause the minimum obstruction of the light falling on the test screen. The fact that the brightness of a diffuse reflector is independent of the distance of observation enables the measurements to be made from a convenient position. One looks at the test surface through a viewing tube whose interior is blackened. The field of view also contains a comparison surface whose illumination can be varied. In the Macbeth *Illuminometer*, shown diagrammatically in Fig. 18–28, fields are compared with the aid of a Lummer-Brodhun cube C, and the brightness of the comparison surface S is varied by adjusting the distance of the lamp L. Other instruments control the brightness of the comparison field by means of filters or variable apertures. These instruments can be calibrated to read illumination directly but the calibration does, of course, apply to one particular test surface which must be kept clean, and renewed when necessary.

It is interesting to note that the illumination on a horizontal surface in England

Fig. 18–28. The Macbeth illuminometer.

at mid-day in summer may reach about 10^4 lumens per sq. ft. The recommended minimum illuminations for a number of surfaces are (in lumens per sq. ft.):

Library table	15
Drawing-board	30
Hospital operating-table	300

For street lighting the optimum height of the lamps is important since if they are high the illumination will tend to be more uniform but rather weak, and if they are low it will be patchy.

CHAPTER XIX

THE ELECTROMAGNETIC THEORY OF LIGHT

19–1. Vector Notation

IN this chapter it will be assumed that the reader is familiar with the laws of electromagnetism and with the fundamentals of vector calculus. With regard to the latter, it is possible for those who are not familiar with the subject to look upon the notation as a form of shorthand. Thus if ϕ is a scalar point function, grad ϕ is a vector whose x, y, and z components are $\partial\phi/\partial x$, $\partial\phi/\partial y$, and $\partial\phi/\partial z$, respectively. If one has a vector $\mathbf{E}$ whose components are E_x, E_y, and E_z, then div $\mathbf{E}$ is the scalar quantity $(\partial E_x/\partial x+\partial E_y/\partial y+\partial E_z/\partial z)$, and curl $\mathbf{E}$ is the vector whose components are $(\partial E_z/\partial y-\partial E_y/\partial z)$, $(\partial E_x/\partial z-\partial E_z/\partial x)$, and $(\partial E_y/\partial x-\partial E_x/\partial y)$. The symbol ∇^2 applied to the scalar ϕ means $(\partial^2\phi/\partial x^2+\partial^2\phi/\partial y^2+\partial^2\phi/\partial z^2)$, and $\nabla^2\mathbf{E}$ is the vector whose components are $\nabla^2 E_x$, $\nabla^2 E_y$, and $\nabla^2 E_z$. If $\mathbf{E}$ and $\mathbf{H}$ are two vectors inclined at angle θ, the *scalar product* is the scalar quantity $EH \cos\theta$ where E and H are the magnitudes of $\mathbf{E}$ and $\mathbf{H}$. The *vector product* is a vector whose magnitude is $EH \sin\theta$, and whose direction is normal to the plane containing $\mathbf{E}$ and $\mathbf{H}$ and such that, to an observer looking along the direction of the vector product, the rotation from $\mathbf{E}$ to $\mathbf{H}$ is clockwise. The scalar product is written $\mathbf{E.H}$ and the vector product $\mathbf{E}\times\mathbf{H}$. It will be seen that $\mathbf{E}\times\mathbf{H}=-\mathbf{H}\times\mathbf{E}$. As indicated above, vectors are printed in heavy type and the magnitudes in italics. Finally it should be pointed out that the right-handed cartesian co-ordinates are employed. That is to say, when looking along the z-axis, a rotation from the x-axis to the y-axis is clockwise. A number of results in vector analysis will be used in what follows, and these will be quoted when they are required.

19–2. Maxwell's Equations. The Displacement Current

The fundamental equations of the electromagnetic field are:

$$\text{div } \mathbf{D}=4\pi\varrho, \quad \ldots \ldots \ldots (19\text{–}1)$$

$$\text{div } \mathbf{B}=0, \quad \ldots \ldots \ldots (19\text{–}2)$$

$$\text{curl } \mathbf{H}=4\pi\mathbf{j}+\frac{1}{c}\frac{\partial\mathbf{D}}{\partial t}, \quad \ldots \ldots (19\text{–}3)$$

$$\text{curl } \mathbf{E}=-\frac{1}{c}\frac{\partial\mathbf{B}}{\partial t}, \quad \ldots \ldots (19\text{–}4)$$

where $\mathbf{D}$ is the electric displacement, ϱ the charge density, $\mathbf{B}$ the magnetic induction, $\mathbf{H}$ the magnetic intensity, $\mathbf{j}$ the current density, and $\mathbf{E}$ the electric intensity. $\mathbf{D}$, $\mathbf{E}$, and ϱ, are measured in e.s.u. and $\mathbf{B}$, $\mathbf{H}$, and $\mathbf{j}$, in e.m.u. The magnitude of the constant c is the ratio of the e.m.u. to the e.s.u. of charge. Equation (19–1) is an expression of Gauss's flux law and (19–2) expresses the fact that isolated magnetic poles do not exist. Equation (19–4) is Maxwell's generalization of Neumann's law of electromagnetic induction. A far more important

429

contribution by Maxwell was the inclusion of the second term on the right-hand side of (19–3). In the absence of this term, the equation follows directly from Ampere's law concerning the work done in taking a magnetic pole round a path linking a current and, in that form, is applicable to steady and slowly varying conditions. Now for any vector **V** div curl $\mathbf{V} \equiv 0$ so that, if curl $\mathbf{H} = 4\pi\mathbf{j}$, it follows that div $\mathbf{j} = 0$. But the equation of continuity of charge is, from (19–1) (using e.s.u. throughout),

$$\operatorname{div} \mathbf{j} = -\frac{\partial \varrho}{\partial t} = -\frac{\partial}{\partial t}\left(\frac{1}{4\pi} \operatorname{div} \mathbf{D}\right), \quad \ldots \ldots \quad (19\text{–}5)$$

i.e. div **j** is zero for the steady state only.

From (19–5) one may write

$$\operatorname{div}\left(\mathbf{j} + \frac{1}{4\pi}\frac{\partial \mathbf{D}}{\partial t}\right) = 0, \quad \ldots \ldots \quad (19\text{–}6)$$

which reduces to div $\mathbf{j} = 0$ in the steady state. Equation (19–6) suggests that, in general, **j** should be replaced by $[\mathbf{j} + (1/4\pi)(\partial \mathbf{D}/\partial t)]$ so that, in the non-steady state, the current density is effectively $[\mathbf{j} + (1/4\pi)(\partial \mathbf{D}/\partial t)]$. **j** is, of course, the conduction current density and $(1/4\pi)(\partial \mathbf{D}/\partial t)$ is called the *displacement current* density. Now the displacement **D** is related to the electric intensity **E** and the polarization **P** by the equation

$$\mathbf{D} = \mathbf{E} + 4\pi\mathbf{P}.$$

Therefore the displacement current may be written

$$\frac{1}{4\pi}\frac{\partial \mathbf{D}}{\partial t} = \frac{\partial \mathbf{P}}{\partial t} + \frac{1}{4\pi}\frac{\partial \mathbf{E}}{\partial t}. \quad \ldots \ldots \quad (19\text{–}7)$$

One can interpret the so-called *polarization current*, $\partial \mathbf{P}/\partial t$, as follows: when a dielectric is polarized by an applied electric field, positive and negative charges are separated. While this separation is taking place the charges are moving and constitute an electric current. The last term of (19–7) is present even when there is no material medium; it is the displacement current in a vacuum. This was called the *aether displacement current* since it was assumed that a polarizable medium, the aether, pervaded all space and was the medium for the transmission of light disturbances. Probably it is better to regard (19–3) (omitting the term $4\pi\mathbf{j}$) simply as an analogue of the more familiar equation (19–4). That is to say, just as a change in magnetic flux induces an electric field, a change in electric flux induces a magnetic field. It is found that it is not necessary to consider the displacement current unless one has rapidly varying fields, i.e. high frequencies.

19–3. Propagation of an Electromagnetic Disturbance in Isotropic Dielectrics

For a non-conducting medium the conduction current **j** is zero. If the medium is isotropic, the electric displacement at any point is in the same direction as the electric intensity, and the magnetic induction is in the same direction as the magnetic intensity, i.e. one may write

$$\mathbf{D} = K\mathbf{E}, \quad \ldots \ldots \ldots \quad (19\text{–}8)$$

$$\mathbf{B} = \mu\mathbf{H}, \quad \ldots \ldots \ldots \quad (19\text{–}9)$$

where K and μ are scalar quantities known respectively as the dielectric constant and the permeability. The medium is assumed to be homogeneous so that K and μ are not functions of position; it is assumed that they are independent of E and H. It is also assumed that there is no volume distribution of charge— $\varrho = 0$. With these assumptions Maxwell's equations reduce to

$$\text{div } \mathbf{E} = 0, \quad \ldots \ldots \ldots \quad (19\text{--}10)$$

$$\text{div } \mathbf{H} = 0, \quad \ldots \ldots \ldots \quad (19\text{--}11)$$

$$\text{curl } \mathbf{H} = \frac{K}{c} \frac{\partial \mathbf{E}}{\partial t}, \quad \ldots \ldots \quad (19\text{--}12)$$

$$\text{curl } \mathbf{E} = -\frac{\mu}{c} \frac{\partial \mathbf{H}}{\partial t}. \quad \ldots \ldots \quad (19\text{--}13)$$

From (19–13) one has

$$\text{curl curl } \mathbf{E} = -\frac{\mu}{c} \text{curl } \frac{\partial \mathbf{H}}{\partial t} = -\frac{\mu}{c} \frac{\partial}{\partial t} (\text{curl } \mathbf{H}).$$

Now it can be shown that for any vector $\mathbf{V}$ curl curl $\mathbf{V} \equiv \text{grad div } \mathbf{V} - \nabla^2 \mathbf{V}$ so that, using (19–12), one has

$$\text{grad div } \mathbf{E} - \nabla^2 \mathbf{E} = -\frac{\mu K}{c^2} \frac{\partial^2 \mathbf{E}}{\partial t^2},$$

and since div $\mathbf{E} = 0$ one has

$$\nabla^2 \mathbf{E} = \frac{\mu K}{c^2} \frac{\partial^2 \mathbf{E}}{\partial t^2}. \quad \ldots \ldots \quad (19\text{--}14)$$

Similarly, E can be eliminated to obtain

$$\nabla^2 \mathbf{H} = \frac{\mu K}{c^2} \frac{\partial^2 \mathbf{H}}{\partial t^2}. \quad \ldots \ldots \quad (19\text{--}15)$$

These equations have the form of the general equation of wave motion and state that variations of E and H are propagated with a speed $c/\sqrt{\mu K}$. It is important to notice that these equations are linear so that the sum of a number of solutions is also a solution. Consequently, the so-called *electromagnetic waves* interfere according to the principle of superposition.

19–4. Plane Waves

The case of a plane wave will now be considered, the values of E and H being constant in wavefronts which are perpendicular to the x-axis. Thus the components of E and H are constant in these planes and their partial derivatives with respect to y and z are zero. Now equation (19–10) is

$$\text{div } \mathbf{E} = \frac{\partial E_x}{\partial x} + \frac{\partial E_y}{\partial y} + \frac{\partial E_z}{\partial z} = 0,$$

$$\therefore \quad \frac{\partial E_x}{\partial x} = 0.$$

Similarly, from (19–11),

$$\frac{\partial H_x}{\partial x} = 0.$$

In addition, (19–12) and (19–13) show that

$$\frac{\partial E_x}{\partial t} = 0 \quad \text{and} \quad \frac{\partial H_x}{\partial t} = 0.$$

Now there may be a constant field superposed on the propagated disturbances, but, as far as the latter are concerned, these equations show that E_x and H_x are zero. The existence of any constant field will be ignored since it is of no interest in the present discussions. Thus at any point both **E** and **H** lie in a plane perpendicular to the x-axis, i.e. in the wavefront. In addition, from (19–14) one has

$$\left.\begin{aligned} \frac{\partial^2 E_y}{\partial x^2} &= \frac{\mu K}{c^2}\frac{\partial^2 E_y}{\partial t^2} \\ \text{and} \quad \frac{\partial^2 E_z}{\partial x^2} &= \frac{\mu K}{c^2}\frac{\partial^2 E_z}{\partial t^2} \end{aligned}\right\} \quad \dots \dots \quad (19\text{–}16)$$

with similar expressions for H_y and H_z. These equations show that the disturbances are propagated along the x-axis, i.e. in the direction of the normal to the wavefront. It follows that **E** and **H** are always perpendicular to the direction of propagation, i.e. one has transverse waves.

It will now be assumed that the variations of **E** are simple harmonic and that **E** is parallel to the y-axis. Then $E_z = 0$ and from (19–16) one may write, for a wave travelling in the positive x-direction,

$$E_y = E_{y0}e^{ik(x-vt)}, \quad \dots \dots \quad (19\text{–}17)$$

where

$$v^2 = \frac{c^2}{\mu K}.$$

A wave in which the variations of **E** are confined to one plane containing the direction of propagation (in this case the xy plane) is known as a *plane-polarized wave*. From (19–12) one has, considering the z components,

$$\frac{\partial H_y}{\partial x} - \frac{\partial H_x}{\partial y} = \frac{K}{c}\frac{\partial E_z}{\partial t} = 0.$$

It has already been stated that $\partial H_x/\partial y$ is zero,

$$\therefore \quad \frac{\partial H_y}{\partial x} = 0.$$

Hence the variations of **H** are confined to the z component. That is to say, **E** and **H** are perpendicular and the direction of propagation, **E**, and **H**, are oriented as in a right-handed co-ordinate system.

From (19–13), considering z components, one has

$$\frac{\partial E_y}{\partial x} - \frac{\partial E_x}{\partial y} = -\frac{\mu}{c}\frac{\partial H_z}{\partial t}.$$

Now $\partial E_x/\partial y = 0$ and E_y is given by (19–17). Hence

$$\frac{\partial H_z}{\partial t} = -\frac{c}{\mu}ikE_{y0}\,e^{ik\left(x-\frac{c}{\sqrt{\mu K}}t\right)},$$

$$\therefore \quad H_z = \sqrt{\frac{K}{\mu}}\,E_{y0}\,e^{ik(x-vt)},$$

i.e.
$$H_z = \sqrt{\frac{K}{\mu}}\,E_y, \quad \ldots \ldots \ldots \quad (19\text{–}18)$$

the constants of integration being omitted since one is not interested in a constant component of the field. Since $\sqrt{K/\mu}$ is a real and positive constant, (19–18) shows that the variations of **H** and **E** are in phase. The properties of an electromagnetic wave depend to a great extent upon the frequency. By comparing the properties predicted by theory with those observed experimentally, many waves are found to be electromagnetic in character. The several divisions into which electromagnetic waves fall are indicated approximately in Fig. 19–1.

Fig. 19–1. The electromagnetic spectrum.

Equation (19–17) shows that $c/\sqrt{\mu K}$ is the phase velocity. In a vacuum μ and K are unity and the phase velocity is c. The refractive index of a material medium is defined as the ratio of the phase velocity in a vacuum to that in the medium.

$$\therefore \quad n = \sqrt{\mu K}. \quad \ldots \quad (19\text{–}19)$$

It will be seen that if μ and K are independent of frequency there is no dispersion. It is found that this is approximately true for wavelengths longer than about 1 cm., but for shorter wavelengths (higher frequencies) the refractive indices of many substances differ widely from those given by (19–19) using values of μ and K appropriate to slowly varying fields. For optical frequencies one may put $\mu = 1$ for transparent media so that $n = \sqrt{K}$. Using the low frequency value of K, one has $\sqrt{K} = 1\cdot405$ for paraffin, which agrees fairly well with the observed refractive index of $1\cdot422$. On the other hand, for water $\sqrt{K} = 9$ whereas n is about $1\cdot33$. For water, and for many other substances, the high value of the static dielectric constant is associated with a contribution to the electric polarization caused by the orientation of polar molecules when an electric field is applied. This is ineffective at optical frequencies, and the refractive index is correspondingly reduced.

19–5. The Poynting Vector

In the presence of a steady electromagnetic field one may say that the energy per unit volume of a homogeneous dielectric is

$$\frac{1}{8\pi}\,(\mathbf{H}.\mathbf{B}+\mathbf{E}.\mathbf{D}).$$

Consider now the volume V which is enclosed by the closed surface S. As the electromagnetic field changes, the rate of increase of energy in V is given by

$$\frac{\partial W}{\partial t} = \frac{\partial}{\partial t}\left\{\iiint \frac{1}{8\pi}(\mathbf{H}.\mathbf{B}+\mathbf{E}.\mathbf{D})dV\right\}$$

and, for an isotropic medium, one has $\mathbf{D}=K\mathbf{E}$ and $\mathbf{B}=\mu\mathbf{H}$ so that $\mathbf{H}.\mathbf{B}=\mu\mathbf{H}^2$ and $\mathbf{E}.\mathbf{D}=K\mathbf{E}^2$. Thus one has

$$\frac{\partial W}{\partial t} = \iiint \frac{1}{4\pi}\left(\mathbf{H}.\frac{\partial \mathbf{B}}{\partial t}+\mathbf{E}.\frac{\partial \mathbf{D}}{\partial t}\right)dV.$$

When the medium is anisotropic, K and μ are tensors (see § 19–7), but $\partial W/\partial t$ is still given by the above expression.

Using (19–3) and (19–4) one has (since $\mathbf{j}=0$ for a dielectric)

$$\frac{\partial W}{\partial t} = -\iiint \frac{c}{4\pi}(\mathbf{H}.\text{curl }\mathbf{E} - \mathbf{E}.\text{curl }\mathbf{H})dV.$$

Now for any two vectors $\mathbf{a}_1$ and $\mathbf{a}_2$ it can be shown that $\mathbf{a}_1.\text{curl }\mathbf{a}_2 - \mathbf{a}_2.\text{curl }\mathbf{a}_1 \equiv \text{div }(\mathbf{a}_2\times\mathbf{a}_1)$,

$$\therefore \quad \frac{\partial W}{\partial t} = -\iiint \frac{c}{4\pi}\text{ div}(\mathbf{E}\times\mathbf{H})dV.$$

Gauss's theorem states that if the surface S encloses the volume V, $\iiint \text{div }\mathbf{a}dV = -\iint\mathbf{a}.d\mathbf{S}$ if the vector $d\mathbf{S}$ has the direction of the inward normal to the surface element dS.

$$\therefore \quad \frac{\partial W}{\partial t} = \iint \frac{c}{4\pi}(\mathbf{E}\times\mathbf{H}).d\mathbf{S}. \quad \ldots \ldots \quad (19\text{–}20)$$

The right-hand side is the integral over the surface S of the normal component of the vector

$$\mathbf{\Pi} = \frac{c}{4\pi}(\mathbf{E}\times\mathbf{H}). \quad \ldots \ldots \quad (19\text{–}21)$$

Now the integral gives the rate at which energy enters the enclosed volume. Hence (assuming conservation of energy) the vector $\mathbf{\Pi}$ can be interpreted as giving the direction of the energy flow at any point and the amount of energy per second crossing unit area perpendicular to the direction of flow. $\mathbf{\Pi}$ is known as *Poynting's vector*. It should be noted that (19–20) indicates that the *integral* on the right-hand side of equation (19–20) gives the *total* energy flow and it has not been proved that $\mathbf{\Pi}$ gives the energy flow across an isolated element of area. However, this interpretation of $\mathbf{\Pi}$ is a very useful one. Now the vector $\mathbf{E}\times\mathbf{H}$ is normal to the plane containing $\mathbf{E}$ and $\mathbf{H}$, so that in an electromagnetic disturbance the energy travels instantaneously in this direction. It will be seen that for a plane wave the energy obviously flows in the direction of propagation. $\mathbf{E}$ and $\mathbf{H}$ are oscillatory and change direction, but $\mathbf{\Pi}$ is unidirectional. However, its magnitude varies and is a maximum when $\mathbf{E}$ and $\mathbf{H}$ are at their maxima and is zero when $\mathbf{E}$ and $\mathbf{H}$ are zero.

For a plane wave in an isotropic medium as discussed in the previous section, $\mathbf{\Pi}$ has magnitude

$$E_y H_z = \frac{c}{4\pi}\sqrt{\frac{K}{\mu}}E_{y0}^2 e^{2ik(x-vt)}.$$

This has mean value

$$\frac{c}{8\pi}\sqrt{\frac{K}{\mu}}E_{y0}{}^2.$$

Now the energy density is $(1/8\pi)(\mu H^2 + KE^2)$ and from equations (19–17) and (19–18) it will be seen that this has mean value $(K/8\pi)E_{y0}{}^2$. Hence the average speed of flow of the energy is given by

$$u = \frac{c}{8\pi}\sqrt{\frac{K}{\mu}}E_{y0}{}^2 \div \frac{K}{8\pi}E_{y0}{}^2,$$

$$\therefore \quad u = \frac{c}{\sqrt{\mu K}}. \qquad \cdots \cdots \quad (19\text{–}22)$$

Thus the average speed of flow of the energy is equal to the phase velocity or speed of propagation of the wave.

It is important to bear in mind that this discussion applies to a monochromatic wave.

19–6. Hertz's Experiments

It has been seen that Maxwell's equations lead to the result that an electromagnetic disturbance can be propagated as a wave motion and that the velocity

(a) Radiator

Spark gap

Receiver

(b) Receiver   (c) Cylindrical Mirrors

Radiator

Fig. 19–2. Apparatus used by Hertz.

is $c/\sqrt{\mu K}$. Maxwell's *Treatise on Electricity and Magnetism* was published in 1873, and in 1887 Hertz discovered waves which were undoubtedly electromagnetic and whose properties resembled those of light. It was later shown that the speed of these waves is equal to the speed of light.

Hertz generated electromagnetic waves by means of an oscillatory discharge across a spark gap. The arrangement is illustrated in Fig. 19–2(a). The spark gap is between two brass knobs connected to rectangular brass plates each of about 40 sq. cm. area. These form a condenser of low capacity, and, when the knobs are connected to the secondary of an induction coil, an oscillatory discharge passes across the gap. This obviously generates an electromagnetic disturbance which, according to the above theory, will be propagated through the air. To detect these waves Hertz used a very simple resonance circuit consisting of a circle of wire broken by a spark gap, as shown in Fig. 19–2(b). The gap between the knobs is regulated by means of a micrometer screw. The diameter of the circle is chosen so that the resonant frequency of this simple circuit is equal to the frequency of the oscillatory discharge across the gap of the source. If the magnetic flux threading the circuit changes, an e.m.f. is induced, and when this is sufficiently large, a spark passes across the gap. Thus Hertz was able to detect the magnetic component of the wave. The maximum length of the gap across which sparks will pass is a measure of the component of the magnetic intensity normal to the plane of the circle. This was found to be a maximum in the direction at right angles to the line joining the knobs of the source, and zero in the direction of propagation and in the direction parallel to the spark gap of the source. This indicates that the waves are transverse and plane polarized. One of the most convincing demonstrations of the existence of a wave motion is to produce interference, and this was done by reflecting the waves from a large metal screen on which they were incident normally. The existence of the resulting stationary waves was shown since the receiver sparked at the antinodes but not at the nodes. Hertz also demonstrated the reflection of the waves from large cylindrical parabolic zinc mirrors, a much stronger spark being obtained when the source was placed at the focus of one and the receiver at the focus of the other. In this case the receiver consisted of two pieces of thick wire placed along the focal line of the receiving mirror and connected to a spark gap behind the mirror. A spark was produced in the receiver when the axes of the mirrors were parallel [Fig. 19–2(c)] but not when they were perpendicular, again indicating that the waves are plane polarized. By interposing a large prism of pitch between the source and receiver, refraction of the waves was demonstrated.

19–7. Electrical Polarization in Anisotropic Media

Many crystals are not isotropic and the above theory cannot describe the propagation of light in such substances. In an anisotropic medium the displacement is not, in general, in the same direction as the electric intensity. That is, the dielectric constant is not a simple scalar constant. The components of $\mathbf{D}$ are related to the components of $\mathbf{E}$ by the equations

$$\left.\begin{array}{l} D_x = K_{xx}E_x + K_{xy}E_y + K_{xz}E_z, \\ D_y = K_{yx}E_x + K_{yy}E_y + K_{yz}E_z, \\ D_z = K_{zx}E_x + K_{zy}E_y + K_{zz}E_z, \end{array}\right\} \quad \text{. . .} \quad (19\text{–}23)$$

where the coefficients are scalar constants if the material is homogeneous.

One writes

$$\mathbf{D} = \mathbf{\Phi}\mathbf{E}, \quad \text{. . . . . . .} \quad (19\text{–}24)$$

where $\mathbf{\Phi}$ is a tensor whose components are K_{xx}, etc. It will be seen that, in general, multiplication by a tensor changes the direction as well as the magnitude of a vector. As with isotropic media, it is assumed that the permeability is unity at optical frequencies, so that only the electrical anisotropy is considered. Since the coefficients of $\mathbf{\Phi}$ vary with frequency, only monochromatic disturbances will be considered in the present discussion.

Maxwell's equations (19–1) to (19–4) remain valid and the energy density is $(1/8\pi)(\mathbf{E}.\mathbf{D} + H^2)$. The energy flux vector is still $(c/4\pi)(\mathbf{E} \times \mathbf{H})$ and it can be shown that it follows that the tensor $\mathbf{\Phi}$ is symmetrical. That is, $K_{xy} = K_{yx}$, $K_{yz} = K_{zy}$, and $K_{xz} = K_{zx}$. That is to say, $\mathbf{\Phi}$ has only six independent coefficients.

The connection between $\mathbf{D}$ and $\mathbf{E}$ can then be described by referring to the so-called *tensor ellipsoid* which represents the properties of $\boldsymbol{\Phi}$. The scalar product of $\mathbf{E}$ and $\mathbf{D}$ is given by

$$\mathbf{E}.\mathbf{D}=\mathbf{E}.(\boldsymbol{\Phi E})=K_{xx}E_x{}^2+K_{yy}E_y{}^2+K_{zz}E_z{}^2$$
$$+2K_{xy}E_xE_y+2K_{yz}E_yE_z+2K_{zx}E_zE_x=p \text{ (say).}$$

If one represents $\mathbf{E}$ in magnitude and direction by the radius vector $\mathbf{r}$ from a fixed origin, $E_x=x$, $E_y=y$, $E_z=z$, and the surface $p=1$ is an ellipsoid known as the tensor ellipsoid since its shape characterizes the tensor $\boldsymbol{\Phi}$. In this particular case it is usually referred to as the *Fresnel Ellipsoid*. It is easily shown that for any value of $\mathbf{E}$ the direction of $\mathbf{D}$ is that of the normal to the surface at the end point of $\mathbf{r}$, and that the magnitude of $\mathbf{D}$ is the reciprocal of the projection of $\mathbf{r}$ on the normal.

If the ellipsoid is referred to its principal axes, the coefficients E_{xy}, E_{yz}, and E_{zx}, vanish and the equation to the ellipsoid becomes

$$K_xx^2+K_yy^2+K_zz^2=1 \quad \ldots \ldots \quad (19\text{–}25)$$

(only single suffixes being necessary). The semi-axes are

$$\frac{1}{\sqrt{K_x}}, \quad \frac{1}{\sqrt{K_y}}, \quad \frac{1}{\sqrt{K_z}}.$$

It will be seen that, of the six independent coefficients of $\boldsymbol{\Phi}$, three define the shape of the Fresnel ellipsoid, so that the other three define its orientation in the medium (i.e. locate the axes of the ellipsoid with respect to the crystal structure). In what follows it will be assumed that the principal axes of the Fresnel ellipsoid are always chosen as the co-ordinate axes.

K_x, K_y, and K_z, are called the *principal dielectric constants* and one now has

$$D_x=K_xE_x, \quad D_y=K_yE_y, \quad D_z=K_zE_z.$$

One defines the *principal velocities* of light by the relations

$$v_x=\frac{c}{\sqrt{K_x}}, \quad v_y=\frac{c}{\sqrt{K_y}}, \quad v_z=\frac{c}{\sqrt{K_z}},$$

so that the axes of the Fresnel ellipsoid are proportional to the principal velocities. These are the velocities in the three principal directions. It is important to remember that they are not the components of the velocity if a disturbance is propagated in another direction.

Since one has $E_x=(1/K_x)D_x$, $E_y=(1/K_y)D_y$, and $E_z=(1/K_z)D_z$, the principal axes of the Fresnel ellipsoid are also the principal axes of the tensor ellipsoid which gives $\mathbf{E}$ as a function of $\mathbf{D}$. One writes $\mathbf{E}=\boldsymbol{\Phi}^{-1}\mathbf{D}$, and the equation to the ellipsoid corresponding to $\boldsymbol{\Phi}^{-1}$ is

$$\frac{x^2}{K_x}+\frac{y^2}{K_y}+\frac{z^2}{K_z}=1. \quad \ldots \ldots \quad (19\text{–}26)$$

Thus its semi-axes are equal to the square roots of the dielectric constants, i.e. to the so-called *principal indices of refraction*, n_x, n_y, and n_z. It is called the *index ellipsoid*.

19-8. Plane Waves in Anisotropic Media

As before, it is assumed that there is no volume charge and no conduction current, and that the permeability is unity. Equations (19-1) to (19-4) then give

$$\text{div } \mathbf{D} = 0 \quad \cdots \cdots \cdots \quad (19\text{-}27)$$

$$\text{div } \mathbf{H} = 0 \quad \cdots \cdots \cdots \quad (19\text{-}28)$$

$$\text{curl } \mathbf{H} = \frac{1}{c}\frac{\partial \mathbf{D}}{\partial t} \quad \cdots \cdots \quad (19\text{-}29)$$

$$\text{curl } \mathbf{E} = \frac{1}{c}\frac{\partial \mathbf{H}}{\partial t} \cdot \quad \cdots \cdots \quad (19\text{-}30)$$

It should be noted that div **E** is not now zero.

In §19-4 it was possible, without loss of generality, to consider a plane wave propagated in the direction of a co-ordinate axis. This is no longer possible since it is assumed that the co-ordinate axes are the principal axes of the Fresnel ellipsoid for the medium. Assume, therefore, that a plane wave advances with phase velocity v along the direction of **n**, the unit vector normal to the planes of equal phase. For a simple harmonic solution one may write

$$\mathbf{E} = \mathbf{E}_0 e^{ik(vt - \mathbf{r} \cdot \mathbf{n})}, \quad \cdots \cdots \quad (19\text{-}31)$$

where **r** is the radius vector from the origin.

From (19-30) one has

$$\frac{\partial \mathbf{H}}{\partial t} = -c \, \text{curl } \mathbf{E}_0 e^{ik(vt - \mathbf{r} \cdot \mathbf{n})}. \quad \cdots \cdots \quad (19\text{-}32)$$

Now it can be shown that if S and $\mathbf{V}$ represent a scalar and a vector field respectively, curl $S\mathbf{V} = S \, \text{curl } \mathbf{V} - \mathbf{V} \times \text{grad } S$.

$$\therefore \quad \frac{\partial \mathbf{H}}{\partial t} = c\mathbf{E}_0 \times \text{grad } e^{ik(vt - \mathbf{r} \cdot \mathbf{n})}$$

since curl $\mathbf{E}_0 = 0$.

Now $\qquad \text{grad } e^{ik(vt - \mathbf{r} \cdot \mathbf{n})} = -ike^{ik(vt - \mathbf{r} \cdot \mathbf{n})} \text{ grad } \mathbf{r} \cdot \mathbf{n}$

and if $\cos \alpha$, $\cos \beta$, and $\cos \gamma$, are the direction cosines of **n**,

$$\text{grad } \mathbf{r} \cdot \mathbf{n} = \left(\mathbf{i}\frac{\partial}{\partial x} + \mathbf{j}\frac{\partial}{\partial y} + \mathbf{k}\frac{\partial}{\partial z}\right)\left(x\cos\alpha + y\cos\beta + z\cos\gamma\right) = \mathbf{n},$$

$$\therefore \quad \frac{\partial \mathbf{H}}{\partial t} = -cike^{ik(vt - \mathbf{r} \cdot \mathbf{n})}\mathbf{E}_0 \times \mathbf{n},$$

$$\therefore \quad \mathbf{H} = \frac{c}{v}e^{ik(vt - \mathbf{r} \cdot \mathbf{n})}(\mathbf{n} \times \mathbf{E}_0) = \mathbf{H}_0 e^{ik(vt - \mathbf{r} \cdot \mathbf{n})} \text{ (say)}. \quad (19\text{-}33)$$

This shows that **H** is normal to the plane of **E** and **n**.

From (19-29) one has

$$\frac{\partial \mathbf{D}}{\partial t} = c \, \text{curl } \mathbf{H} = c \, \text{curl } \mathbf{H}_0 e^{ik(vt - \mathbf{r} \cdot \mathbf{n})}.$$

This is the analogue of (19–32) so that, proceeding as above, one has

$$\frac{\partial \mathbf{D}}{\partial t} = -cike^{ik(vt - \mathbf{r}.\mathbf{n})}(\mathbf{n} \times \mathbf{H}_0).$$

Integrating, and substituting for $\mathbf{H}_0$,

$$\mathbf{D} = -\frac{c^2}{v^2}\mathbf{n} \times (\mathbf{n} \times \mathbf{E}). \quad \ldots \ldots \quad (19\text{–}34)$$

This shows that $\mathbf{D}$ is normal to $\mathbf{n}$ and to $\mathbf{H}$. Thus both $\mathbf{H}$ and $\mathbf{D}$ are normal to $\mathbf{n}$, i.e. lie in the wavefront. Hence with respect to $\mathbf{H}$ and $\mathbf{D}$ one has transverse waves. Since $\mathbf{H}$ is normal to $\mathbf{D}$, $\mathbf{E}$, and $\mathbf{n}$, these three must be coplanar. Now if $\mathbf{V}_1$, $\mathbf{V}_2$, and $\mathbf{V}_3$, are three vectors, it can be shown that $\mathbf{V}_1 \times (\mathbf{V}_2 \times \mathbf{V}_3) = \mathbf{V}_2(\mathbf{V}_1.\mathbf{V}_3) - \mathbf{V}_3(\mathbf{V}_1.\mathbf{V}_2)$. Hence from (19–34)

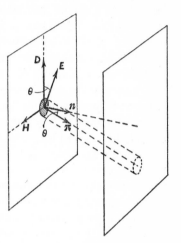

$$\mathbf{D} = \frac{c^2}{v^2}[\mathbf{E} - \mathbf{n}(\mathbf{n}.\mathbf{E})], \quad (19\text{–}35)$$

which again shows that $\mathbf{D}$, $\mathbf{E}$, and $\mathbf{n}$, are coplanar.

Now the Poynting vector

$$\mathbf{\Pi} = \frac{c}{4\pi}\mathbf{E} \times \mathbf{H}$$

is normal to the plane of $\mathbf{E}$ and $\mathbf{H}$ and therefore $\mathbf{D}$, $\mathbf{E}$, $\mathbf{n}$, and $\mathbf{\Pi}$, are coplanar. Also, since $\mathbf{n}$ is normal to $\mathbf{D}$ and $\mathbf{\Pi}$ is normal to $\mathbf{E}$, the angle between $\mathbf{\Pi}$ and $\mathbf{n}$ is equal to the angle between $\mathbf{E}$ and $\mathbf{D}$. The direction of $\mathbf{\Pi}$ is the direction of

Fig. 19–3. Orientation of ray and wave normal.

energy flow, i.e. the direction of the ray. One may say that a given element of wave travels in this direction (see Fig. 19–3). Its velocity—the ray velocity V—is obviously $v/\cos\theta$.

Equation (19–35) gives

$$D_x = \frac{c^2}{v^2}(E_x - (\mathbf{n}.\mathbf{E})\cos\alpha) \left.\right\} \quad \ldots \ldots \quad (19\text{–}36)$$

with similar expressions for D_y and D_z.

Now $E_x = D_x/K_x = D_x v_x{}^2/c^2$ and E_y and E_z can similarly be expressed in terms of the other principal velocities v_y and v_z.

Making these substitutions in (19–36), one obtains

$$\left.\begin{aligned} D_x &= \frac{c^2(\mathbf{n}.\mathbf{E})\cos\alpha}{v_x{}^2 - v^2}, \\[2mm] D_y &= \frac{c^2(\mathbf{n}.\mathbf{E})\cos\beta}{v_y{}^2 - v^2}, \\[2mm] D_z &= \frac{c^2(\mathbf{n}.\mathbf{E})\cos\gamma}{v_z{}^2 - v^2}. \end{aligned}\right\} \quad \ldots \ldots \quad (19\text{–}37)$$

Now $\mathbf{D}$ is normal to $\mathbf{n}$

$$\therefore \quad \mathbf{D} \cdot \mathbf{n} = D_x \cos \alpha + D_y \cos \beta + D_z \cos \gamma = 0.$$

Using (19–37), this gives

$$\frac{\cos^2 \alpha}{v_x{}^2 - v^2} + \frac{\cos^2 \beta}{v_y{}^2 - v^2} + \frac{\cos^2 \gamma}{v_z{}^2 - v^2} = 0. \quad \ldots \quad (19\text{–}38)$$

It will be seen that, in general, the phase velocity v can have two values in any given direction. However, for most anisotropic media, it is found that there are two directions for which (19–38) has only one solution, i.e. gives only one phase velocity. These directions are called the *optic axes*, and the medium is said to be *biaxial*. As a special case, there are also *uniaxial* crystals, in which there is only one optic axis. It will be seen that the optic axis is a *direction* in the medium and not a line. If, for any direction other than an optic axis, the values of v obtained from (19–38) are substituted into (19–37), the corresponding directions of $\mathbf{D}$ can be obtained. It is found that they are at right angles. It is important to notice that these are the only possible directions $\mathbf{D}$. That is to say, the disturbances that can be propagated in the medium are limited to those in which $\mathbf{D}$ has one of these directions. Since, in general, there are two possible directions for $\mathbf{D}$ for a given direction of the wave normal, there are also two possible ray directions (see Fig. 19–3). Conversely, for a given direction of the ray there are, in general, two possible directions for the wave normal. Consequently, if one has a point source of light in the medium, the rays spread out from the point in straight lines (assuming the medium is homogeneous), but there is not a single expanding spherical wave as in isotropic media. The form of the expanding wavefront will be discussed in the next section.

19–9. Wave Surface Expanding from a Point Source

In a homogeneous medium the rays from a point source are directed radially outwards. After a time t the disturbances from the source are located at distances along the rays determined by the ray velocities in the appropriate directions. To find the surface of constant phase (the wavefront) it is therefore necessary to plot the ray velocity V (not the wave or phase velocity) on a polar diagram.

It was shown in § 19–8 that $\mathbf{D}$, $\mathbf{E}$, and $\boldsymbol{\Pi}$, lie in the same plane. Thus one may write

$$\mathbf{D} + l\mathbf{E} + m\boldsymbol{\pi} = 0 \quad \ldots \ldots \quad (19\text{–}39)$$

where l and m are scalars and $\boldsymbol{\pi}$ is the unit vector. Taking the scalar product with $\boldsymbol{\pi}$, one has

$$\boldsymbol{\pi} \cdot \mathbf{D} + m = 0 \quad \ldots \ldots \quad (19\text{–}40)$$

since $\boldsymbol{\pi} \cdot \boldsymbol{\pi} = 1$, and $\boldsymbol{\pi} \cdot \mathbf{E} = 0$ because $\boldsymbol{\pi}$ is normal to $\mathbf{E}$.

$$\therefore \quad \mathbf{D} + l\mathbf{E} - (\boldsymbol{\pi} \cdot \mathbf{D})\boldsymbol{\pi} = 0.$$

Taking the scalar product with $\mathbf{n}$, one has $\mathbf{n} \cdot \mathbf{D} = 0$ because $\mathbf{n}$ is normal to $\mathbf{D}$, and this leaves

$$l(\mathbf{n} \cdot \mathbf{E}) = (\boldsymbol{\pi} \cdot \mathbf{D})(\mathbf{n} \cdot \boldsymbol{\pi})$$

or $\qquad\qquad l = \dfrac{(\boldsymbol{\pi} \cdot \mathbf{D})(\mathbf{n} \cdot \boldsymbol{\pi})}{(\mathbf{n} \cdot \mathbf{E})} . \quad \ldots \ldots \quad (19\text{–}41)$

Also, taking the scalar product of (19–35) with $\boldsymbol{\pi}$ and remembering that $\boldsymbol{\pi} . \mathbf{E}=0$, one has

$$\boldsymbol{\pi} . \mathbf{D} = -\frac{c^2}{v^2}(\boldsymbol{\pi} . \mathbf{n})(\mathbf{n} . \mathbf{E}). \quad \ldots \ldots \quad (19\text{–}42)$$

(19–41) and (19–42) give

$$l = -\frac{c^2}{v^2}(\mathbf{n} . \boldsymbol{\pi})^2 = -\frac{c^2}{v^2}\cos^2\theta = -\frac{c^2}{V^2}, \quad \ldots \quad (19\text{–}43)$$

since $\mathbf{n}$ and $\boldsymbol{\pi}$ are unit vectors inclined at angle θ. Substituting for l and m from (19–40) and (19–43), (19–39) gives

$$\mathbf{D} - \frac{c^2}{V^2}\mathbf{E} - (\boldsymbol{\pi} . \mathbf{D})\boldsymbol{\pi} = 0,$$

or

$$\mathbf{E} = \frac{V^2}{c^2}[\mathbf{D} - \boldsymbol{\pi}(\boldsymbol{\pi} . \mathbf{D})]. \quad \ldots \ldots \quad (19\text{–}44)$$

On comparing this with (19–35), it will be seen that $\mathbf{D}$, $\mathbf{E}$, $\mathbf{n}$, and v^2/c^2, are simply replaced by $\mathbf{E}$, $\mathbf{D}$, $\boldsymbol{\pi}$, and c^2/V^2. Proceeding in a similar manner, one has, if ξ, η, and ζ, are the direction cosines of $\boldsymbol{\pi}$, i.e. of the ray,

$$E_x = \frac{V^2}{c^2}(D_x - (\boldsymbol{\pi} . \mathbf{D})\cos\xi) \left.\right\} \quad \ldots \ldots \quad (19\text{–}45)$$

with similar expressions for E_y and E_z.

And since

$$D_x = K_x E_x = \frac{c^2 E_x}{v_x{}^2}, \text{ etc.}$$

one has

$$\left.\begin{aligned} E_x &= \frac{v_x{}^2 V^2(\boldsymbol{\pi} . \mathbf{D})\cos\xi}{c^2(V^2 - v_x{}^2)}, \\[2mm] E_y &= \frac{v_y{}^2 V^2(\boldsymbol{\pi} . \mathbf{D})\cos\eta}{c^2(V^2 - v_y{}^2)}, \\[2mm] E_z &= \frac{v_z{}^2 V^2(\boldsymbol{\pi} . \mathbf{D})\cos\zeta}{c^2(V^2 - v_z{}^2)}. \end{aligned}\right\} \quad \ldots \ldots \quad (19\text{–}46)$$

Now $\mathbf{E}$ is normal to $\boldsymbol{\pi}$ so that

$$\mathbf{E} . \boldsymbol{\pi} = E_x\cos\xi + E_y\cos\eta + E_z\cos\zeta = 0$$

and, using (19–46), this gives

$$\frac{v_x{}^2\cos^2\xi}{v_x{}^2 - V^2} + \frac{v_y{}^2\cos^2\eta}{v_y{}^2 - V^2} + \frac{v_z{}^2\cos^2\zeta}{v_z{}^2 - V^2} = 0, \quad \ldots \quad (19\text{–}47)$$

which gives the ray velocity V for any direction of the ray. One can now find the shape of the wavefront by representing V by the length of the radius vector drawn in direction (ξ, η, ζ). Thus, putting $V=r$, $\cos\xi = x/r$, $\cos\eta = y/r$, and $\cos\zeta = z/r$, one has, for the equation to the wavefront,

$$v_x{}^2(v_y{}^2 - r^2)(v_z{}^2 - r^2)x^2 + v_y{}^2(v_z{}^2 - r^2)(v_x{}^2 - r^2)y^2 + v_z{}^2(v_x{}^2 - r^2)(v_y{}^2 - r^2)z^2 = 0,$$

i.e.

$$(v_x{}^2 x^2 + v_y{}^2 y^2 + v_z{}^2 z^2)r^2 - v_x{}^2(v_y{}^2 + v_z{}^2)x^2$$
$$- v_y{}^2(v_z{}^2 + v_x{}^2)y^2 - v_z{}^2(v_x{}^2 + v_y{}^2)z^2 + v_x{}^2 v_y{}^2 v_z{}^2 = 0. \quad (19\text{–}48)$$

This surface, which is a wavefront, is frequently referred to as the *wave surface*; since it is obtained from the ray velocity, it is sometimes called the *ray* (or *ray velocity*) *surface*. To obtain an idea of the shape of the surface, consider the sections in the co-ordinate planes. It will be assumed that $v_x > v_y > v_z$. The intersection with the xz plane ($y=0$) is given by

$$(r^2 - v_y^2)(x^2 v_x^2 + z^2 v_z^2 - v_x^2 v_z^2) = 0,$$

i.e. the circle

and the ellipse

$$\left. \begin{array}{l} r^2 = x^2 + z^2 = v_y^2 \\[2mm] \dfrac{x^2}{v_z^2} + \dfrac{z^2}{v_x^2} = 1. \end{array} \right\} \qquad \cdots \cdots \quad (19\text{-}49)$$

Since $v_x > v_y > v_z$, the two curves intersect in four points A,B,C,D [Fig. 19-4(a)]. The directions AOC and DOB are the *ray axes* or directions in which there is a

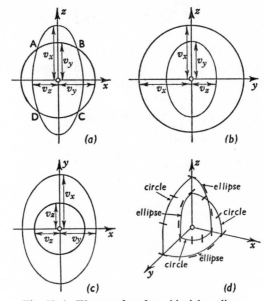

Fig. 19-4. Wave surface for a biaxial medium.

single ray velocity; they are not the *optic axes*. The latter are the directions in which there is only one phase velocity. This will be discussed further in § 22-9. It will be seen from the symmetrical nature of (19-48) that the intersection with each of the planes $x=0$ and $z=0$ is also a circle and an ellipse. Thus in the yz plane, one has

$$y^2 + z^2 = v_x^2$$

and

$$\frac{y^2}{v_z^2} + \frac{z^2}{v_y^2} = 1,$$

i.e. a circle entirely enclosing an ellipse [Fig. 19-4(b)]. In the xy plane one has

$$x^2 + y^2 = v_z^2$$

and

$$\frac{x^2}{v_y^2} + \frac{y^2}{v_x^2} = 1,$$

i.e. an ellipse entirely enclosing a circle [Fig. 19-4(c)].

The direction of **D** can be deduced from the fact that, at any point, **D** is in the tangent plane of the wave and is coplanar with the ray and the wave normal. On the elliptic sections it is therefore in the plane of the diagram, and is consequently normal to this plane on the circular sections. The shape of the wave surface and the directions of **D** are illustrated in Fig. 19–4(d), which shows quadrant sections of the wave surface. In all these diagrams the differences between the velocities v_x, v_y, and v_z, are very much greater than those encountered in practice.

19-10. Uniaxial Media

If the difference between v_x and v_y is reduced, the ray axes (and the optic axes) approach the z-axis, and when $v_x = v_y = v_{xy}$ (say) there is only one optic axis. Since $v_{xy} > v_z$ it will be seen from Fig. 19–4 that the sections in both the xz and

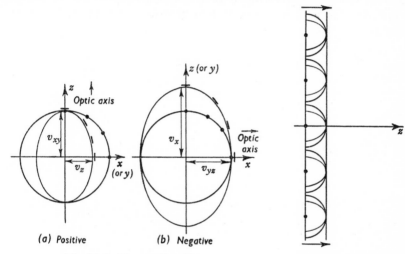

(a) Positive   (b) Negative

Fig. 19–5. Wave surface for uniaxial media.

Fig. 19–6. Propagation of a plane wave along the optic axis.

yz planes consist of a circle which touches an inscribed ellipse on the z-axis. The section in the xy plane consists of two concentric circles. Thus the complete wave surface consists of a sphere which touches an inscribed prolate spheroid on the axis of the latter. It is generated by rotating Fig. 19–5(a) about the z-axis. One is said to have a *positive uniaxial medium*. On the other hand, if the difference between v_y and v_z is reduced until $v_y = v_z = v_{yz}$ (keeping $v_x > v_{yz}$), one obtains a so-called *negative uniaxial medium* and the x-axis becomes the optic axis. The sections in both the xz and xy planes consist of an ellipse which touches an inscribed sphere on the x-axis [Fig. 19–5(b)]. The section in the yz plane consists of concentric circles, and the complete wave surface is generated by rotating Fig. 19–5(b) about the x-axis. That is, one has an oblate spheroid and an inscribed sphere.

The fact that for a uniaxial medium the optic axis coincides with the ray axis is easily shown as follows. Suppose that for a positive uniaxial medium one has a plane wave whose normal lies along the ray axis. Then according to Huygens' principle each element of a wavefront acts as a source of secondary waves and the two waves from each source spread out as shown in Fig. 19–6; the plane envelope of the elliptic sections obviously coincides with that of the circular sections. That is, the wavefront associated with the former has the same wave velocity as that associated with the latter. Further examples of the application of Huygens' principle to anisotropic media are discussed in Chapter XXII.

One should point out, in conclusion, that the discussion in §§ 19–9 and 19–10 is not entirely satisfactory. The aim was to find the shape of the wavefront expanding from a point source in an anisotropic medium. What is derived is the ray velocity surface, describing the variation with direction of the ray velocity, but it is, in fact, the ray velocity appropriate to a plane wave. That is to say, it has been assumed, without proof, that the ray velocity with which a disturbance spreads out in any direction from a point source is equal to the ray velocity in that direction for a plane wave. It is a plausible assumption, but it is an assumption.

CHAPTER XX

ABSORPTION, DISPERSION, AND SCATTERING

WHEN a beam of light is propagated in a material medium its velocity is less than its velocity in a vacuum and its intensity gradually decreases as it progresses through the medium. The velocity of light in a material medium varies with the wavelength, and this variation is referred to as *dispersion*. The reduction in the intensity of a beam traversing a medium is partly due to the fact that some light is *scattered*, and partly due to *absorption*. In true absorption the light disappears, the energy being converted into heat. The phenomena of scattering, absorption, and dispersion, are inseparably connected as will be seen from the discussions which follow.

20-1. General and Selective Absorption

All media show some absorption. Those which are referred to as being transparent simply have very small absorptions. Some media absorb all wavelengths more or less equally; they are said to show *general absorption*. Others show *selective absorption*—they absorb some wavelengths very much more strongly than others. Lamp black shows very general absorption, whereas dyes and pigments are obvious examples of materials showing selective absorption. Metals show very strong general absorption although many also show selective absorption; the associated selective reflection accounts for their colour. For example, a thick film of gold appears opaque, but a thin film appears blue-green by transmission, showing that although all wavelengths are strongly absorbed blue-green light is absorbed rather less strongly than the rest. Again, it is found that thin films of silver transmit wavelengths in the region of 3160 angstroms. Glasses and other optical materials which are transparent throughout the visible region show very strong absorption in the infra-red and ultra-violet regions. For example, crown glass is transparent from $\lambda 0.35\mu$ to $\lambda 2\mu$, quartz from 0.19μ to 4μ, fluorite from 0.125μ to 9.5μ, and rock salt from 0.175μ to 17μ. Air absorbs wavelengths below 0.185μ so that spectroscopes intended for use in this region must be evacuated.

It is fairly obvious how selective absorption influences the colour of a substance viewed by transmission. The colour of an opaque body depends upon selective absorption in a less obvious manner. For most coloured objects such as paints or flowers, the light penetrates a short distance below the surface and is reflected, refracted, diffracted, and scattered, within the body before emerging minus the selectively absorbed wavelengths. Such a body is said to have *pigment* or *body colour*; it appears to have the same colour by transmission if a sufficiently thin layer is employed. If the surface of such a body is highly polished, the specularly reflected light is almost white. If, however, the selective absorption of a substance is extremely strong, it shows true *selective reflection* and the colour of the specularly reflected light is found to be complementary to the colour of a thin film viewed by transmission. The wavelengths that are selectively absorbed are also selectively reflected to give the *surface colour*. Thus gold shows surface colour in addition to the high absorption and consequent high reflectivity for all wavelengths which characterizes metals. Powerful aniline dyes illustrate the way in which extremely strong selective absorption is associated with selective reflection. Thus a dye which absorbs green light appears purple by transmission when in solution, and green by reflection when in the solid state.

The *absorption spectrum* of a substance can be observed by passing white light through it and examining the transmitted light with a spectroscope. In general, light will be removed from the transmitted beam by scattering as well as absorption, but the scattering is reduced if the substance is in a homogeneous state such as a single crystal, a liquid, or an amorphous solid. Dielectrics show pronounced selective absorption. For solids and liquids this usually takes the form of *absorption bands* spreading over continuous bands of wavelengths. Speaking generally, it may be said that most insulators are more or less transparent to γ-rays and X-rays; show very strong absorption in the far ultra-violet (sometimes spreading up to or through the visible region); become transparent in or near the visible region; show strong absorption bands in the infra-red; and become almost completely transparent in the region of radio waves.

Fig. 20–1.
Penetration of light into a surface.

The absorption spectra of all gases at ordinary pressures show narrow absorption lines. Sometimes regions of continuous absorption can also be observed. The lines in the absorption spectra correspond to lines in the emission spectra, and if the gas consists of diatomic or polyatomic molecules, the sharp lines form the structure of the bands characteristic of molecular spectra. The absorption of an insulator in an absorption band can be comparable *in magnitude* to the absorption of a metal. It is completely different in origin.

Under certain circumstances, a body composed of a highly absorbing and therefore highly reflecting material such as a metal is almost completely non-reflecting. For example, chemically deposited silver appears black. The effect is due to the surface structure of the body. If the surface has the form represented by Fig. 20–1, the light is multiply reflected down the interstices between the needle-like structures and gradually becomes absorbed. A surface of platinum black has a spongy texture and light penetrates into the surface in this way and becomes almost completely absorbed. Near grazing incidence the light will not usually enter the interstices to any great extent. For example, a smoked glass plate has high specular reflectivity near grazing incidence.

20–2. Lambert's Law

Lambert's law states that equal paths in the same absorbing medium absorb equal fractions of the light that enters them. Suppose, then, that in traversing a path of length dx in a medium the intensity is reduced from I to $I-dI$. Then

Lambert's law states that dI/I is the same for all elementary paths of length dx. One can put

$$\frac{dI}{I} = -K . dx,$$

where K is a constant and is known as the *absorption coefficient*.

$$\therefore \quad \log I = -Kx + C,$$

where C is a constant. If $I = I_0$ at $x = 0$, $C = \log I_0$ and one has

$$I = I_0 e^{-Kx}. \quad \ldots \ldots \ldots \quad (20\text{–}1)$$

This expresses Lambert's law.

It is sometimes more convenient to specify the absorption of a medium by means of the *extinction coefficient* $\varkappa$. This is defined by saying that if a beam of light traverses a path whose length is equal to the wavelength of the light in the medium (λ_m), the intensity is multiplied by $e^{-4\pi\varkappa}$. Thus after traversing a path x one has

$$I = I_0 e^{-(4\pi/\lambda_m)\varkappa x}. \quad \ldots \ldots \ldots \quad (20\text{–}2)$$

On comparing (20–2) and (20–1) it will be seen that $\varkappa = K\lambda_m/4\pi$. In terms of the amplitudes one has

$$A = A_0 e^{-(2\pi/\lambda_m)\varkappa x}. \quad \ldots \ldots \ldots \quad (20\text{–}3)$$

Since for a given frequency the wavelength is different in different media, the factor $e^{-4\pi\varkappa}$ corresponds to different path lengths in different media. This difficulty can be overcome by referring to the absorption in a path whose length is equal to the wavelength of the light in a vacuum. The factor is then $e^{-4\pi n\varkappa x}$, and in terms of amplitudes one has

$$A = A_0 e^{-(2\pi/\lambda)n\varkappa x},$$

λ being the wavelength in a vacuum. $n\varkappa$ is sometimes called the *absorption index*.*

If one has a solution of an absorbing substance, the absorption coefficient of the solution will depend upon the concentration. Beer's law states that it is directly proportional to the concentration. This will be true only if the absorbing power of a molecule is not influenced by the proximity of its neighbours. Thus, whilst Lambert's law always holds, Beer's law sometimes doesn't.

When attempting to determine the absorption coefficient, it must be remembered that in (20–1) I_0 is the intensity of the light that enters the body; since some light is reflected at the first surface, it is not the intensity of the incident light. Again, owing to reflection at the second surface, I is not the emergent intensity for a body of total thickness x. The losses due to reflection can be eliminated by measuring the emergent intensity for two different thicknesses. Let I_0 be the incident intensity and I_1 and I_2 the emergent intensities for path lengths x_1 and x_2 respectively. Let A_1 and A_2 be the corresponding absorbed fractions of the light that enters the medium, and let R be the fraction of the incident energy that is reflected at each surface. The intensity of the light actually entering the medium

---

* There seems to be no general agreement regarding the names to be given to the various constants that can be used to specify the absorption of a medium.

is $I_0(1-R)$, the intensity incident on the second surface after traversing a path of length x_1 is $I_0(1-R)(1-A_1)$, and the emergent intensity is $I_1=I_0(1-R)^2(1-A_1)$. Similarly, the emergent intensity for a thickness x_2 is $I_2=I_0(1-R)^2(1-A_2)$. Now $A_1=1-e^{-Kx_1}$, and $A_2=1-e^{-Kx_2}$,

$$\therefore \quad \frac{I_2}{I_1}=e^{-K(x_2-x_1)} \quad \quad \ldots \ldots \quad (20\text{–}4)$$

and K can be found by measuring I_1 and I_2.

20–3. Dichromatism

Suppose one has a medium which very strongly absorbs the yellow and the blue regions of the spectrum, weakly absorbs the green region, and is almost transparent to red light. A fairly small thickness of the medium will be sufficient to absorb the yellow and blue regions of the spectrum, and when viewed by transmission with incident white light, the emergent red and green light cause it to appear yellow (see § 17–9). If a thick layer of the medium is viewed by transmission, the green light will be absent and it will appear red. Thus the colour of the emergent light changes as the thickness is increased. This phenomenon is referred to as *dichromatism*. Certain mixtures of dyes show the effect.

20–4. The Scattering of Light by Small Particles

The scattering of light by a particle that is large compared with the wavelength simply consists of a mixture of diffraction and diffuse reflection and refraction. The scattering from a cloud of such particles is more or less independent of the wavelength unless the particles themselves are large and selectively absorbing. The path of a beam of sunlight entering a room is rendered visible by the white light scattered by the dust particles in the air. A far more interesting phenomenon is the scattering of light from particles that are small compared with the wavelength. Tobacco smoke consists of a cloud of such particles and its characteristic blue colour is caused by the dependence of the scattering upon the wavelength. The scattering of light by very small particles was investigated experimentally by Tyndall and is sometimes referred to as the *Tyndall effect*. The theory was studied by Rayleigh, so that it is frequently referred to as *Rayleigh scattering*. It is found that the scattered intensity is proportional to the square of the volume of the particle and proportional to $1/\lambda^4$. Thus the scattering for light at the blue end of the spectrum is about ten times as great as that for light at the red end. This explains the blue appearance of tobacco smoke. As will be seen below, it also explains the blue colour of the sky.

It will be seen from above that as the particle size is reduced the intensity of the scattered light decreases rapidly. For particles of atomic and molecular dimensions the scattering is very small, but it is still observable. Thus if a strong beam of white light is passed through a pure liquid which is completely free from suspended particles, it is possible to observe the bluish light which is scattered laterally by the molecules themselves. The effect is less marked with a gas since there are fewer molecules per c.c. However, Rayleigh has shown that almost all the light seen in a clear sky is due to this *molecular scattering* by the air molecules. Here one has a very large number of particles so that the total intensity of the scattered light is easily observable. If it were not for the scattering of the molecules of air, a cloudless sky would appear completely black except in the direction of the sun.

The red colour of the sun itself at sunset can be explained in a similar manner. Fig. 20–2 shows that in this case the direct sunlight traverses an extra long path through the lowest and densest parts of the atmosphere. Since more blue than red light is scattered out of the direct sunlight, the sun appears red. The effect is enhanced by the presence of dust or mist particles. In a fine mist the same effect explains why one can obtain clearer photographs of distant objects by using light of longer wavelength, infra-red photographs being clearer than those taken with visible light. In a thick fog the particles are usually not small compared with the wavelength and there is little advantage in using red or infra-red light.

Fig. 20–2. Sunlight at grazing incidence.

20–5. The Quantum Theory of Absorption and Scattering

Absorption and molecular scattering are processes which are concerned with the interaction between light and matter, and it is only in terms of the quantum theory that one can give an adequate account of them. The present book is chiefly concerned with classical theory, and only a brief description of the phenomena can be given.

When discussing the interchange of energy between light and matter, it is found to be necessary to assume that the light consists of discrete packets of energy. These are referred to as *photons* and, if v is the frequency of the light in terms of the wave theory, each photon has energy hv where h is *Planck's constant*. Thus in some respects light behaves as a wave motion and in others it behaves as if it consisted of particles. These wave and particle aspects are not now associated with rival theories of light, but are complementary. Modern quantum mechanics includes a complete theory of light and shows when and to what extent light behaves as particles, and when and to what extent it behaves as waves. The theory is beyond the scope of the present book.

Rayleigh scattering results from an *elastic collision* between a photon and an atom or molecule. Here the photon is scattered without loss or gain in energy, so that there is no change of frequency. This is sometimes referred to as *coherent scattering* since the scattered light is coherent with the incident light.

Absorption also results from a collision between a photon and an atom. If the energy of the incident photon is exactly equal to an excitation energy of the atom, the photon is absorbed. The fact that the photon must have exactly the right energy accounts for the narrow absorption lines observed for gases at low pressures. For gases at high pressures, and for liquids and solids, the relative closeness of the molecules causes the excitation energies of different molecules to be slightly different. Hence the medium can absorb photons over a finite range of energies (i.e. over a finite range of frequencies). This accounts for the broader absorption lines. A number of close lines can merge to give a broad absorption band. For media of this type there is considerable interaction between molecules, and the energy of the excited molecules is quickly dissipated.

This gives true absorption. For gases at low pressures intermolecular collisions are relatively rare and the excited atom is undisturbed for long enough to be able to reradiate and return to its unexcited state. In doing so, the frequency of the emitted radiation is exactly the same as that of the light originally absorbed. This is referred to as *resonance radiation* for a reason which becomes obvious in the next section. The light is not simply radiated in the direction of the incident light, and the effect is of pronounced scattering of light of that particular frequency. It is also possible for an excited atom to return to its unexcited state via some intermediate state. In this case the energy (and therefore the frequency) of the emitted light must be lower than that of the light originally absorbed. This is known as *Stokes' Law* and the phenomenon is referred to as fluorescence; it is exhibited by solids, liquids, and gases.

In the phenomena described above, the incident photon is completely absorbed. Another possibility is that the incident photon has more than enough energy to excite the atom. In this case it is possible for the excess energy to be carried away as a photon of smaller energy (lower frequency). It is also possible for a photon to collide with an excited atom which falls to a lower state and gives some energy to the photon so that the frequency is increased. It will be seen that in this *inelastic collision* the frequency of the scattered light can be either lower than, or higher than, that of the incident light. This is known as the *Raman Effect*. It is sometimes referred to as *incoherent scattering* since the scattered light is not coherent with the incident light. Since the probability of this type of collision occurring is rather small, the effect is best observed in gases at high pressure, or in liquids or solids.

In the ordinary absorption process a photon raises an atom from a lower to a higher state, and in spontaneous emission the photon is emitted as the atom falls from the higher to the lower state. If, however, an identical photon strikes the atom while it is in the higher state, it can trigger the transition so that a second photon is emitted. It will be seen that as a result of this *stimulated emission* process the total light intensity will increase if there is what is known as a *population inversion* where there are more atoms in the higher state than there are in the lower—there can be said to be negative absorption. This is the principle of the *laser* (*l*ight *a*mplification by the *s*timulated *e*mission of *r*adiation). It is found that the light emitted is in phase with the incident light, so that a strong coherent beam can build up. The population inversion can be achieved by *optical pumping* where light from a separate source raises the atoms to the higher state before the initial stimulating light is applied. To obtain a large amplification a long light path is required, and the medium is enclosed within a Fabry-Perot etalon.

20-6. The Electromagnetic Theory of Absorption and Scattering

Although a completely satisfactory theory of absorption and scattering can only be given in terms of the processes outlined in the previous section, the simpler classical picture is adequate for many purposes. It is assumed that the molecules in a dielectric may be represented as *dipoles* or *bound charges*, i.e. charges that are bound to their centres of equilibrium by an elastic force. For an uncharged medium there must be equal numbers of positive and negative charges. When an electromagnetic wave impinges on a bound charge it is caused to oscillate and therefore to radiate. If the frequency of the wave is not equal to the natural frequency of the bound charge, one has forced oscillation of small amplitude, and the radiation from the charge is therefore weak and of the same frequency as that of the wave. This corresponds to molecular scattering. If the frequency of the wave is equal to the natural frequency of the bound charge, one has resonance, and a much larger amount of energy from the wave goes into the vibrating charge. In a solid, liquid, or gas at high pressure, there is strong inter-molecular action and friction type forces cause heavy damping of the dipole with the result that its energy is quickly dissipated. This corresponds to true absorption. In a gas at low pressure the motion of the charge or dipole is relatively undamped and it radiates strongly. This is resonance radiation.

It is possible to extend this theory to give a qualitative explanation of fluorescence and the Raman effect by assuming that the charges are bound by forces which do not obey Hooke's law.

The absorption of an electromagnetic wave by a conducting medium is easily explained by assuming that a conductor has a large number of *free electrons*. When the wave arrives, its energy goes into causing the charges to move. The moving charges constitute currents and the usual dissipation of energy by these currents explains the absorption of the radiant energy. It will be seen that although the absorption in an absorption band of an insulator may be comparable in magnitude with the absorption of a metal, the two processes are rather different.

The electromagnetic theory gives a simple explanation of the distribution of the scattered light in different directions. Suppose, for example, that plane polarized light with the electric vector parallel to the y-axis is travelling along the x-axis and is incident on a small particle at the origin O (Fig. 20–3). Since the incident light has no component of E perpendicular to the y-axis, there can be no scattered light along this axis. Light can obviously be scattered in all directions in the xz plane and will be plane polarized with E parallel to that of the incident light. For light scattered in the direction OP the incident light has component $E \cos \theta$ perpendicular to the direction of propagation. Thus the intensity of the light scattered in a direction making angle θ with the xz plane is proportional to $\cos^2 \theta$. If the incident light is unpolarized, it has equal components of E in all directions perpendicular to the x-axis. The light scattered along the x-axis is unpolarized, and that scattered in any direction in the yz plane is plane polarized with E transverse and in that plane.

Fig. 20–3.
Polarization of scattered light.

In some cases of the molecular scattering of polarized incident light, the scattered light is found to be only partially polarized. This depolarization has been explained by assuming that the molecules are anisotropic, so that the moment of the induced dipole is not in the direction of the electric vector of the incident light.

20-7. Normal Dispersion. Cauchy's Formula

It is not surprising that the earliest measurements of dispersion were for visible light and that the materials whose dispersions were investigated first were those which are transparent throughout the visible region. Thus the earliest measurements of dispersion were for a range of wavelengths in or near which the medium has no absorption band. It was found that, although the absolute value of the refractive index is different for different substances, its variation with wavelength is always of approximately the same form. Fig. 20-4 shows the dispersion curves in the visible region for a number of colourless transparent substances. It will be seen that in each case both n and $dn/d\lambda$ decrease in magnitude as λ increases. It should be noted, however, that the curves are *not exactly* the same shape. Although there are many exceptions, it is useful to note that, in general, denser materials have higher refractive indices than less dense media.

Fig. 20-4. Normal dispersion.

Dispersion of the form described above was later referred to as *normal dispersion*, to distinguish it from the *anomalous dispersion* which was observed in the region of an absorption band. It was found that the refractive index increases with increasing wavelength as one passes through an absorption band. It must be pointed out at once that there is nothing abnormal about anomalous dispersion. All substances exhibit normal dispersion for wavelengths that are far removed from absorption bands, and anomalous dispersion in the region of a band.

It was shown by Cauchy in 1836 that in a region of normal dispersion the variation of refractive index with wavelength for a given medium can be represented by an expression of the form

$$n = A + \frac{B}{\lambda^2} + \frac{C}{\lambda^4}, \quad \cdots \cdots \quad (20\text{--}5)$$

where A, B, and C, are constants characteristic of the medium concerned, and λ is usually the wavelength in a vacuum. The constants can be determined experimentally by measuring n for three values of λ. For many purposes it is sufficiently accurate to include the first two terms only. Then

$$n = A + \frac{B}{\lambda^2} \quad \cdots \cdots \cdots \quad (20\text{–}6)$$

and

$$\frac{dn}{d\lambda} = -\frac{2B}{\lambda^3}. \quad \cdots \cdots \cdots \quad (20\text{–}7)$$

Since A and B are positive, these equations express the fact that n decreases as λ increases, and that the slope of the dispersion curve is negative, its magnitude decreasing as λ increases.

The following alternative expression for the dispersion of glasses has been given by Hartmann:

$$n = n_0 + \frac{A}{(\lambda - \lambda_0)^{1 \cdot 2}}. \quad \cdots \cdots \quad (20\text{–}8)$$

This gives better agreement with observation than the formula of the Cauchy type that also has three constants.

For a gas, Gladstone and Dale showed experimentally that

$$\frac{n-1}{\varrho} = \text{constant}, \quad \cdots \cdots \quad (20\text{–}9)$$

where ϱ is the density of the gas.

20–8. Anomalous Dispersion. Sellmeier's Formula

For a substance that is transparent throughout the visible region, the refractive index in that region is represented very accurately by (20–5). If, however, the refractive index measurements are extended into the infra-red region, it is found

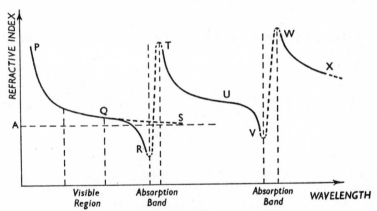

Fig. 20–5. Anomalous dispersion.

that, as one approaches wavelengths which the medium absorbs, the refractive index begins to decrease much more rapidly than is indicated by Cauchy's formula. In Fig. 20–5 the curve PQR represents the dispersion curve actually obtained and the broken line QS is that indicated by Cauchy's formula. Measurements beyond R become difficult owing to the absorption of the medium, but for wavelengths beyond the absorption band measurements can again be made quite easily; they yield a curve of the form TU. If there is a second absorption band, the curve continues along UV and, beyond this band, along WX. A more complete investigation shows that the curves PQR, TUV, and WX, are connected up as indicated to form a continuous curve. Since the light is absorbed very strongly, measurements within a band must be made with very thin layers of the substance. It will be seen that as one passes through an absorption band n increases as λ increases. As already stated, this is referred to as anomalous dispersion.

In order to obtain a satisfactory dispersion formula, it is necessary to consider the mechanism by which the light is absorbed by the medium. Sellmeier (1871) assumed that the medium contains elastically bound particles which have a natural frequency of vibration, and that if light of this frequency is passed through the medium, the particles resonate and energy is absorbed. For light of other frequencies the particles execute forced oscillations, the amplitudes increasing as the frequency of the light approaches the resonant frequency.

Fig. 20–6. Dispersion curve given by Sellmeier's formula, assuming two absorption bands.

These vibrations cause a change in the velocity of the light in a manner which will be discussed briefly later (see § 20–14). If all the elastically bound particles in the medium have a natural frequency corresponding to light of wavelength λ_0 in a vacuum, Sellmeier's theory gives

$$n^2 = 1 + \frac{A\lambda^2}{\lambda^2 - \lambda_0^2}, \quad \cdots \cdots \quad (20\text{--}10)$$

where A is a constant. This would correspond to a medium having only one absorption band. The existence of several bands corresponds to the existence of particles with several different natural frequencies. This gives

$$n^2 = 1 + \sum \frac{A_j \lambda^2}{\lambda^2 - \lambda_j^2}, \quad \cdots \cdots \quad (20\text{--}11)$$

where A_j is proportional to the number of particles whose natural frequency corresponds to λ_j. Fig. 20–6 shows the form of the dispersion curve given by Sellmeier's formula, assuming there are two absorption bands.

Although Sellmeier's equation represents a considerable improvement over Cauchy's formula, it has an obvious important defect: it indicates that n is infinite and discontinuous at λ_1, λ_2, etc. Thus Sellmeier's formula breaks down in the region of an absorption band. In regions remote from an absorption band Sellmeier's formula gives better agreement with observation than a formula of the Cauchy type having the same number of constants. It will be seen below that Sellmeier's equation can be derived from the more exact results obtained from electromagnetic theory. It is easily shown that Sellmeier's equation reduces to Cauchy's, when certain approximations are made. If there is one absorption band and this is a considerable distance to the short wavelength side of the region for which the dispersion is required, one can write $\lambda^2 \gg \lambda_0^2$ in (20–10) and obtain

$$n^2 = 1 + A\left(1 - \frac{\lambda_0^2}{\lambda^2}\right)^{-1} = 1 + A + \frac{A\lambda_0^2}{\lambda^2} + \frac{A\lambda_0^4}{\lambda^4},$$

which is of the same form as Cauchy's equation.

20–9. Experimental Demonstration of Anomalous Dispersion

The anomalous dispersion of sodium vapour was demonstrated by R. W. Wood by means of the following experiment. The apparatus is shown schematically in Fig. 20–7(a). T is a steel tube with a water-cooled glass window at each end. Pieces of sodium are placed along the bottom of this tube, which is partially evacuated and heated from the bottom as indicated. As the sodium is heated, vapour diffuses upwards across the tube. Thus the density of the vapour gradually increases from top to bottom and this is equivalent to a prism of the

(a) Experimental Arrangement

Blue   Green   Yellow   Red
(b) Result

Fig. 20–7. The anomalous dispersion of sodium vapour.

vapour whose thickness increases downwards, the refracting edge being perpendicular to the axis of the tube. White light from the horizontal slit S_1 is collimated by the lens L_1 and is brought to a focus in the plane of the vertical slit S_2 by means of the lens L_2. S_2, L_3, P, and L_4, represent a simple prism spectroscope, the refracting edge of P being vertical. When the tube is cold it contains a homogeneous gas, and a white image of S_1 is produced across the spectroscope slit S_2, giving a continuous spectrum along a horizontal strip of the focal plane of the spectroscope. When the sodium is vaporized, the prismatic action of the tube of vapour causes the images of S_1 to be dispersed along the length of

S_2. For wavelengths remote from the D lines the refractive index of the vapour is approximately unity, and the horizontal continuous spectrum in the spectroscope is unaffected. As the D lines are approached from the short wavelength side, the refractive index of the vapour becomes less than one, and the light is deviated upwards by the vapour. The inversion introduced by the spectroscope lenses causes a downward displacement of the narrow continuous spectrum. Thus displacements upwards and downwards of the spectrum correspond to increases and decreases of the refractive index of the vapour, and the narrow spectrum gives a qualitative representation of a dispersion curve (such as Fig. 20–5) for the two neighbouring absorption lines D_1 and D_2 at 5896 and 5890 angstroms. The result is represented by Fig. 20–7(b). If the density of the vapour in the tube is high, the absorption lines broaden and it is not possible to distinguish the part of the curve that lies between them. A diaphragm immediately after lens L_1 is used to select a section of the tube across which the density gradient is uniform.

20–10. Propagation of Light in an Absorbing Medium

It follows from §19–4 that, for a plane polarized plane wave travelling with velocity v in the positive x-direction in a non-absorbing medium, one can write

$$E_y = E_{y0} e^{ik(vt-x)} = E_{y0} e^{i\omega\left(t-\frac{x}{v}\right)} = E_{y0} e^{i\omega\left(t-\frac{n}{c}x\right)}, \quad . \quad . \quad (20\text{–}12)$$

where n is the refractive index of the medium. Suppose now that E_{y0} is the amplitude at $x=0$ in an absorbing medium whose extinction coefficient is $\varkappa$. Then it follows from (20–3) that the disturbance at x is represented by

$$E_y = E_{y0} e^{-k\varkappa x} e^{i\omega\left(t-\frac{n}{c}x\right)}$$

$$= E_{y0} e^{i\omega\left(t-\frac{n(1-i\varkappa)}{c}x\right)},$$

since $k=\omega/v=n\omega/c$. This can be written

$$E_y = E_{y0} e^{i\omega\left(t-\frac{\mathbf{n}}{c}x\right)}, \quad . \quad . \quad . \quad . \quad (20\text{–}13)$$

where $\qquad\qquad\qquad \mathbf{n}=n(1-i\varkappa). \quad . \quad . \quad . \quad . \quad (20\text{–}14)$

Owing to the formal similarity between (20–12) and (20–13), $\mathbf{n}$ is often called the *complex index*. This is not entirely satisfactory because the real part of $\mathbf{n}$ is only indirectly related to the angles of refraction with absorbing media.

It will be seen in the next section that when an electromagnetic wave passes through an absorbing dielectric the ratio of the polarization to the electric intensity is complex [see equation (20–19)]. This means that the dielectric constant is complex. It is easily shown that a complex dielectric constant implies absorption and that $\sqrt{K}$ becomes $\mathbf{n}$ instead of n. Thus the components of the field vectors satisfy equations of the form of (19–16) where K is complex. For example, for a plane polarized plane wave travelling in the positive x-direction one has, setting $\mu=1$,

$$E_y = E_{y0} e^{i(\omega t - k'x)},$$

where $\qquad\qquad k' = (\omega/c)\sqrt{K} = (\omega/c)(\alpha - i\beta) \text{ (say)}.$

$$\therefore \quad E_y = E_{y0} e^{-(k\beta/n)x} e^{i\omega\left(t-\frac{\alpha}{c}x\right)}.$$

The first term obviously represents absorption and it will be seen that $\beta = n\varkappa$ and $\alpha = n$. That is to say, $K = \mathbf{n}^2$.

20–11. The Theory of Dispersion in Dielectrics

The electromagnetic theory of Maxwell is based on the assumption that the light is propagated in a medium that is continuous and has a certain dielectric constant and permeability. It follows from that theory that the refractive index of a dielectric is also constant, so that the phenomenon of dispersion is excluded from the theory. It has already been pointed out that the dielectric constant is, in fact, not a constant but that it depends upon the frequency. This agrees with the well known fact that the refractive index depends upon the frequency.

Now it is known that matter consists of electrically charged particles, and it should be possible to explain the electrical properties of matter (such as the way in which electromagnetic waves are propagated) directly in terms of the electronic structure. That is to say, it ought not to be necessary to resort to empirical relations such as that implied by a constant or variable dielectric constant. The first attempt to derive the electrical properties of matter from the electron theory was made by H. A. Lorentz. In this theory it is impossible to take into account the actual contribution of each electron or dipole of which the medium is composed, but the average effect of a large number can be found. Thus in discussing the polarization $\mathbf{P}$, one is concerned with its average value over a volume which is sufficiently large to contain many dipoles although the linear dimensions of the volume are considerably smaller than the wavelength of the light.

Let $\mathbf{E}$ be the electric vector of an incident light wave and let $\mathbf{P}$ be the resulting polarization. Then one has

$$\mathbf{D}=K\mathbf{E}=\mathbf{E}+4\pi\mathbf{P}$$

and, as shown in §20–10, one has, in general,

$$4\pi\frac{\mathbf{P}}{\mathbf{E}}=K-1=n^2-1. \qquad \ldots \ldots \quad (20\text{--}15)$$

It can be shown that the total electric intensity acting on a charge at any point within a polarized isotropic medium is $\mathbf{E}+(4\pi/3)\mathbf{P}$. (Actually this is the average value for charges contained within a small volume surrounding the point in question.) Suppose that the bound charges are electrons, each of which has mass m and charge e. If the medium is isotropic and the magnetic force on an electron associated with its own motion is neglected (there being no external magnetic field), the displacement of the electron x is along the same straight line as $\mathbf{E}$ and $\mathbf{P}$. Suppose the electron is subject to an elastic restoring force which is proportional to the displacement from the equilibrium position, and that the free period is $2\pi/\omega_0$. In addition, there will be a damping force, and the equation of motion for an "average electron" is therefore of the form

$$\ddot{x}+r\dot{x}+\omega_0^2 x = \frac{1}{m}\left(E+\frac{4\pi}{3}P\right)e, \qquad \ldots \quad (20\text{--}16)$$

where r is the resisting force per unit mass per unit velocity, the right-hand side being the applied force per unit mass.

Now the polarization is equal to the dipole moment per unit volume, so that if there are N electrons per unit volume one has

$$P=Nex. \qquad \ldots \ldots \ldots \quad (20\text{--}17)$$

16*

Using (20–16), this gives

$$\ddot{P} + r\dot{P} + \omega_0^2 P = \frac{Ne^2}{m}\left(E + \frac{4\pi}{3}P\right). \quad \cdots \quad (20\text{–}18)$$

It is now assumed that P has the same frequency as E but that there may be a phase difference between them. Thus if

$$E = E_0 e^{i\omega t}$$

one has

$$P = z E_0 e^{i\omega t},$$

where z is a constant which is, in general, complex. Hence from (20–18)

$$z(-\omega^2 + ir\omega + \omega_0^2) = \frac{Ne^2}{m}\left(1 + \frac{4\pi}{3}z\right).$$

Thus from (20–15) one has

$$\mathbf{n}^2 - 1 = 4\pi\frac{P}{E} = 4\pi z = \frac{4\pi Ne^2}{m} \cdot \frac{1}{\omega_0^2 - \omega^2 - \dfrac{4\pi}{3}\cdot\dfrac{Ne^2}{m} + ir\omega}, \quad (20\text{–}19)$$

or

$$\frac{\mathbf{n}^2 - 1}{\mathbf{n}^2 + 2} = \frac{4\pi z}{4\pi z + 3} = \frac{4\pi Ne^2}{3m}\cdot\frac{1}{\omega_0^2 - \omega^2 + ir\omega}. \quad \cdots \quad (20\text{–}20)$$

Now in deriving these results it was assumed that the medium contained a distribution of oscillators all of which had the same natural frequency. This would correspond to the existence of only one absorption line. To generalize the result, suppose that there are N molecules per unit volume and that there are f_1 electrons of type 1, f_2 of type 2, etc. Then (20–17) becomes

$$P = Ne\sum_j f_j x_j, \quad \cdots \quad \cdots \quad (20\text{–}21)$$

and (20–20) becomes

$$\frac{\mathbf{n}^2 - 1}{\mathbf{n}^2 + 2} = \frac{4\pi}{3}\cdot\frac{Ne^2}{m}\sum_j\frac{f_j}{\omega_j^2 - \omega^2 + ir_j\omega}, \quad \cdots \quad (20\text{–}22)$$

and (20–19) can be written

$$\mathbf{n}^2 - 1 = 4\pi\frac{Ne^2}{m}\sum_j\frac{f_j}{\omega_j'^2 - \omega^2 + ir_j\omega}, \quad \cdots \quad (20\text{–}23)$$

where

$$\omega_j'^2 = \omega_j^2 - \frac{4\pi}{3}\cdot\frac{Ne^2}{m}f_j. \quad \cdots \quad \cdots \quad (20\text{–}24)$$

For stationary or slowly varying fields one can put $\omega = 0$ so that (20–23) gives

$$\mathbf{n}^2 - 1 = K - 1 = 4\pi\frac{Ne^2}{m}\sum_j\frac{f_j}{\omega_j'^2}. \quad \cdots \quad (20\text{–}25)$$

As introduced above, the f's are integers, but it is found that in order to obtain agreement between the observed and calculated values of the dielectric constant, non-integral values must be substituted into (20–25). It is then supposed that each molecule contains only one oscillator of each type, the f's being the strengths of the various oscillators. In the classical theory the ω_j's correspond to the natural frequencies of oscillators that are distributed throughout the medium. In quantum mechanics these oscillators are associated with the transitions that an atom can undergo. With each transition there is associated an oscillator strength defined as the number of classical oscillators per atom which would absorb the same amount of radiation from a parallel beam of light. Although it involves a different interpretation of the quantities that occur, the quantum theory of dispersion yields results which are similar to those given by classical theory. A detailed discussion of the quantum theory is beyond the scope of the present book.

20–12. Regions Remote from Absorption Bands

If $\omega_j'^2-\omega^2 \gg r\omega$, the absorption may be neglected and n is real. (20–23) gives

$$n^2-1=\frac{4\pi Ne^2}{m}\sum_j \frac{f_j}{\omega_j'^2-\omega^2}. \quad \ldots \quad (20\text{–}26)$$

Now the wavelength in a vacuum is given by $\lambda=2\pi c/\omega$, and if $\lambda_j'=2\pi c/\omega'$ one has

$$n^2=1+\frac{Ne^2}{\pi c^2 m}\sum_j \frac{f_j \lambda^2 \lambda_j'^2}{\lambda^2-\lambda_j'^2} \quad \ldots \quad (20\text{–}27)$$

or, putting

$$A_j=\frac{Ne^2}{\pi c^2 m}f_j \lambda_j'^2,$$

$$n^2=1+\sum_j \frac{A_j \lambda^2}{\lambda^2-\lambda_j^2}, \quad \ldots \quad (20\text{–}28)$$

which is Sellmeier's formula.

Since the density ϱ of a substance is proportional to N, (20–22) shows that for light of a given frequency

$$\frac{n^2-1}{(n^2+2)\varrho}=\text{constant.} \quad \ldots \quad (20\text{–}29)$$

This is known as the Lorenz-Lorentz law. It is confirmed experimentally for a wide range of substances, even through a change of state such as the transition from liquid to vapour. For low frequencies it follows that the dielectric constant is related to the density by the equation

$$\frac{K-1}{(K+2)\varrho}=\text{constant.} \quad \ldots \quad (20\text{–}30)$$

Equation (20–29) gives

$$\frac{(n-1)}{\varrho}\cdot\frac{(n+1)}{(n^2+2)}=\text{constant.}$$

Now for a gas the refractive index does not differ widely from unity, so that the second factor is almost constant. Hence for a gas one has

$$\frac{n-1}{\varrho}=\text{constant,} \quad \ldots \quad (20\text{–}31)$$

which is the law of Gladstone and Dale.

The quantity $(n^2-1)/(n^2+2)\varrho$ has been termed the *specific refraction* and the product of this and the molecular weight M of a substance is known as the *molecular (or molar) refraction*. If N_0 is Avogadro's number one has

$$N = \frac{N_0 \varrho}{M}$$

so that (20–22) gives, for the molecular refraction,

$$[n] = \frac{(n^2-1)M}{(n^2+2)\varrho} = \frac{4\pi N_0 e^2}{3m} \sum_j \frac{f_j}{\omega_j^2 - \omega^2}. \quad . \quad . \quad (20\text{–}32)$$

This suggests that in a mixture of substances which do not interact the molar refractions are additive, a result which is confirmed experimentally. When there is chemical reaction between two or more substances, it is sometimes possible to add the molar refractions plus some extra terms which take account of the electrons which are associated with the chemical bond.

20–13. Regions Close to Absorption Bands

For simplicity it is assumed initially that there is only one absorption band, so that (20–23) becomes

$$\mathbf{n}^2 = n^2(1-i\varkappa)^2 = 1 + \frac{4\pi Ne^2}{m} \frac{f}{\omega_0'^2 - \omega^2 + ir\omega}. \quad . \quad . \quad (20\text{–}33)$$

On equating the real parts, one obtains

$$n^2 - n^2\varkappa^2 = 1 + \frac{4\pi Ne^2}{m} \frac{(\omega_0'^2 - \omega^2)f}{(\omega_0'^2 - \omega^2)^2 + r^2\omega^2}, \quad . \quad . \quad (20\text{–}34)$$

and on equating the imaginary parts,

$$n^2\varkappa = \frac{2\pi Ne^2}{m} \frac{r\omega f}{(\omega_0'^2 - \omega^2)^2 + r^2\omega^2}. \quad . \quad . \quad (20\text{–}35)$$

If one has a weak absorption band, $\varkappa$ is small and $n^2\varkappa^2 \ll n^2$. Hence, putting $\omega_0' = 2\pi c/\lambda_0$ and $\omega = 2\pi c/\lambda$, where c and λ refer to the light in a vacuum, (20–34) gives

$$n^2 = 1 + \frac{4\pi Ne^2}{m} \cdot \frac{\lambda_0^2\lambda^2(\lambda^2 - \lambda_0^2)f}{4\pi^2 c^2(\lambda^2 - \lambda_0^2)^2 + r^2\lambda_0^4\lambda^2}. \quad . \quad . \quad (20\text{–}36)$$

Now in the region of the absorption band $\lambda \doteq \lambda_0$ and one can write $\lambda_0^2\lambda^2 \doteq \lambda_0^4$, $\lambda_0^4\lambda^2 \doteq \lambda_0^6$, and $(\lambda + \lambda_0) \doteq 2\lambda_0$. Hence, since n does not differ widely from unity (20–36) is approximately of the form

$$n = 1 + \frac{A(\lambda - \lambda_0)}{B(\lambda - \lambda_0)^2 + C}. \quad . \quad . \quad . \quad . \quad (20\text{–}37)$$

Also, since $n \doteq 1$ (20–35) gives, for the absorption index,

$$n\varkappa = \frac{Ne^2}{cm} \frac{\lambda_0^4\lambda^3 rf}{4\pi^2 c^2(\lambda^2 - \lambda_0^2)^2 + r^2\lambda_0^4\lambda^2}, \quad . \quad . \quad (20\text{–}38)$$

which is approximately of the form

$$n\varkappa = \frac{P}{Q(\lambda - \lambda_0)^2 + R}. \quad . \quad . \quad . \quad . \quad (20\text{–}39)$$

Fig. 20–8(a) shows the variation of n and $n\varkappa$ in the region of a single weak absorption band. This is typical of the results found experimentally for gases, the refractive index never being very different from unity. It can be shown that for a strong absorption band the variation of n takes the form shown in Fig. 20–8(b). It will be seen that n does not approach unity beyond the absorption band, so that if there is a second band at a longer wavelength, there will be a displacement of the curve of the form already shown in Fig. 20–5. The above figures show the anomalous dispersion (increase of n with λ) which is observed as one passes through an absorption band. In a complete theory it would be possible to calculate the values of the constants in the above equations from the atomic structure.

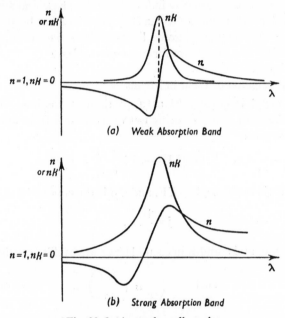

(a)   Weak Absorption Band

(b)   Strong Absorption Band

Fig. 20–8. Anomalous dispersion.

20–14. Connection Between Dispersion and Molecular Scattering

It has already been remarked that in molecular scattering the scattered light is coherent with the incident light. When the incident light impinges on a "molecular oscillator", the latter executes forced oscillations and sends out secondary waves in all directions. Referring to Fig. 20–9(a), it will be seen that

(a)   (b)

Fig. 20–9. Molecular scattering.

for a random distribution of scattering centres there will be a random variation of optical path for light scattered laterally from different oscillators to the point P. Hence the resultant intensity at P will be small. On the other hand, the light that is scattered more or less straight ahead arrives almost in phase at Q [Fig. 20-9(b)]. The disturbance at Q due to the scattered light can then interfere with the primary wave. The amplitude of the scattered disturbance is small and the resultant has an amplitude and phase which is not very different from that of the primary wave. Now if the phase of the resultant at Q is ahead of that of the primary wave, it means that the effect of the scattered disturbances is an increase in the phase velocity of the light—the disturbance at Q has a given phase earlier than it would have had in the absence of scattering. That is to say, the scattered light affects the refractive index. Now the phase and amplitude of the scattered light depends upon the frequency of the incident beam, and it can be shown that the effect of the scattered light on the refractive index is precisely that represented by the dispersion formulae given above.

20-15. The Propagation of Light in Metals

Initially, a metal is considered as a continuous medium with large conductivity, the dielectric constant being not very different from unity. Maxwell's equation (19–3) gives

$$\text{curl } \mathbf{H} = 4\pi\mathbf{j} + \frac{1}{c}\frac{\partial \mathbf{D}}{\partial t}.$$

If the medium is isotropic, $\mathbf{D} = K\mathbf{E}$, and if σ is the conductivity

$$\mathbf{j} = \frac{1}{c}\sigma\mathbf{E},$$

where $\mathbf{j}$ is in e.m.u. and σ and $\mathbf{E}$ in e.s.u. Hence Maxwell's equation becomes

$$\text{curl } \mathbf{H} = \left(\frac{4\pi}{c}\sigma + \frac{K}{c}\frac{\partial}{\partial t}\right)\mathbf{E}.$$

It has already been seen that for any vector $\mathbf{V}$ curl curl $\mathbf{V} = \text{grad (div } \mathbf{V}) - \nabla^2\mathbf{V}$. Now one may put $\mu = 1$ for optical frequencies so that equation (19–4) becomes curl $\mathbf{E} = -(1/c)\partial\mathbf{H}/\partial t$, and if there is no volume charge (19–1) gives div $\mathbf{E} = 0$.

Hence
$$\nabla^2\mathbf{E} = \frac{1}{c}\frac{\partial}{\partial t}\left(\frac{4\pi}{c}\sigma + \frac{K}{c}\frac{\partial}{\partial t}\right)\mathbf{E}$$

$$= \frac{K}{c^2}\frac{\partial^2\mathbf{E}}{\partial t^2} + \frac{4\pi\sigma}{c^2}\frac{\partial\mathbf{E}}{\partial t}. \quad \cdots \cdots \quad (20\text{--}40)$$

This is satisfied by
$$E_y = E_{y0}e^{i\omega\left(t - \frac{\mathbf{n}}{c}x\right)}, \quad \cdots \cdots \quad (20\text{--}41)$$

where
$$\mathbf{n}^2 = K - i\frac{4\pi\sigma}{\omega}. \quad \cdots \cdots \quad (20\text{--}42)$$

(20–41) is of the same form as (20–13), which applies to any absorbing medium whose extinction coefficient is given by

$$\mathbf{n}^2 = n^2(1 - i\varkappa)^2. \quad \cdots \cdots \quad (20\text{--}43)$$

Equating the real parts and the imaginary parts in (20–42) and (20–43), one obtains

$$n^2(1-\varkappa^2)=K \qquad \cdots \cdots \quad (20\text{–}44)$$

and

$$n^2\varkappa= \frac{2\pi\sigma}{\omega} =\sigma T= \frac{\sigma\lambda}{c}, \qquad \cdots \cdots \quad (20\text{–}45)$$

where T is the period of the light and λ its wavelength in a vacuum. On eliminating $\varkappa$ one has

$$n^2= \frac{K+\sqrt{K^2+4\sigma^2T^2}}{2}. \qquad \cdots \cdots \quad (20\text{–}46)$$

Except for electromagnetic waves of very low frequency, the observed values of n and $\varkappa$ do not agree with the values calculated from these equations. The above theory is obviously concerned with the general absorption exhibited by metals, and does not deal with the selective absorption which they also exhibit. The fact that the experimental results agree fairly well with the above theory for long wavelengths indicates that the selectively absorbed frequencies are confined to the higher (e.g. optical) frequencies. As for dielectrics, it is necessary, for a more complete theory, to consider the structure of the medium.

20–16. The Dispersion of Metals

It is assumed that metals possess free electrons which when in motion give the conduction current, and that they also have bound charges as possessed by dielectrics. Suppose, then, that there are N atoms per unit volume and f_e free electrons per atom. When an electric field E is applied, each free electron is given an acceleration Ee/m. Hence a drift is superposed on the random motion of the free electrons which is assumed to exist in the absence of a field. If the free electrons move under the influence of the field for time t, they attain a velocity of Eet/m, but collisions between the free electrons and the atoms quickly destroy this drift and the collisions increase the random (thermal) motion. It is in this way that energy is dissipated. At any instant the average velocity of the electrons depends on the average time between collisions. If the average velocity is $Ee\tau/m$, τ is the *relaxation time* and the current is $(Nf_e e)(Ee\tau/m)$ $=Nf_e e^2\tau E/m$. Hence the conductivity is given by

$$\sigma= \frac{\text{current}}{\text{field}} = \frac{Nf_e e^2\tau}{m}. \qquad \cdots \cdots \quad (20\text{–}47)$$

If the field E is due to an incident electromagnetic wave of period T, one would expect (20–47) to hold only if $T\gg\tau$.

The effect of the free electrons can be included in the dispersion formula simply by assuming that they correspond to electrons whose natural frequency is zero. This gives one extra term in equation (20–23). It is also assumed that the field within the metal is E and not $E+(4\pi/3)P$, so that ω_j' reduces to ω_j and (20–23) gives

$$n^2-1= \frac{4\pi Ne^2}{m} \left[\frac{f_e}{-\omega^2+ir_e\omega} + \sum_j \frac{f_j}{\omega_j^2-\omega^2+ir_j\omega} \right]. \qquad (20\text{–}48)$$

Suppose the frequency is low so that $\omega \ll r_e$. If the effect of the bound electrons can be neglected, one then has

$$\mathbf{n}^2 - 1 = \frac{4\pi N e^2 f_e}{imr_e\omega}. \qquad \ldots \ldots \quad (20\text{--}49)$$

Also, if the effect of the bound electrons is neglected, one has $K=1$. (20-42) gives

$$\mathbf{n}^2 = 1 - i\frac{4\pi\sigma}{\omega}. \qquad \ldots \ldots \quad (20\text{--}50)$$

(20-49) and (20-50) give

$$r_e = \frac{Ne^2 f_e}{m\sigma} \qquad \ldots \ldots \quad (20\text{--}51)$$

or, from (20-47),

$$r_e = \frac{1}{\tau}. \qquad \ldots \ldots \quad (20\text{--}52)$$

Suppose now that the frequency is sufficiently high to write $r_e \ll \omega$. This corresponds to a very small dissipation of energy by the free electrons associated with the fact that the time between collisions is much larger than the period of the wave. If the effect of the bound electrons can again be neglected, (20-48) gives

$$\mathbf{n}^2 = 1 - \frac{4\pi N e^2 f_e}{m\omega^2}. \qquad \ldots \ldots \quad (20\text{--}53)$$

This equation indicates that there is a transition wavelength for which $\mathbf{n}=0$. For shorter wavelengths $\mathbf{n}$ is real so that there is no absorption and n is less than unity. For longer wavelengths $\mathbf{n}$ is purely imaginary so that no periodic wave can be propagated in the metal. Thus when the wave strikes the metal the refracted disturbance dies away exponentially and there is almost total reflection for all angles of incidence. The reflection coefficient for normal incidence changes suddenly from almost zero to almost unity at the transition wavelength. Although a transition of this extreme nature does not occur in practice, a very sudden change has been observed with some metals.

In general it is found that if one neglects the terms corresponding to the bound electrons, the absorption given by (20-48) is smaller than the observed value. It is also found that the variation of $\varkappa$ with temperature does not correspond to the temperature coefficient of σ. It must be concluded that the absorption of many metals is associated with bound electrons as well as free electrons, i.e. that the metals absorb selectively as well as generally. This is obvious anyway if they are markedly coloured.

The experimental results give a qualitative agreement with the theory given above but it is only in terms of the quantum theory that one can give a satisfactory account of the optical properties of metals. In particular, the above theory is not able to predict the natural frequencies of the bound electrons. In the infra-red region the effect of the bound electrons may be neglected, but even here the above theory gives only a qualitative agreement with observation.

CHAPTER XXI

REFLECTION AND REFRACTION

21-1. Boundary Conditions

WHEN an electromagnetic wave strikes the boundary between two media, there are reflected and refracted disturbances. The total electromagnetic field in the first medium therefore includes both the incident and the reflected waves. Now it is known from electromagnetic theory that at any boundary separating two media the tangential components of $\mathbf{E}$ and $\mathbf{H}$ and the normal components of $\mathbf{D}$ and $\mathbf{B}$ are continuous. These boundary conditions determine the reflected and refracted disturbances. At optical frequencies all materials can be regarded as non-magnetic so that $\mu=1$ and $\mathbf{B}=\mathbf{H}$. For isotropic media $\mathbf{D}=K\mathbf{E}$. Thus at an interface E_t, H_t, KE_n, and H_n, are continuous.

It will be assumed that the plane boundary separating the two media occupies the xy plane. Thus if $\mathbf{E}_1$ and $\mathbf{H}_1$, $\mathbf{E}_2$ and $\mathbf{H}_2$, and $\mathbf{E}_3$ and $\mathbf{H}_3$, represent the incident, reflected, and refracted disturbances respectively, the boundary conditions give

$$E_{1x}+E_{2x}=E_{3x}, \quad \ldots \ldots \ldots \text{(21-1)}$$

$$E_{1y}+E_{2y}=E_{3y}, \quad \ldots \ldots \ldots \text{(21-2)}$$

$$H_{1x}+H_{2x}=H_{3x}, \quad \ldots \ldots \ldots \text{(21-3)}$$

$$H_{1y}+H_{2y}=H_{3y}, \quad \ldots \ldots \ldots \text{(21-4)}$$

$$KE_{1z}+KE_{2z}=K'E_{3z}, \quad \ldots \ldots \ldots \text{(21-5)}$$

$$H_{1z}+H_{2z}=H_{3z}, \quad \ldots \ldots \ldots \text{(21-6)}$$

where K and K' are the dielectric constants for the first and second media respectively. These conditions supply only four new independent equations since the last two conditions can be deduced from the first four using Maxwell's equations.

21-2. Reflection and Refraction by Transparent Isotropic Dielectrics

It will be assumed that the incident disturbance is a monochromatic plane polarized plane wave. The boundary between media whose dielectric constants are K and K' is taken as the xy plane and the incident ray is assumed to be in the xz plane, the z-axis being directed into the first medium. The angles of incidence, reflection, and refraction, are denoted by I_1, I_2, and I_3, respectively. One can then write, for the y components of the electric vectors,

$$E_{1y}=A_{1y}e^{i\{\omega_1 t-k_1(l_1 x+m_1 y+n_1 z)\}}, \quad \ldots \ldots \text{(21-7)}$$

$$E_{2y}=A_{2y}e^{i\{\omega_2 t-k_2(l_2 x+m_2 y+n_2 z)\}}, \quad \ldots \ldots \text{(21-8)}$$

$$E_{3y}=A_{3y}e^{i\{\omega_3 t-k_3(l_3 x+m_3 y+n_3 z)\}}, \quad \ldots \ldots \text{(21-9)}$$

where A_1, A_2, and A_3, are used instead of E_{10}, E_{20}, and E_{30}, for the amplitudes at the surface in order to reduce the number of suffixes. (With absorbing media the E's would require suffixes $z=0$.) If A_1 is assumed to be real and positive, a real and negative value of A_2 or A_3 will indicate a phase change of π at the boundary, and a complex value will indicate a phase change other than π. Since the incident ray is in the xz plane as defined above,

$$l_1=\sin I_1, \qquad m_1=0, \qquad n_1=-\cos I_1. \qquad . \quad . \quad (21\text{--}10)$$

Now at the boundary (that is, at $z=0$) the condition (21–2) must be satisfied for all values of x, y, and t. Hence one must have the same coefficients of x, y, and t, in the exponentials of (21–7), (21–8), and (21–9). On equating the coefficients of t one has

$$\omega_1=\omega_2=\omega_3, \quad . \quad . \quad . \quad . \quad . \quad . \quad (21\text{--}11)$$

which shows that the incident, reflected, and refracted disturbances have the same frequency. The numerical suffixes can therefore be omitted. Since the incident and reflected disturbances are in the same medium (and therefore have the same velocity) it also follows that

$$k_1=k_2=k \text{ (say).} \quad . \quad . \quad . \quad . \quad . \quad (21\text{--}12)$$

Again, if the velocities in the first and second media are c and c' respectively, one has $\omega=kc=k'c'$ where k' is now written for k_3.

$$\therefore \quad \frac{k'}{k}=\frac{c}{c'}=\frac{n'}{n}, \quad . \quad . \quad . \quad . \quad . \quad (21\text{--}13)$$

where n and n' are the refractive indices of the media. On equating coefficients of y in (21–7), (21–8), and (21–9), one has, in view of (21–10),

$$m_2=m_3=0. \quad . \quad . \quad . \quad . \quad . \quad . \quad (21\text{--}14)$$

This confirms one of the classical laws of reflection and refraction: the reflected and refracted rays lie in the plane of incidence. One can therefore represent the rays on a plane figure (Fig. 21–1) and write

$$\left.\begin{array}{l} l_2=\sin I_2 \quad l_3=\sin I_3, \\ n_2=\cos I_2 \quad n_3=-\cos I_3. \end{array}\right\} \quad . \quad . \quad . \quad (21\text{--}15)$$

Equating coefficients of x in (21–7), (21–8), and (21–9), gives

$$\sin I_1=\sin I_2=\sin I \text{ (say)} \quad . \quad . \quad . \quad (21\text{--}16)$$

and $$k \sin I_1=k' \sin I_3=k' \sin I' \text{ (say)} \quad . \quad . \quad (21\text{--}17)$$

or $$n \sin I=n' \sin I', \quad . \quad . \quad . \quad . \quad . \quad (21\text{--}18)$$

which is Snell's law.

The above results would follow from any self-consistent wave theory and do not depend on the particular boundary conditions given in §21–1. Whatever boundary conditions one has, the relationship between E_1, E_2, and E_3, must be independent of x, y, and t, and the above results must follow. A far more important test of the theory is made when it is used to calculate the intensities and states of polarization of the reflected and refracted disturbances.

Whatever the direction of the electric vector of the incident beam, it can be resolved into components in and perpendicular to the plane of incidence. Since the angle of incidence is specified, the disturbance is completely determined by specifying these *two* components. Hence these are used instead of the *three* components parallel to the co-ordinate axes. The latter must, however, be introduced in order to apply the boundary conditions. The components of E_1 parallel to and perpendicular to the plane of incidence are denoted by E_{1l} and E_{1r} respectively (the initial letters being unsatisfactory suffixes) and the components of E_2 and E_3 are similarly represented. Obviously E_r is parallel to the y-axis in each case but it is also necessary to specify the directions in which E_r and E_l are positive. The obvious choice for the perpendicular component is to

Fig. 21-1.   Reflection and refraction at a plane surface.

Fig. 21-2. Definition of the *l*-directions.

make it positive when in the positive direction of y so that $E_{1r} \equiv E_{1y}$, $E_{2r} \equiv E_{2y}$, and $E_{3r} \equiv E_{3y}$. The directions in which E_{1l}, E_{2l}, and E_{3l} are positive are shown in Fig. 21-2. Thus for the incident disturbance one has

$$\left. \begin{array}{l} E_{1l} = A_{1l}e^{i\{\omega t - k(x \sin I - z \cos I)\}}, \\ E_{1r} = A_{1r}e^{i\{\omega t - k(x \sin I - z \cos I)\}}, \end{array} \right\} \quad \cdots \quad (21\text{--}19)$$

with similar expressions for E_{2l}, E_{2r}, E_{3l}, and E_{3r}. The boundary condition (21-2) gives, at $z=0$,

$$E_{1r} + E_{2r} = E_{3r} \quad \cdots \cdots \quad (21\text{--}20)$$

and (21-3) gives

$$-H_{1l} \cos I + H_{2l} \cos I = -H_{3l} \cos I'. \quad \cdots \quad (21\text{--}21)$$

Now it follows from equation (19-18) (page 433) that $H_{1l} = -\sqrt{K}E_{1r}$, $H_{2l} = -\sqrt{K}E_{2r}$, and $H_{3l} = -\sqrt{K'}E_{3r}$, where K and K' are the dielectric constants of the first and second media, the negative signs being due to the orientation of the positive l-directions. Hence (21-21) gives

$$(E_{1r} - E_{2r}) n \cos I = E_{3r} n' \cos I' \quad \cdots \quad (21\text{--}22)$$

since $n = \sqrt{K}$ and $n' = \sqrt{K'}$.

The boundary condition (21-1) gives

$$(E_{1l} - E_{2l}) \cos I = E_{3l} \cos I' \quad \cdots \cdots \quad (21\text{--}23)$$

and (21-4) gives

$$H_{1r} + H_{2r} = H_{3r}.$$

But $H_{1r}=\sqrt{K}E_{1l}$, $H_{2r}=\sqrt{K}E_{2l}$, and $H_{3r}=\sqrt{K'}E_{3l}$, so that one has

$$(E_{1l}+E_{2l})n=E_{3l}n'. \qquad \ldots \ldots \quad (21\text{–}24)$$

Now in the expressions (21–19) for E_1, and in the corresponding expressions for E_2 and E_3, one has an exponential factor and all these factors are equal at $z=0$. Hence in (21–20), (21–22), (21–23), and (21–24), one may replace E's by A's to give relationships between the amplitudes.

Division of (21–23) by (21–24) gives

$$\frac{(A_{1l}-A_{2l})\cos I}{(A_{1l}+A_{2l})n}=\frac{\cos I'}{n'}$$

or, using Snell's law,

$$(A_{1l}-A_{2l})\sin I \cos I=(A_{1l}+A_{2l})\sin I' \cos I'.$$

$$\therefore \quad A_{2l}=A_{1l}\frac{\sin 2\,I-\sin 2\,I'}{\sin 2\,I+\sin 2\,I'}, \quad \ldots \ldots \quad (21\text{–}25)$$

or $$A_{2l}=A_{1l}\frac{\tan (I-I')}{\tan (I+I')}. \qquad \ldots \ldots \quad (21\text{–}26)$$

Division of (21–22) by (21–20) gives

$$\frac{(A_{1r}-A_{2r})n\cos I}{(A_{1r}+A_{2r})}=n'\cos I'$$

or, using Snell's law,

$$A_{2r}\left(\frac{\sin I'}{\cos I'}+\frac{\sin I}{\cos I}\right)=A_{1r}\left(\frac{\sin I'}{\cos I'}-\frac{\sin I}{\cos I}\right),$$

$$\therefore \quad A_{2r}(\sin I' \cos I+\cos I' \sin I)=A_{1r}(\sin I' \cos I-\cos I' \sin I)$$

or $$A_{2r}=-A_{1r}\frac{\sin (I-I')}{\sin (I+I')}. \qquad \ldots \ldots \quad (21\text{–}27)$$

From (21–25) and (21–23)

$$A_{3l}\cos I'=A_{1l}\cos I\left(\frac{2\sin 2I'}{\sin 2I+\sin 2I'}\right),$$

$$\therefore \quad A_{3l}=A_{1l}\frac{2\sin I' \cos I}{\sin (I+I')\cos (I-I')}. \qquad \ldots \quad (21\text{–}28)$$

Finally, from (21–20) and (21–27),

$$A_{3r}=A_{1r}\frac{\sin (I+I')-\sin (I-I')}{\sin (I+I')}$$

or $$A_{3r}=A_{1r}\frac{2\sin I' \cos I}{\sin (I+I')}. \qquad \ldots \ldots \quad (21\text{–}29)$$

(21–26), (21–27), (21–28), and (21–29), are known as *Fresnel's equations*; they were first derived by Fresnel from the elastic solid theory.

21-3. Normal Incidence

Fresnel's equations as given above are indeterminate at normal incidence but (21-20), (21-22), (21-23), and (21-24) are easily solved directly. Thus, putting $\cos I = \cos I' = 1$, (21-23) and (21-24) give

$$(A_{1l} + A_{2l})n = (A_{1l} - A_{2l})n',$$

$$\therefore \quad A_{2l} = A_{1l}\frac{n'-n}{n'+n}. \quad \cdots \cdots \quad (21\text{-}30)$$

(21-22) and (21-20) give

$$(A_{1r} - A_{2r})n = (A_{1r} + A_{2r})n',$$

$$\therefore \quad A_{2r} = -A_{1r}\frac{n'-n}{n'+n}. \quad \cdots \cdots \quad (21\text{-}31)$$

(21-30) and (21-23) give

$$A_{3l} = A_{1l}\frac{2n}{n'+n}. \quad \cdots \cdots \quad (21\text{-}32)$$

(21-31) and (21-20) give

$$A_{3r} = A_{1r}\frac{2n}{n'+n}. \quad \cdots \cdots \quad (21\text{-}33)$$

For normal incidence the plane of incidence is indeterminate and at first sight it may be surprising that (21-31) contains a negative sign and (21-30) does not. The explanation is simply that, as defined above, the positive direction of l is reversed on reflection at normal incidence whereas the direction of the y-axis (i.e. of r) is fixed in space.

21-4. Discussion of Results

The equations deduced in the previous two sections give the magnitude and direction of the electric vector in the reflected and refracted disturbances. These are sufficient to specify the disturbances completely since in any wave **E** and **H** are not independent. It is more useful to specify **E** than **H** since it is found that it is the magnitude of **E** which determines the observed intensity (see §21-10).

Whatever the state of polarization of the incident light, **E** can be resolved into components in and perpendicular to the plane of incidence as indicated in Chapter VI. Fresnel's equations then give the components of the reflected and refracted disturbances, and therefore give the intensities and states of polarization of these waves. For example, equation (21-26) shows that A_{2l} is always zero when $I + I' = 90°$, i.e. when the reflected and refracted rays are at right angles. Hence, whatever the state of polarization of the incident light, the reflected disturbance has no component in the plane of incidence—it is plane polarized with **E** perpendicular to that plane. This corresponds to Brewster's law as given in §6-15 if the vibrations associated with the light in Chapter VI correspond to the variations of **E**.

To find the intensity and state of polarization of the reflected and refracted rays, it is necessary to know the amplitudes and phases of the components in and perpendicular to the plane of incidence. If $n'>n$ the expressions for A_2 and A_3 are real. Hence the phases are either 0 or π with respect to that of the incident light and are indicated simply by the signs of the amplitudes. Fig. 21–3 shows the amplitudes for the reflected and refracted disturbances as fractions of the incident amplitudes in the corresponding planes for $n'/n=1\cdot5$. That is, the figure gives the ratios A_{2r}/A_{1r}, A_{2l}/A_{1l}, etc., and corresponds to light incident from air to glass.

The reflection coefficients are the ratios of the intensities of the reflected and incident disturbances and are simply obtained by squaring the ordinates for the A_{2l} and A_{2r} curves. They are shown in Fig. 21–4.

Fig. 21–3. Reflected and refracted amplitudes for $n'/n=1\cdot5$.

Fig. 21–4. Reflected intensities.

It must be remembered that the intensity is defined as the energy in unit time crossing unit area perpendicular to the direction of propagation. It is proportional to the product of the refractive index and the square of the amplitude (see § 19–5) and, since the incident and reflected beams are in the same medium, the ratio of the squares of the amplitudes is equal to the ratio of the intensities. It is also the ratio of the energy fluxes since the two beams have the same cross-section area. On the other hand, when a beam is refracted the cross-section area is increased by a factor ($\cos I'/\cos I$) so that the total energy in the refracted beam is proportional to the intensity multiplied by ($\cos I'/\cos I$). It should be noted that it is the total energy fluxes in the reflected and refracted beams which are complementary—not the intensities nor the squares of the amplitudes (see Fig. 21–3).

Fig. 21–4 shows that the reflecting power at normal incidence is about 4%, and that when it falls to zero at the polarizing angle ($56\cdot3°$) for light having $\mathbf{E}$ in the plane of incidence, it is about 15% for light having $\mathbf{E}$ perpendicular to the plane of incidence. All the incident light is reflected at grazing incidence.

Fig. 21–3 shows that for all angles of incidence there is a phase change of π on reflection for light whose vibration direction is perpendicular to the plane of incidence. On the other hand, E_{2l} is in phase with E_{1l} for angles of incidence less than the polarizing angle and is π out of phase for larger angles of incidence.

In interpreting this result one must be careful to take into account the definition of the positive *l*-direction. This is shown in Fig. 21–2. For light near grazing incidence the positive directions of *l* for the incident and reflected disturbances are roughly parallel as in Fig. 21–5(*a*), and the phase change of π means that, to an observer somewhere along the *x*-axis, the direction of E_l is suddenly reversed on reflection. For light near normal incidence, the positive directions of *l* for the incident and reflected rays are roughly in opposite directions [Fig. 21–5(*b*)], and, for an observer somewhere along the *z*-axis, a zero phase change for E_l really means a reversal of its direction on reflection. Thus there is a sense in which one always has a phase change of π on reflection (see also §21–3). This is important in certain interference experiments (see Chapters VII and VIII).

Fig. 21–5. The *l*-directions near grazing and normal incidence.

If the incident light is unpolarized, it can be resolved into incoherent components of equal amplitude in and perpendicular to the plane of incidence. Fig. 21–4 shows that at normal incidence the reflection coefficients are equal. This must be so because the plane of incidence is indeterminate and there is no real distinction between the components. Hence the reflected and refracted disturbances are unpolarized. The totally reflected light at grazing incidence is also unpolarized. For all other angles of incidence the reflection coefficients for the components are different. For light incident at the polarizing angle the reflected light is plane polarized and the refracted light partially plane polarized. For other angles of incidence both the reflected and refracted beams are partially plane polarized. The *degree of polarization* is defined as $(A^2_{max}-A^2_{min})/$ $(A^2_{max}+A^2_{min})$ where A_{max} and A_{min} are the maximum and minimum amplitude components of the electric vector. It can be calculated from Fresnel's formulae for the reflected and refracted beams.

If the incident light is plane polarized one can again discuss the reflection and refraction of the separate components. For the reflected light Fig. 21–3 shows that, except for normal or grazing incidence, $|A_{2r}/A_{2l}|$ is always greater than $|A_{1r}/A_{1l}|$. This means that the plane of the electric vector is inclined to the plane of incidence at a larger angle in the reflected than in the incident light. For the refracted light $|A_{3r}/A_{3l}|<|A_{1r}/A_{1l}|$ so that the plane of vibration is rotated towards the plane of incidence.

Generally speaking, the results predicted by the theory are found to be in very close agreement with the experimental results. (Methods of determining the state of polarization of a beam of light are discussed in Chapters XXII and XXIII.) In practice, light reflected at the polarizing angle is found to be elliptically polarized, although the ellipse is a very thin one. Measurements on freshly formed liquid surfaces show that the ellipse is made more slender when the surfaces are cleaner. The residual ellipticity is associated with the arrangement of the molecules in the surface film.

21-5. Total Internal Reflection

Except for the reference to Brewster's law, the discussion of the previous section was concerned only with the case $n' > n$. When $n' < n$ one has the well known phenomenon of total internal reflection for angles of incidence greater than the critical angle.

For angles of incidence less than the critical angle Fig. 21-6 shows the amplitudes of the reflected components as fractions of the incident amplitudes for $n/n' = 1 \cdot 5$. Fig. 21-7 shows the reflection coefficients. At normal incidence the reflection coefficients for both components are 4%—the same as for light incident on the same boundary from the other side. The polarizing angle (33·7°) is simply the complement of that for light incident from the less dense side of the boundary, and is also such that the ratio of their sines is 1·5. That is, if the angle of incidence

Fig. 21-6. Internally reflected
amplitudes for $n/n' = 1 \cdot 5$.

Fig. 21-7. Reflected intensities
for $n/n' = 1 \cdot 5$.

for light in one direction is the polarizing angle and the directions of the incident and refracted rays are reversed, the new angle of incidence is the polarizing angle for light in the reverse direction. This follows at once from the original statement of Brewster's law.

For angles of incidence greater than the critical angle (41·8°), the sine of the angle of refraction as given by Snell's law is greater than unity. One has

$$\sin I' = \left(\frac{n}{n'}\right) \sin I.$$

$$\therefore \quad \cos I' = \sqrt{1 - (n/n')^2 \sin^2 I}$$

$$= i\sqrt{(n/n')^2 \sin^2 I - 1}. \quad . \quad . \quad . \quad (21\text{--}34)$$

Using this value of $\cos I'$, equation (21-27) gives, for the *reflected* light,

$$A_{2r} = -A_{1r} \frac{i \sin I \sqrt{(n/n')^2 \sin^2 I - 1} - \cos I\,(n/n')\sin I}{i \sin I \sqrt{(n/n')^2 \sin^2 I - 1} + \cos I\,(n/n')\sin I}$$

$$= A_{1r} \frac{(n/n') \cos I - i\sqrt{(n/n')^2 \sin^2 I - 1}}{(n/n') \cos I + i\sqrt{(n/n')^2 \sin^2 I - 1}}.$$

Now $\dfrac{a-ib}{a+ib}=e^{-i\delta}$, where $\tan\dfrac{\delta}{2}=\dfrac{b}{a}$. Hence one may write

$$A_{2r}=A_{1r}e^{-i\delta_r} \qquad . \quad . \quad . \quad . \quad . \quad . \quad (21\text{--}35)$$

or $$E_{2r}=A_{1r}e^{i\{\omega t-k(x\,\sin\,I+z\,\cos\,I)-\delta_r\}}, \qquad . \quad . \quad . \quad (21\text{--}36)$$

where $$\tan\left(\frac{\delta_r}{2}\right)=\frac{\sqrt{(n/n')^2\,\sin^2\,I-1}}{(n/n')\,\cos\,I}. \qquad . \quad . \quad . \quad (21\text{--}37)$$

Similarly, from (21–25),

$$A_{2l}=A_{1l}\,\frac{\sin\,I\,\cos\,I-i(n/n')\,\sin\,I\sqrt{(n/n')^2\,\sin^2\,I-1}}{\sin\,I\,\cos\,I+i(n/n')\,\sin\,I\sqrt{(n/n')^2\,\sin^2\,I-1}}$$

$$=A_{1l}\,\frac{\cos\,I-i(n/n')\sqrt{(n/n')^2\,\sin^2\,I-1}}{\cos\,I+i(n/n')\sqrt{(n/n')^2\,\sin^2\,I-1}}$$

or $$E_{2l}=A_{1l}e^{i\{\omega t-k(x\,\sin\,I+z\,\cos\,I)-\delta_l\}}, \qquad . \quad . \quad . \quad (21\text{--}38)$$

where $$\tan\left(\frac{\delta_l}{2}\right)=\frac{(n/n')\sqrt{(n/n')^2\,\sin^2\,I-1}}{\cos\,I}. \qquad . \quad . \quad (21\text{--}39)$$

Thus the components of **E** parallel to and perpendicular to the plane of incidence experience phase retardations of δ_l and δ_r respectively, the amplitudes of the reflected components being equal to those of the incident components. For example, if the incident light is plane polarized, the incident components are in phase and the totally reflected components are out of phase. Hence the reflected light is elliptically polarized, the phase difference (δ) between the components being given by

$$\tan\left(\frac{\delta}{2}\right)=\tan\left(\frac{\delta_l}{2}-\frac{\delta_r}{2}\right)$$

$$=\frac{\tan\,(\delta_l/2)-\tan\,(\delta_r/2)}{1+\tan\,(\delta_l/2)\tan\,(\delta_r/2)}$$

$$=\frac{\dfrac{[(n/n')^2-1]\sqrt{(n/n')^2\,\sin^2\,I-1}}{(n/n')\,\cos\,I}}{\dfrac{(n/n')\,\cos^2\,I+(n/n')[(n/n')^2\,\sin^2\,I-1]}{(n/n')\,\cos^2\,I}}$$

$$=\frac{\cos\,I\sqrt{(n/n')^2\,\sin^2\,I-1}}{(n/n')\,\sin^2\,I}. \qquad . \quad . \quad . \quad (21\text{--}40)$$

Fig. 21–8 shows the phase changes for the reflected components of internally reflected light for $n/n'=1\cdot5$ (corresponding to internal reflection at a glass-air surface). For angles of incidence less than the critical angle they are 0 or π as indicated by Fig. 21–6, and for total reflection they are given by (21–37) and (21–39). The figure also shows the phase difference δ between the reflected components when the incident components are in phase.

Suppose one has plane polarized light incident on a glass-air surface and that the plane of E is inclined at 45° to the plane of incidence. The components parallel to and perpendicular to the plane of incidence are then equal. Using (21–40) it is found that for $n/n'=1{\cdot}5$ the phase difference between the reflected components is 45° when the angle of incidence is either 53°15′ or 50°14′ (see Fig. 21–8). The reflected light is, of course, elliptically polarized. If there is now a second internal reflection at one of these angles a further 45° phase difference is introduced, so that a total phase difference of 90° is introduced between the two perpendicular components. Since the components have equal amplitudes the light is circularly polarized. *Fresnel's rhomb* produces circularly polarized

Fig. 21–8. Phase changes for internal reflection ($n/n'=1{\cdot}5$).

Fig. 21–9. Fresnel's rhomb.

light in this way (Fig. 21–9). The example illustrated employs glass of index 1·5 and has angles of incidence of 53°15′. Light is incident normally on the first face, the plane of vibration being at 45° to the plane of the diagram.

21–6. Disturbance in the Second Medium

When one has total internal reflection the phase difference between the incident and reflected disturbances is not π. That is to say, there is a resultant field in the first medium at the boundary. It follows that in order to satisfy the boundary conditions there must also be a disturbance in the second medium. The component perpendicular to the plane of incidence is represented by

$$E_{3r}=A_{3r}e^{i\{\omega t-k'(x\,\sin\,I'-z\,\cos\,I')\}}$$

(see 21–19) where, from (21–20) and (21–35),

$$A_{3r}=A_{1r}(1+e^{-i\delta_r})$$

$$=A_{1r}e^{-i(\delta_r/2)}(e^{+i(\delta_r/2)}+e^{-i(\delta_r/2)})$$

$$=2A_{1r}\cos\left(\frac{\delta_r}{2}\right)e^{-i(\delta_r/2)}.$$

Substituting for $k'\sin I'$ from (21–17) and for $\cos I'$ from (21–34), one has

$$E_{3r}=2A_{1r}\cos\left(\frac{\delta_r}{2}\right)e^{-i(\delta_r/2)}e^{i\{\omega t-kx\,\sin\,I+k'\,zi\sqrt{(n/n')^2\,\sin^2\,I-1}\}}$$

$$=2A_{1r}\cos\left(\frac{\delta_r}{2}\right)e^{-k'z\sqrt{(n/n')^2\,\sin^2\,I-1}}e^{i\{\omega t-kx\,\sin\,I-(\delta_r/2)\}}.\quad(21\text{–}41)$$

Thus E_{3r} is not periodic in z; the expression does not represent a wave whose direction of propagation has a component in the z-direction. The amplitude of E_{3r} decreases exponentially with increasing distance beyond the boundary and becomes negligibly small after a distance of a few wavelengths. It follows that, although there is a finite disturbance beyond the boundary, no energy is conveyed away from the surface and none is absorbed since the media are transparent. It is all reflected as indicated by the equations given above for the reflected wave.

It has been shown both theoretically and experimentally that if one has only a very thin film of the low-index medium followed by a high-index medium, it is possible for light to be propagated across the gap into the third medium, even if the angle of incidence at the first boundary exceeds the critical angle. The effect can be demonstrated with the simple prism system shown in Fig. 21–10. P_1 is an ordinary right-angled isosceles prism and P_2 is a prism whose hypotenuse face has a very shallow convex surface. On placing the prisms in contact, it is found that light is transmitted across the narrow gap surrounding the actual point of contact. One refers to this as *frustrated total reflection*. The transmitted light gets weaker as the thickness of the film increases, being negligible if the air gap exceeds a few wavelengths. If both hypotenuse faces are plane and

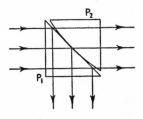

Fig. 21–10. Demonstration of frustrated total reflection.

can be kept accurately parallel and brought very close together, one can obtain uniform transmitted and reflected beams of any desired relative intensity. Since there is no absorption one has a very efficient beam splitter. A convenient method of spacing the prisms is to coat one with a low-index solid film of the necessary thickness and to place the other in contact with it. Non-absorbing, semi-reflecting films of this type have been used in the production of interference filters (see § 9–16).

21–7. Reflection by an Absorbing Medium

It was shown in § 20–10 that the expression representing a disturbance in an absorbing medium is formally the same as for a transparent medium, the refractive index being complex. The results of §§ 21–2 and 21–3 can therefore be used for light incident on an absorbing medium. It will be assumed that the first medium is air (or, more strictly, a vacuum) so that $n=1$. Then, if $\mathbf{n}$ is the complex index of the second medium, one can write

$$E_{1r}=A_{1r}e^{i\omega\{t-\frac{1}{c}(x\sin I-z\cos I)\}}, \quad \ldots \ldots \quad (21\text{--}42)$$

$$E_{2r}=A_{2r}e^{i\omega\{t-\frac{1}{c}(x\sin I+z\cos I)\}}, \quad \ldots \ldots \quad (21\text{--}43)$$

$$E_{3r}=A_{3r}e^{i\omega\{t-\frac{1}{c}(x\sin I'-z\cos I')\}}. \quad \ldots \ldots \quad (21\text{--}44)$$

In order to satisfy the boundary condition (21–20) one must have

$$\sin I'=\frac{\sin I}{\mathbf{n}} \quad \ldots \ldots \ldots \quad (21\text{--}45)$$

and, except for normal incidence, I' is complex. A_{2r} and A_{3r} are also complex, and are given by the expressions in §§ 21–2 and 21–3 where I' is as given above. One has

$$\cos I' = \frac{\sqrt{n^2 - \sin^2 I}}{n} \qquad \dots \dots \quad (21\text{–}46)$$

and

$$\tan I' = \frac{\sin I}{\sqrt{n^2 - \sin^2 I}}. \qquad \dots \dots \quad (21\text{–}47)$$

The reflection coefficient or reflecting power (R) is the ratio of the reflected to the incident intensity and, for normal incidence, it follows at once from equation (21–31) on putting $n=1$, $n'=\mathbf{n}$. A_{2r} is complex and the reflected intensity is the product of A_{2r} with its conjugate so that

$$R = \frac{A_{2r}\bar{A}_{2r}}{A^2{}_{1r}} = \frac{\mathbf{n}-1}{\mathbf{n}+1} \cdot \frac{\bar{\mathbf{n}}-1}{\bar{\mathbf{n}}+1}, \qquad \dots \dots \quad (21\text{–}48)$$

$$\therefore \quad R = \frac{(n-1)^2 + n^2 \varkappa^2}{(n+1)^2 + n^2 \varkappa^2}. \qquad \dots \dots \quad (21\text{–}49)$$

For oblique incidence R depends, of course, on the polarization of the incident beam. R_r and R_l can be deduced from the expressions given in § 21–2 but the calculations are rather tedious. It can be shown that when $n^2 + n^2 \varkappa^2 \gg 1$ one has

$$R_r = \frac{(n - \cos I)^2 + n^2 \varkappa^2}{(n + \cos I)^2 + n^2 \varkappa^2}, \qquad \dots \dots \quad (21\text{–}50)$$

$$R_l = \frac{\left(n - \dfrac{1}{\cos I}\right)^2 + n^2 \varkappa^2}{\left(n + \dfrac{1}{\cos I}\right)^2 + n^2 \varkappa^2}. \qquad \dots \dots \quad (21\text{–}51)$$

Fig. 21–11 shows, qualitatively, the form of the variation of R_r and R_l with angle of incidence. Equations (21–49), (21–50), and (21–51), show that a high reflecting power is associated with strong absorption. It will be seen that when the absorption is very strong the reflecting power approaches unity. It has already been pointed out in § 20–1 that a body selectively absorbs those wavelengths which it selectively reflects, and that metals reflect and absorb strongly over a wide range of wavelengths. It was also pointed out that it is only when the selective absorption is very strong that the selective reflection determines the colour (surface colour). For less powerful absorption even the maximum reflection coefficient is relatively small and the colour observed is body colour.

Fig. 21–11. Reflection coefficients for an absorbing medium.

The phenomenon of selective reflection has been used as a method of isolating the wavelengths concerned. For example, in their famous determinations of emissivities Hagens and Rubens made use of the fact that after three reflections by fluorite crystals the thermal radiation is reduced to a narrow band of wavelengths in the region of $25 \cdot 5\mu$. Radiations isolated in this way are referred to as the *residual rays* or *reststrahlen*.

The propagation of light in metals was discussed in § 20–15, the metal being regarded simply as a continuous medium of finite electrical conductivity. It follows from equations (20–45) and (20–46) that, if $K \ll \sigma T$, $n = \sqrt{\sigma T}$ and $\varkappa = 1$. If $\sigma T \gg 1$ (21–49) gives, for the reflecting power at normal incidence,

$$R = 1 - \frac{2}{\sqrt{\sigma T}} = 1 - \sqrt{\frac{c}{\sigma \lambda}}. \qquad \dots \dots \quad (21\text{–}52)$$

Since the reflecting powers of metals are very high, direct measurements of R do not give a sufficiently accurate method of investigating the variations of R from metal to metal, nor of the variation of R with temperature. In consequence, it is better to measure the emissivity E which, according to Kirchhoff's law, is given by

$$E = 1 - R.$$

Experiments by Hagens and Rubens and subsequent workers have given results in fairly good agreement with (21–52) for wavelengths greater than about 4μ. The results show a variation of R with temperature which agrees fairly well with that indicated by the variation of the conductivity.

For wavelengths in the visible region the experimental values of R differ widely from those given by (21–52). In this region metals show selective reflection and absorption so that they must have bound as well as free electrons. (See §§ 20–15 and 20–16.)

21–8. The Reflected Disturbance

For all metals the reflection coefficients for disturbances (or components) whose electric vector is in or perpendicular to the plane of incidence are of the form illustrated in Fig. 21–11. The curves show a resemblance to those for transparent media but there is one important difference: for metals R falls to a minimum for a particular angle of incidence but does not fall to zero as it does for dielectrics. Both components undergo a change of phase on reflection and the difference (δ) between these phase changes varies from 180° at normal incidence to zero at grazing incidence. Whereas for transparent media δ changes from 180° to zero at the polarizing angle, the value of δ for a metal changes gradually. If, as usual, $n^2(1 + \varkappa^2) \gg 1$, δ is almost exactly 90° when R_l is a minimum. δ is exactly 90° at the so-called *principal angle of incidence* (I_p).

It will be seen that if plane polarized light is incident on a metal the reflected components are, in general, unequal and out of phase—one has elliptically polarized reflected light. In particular, suppose plane polarized light is incident at the principal angle of incidence and that its electric vector is at 45° to the plane of incidence. The reflected components will be unequal and will be 90° out of phase. Hence the reflected light will be elliptically polarized and one of the axes of the ellipse will be in the plane of incidence. Since the incident light has equal components in and perpendicular to the plane of incidence, the ratio of the axes is simply $|A_{2l}| / |A_{2r}|$ (i.e. $\sqrt{R_l / R_r}$). In general, to analyse elliptically polarized light the phase difference is compensated to give plane polarized light, and the plane of vibration of this light is determined by means of an analyser (see § 22–16). In the particular case under discussion here the compensation can be effected by a quarter-wave plate and the angle between the plane of incidence and the plane perpendicular to the plane of vibration of the resulting plane polarized light is known as the *principal azimuth* (ψ_p).* In Fig. 21–12, AB represents the vibration direction of the plane polarized light and it will be seen that tan ψ_p is the ratio of the axes of the ellipse, i.e. tan $\psi_p = \sqrt{R_l/R_r}$.

If circularly polarized light (from a Fresnel rhomb, for example) is incident at the principal angle of incidence, the 90° phase difference between the components in and perpendicular to the plane of incidence becomes zero (or 180°) after reflection. Hence the reflected light is plane polarized and the angle between the plane of incidence and the plane perpendicular to the electric vector is the principal azimuth.

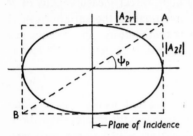

Fig. 21–12. The principal azimuth.

If the principal angle of incidence and the principal azimuth are known, n and $\varkappa$ can be calculated as shown below, and hence the normal reflecting power can be found from (21–49). This can then be compared with the experimental value.

To find n and $\varkappa$ from I_p and ψ_p one proceeds as follows. If a is the ratio of the amplitudes of the reflected components and δ is their phase difference one has, in general,

$$ae^{i\delta} = \frac{A_{2l}}{A_{2r}}. \qquad \ldots \ldots \ldots \quad (21\text{–}53)$$

If the incident light has its electric vector at 45° to the plane of incidence $A_{1l} = A_{1r}$, and if the angle of incidence is I_p, $\delta = 90°$ and $e^{i\delta} = i$. Hence, using (21–26) and (21–27), one has

$$ia = -\frac{\cos{(I_p + I')}}{\cos{(I_p - I')}}$$

$$= \frac{\tan I_p \tan I' - 1}{\tan I_p \tan I' + 1}.$$

$$\therefore \quad \frac{1 + ia}{1 - ia} = \tan I_p \tan I'$$

or, using (21–47) and assuming that $n^2 + n^2\varkappa^2 \gg \sin^2 I_p$, one has

$$\frac{1 + ia}{1 - ia} = \frac{\tan I_p \sin I_p}{n}.$$

* The reason for this rather clumsy definition is that the term *plane of polarization* was at one time used for the plane perpendicular to the plane of the electric vector and ψ_p was naturally defined as the angle between the plane of polarization and the plane of incidence. It is convenient to retain this angle rather than to use the complementary angle between the plane of incidence and the plane of the electric vector itself.

As has already been shown (Fig. 21–12),

$$a = \tan \psi_p.$$

$$\therefore \quad \tan I_p \sin I_p = \mathbf{n} \frac{1 + i \tan \psi_p}{1 - i \tan \psi_p}$$

$$= \mathbf{n} \frac{\cos \psi_p + i \sin \psi_p}{\cos \psi_p - i \sin \psi_p}$$

$$= \mathbf{n} e^{2i\psi_p}$$

$$= n(1 - i\varkappa)(\cos 2\psi_p + i \sin 2\psi_p).$$

$$\therefore \quad \tan I_p \sin I_p = (n \cos 2\psi_p + n\varkappa \sin 2\psi_p)$$

$$+ i \, (n \sin 2\psi_p - n\varkappa \cos 2\psi_p). \quad . \quad (21\text{–}54)$$

Now the left-hand side of (21–54) is real so that one may equate the imaginary part of the right-hand side to zero. This gives

$$\varkappa = \tan 2\psi_p. \quad \cdot \quad \cdot \quad \cdot \quad \cdot \quad \cdot \quad \cdot \quad (21\text{–}55)$$

On equating the real parts of (21–54) and using this value of $\varkappa$, one has

$$\tan I_p \sin I_p = n \cos 2\psi_p + n \sin 2\psi_p \tan 2\psi_p$$

$$= \frac{n}{\cos 2\psi_p} (\cos^2 2\psi_p + \sin^2 2\psi_p),$$

or

$$n = \tan I_p \sin I_p \cos 2\psi_p. \quad \cdot \quad \cdot \quad \cdot \quad (21\text{–}56)$$

As pointed out above, the values of n and $\varkappa$ given by these equations can be used to calculate the normal reflecting power. The values of R calculated in this way from the observed values of I_p and ψ_p give fairly good agreement with the values of R observed directly. An important difficulty encountered in this work is that the properties of a metal surface depend upon the method used to polish it since this affects the structure of the surface films. It is also very important to ensure that the surface is clean. By using thin films and thin prisms, direct measurements of n and $\varkappa$ have been made but here one encounters the additional difficulty that the properties of thin films differ from those of the metal in bulk. The results of these investigations will not be discussed in detail but it is interesting to note that for some metals n is less than unity.

21–9. The Refracted Disturbance

Fig. 21–13 represents the refraction of a plane wave at a surface separating an absorbing medium and air (or more strictly, a vacuum). When the edge B of the wave reaches the boundary the edge A has already travelled into the medium. Hence the amplitude decreases across the wavefront from B to A. It can be shown that, in a direction normal to the wavefront, a wave of this type is propagated with a wave velocity which depends upon the rate at which the amplitude decreases across the wave. That is, the wave velocity depends on the angle between the surface of constant phase (the wavefront) and the surfaces of constant amplitude (which are parallel to the refracting surface). Hence the wave velocity in the medium depends upon the angle of incidence. It differs in

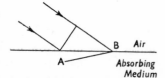

Fig. 21–13. Refraction into an absorbing medium.

magnitude and direction from the ray velocity, and the propagation of the wave resembles that of an extraordinary wave in a crystal (see Chapter XXII). Snell's law is not obeyed, and the ratio of the sines of I' and I is not equal to the real part of **n**.

To show that the velocity of the refracted wave depends upon the angle of incidence one proceeds as follows. According to equations (21–44), (21–45), and (21–46), the perpendicular component of the refracted disturbance is given by

$$E_{3r} = A_{3r} e^{i\omega \left\{ t - \frac{\mathbf{n}}{c}(x \sin I' - z \cos I') \right\}},$$

where

$$\mathbf{n} \sin I' = \sin I$$

and

$$\mathbf{n} \cos I' = \sqrt{\mathbf{n}^2 - \sin^2 I} = a - ib \text{ (say)}.$$

$$\therefore \quad E_{3r} = A_{3r} e^{\frac{\omega b z}{c}} e^{i\omega \left\{ t - \frac{x \sin I - az}{c} \right\}}.$$

Hence the direction cosines of the normal to the wavefront are

$$\frac{\sin I}{\sqrt{a^2 + \sin^2 I}}, \quad 0, \quad \frac{-a}{\sqrt{a^2 + \sin^2 I}}$$

and the wave velocity is

$$\frac{c}{\sqrt{a^2 + \sin^2 I}}$$

and obviously depends on the angle of incidence.

21–10. Stationary Light Waves

It was shown in §6–12 that when one has wave trains of equal velocity, amplitude, and frequency, travelling in opposite directions, a system of standing

Fig. 21–14. Standing waves—normal incidence.

waves is set up. Now when a beam of light is incident normally on a plane reflecting surface, the incident and reflected disturbances can interfere in this way to give stationary waves. The existence of these stationary light waves was first demonstrated by Wiener in 1890. If the reflecting surface is only partially reflecting, the superposed wave trains have unequal amplitudes and, superposed on the stationary waves, there is a progressive component towards the surface. The present discussion is concerned only with the stationary waves.

The arrangement used by Wiener is illustrated in Fig. 21–14. W represents a plane wave incident on the plane reflecting surface AB. Whatever its direction in the incident light, the electric vector is reversed on reflection if AB is the surface of a dielectric (see § 21–4). This is approximately true if AB is the surface of a highly reflecting metal. In consequence, one has a node at the surface as far as the electric vector is concerned. It can be shown that for the magnetic intensity there is an antinode at the reflecting surface. The figure shows the formation of the nodes and antinodes for the electric intensity. Wiener showed the existence of the nodes and antinodes by placing a very thin photographic film in an inclined position such as PQ. It was found that the film showed a series of fringes corresponding to planes of maximum light intensity. The spacing of the fringes across PQ is obviously increased if the angle between PQ and AB is decreased and this makes it easier to resolve the fringes. It is found

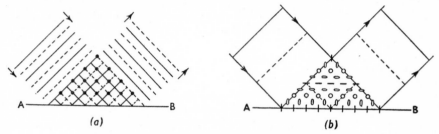

(a)   (b)

Fig. 21–15. Stationary waves with light incident at 45°.

that the blackening of the photographic film is a maximum at the electric antinodes as opposed to the magnetic ones, which indicates that the "effective light disturbance" is determined by the magnitude of the electric intensity associated with the wave.

Drude and Nernst repeated Wiener's experiment with a fluorescent film in place of the photographic film and obtained similar results. They also found that no fluorescence was observed in a very thin film of fluorescent material placed on a silver reflecting surface. This also shows that there is no fluorescence where the total electric intensity is zero.

Fig. 21–15 shows another experiment due to Wiener. In (a) plane polarized light is incident on a reflecting surface AB at an angle of incidence of 45°, the electric vector being perpendicular to the plane of incidence. Although the incident and reflected beams are perpendicular, their electric vectors are parallel and there will be destructive interference in planes parallel to AB. Hence fringes can be observed with an inclined photographic film as in Wiener's first experiment. In the figure crests and troughs (in both the incident and reflected waves) are represented by full and broken lines respectively. A trough is reflected as a crest and a crest as a trough. Destructive interference occurs where an incident crest coincides with a reflected trough and vice versa. If the electric vector is in the plane of incidence as in (b), the vectors for the incident and reflected beams are at right angles. In this case there is no destructive interference, the resultants being circles, ellipses, or straight lines, according to the phase difference as indicated in the figure. No fringes are observed with this arrangement whatever form of detector—photographic emulsion, flourescent screen, or photo-electric cell—is used to examine the light distribution. It is important to notice that the effect of the superposition of the magnetic vectors in the first experiment is represented by the second figure, and that for the second experiment it is represented by the first figure. That is to say, observable fringes are caused by a variation of the amplitude of the electric intensity but not by a variation of the amplitude of the magnetic intensity.

It will be seen that the experiments on standing waves suggest that it is the magnitude of the electric vector rather than that of the magnetic vector which determines the intensity of the observed light. It is often convenient to refer to the oscillatory electric intensity simply as the light vibration.

CHAPTER XXII

THE PROPAGATION OF LIGHT IN CRYSTALS

ALTHOUGH some results from Chapter XIX are used, it is not essential to have a knowledge of the electromagnetic theory of light before reading the present chapter. The chief result assumed is the nature of the wave surface in a crystal. The nature of polarized light is discussed in simple terms in Chapter VI. The vibration direction introduced there is the same as the direction of the electric displacement as indicated by electromagnetic theory.

22–1. Waves in Anisotropic Media

The path of a wave through a medium can be found by applying Huygens' Principle. In its simple form, which can be used when there is no diffraction, this principle states that each point on a wavefront acts as a source of secondary waves and that these are effective only on their forward envelope. It has already been seen that for isotropic media the disturbance from a point source spreads out as a spherical wave so that, from each point on a wavefront, one has spherical secondary waves. The rays (lines of energy flow) are then the wave normals and obey the classical laws of refraction. Huygens' principle can be applied in the same way in order to find the path of a disturbance in an anisotropic medium. When light enters such a medium it is found that there are, in general, two refracted paths. The medium is said to be *doubly refracting* or *birefringent*.

For a uniaxial medium, it was shown in § 19–10 that the disturbance from a point source can spread out as two waves—a sphere and a spheroid—and that each is plane polarized. It will be seen that there can be a disturbance propagated by means of spherical secondary waves as in isotropic media. One speaks of *ordinary* rays and waves since the rays are wave normals and obey the classical laws of refraction when a disturbance enters the anisotropic medium from one which is isotropic. The disturbances that are propagated by the spheroidal secondary waves behave in a rather different manner and one speaks of *extraordinary* waves and rays. In general, the rays are no longer wave normals and do not obey Snell's law of refraction. The refracted extraordinary ray is not, in general, in the plane of incidence.

For biaxial media the situation is different. As shown in § 19–9, there is no spherical sheet in the wave surface expanding from a point source. Consequently there are no spherical secondary waves and therefore, in general, no ordinary rays or waves. Fig. 19–4 showed that even with a biaxial crystal the wave surface has one circular section in each of three mutually perpendicular planes. If light is incident on the crystal from an isotropic medium such that one of these planes is the plane of incidence, one of the refracted disturbances is propagated by waves having a circular section and, in that plane, $\sin I'/\sin I$ is constant. That is, one has an ordinary ray.

The directions of the electric displacement D in the polarized disturbances are as given in §§ 19–9 and 19–10. As has already been pointed out, D and H are not independent when the direction of propagation is specified, so that it is sufficient to specify only **D**. **D** is chosen and is often referred to as the light vibration because, as indicated by Wiener's experiment, it is more directly related to the light intensity as ordinarily observed (see § 21–10).

22–2. Double Refraction in Uniaxial Crystals

Fig. 22–1 shows a plane wave incident normally on the plane interface AB between an isotropic medium, such as air, and a negative uniaxial crystal. An example of the latter is calcite or iceland spar—naturally occurring forms of calcium carbonate. The figure shows a section through the crystal which is normal to the crystal surface and parallel to the optic axis. (A section containing

Fig. 22–1. Double refraction at normal incidence.

the optic axis is called a *principal section.*) The direction of the optic axis (which is a *direction* and not a single line) is indicated by the broken lines. It should be noted that in all these figures the eccentricity of the elliptic section of the wave surface is very much exaggerated. When the wave strikes the interface, each point such as P_1, P_2, and P_3, acts as a source of secondary waves. In the crystal the wave from each of these points takes the form of a sphere inscribed within an oblate spheroid. These touch on the axis of rotation of the latter and this is parallel to the optic axis. For the circular wave section the direction of **D** is perpendicular to the plane of the figure; for the elliptic wave section it is in the plane of the figure. If the incident wave has components of **D** in both these directions, both waves spread out from each point and the two sets of secondary waves give two forward envelopes. These are the ordinary and extraordinary waves W_O and W_E. If the incident wave is plane polarized with the direction of **D** either in or perpendicular to the principal section, there will be only one wave in the crystal—that for which the direction of **D** is the same as that in the incident wave. The other refracted wave will be absent since, in the incident wave, there is no component of **D** in the appropriate direction. If the incident wave is polarized in any other way, or is unpolarized, it will have components in and perpendicular to the principal section, and there will be double refraction. Thus one may say that for each ray such as O_1P_1 incident on the interface there will be two refracted rays—the ordinary ray P_1Q_1 for which **D** is perpendicular to the principal section, and the extraordinary ray P_1R_1 for which **D** is in the principal section. It will be seen that the ordinary ray is normal to the wave and enters the crystal without deviation as would a ray entering an isotropic medium at normal incidence. The extraordinary ray is refracted in the principal section as shown. The ray velocities are proportional to P_1Q_1 and P_1R_1, and the wave velocities are measured along the wave normals and are proportional to P_1Q_1 and P_1S_1. Thus the velocities of the extraordinary ray and wave are greater than those of the ordinary ray and wave. The reverse is true for positive uniaxial crystals in which the spherical sheet of the wave surface encloses the spheroidal sheet. Except for disturbances propagated in directions close to the optic axis, quartz behaves as a positive uniaxial crystal. The properties of quartz will be discussed later.

Fig. 22–2.
Crystal cut perpendicular to the axis.

Two special cases of normal incidence should be mentioned. These are illustrated for negative crystals by Figs 22–2 and 22–3. In the first, light is incident normally on a crystal face cut perpendicular to the optic axis, i.e. the light is travelling along the axis. It will be seen that the two ray velocities are equal and equal to the two wave velocities. There is no double refraction and the O- and E-waves advance together. Figs 22–3(a) and (b) show light incident normally on a crystal face cut parallel to the optic axis. (a) shows a principal section and (b) a section at right angles. It will be seen that, again, neither the O- nor the E-rays are refracted but the waves advance with different speeds. The direction of **D** for each ray is as shown. These follow from the discussions of §§ 19–9 and 19–10 but may alternatively be described, by referring to the so-called *principal planes*, as follows. The principal section that contains the ordinary ray is sometimes called the principal plane of the ordinary ray. The principal plane of the E-ray is similarly defined, i.e. it is the plane containing the E-ray and the optic axis. The direction of **D** for the O-ray is always perpendicular to the principal

Fig. 22–3. Crystal cut parallel to the axis.

plane of the O-ray, whereas for the E-ray **D** is *in* the corresponding principal plane. Since the ordinary wave surface is spherical, the ordinary ray and wave velocities are equal and the same in all directions. This velocity (v_0) is one of the two *principal velocities* for the uniaxial medium (see Chapter XIX). The corresponding principal refractive index, known as the *ordinary index,* is therefore given by

$$n_0 = \frac{\text{velocity of light in a vacuum}}{\text{ordinary wave velocity}}.$$

Along the optic axis the E-wave and ray velocities are equal and equal to the ordinary velocity (see Fig. 22–2). As one moves away from the axis, the velocity of the E-wave becomes less than that of the E-ray. For positive crystals both become smaller than the ordinary velocity, and for negative crystals both become larger than v_0 (see Fig. 22–1). The E-wave and ray velocities again become equal in directions at right angles to the optic axis, reaching a maximum value for negative crystals (Fig. 22–3) and a minimum for positive crystals. Thus for positive crystals the second principal refractive index (the *extraordinary index*) is given by

$$n_E = \frac{\text{velocity of light in a vacuum}}{\text{minimum velocity of E-wave}}$$

and for negative crystals,

$$n_E = \frac{\text{velocity of light in a vacuum}}{\text{maximum velocity of E-wave}}.$$

For sodium light ($\lambda\,5893$) one has, for calcite at $18°$ C., $n_0 = 1·65836$, $n_E = 1·48641$ and for quartz $n_0 = 1·54425$, $n_E = 1·55336$. (For fused quartz, which is isotropic, one has $n = 1·45845$.)

22–3. Plane Waves at Oblique Incidence

Fig. 22–4 shows parallel rays (i.e. a plane wave) incident obliquely on the plane surface of a negative uniaxial crystal. It is assumed that the plane of

Fig. 22–4. Double refraction at oblique incidence.

incidence is a principal section, so that the optic axis lies in the plane of the figure; its direction is indicated by the broken lines. To find the refracted path of the wave one proceeds in the same way as for isotropic media (see § 1–7). The wave W reaches P_1 before it reaches P_2, and, during the time taken for the disturbance to travel from Q to P_2 (assumed, for convenience, to be in air), the secondary waves expand from P_1 into the crystal. One draws the circular section of the O-wave surface with radius $P_1A = QP_2/n_0$, the major axis of the E-wave surface being $P_1B = QP_2/n_E$. The refracted wavefronts W_0 and W_E are then found by drawing, from P_2, a tangent to each sheet of the wave surface. In terms of rays, the ray incident at P_1 is doubly refracted along P_1O (the O-ray) and P_1E (the E-ray), the directions of **D** being as indicated. As before, both refracted rays are present if the incident ray has a component of **D** in the appropriate directions. The special cases of a crystal cut with its surface (i) parallel to and (ii) perpendicular to the optic axis are shown in Figs 22–5 and 22–6 respectively.

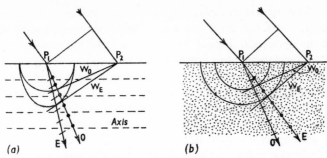

Fig. 22-5. Double refraction with crystal cut parallel to the axis.

In the examples illustrated the optic axis is either in or perpendicular to the plane of incidence, and in each case the E-ray lies in the plane of incidence. When the plane of incidence is not a principal section the extraordinary ray does not lie in the plane of incidence. It will be seen, from above, that Snell's law does not apply to the E-ray.

Fig. 22-6. Double refraction with crystal cut perpendicular to the axis.

22-4. Observation of Double Refraction in Calcite

The fundamental crystal form of calcite is a rhombohedron as shown in Fig. 22-7. Each rhombic face has angles of approximately 78° and 102°. Large

Fig. 22-7.
Calcite crystal.

Fig. 22-8. Double refraction in a calcite crystal.

crystals may be reduced by cleavage to parallelopipeds or rhombohedra containing these angles. It will be seen that there are two diametrically opposite corners (A and B) which are bounded by three obtuse (102°) angles. The direction of the optic axis is such that, passing through A or B, it makes equal angles with all three faces. In the rhombohedral form the diagonal AB is in the direction of the optic axis. Fig. 22–8(*a*) illustrates the double refraction of a ray of unpolarized light incident in a principal section (a parallelogram with angles of about 109° and 71°). Looking along the emergent rays from the right, the principal sections are as indicated in 22–8(*b*).

Suppose that a calcite crystal is placed over a dot on a piece of paper, and that the dot is viewed normally through the crystal. Two images are seen and these are at different apparent depths in the crystal (see Fig. 22–9). If the crystal is now rotated about a vertical axis, one image remains stationary and the other

(*a*) Side view

(*b*) Plan view

Fig. 22–9.
Demonstration of double image.

moves round it. The former is, of course, the ordinary, and the latter the extra-ordinary image.

An interesting experiment with two equal calcite crystals is illustrated by Fig. 22–10. A ray of unpolarized light is incident normally on the first crystal and is doubly refracted. Two plane polarized rays emerge from the crystal with directions of **D** as indicated. If the second crystal is similarly orientated, these beams are further separated, but each passes through the second crystal as a single ray [see Fig. 22–10(*a*)]. This is because a ray incident on a crystal can give rise to two refracted rays only if it has a component of **D** in *each* of the perpendicular directions which correspond to the O- and the E-rays. If the second crystal is rotated 180° to the position shown in (*b*), the two rays are reunited as shown and the emergent ray shows all the properties of unpolarized light. If the second crystal is rotated 90° so that the principal sections of the two crystals are at right angles, the direction of **D** for the ordinary ray emerging from the first crystal is exactly the direction of **D** for the extraordinary ray in the second crystal. It is therefore singly refracted as an E-ray. Similarly, the ray which was the E-ray in the first crystal becomes the O-ray in the second. It should be remembered that there is nothing ordinary or extraordinary about the rays themselves—in the air between the crystals they are simply rays which are plane polarized at right angles. They behave as E or O disturbances in the crystals only because of the directional properties of the latter. Thus the E-ray emerging from the first crystal passes straight through the second crystal, and the O-ray becomes the E-ray and is refracted. The positions and vibration directions of the emergent rays are shown by the end-on view in (*c*). The rays are denoted by OE and EO, signifying that one is the O-ray in the first crystal and the E-ray in the second, and the other is the E-ray in the first and the O-ray in the second.

If the angle between the principal planes of the crystals is between 0° and 90° (or between 90° and 180°), each ray incident on the second crystal has a component of **D** both in and perpendicular to the principal section. Each ray is therefore doubly refracted as an O- and an E-ray. Figs 22–10(*d*) and (*e*) show the positions of the four emergent rays when the principal sections of the crystals are inclined at 45° and 135°. In general, the relative intensities of the four rays emerging from the second crystal are determined by the components of **D** in and perpendicular to the principal section of the second crystal. Suppose the angle between the principal sections is θ. Then, for the E-ray from the first crystal, **D** is in the principal section of that crystal; it has components proportional to $\cos \theta$ and $\sin \theta$ respectively in and perpendicular to the principal section of the second crystal. The intensity of the emergent ray EE is therefore proportional to $\cos^2 \theta$ (Law of Malus—see § 6–14), and that of the ray EO is proportional to $\sin^2 \theta$. Similarly, the intensities of the rays OO and OE are also proportional to $\cos^2 \theta$ and $\sin^2 \theta$ respectively. Thus as θ is increased from 0 to 90° the intensities of the rays OO and EE gradually decrease from a maximum down to zero,

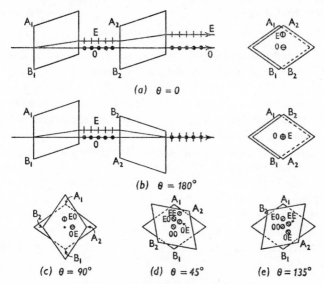

Fig. 22–10. Two calcite crystals in series.

while the intensities of the rays OE and EO gradually increase from zero to a maximum. When θ is 45° or 135° [Figs 22–10(d) and (e)] all four emergent rays have the same intensity. It has been assumed here that unpolarized light is incident on the first crystal. If the original beam is polarized, the O- and E-rays from the first crystal may have unequal intensities and the relative intensities of the final emergent rays will be changed accordingly.

22–5. The Nicol Prism

It is frequently desirable to be able to produce a single plane polarized beam of light. Obviously this can be done by double refraction if one of the refracted beams can be suitably removed. Now the O- and E-rays in a calcite crystal travel with different speeds, corresponding to different refractive indices. In the Nicol prism (Fig. 22–11) a calcite crystal is cut across a diagonal as shown and the halves cemented together with canada balsam or some similar material. This material has a refractive index intermediate between the indices of calcite for the O- and E-rays so that at the balsam layer one (E) can be transmitted while the other (O) is totally reflected and absorbed by the black coating which is applied

17*

to the edges of the prism. The details of the construction of a Nicol are as follows. A crystal is chosen whose long edges are about three times as long as its short edges. It was pointed out in § 22–4 that a principal section is a parallelogram with angles of approximately 109° and 71°. The end faces of the crystal

(a) Principal Section   (b) View showing direction of Cut

Fig. 22–11. The Nicol prism.

are now ground and polished to reduce the acute angle to 68°, and the crystal is cut across the plane that is perpendicular to the principal section and to the end faces (see Fig. 22–11). If light is incident parallel to the long edges of the prism, the O-ray is totally reflected at the calcite-balsam surface as shown in the figure. A clockwise rotation of the rays will increase the angles of incidence at the cemented surface, and when that of the E-ray exceeds the critical angle, both rays will be totally reflected. An anti-clockwise rotation will eventually reduce the angle of incidence of the O-ray below the critical angle, and both rays will then be transmitted. It will be seen that the O- and E-rays will be separated for only a small range of directions of the ray entering the crystal. In the Nicol prism the end faces are ground as described above in order to make the ray AB (incident parallel to the long edges) lie in the middle of this range of about 24°. It will be appreciated that this angular field will depend upon the cement employed.

22–6. Two Nicols in Series

Suppose that the plane polarized ray emerging from one Nicol prism enters another, the long edges of the prisms being parallel. If the principal sections of the prisms are parallel [Fig. 22–12(a) or

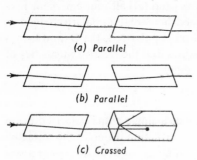

(a) Parallel

(b) Parallel

(c) Crossed

Fig. 22–12. Two Nicols in series.

(b)], the ray will pass through the second prism unaffected (apart from the normal reflection and absorption losses). If the principal sections are perpendicular [Fig. 22–12(c)], the prisms are said to be crossed, and the ray which was the E-ray in the first prism becomes the O-ray in the second crystal and is totally reflected. That is, no light is transmitted by a pair of crossed Nicols. Frequently one employs two Nicols in series, with some optical system between them. The purpose of the first Nicol—the polarizer— is to plane-polarize the light. The system between the Nicols may change the state of polarization. For example, it may rotate the plane of vibration. By rotating the second Nicol about an axis parallel to the long edges, one can then find the new plane of vibration—it is perpendicular to the principal section of the second Nicol when the intensity of the emergent beam falls to zero. The second Nicol, which is used to examine the state of polarization of the light emerging from the system, is referred to as the *analyser*. More complicated arrangements involving the use of a polarizer and an analyser will be described later. With only a fixed polarizer and a rotating analyser, the component of the vibrations (i.e. of **D**) which can be transmitted by the analyser is proportional to $\cos \theta$ where θ is the angle between the principal sections of the Nicols. The intensity of the light emerging from the analyser is therefore proportional to $\cos^2 \theta$ and is independent of the orientation of the polarizer if the original light is unpolarized. If the original incident beam contains plane or elliptically polarized light, the intensity of the beam emerging from the polarizer will depend upon the orientation of the latter, and the intensity of the final emergent beam will not depend simply upon the angle between the principal sections of the two crystals.

22–7. Other Polarizing Prisms

In the previous section, only a single incident ray was discussed and it was assumed that this was incident parallel to the long edges of the polarizer. It was stated in §22–5 that a Nicol has an angular field of about 24°; but if two Nicols are placed in series, it is found that the whole field of view does not go

(a) Thompson and Glazebrook   (b) Ahrens

Fig. 22–13. Square-ended prisms.

uniformly dark when the Nicols are crossed. As the analyser is rotated, a dark shadow crosses the field of view. The reason is that the light emerging from a Nicol is not uniformly plane polarized. Another disadvantage of the simple Nicol prism is that, since the E-ray passes obliquely through a parallel-sided plate, the emergent ray is displaced laterally. This latter defect can be overcome by making the end faces perpendicular to the long edges. A prism of this type is often said to be square ended but this does not, of course, mean that the cross-section is a square. The square ended Nicol has the additional advantage of a smaller loss of light by reflection at the end face since less light is reflected at normal incidence.

In order to obtain more uniformly plane polarized light, the square ended prism shown in Fig. 22–13(a) was used by S. P. Thompson and by Glazebrook; it is rather longer than an ordinary Nicol of the same width. Other prisms of this type have been cut with the optic axis parallel to AB instead of AD. A prism which has been widely used is that due to Ahrens [Fig. 22–13(b)]. This has three calcite components cemented with balsam and obviously can be regarded as a combination of Thompson prisms. It has a field of about 26° and, for a given width, has a length only about half that of a Nicol. Ahrens prisms have also been cut with the optic axis parallel to AB instead of AD.

Nicol prisms and others employing Canada balsam cannot be used in the ultra-violet because the balsam absorbs in that region. Foucault devised a

(a) Rochon   (b) Wollaston

Fig. 22–14. Quartz double image prisms.

prism of the Nicol type but with an air gap and this had the advantage of shortening the prism. However, the angular field was small (about 8°) and the intensity of the E-ray was reduced by reflections. Square ended Foucault prisms were also employed, and that due to Glan bears the same relation to the Thompson prism as does the Foucault to the Nicol. All have the disadvantage of multiple reflections in the air film.

Most of the prisms used in the ultra-violet have been of the double image type. Fig. 22–14 shows those due to Rochon and Wollaston. Each of these employs a pair of quartz prisms, the directions of the optic axes being as shown. In each case the plane polarized components are separated by double refraction at the interface. In the Rochon prism the O-ray is transmitted without deviation for all wavelengths. In the Wollaston prism the ray labelled O is, in fact, the extraordinary ray in the first prism, so that both rays are deviated at the interface. With this arrangement a greater separation is obtained. It should be noted that with the Rochon prism the light must pass through in the direction indicated. If the right-hand component is traversed first the plane of vibration will be rotated by the left-hand component and this rotation depends upon wavelength (see Chapter XXIII).

22–8. Polarization by Selective Absorption (Dichroism)

The prisms described above provide methods of obtaining plane polarized light by double refraction, one of the components being removed by reflection or mechanical obstruction. Now some materials show different absorptions for the O- and E-rays. This effect (discovered in 1815 by Biot) is known as *Dichroism* and, if it is very marked, it provides a means of producing partially plane polarized light. One of the best known materials of this kind is tourmaline—a naturally occurring mineral. In this uniaxial crystal the O-ray is much more strongly absorbed than the E-ray, and a single crystal cut parallel to the axis can be used as a polarizer or analyser. To a first approximation, the intensity of

Fig. 22–15.
Two tourmaline plates in series.

the light emerging from the analyser is again proportional to $\cos^2 \theta$ (see Fig. 22–15). Unfortunately, neither the absorption of the O-ray nor the transmission of the E-ray is complete, and the absorption depends on the wavelength. More satisfactory selectively absorbing screens have been synthesized, particularly by the Polaroid Corporation, U.S.A. Ultramicroscopic crystals are contained in a film and the crystals can be orientated by stretching the film.

There are now several forms of sheet-type dichroic polarizer and the transmittance ratio for perpendicularly polarized components can be as high as 10^5. These polarizers have now superseded birefringent polarizers in most applications; they can have larger angular apertures and enormously larger linear apertures—it is possible to produce sheets 18 inches wide with virtually unlimited length.

22–9. Ray and Wave Velocity for Biaxial Crystals

The occurrence of double refraction in a biaxial crystal can be demonstrated by using Huygens' principle as for uniaxial media. Fig. 22–16 shows the special

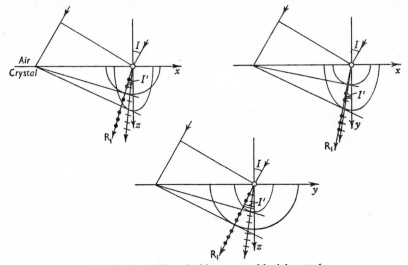

Fig. 22–16. Oblique incidence on a biaxial crystal.

cases where the plane of incidence contains two of the principal axes (see Chapter XIX). In each plane, one of the sections of the wave surface is circular and, as pointed out in § 22–1, one has $\sin I'/\sin I = $ constant for one of the refracted rays (OR_1).

As defined in Chapter XIX, the phase or wave velocity is the velocity with which a plane wave advances in the direction of the wave normal, and an optic axis is a direction in which there is only one possible phase velocity. In Fig. 22–17, OB is a direction of single ray velocity but it is not an optic axis. Fig. 22–18 shows that a plane wave parallel to T_1T_2 is propagated with the same phase (wave normal) velocity by means of secondary waves having either the elliptic or the circular sections. That is to say, one of the optic axes is the direction OT_2 which is normal to T_1T_2, the tangent common to the ellipse and the circle. The other optic axis is the direction OT_4. Let the direction of the optic axis OT_2 be defined by the angle ϕ which it makes with the x-axis. The equations to the circular and elliptic sections of the wave surface are, respectively,

$$x^2 + z^2 = v_y{}^2$$

and

$$\frac{x^2}{v_z{}^2} + \frac{z^2}{v_x{}^2} = 1.$$

Fig. 22–17. The optic axes.

Fig. 22–18.
Propagation of plane waves along an axis.

Now T_2 is the point $(v_y \cos \phi, v_y \sin \phi)$ so that the equation to the tangent to the circle at T_2 is

$$x \cos \phi + z \sin \phi = v_y.$$

If this touches the ellipse one has*

$$v_z^2 \cos^2 \phi + v_x^2 \sin^2 \phi = v_y^2,$$

$$\therefore \quad v_z^2 \cos^2 \phi + v_x^2 - v_x^2 \cos^2 \phi = v_y^2$$

or

$$\cos \phi = \sqrt{\frac{v_x^2 - v_y^2}{v_x^2 - v_z^2}}. \quad \cdots \quad (22\text{--}1)$$

Fig. 22–19.
Connection between
wave surface and
wave velocity surface.

This defines the direction of the optic axis OT_2. The angle between the optic axes is usually taken to be acute. That is to say, it is 2ϕ if $(v_x^2 - v_y^2) > (v_y^2 - v_z^2)$ and $2(\pi/2 - \phi)$ if $(v_x^2 - v_y^2) < (v_y^2 - v_z^2)$; the former inequality defines a negative, and the latter a positive biaxial crystal.

If, in general, one draws a tangent to the elliptic section of the wave surface, the perpendicular distance from O to that tangent represents the wave velocity in that direction. If one does this for each point on the ellipse, one obtains a polar diagram of the wave velocity. This is the *wave velocity surface* (sometimes called the *normal surface*). It will be seen from Fig. 22–19 that, conversely, the wave surface (or ray velocity surface) is the envelope of the plane wavefronts that advance in all directions through the origin.

22–10. Internal Conical Refraction

Suppose a narrow, collimated pencil of unpolarized light is incident normally on a biaxial crystal cut perpendicular to the optic axis [Fig. 22–20(a)]. The paths of the refracted pencils can be found as follows. Take the point O in the middle

* The straight line $lx + my = n$ touches the ellipse $\dfrac{x^2}{a^2} + \dfrac{y^2}{b^2} = 1$ if $a^2 l^2 + b^2 m^2 = n^2$.

of the small plane wave striking the crystal. The line T_1T_2 is the tangent common to the elliptic and circular sections of the wave surface for a disturbance spreading out from O, and T_1T_2 is parallel to the crystal surface. It follows from Huygens' principle that if O is moved over the element of plane wave striking the crystal surface, T_1 and T_2 generate the refracted elements of the wave. Hence the pencil of light is refracted as shown. Actually this is an over-simplification because it can be shown that the tangent plane T_1T_2 actually touches the three-dimensional wave surface in a circle of which T_1T_2 is the diameter. (In the diagram the circle is perpendicular to the paper.) Thus while disturbances travel from O to T_1 and to T_2 they also travel to each point on the circumference of

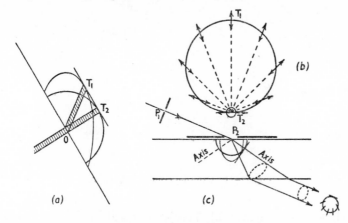

Fig. 22–20. Internal conical refraction.

this circle; as O generates the incident plane wave element, each point on the circumference of the circle generates a similar wave element. Consequently, light spreads into the crystal from O towards each point on the circumference of the circle whose diameter is T_1T_2. That is to say, a hollow cone of light is propagated in the crystal. For each of the generating rays of this cone, the direction of **D** is coplanar with the ray and the wave normal. Thus, viewing the oncoming light, the direction of **D** is as represented by Fig. 22–20(*b*).

If the second surface of the crystal is parallel to the first, a hollow cylinder of light will emerge. The phenomenon, known as *internal conical refraction*, was predicted by Sir William Hamilton and verified by Lloyd using a plate of arragonite ($CaCO_3$) cut with its faces equally inclined to the two optic axes. That is, oblique incidence was used as in Fig. 22–20(*c*). If pinhole P_1 is kept stationary and P_2 is moved about on the crystal surface, there will, in general, be two refracted rays. When the correct position for P_2 is found, the refracted light spreads out into a hollow cone as indicated. In practice, only an infinitesimal amount of light is incident in *precisely* the correct direction, so that the cone of light predicted by the theory is not seen. Rays in closely neighbouring directions of incidence give light close to the hollow cone referred to and the cone itself is observed as a *dark* cone, i.e. the emerging hollow cylinder has "walls" of finite thickness and the end-on view shows a fine dark ring dividing inner and outer rings of light.

22–11. External Conical Refraction

At the point B [Fig. 22–21(a)], which on the three-dimensional wave surface has the appearance of a dimple, one can draw an infinite number of tangent planes to the wave surface. Hence, for a narrow pencil of rays travelling along the ray axis, there are an infinite number of possible directions of the wave

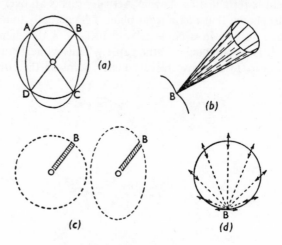

Fig. 22–21. External conical refraction.

normal. These are indicated in (b). Pencils of rays along OB with the two wave normals that lie in the plane of Fig. (a) are of the form shown in (c). Suppose a pencil of rays along OB in the crystal contains plane wave elements with every possible orientation of wave normal. Suppose, further, that the surface of the crystal is at B. There are then an infinite number of emergent rays, and each corresponds to the ray OB and one of the possible associated wave normals in the crystal. The emergent rays constitute a hollow cone of light spreading out from B. For each of the wave normals that can be associated with the ray OB, there is only one possible vibration direction—it is in the plane defined by the

Fig. 22–22. Observation of external conical refraction.

ray and the wave normal. This determines the vibration direction of each of the emergent rays. Looking towards the oncoming cone of rays, the vibration directions are as indicated by (d). Conversely, a hollow cone of suitably polarized rays incident at B from outside the crystal will unite to give a single ray BO inside.

Experimentally, the phenomenon of *external conical refraction* can be observed as follows. A convergent cone of unpolarized light is incident on the crystal through the pinhole P_1 (Fig. 22–22). Those rays in the incident cone that have the appropriate vibration directions combine into a single ray, and others give other refracted rays. If the position of P_2 is adjusted until P_1P_2 is the ray axis, the single ray P_1P_2 gives an emergent cone of rays, and all other rays in the crystal are obstructed.

22–12. Passage of Light Through Crystal Plates

Suppose a plane polarized beam of light is incident normally on the surface of a plane parallel uniaxial crystal plate. Fig. 22–23 shows a principal section of the crystal and indicates the passage of the light through the plate. In general, there will be two emergent rays, one (O) with the plane of vibration perpendicular to the principal section, and the other (E) with **D** in the principal section. If, however, the plane of vibration of the incident light is in or perpendicular to the principal section, there will be only one plane polarized emergent beam. The two directions of vibration of the incident light which correspond to a single plane polarized emergent beam are sometimes referred to as the *privileged directions* of the crystal. One corresponds to the vibration direction of the O-ray, and the other is the vibration direction of the E-ray. These two rays have

Fig. 22–23. Passage of light through a crystal plate.

different velocities, and the privileged direction corresponding to **D** for the faster ray is called the *fast axis* and the other is the *slow axis*. These correspond to the O- and E-rays respectively for a positive crystal and vice versa for a negative crystal. If the incident light is unpolarized, there will always be two plane polarized emergent rays, and their intensities will not change as the crystal is rotated about the incident ray as axis.

If the crystal plate is cut perpendicular to the optic axis, the state of polarization of the emergent beam is always the same as that of the incident beam, and there are no privileged directions.

If the crystal plate is cut parallel to the optic axis, the O- and E-rays travel along the same line but with different speeds. Fig. 22–24 shows a collimated incident beam of light plane polarized with **D** neither in nor perpendicular to the principal section of a negative crystal. In this case the O and E disturbances will emerge from the plate with different phases and, since they are coherent and along the same path, the perpendicular vibrations are superposed to give plane, circularly, or elliptically polarized light (see below). If the incident light is unpolarized, it can be resolved into *incoherent* plane polarized components with any two mutually perpendicular vibration directions. That is, incoherent O and E disturbances are propagated through the crystal and emerge as unpolarized light. (One can, in fact, be said to have unpolarized light at all points through the plate.)

Fig. 22–24. Plate cut parallel to the axis.

Consider, again, the case of a plane polarized incident beam. With the negative crystal shown in the figure, the privileged directions of the plate will be along and perpendicular to the optic axis, the former being the fast and the latter the slow axis. If the vibration direction of the incident light is not in one of the privileged directions, it will have components in both these directions. For example, if the vibration direction of the incident beam makes angle θ with the optic axis, the amplitudes of the O- and E-waves will be $A \sin \theta$ and $A \cos \theta$ respectively, where A is the amplitude of the incident light. Fig. 22–25 shows the end-on view looking against the oncoming light. Suppose the thickness of the crystal plate is d and let n_O and n_E be the ordinary and extraordinary refractive indices. Then the optical path through the crystal is $n_O d$ for the O-ray and $n_E d$ for the E-ray. That is to say, the O- and E-rays pass through optical paths which

differ by $(n_O - n_E)d$. Now the vibrations of the O and E disturbances commence in phase since they are components of a linear vibration. Consequently, they emerge from the plate with phase difference given by

$$\delta = \frac{2\pi}{\lambda} (n_O - n_E)d, \quad \cdot \quad \cdot \quad (22\text{–}2)$$

Fig. 22–25. Resolution along fast and slow axes.

where λ is the wavelength in air.

When the coherent O and E disturbances emerge from the crystal, their perpendicular linear simple harmonic vibrations are superposed. Imagine now that the thickness of the crystal can be increased gradually. When $\delta = 0$ (or $2p\pi$, where p is an integer) the resultant is a linear vibration identical to that of the incident light. As δ increases from zero, the resultant becomes an elliptic motion, and, as δ continues to increase, the eccentricity changes and the axes rotate as indicated in Fig. 22–26. When δ reaches π [or $(2p+1)\pi$] the resultant is again linear so that the emergent light is plane polarized, although it does not have the same vibration direction as the incident light. Further increase of δ gives the elliptic resultants shown until one returns to the plane polarization of the incident light when $\delta = 2\pi$. Fig. 22–26 can be looked upon as giving the state of polarization at different distances through a thick crystal as the light traverses it. It should be noted that between $\delta = 0$ and $\delta = \pi$ the elliptic motion is anticlockwise, and between $\delta = \pi$ and $\delta = 2\pi$ it is clockwise. Obviously, the reverse is true if the vibration direction of the incident light is inclined in the opposite direction, or if one looks along the rays from the opposite direction. It should be noted also that if, in the above example, the vibration direction of the incident

Fig. 22–26. State of polarization of light passing through a crystal plate. (y lags.)

light had been inclined to the optic axis at $\theta = 45°$, one would have obtained circularly polarized emergent light when $\delta = \pi/2$ [or $(2p+\frac{1}{2})\pi$] and $\delta = 3\pi/2$ [or $(2p+3/2)\pi$].

If the light emerging from the crystal plate is passed into an analyser (such as a Nicol), only the component parallel to the principal section of the analyser will be transmitted. That is to say, after compounding the O and E disturbances from the plate the resultant must be resolved into a new pair of perpendicular directions—that for which the analyser is opaque, and that for which it is transparent. This can be done by resolving the O and E disturbances from the plate in the relevant directions. Thus to find the disturbance transmitted by the analyser, one finds the components of the O and E vibrations in the direction for which the analyser is transparent and, allowing for the phase difference between them, the two components are superposed (see also § 22–17).

Before proceeding further with a discussion of the effect of crystal plates on polarized light, it should be pointed out that elliptically polarized light can be resolved into any two perpendicularly polarized plane components. If it is resolved into plane polarized components whose vibration directions are parallel to the axes of the ellipse, the components are $\pi/2$ out of phase, but if it is resolved into any other perpendicular directions, the components are not $\pi/2$ out of phase. That is to say, when elliptically polarized light enters a crystal plate cut parallel to the optic axis, the phase difference between the O and E components depends on the orientation of the ellipse. The relation between the orientation of the axes of the ellipse and the phase difference between its components has already been given [equation (6–41)].

If unpolarized light enters the crystal the components are incoherent and the emergent light is also unpolarized.

22–13. Quarter- and Half-wave Plates

A crystal plate that introduces a phase difference of $\pi/2$ (a quarter of a cycle) between the O and E disturbances is called a *quarter-wave plate*. One also has half-wave plates, which introduce a phase difference of π, and so on.

From the discussion of the previous section it will be seen that for a full-wave plate the state of polarization of the emergent light is always identical to that of the incident light.

With a half-wave plate the general state of polarization of the emergent light is the same as that of the incident light, but usually with a different orientation. For example, suppose that the incident light is plane polarized and that the vibration direction makes angle θ with the optic axis. The plate introduces a phase retardation of π in the O-ray relative to the E-ray so that, on emergence, the vector representing the O vibration (Fig. 22–25) is reversed. Thus the resultant is in the direction $-\theta$. That is to say, the plane of vibration is rotated 2θ. There is, of course, no rotation if the plane of vibration of the incident light is in one of the privileged directions, i.e. if $\theta=0$ or $\pi/2$. Reference to Fig. 22–26 will also illustrate the fact that, unless the axes are in the privileged directions, an elliptically polarized incident beam gives a similarly polarized emergent beam, the axes of the ellipse being rotated.

Consider now a quarter-wave plate. When the incident light is plane polarized one has, in general, elliptically polarized emergent light, the axes of the ellipse being parallel to the privileged directions. There are two special cases: if the incident light has its vibration direction parallel to, or perpendicular to, the optic axis, the emergent light is identically polarized; and if the vibration direction is initially at 45° to the optic axis, the emergent light is circularly polarized.

If, with a quarter-wave plate, the incident light is circularly polarized, or elliptically polarized with axes parallel to the privileged directions of the plate, the incident disturbance can be resolved into plane polarized O and E components which are $\pi/2$ out of phase. The plate then removes this phase difference so that plane polarized light emerges. With elliptically polarized incident light, the O and E components are not, in general, $\pi/2$ out of phase, so that they do not emerge in phase. That is, one has elliptically polarized emergent light.

Quarter-wave plates are frequently made of quartz or mica. Actually mica is biaxial but there is a clear colourless form for which the angle between the optic axes is vanishingly small. Mica splits easily into thin sheets and by trial and error one can select a sheet of the thickness necessary to give a quarter-wave plate. It is not always easy to cleave a mica plate for which the optic axis is parallel to the surface, but with quartz—which has to be cut and polished—it is usual to produce a plate in which the axis is so orientated. The principal refractive indices of quartz for sodium light are 1·55336 and 1·54425. Hence, since $\delta = (2\pi/\lambda)(n_E - n_O)d$, one has $d \doteq 0\cdot0164$ mm. when $\delta = \pi/2$. One can, of course, use more robust plates giving $\delta = 5\pi/2$, $9\pi/2$, etc. Such plates give identical effects with polarized light but it is easy to distinguish between them with a micrometer screw gauge.

22–14. Use of a Quarter-wave Plate in the Analysis of Polarized Light

A theorem due to Stokes states that there are only seven possible states of polarization of a beam of light: unpolarized, plane polarized, elliptically polarized, circularly polarized, and three mixtures—each of unpolarized and one of the other three types. On passing the light through an analyser which can rotate about the direction of the light as axis, one can detect the presence of elliptically or plane polarized light since this will cause the intensity of the transmitted light to vary with the orientation of the analyser. If there is no variation with orientation, the original light is unpolarized, circularly polarized, or a mixture of the two. By combining an analyser (such as a Nicol) and a quarter-wave plate, it is possible to make a complete systematic qualitative analysis of the light. One proceeds as follows:

I. Insert analyser and rotate it. There are three possibilities:

   (a) No light is transmitted for one orientation of the analyser.
   (b) The intensity of the transmitted light is independent of the orientation of the analyser.
   (c) The intensity varies with orientation but never falls to zero.
      (a) indicates that the light is completely plane polarized; (b) indicates that the light is unpolarized, circularly polarized, or a mixture of the two; (c) indicates elliptically polarized light, a mixture of elliptically polarized and unpolarized light, or a mixture of plane polarized and unpolarized light.

II. To investigate I (b) further, pass the light through a quarter-wave plate followed by an analyser, and rotate the analyser. There are the same three possibilities: (a), (b), and (c). (a) indicates that the original beam is circularly polarized; (b) indicates that it is unpolarized; (c) indicates that it is a mixture of circularly polarized and unpolarized light.

III. To investigate I (c) further, one again uses a quarter-wave plate and an analyser but, now, the plate and analyser are rotated independently. There are only two possibilities:

(a) The light is extinguished for one setting.

(b) The intensity of the light varies as the components are rotated, but never falls to zero.

In this case (a) indicates that the light is elliptically polarized and that the axes of the ellipse are parallel to the privileged directions of the plate when the light is extinguished; (b) indicates that the light is a mixture of elliptically polarized and unpolarized light, or a mixture of plane polarized and unpolarized light. For the former, when the intensity is a minimum the privileged directions of the plate are parallel to the axes of the ellipse, and the position of the analyser gives the ratio of the axes (see § 22–16). A mixture of plane polarized and unpolarized light emerges as a special case of the last mixture and is indicated by the fact that the analyser is parallel to one of the privileged directions of the plate when the intensity is a minimum. That is to say, one of the axes of the ellipse contracts to zero.

The student should satisfy himself that he understands why the effects described lead to the conclusions stated. Note that, after passage through a quarter-wave plate, circularly polarized light becomes plane polarized; plane polarized light can become elliptically, circularly, or plane polarized, according to the orientation of the plate; elliptically polarized light emerges either plane or elliptically polarized; and unpolarized light remains unpolarized.

22–15. The Babinet and Soleil Compensators

It is convenient, for the production and analysis of elliptically polarized light, to have a crystal plate of variable thickness. Such plates are known as compensators. Fig. 22–27 shows the Babinet and Soleil compensators. In the former one has two quartz wedges of small angle, the optic axes being as shown. Light enters from above and, in contrast with the Wollaston prism, the wedge angles are sufficiently small for one to be able to neglect the separation of

(a) Babinet   (b) Soleil

Fig. 22–27. Compensators.

the O- and E-rays. The upper wedge is fixed and, by means of a micrometer screw, the lower can be moved as indicated. On entering the first wedge, the O-ray travels faster than the E-ray (quartz being a positive crystal). Since the optic axis of the second wedge is perpendicular to that of the first, the O-ray for the first wedge becomes the E-ray for the second and vice versa. That is to say, the rays exchange speeds on passing into the second wedge. By moving the point of incidence along the upper wedge, or by moving the lower wedge, one can cause the paths in the wedges to be different. In this way one can control the phase difference between the emergent rays so that one has, in effect, a plate of variable thickness.

The fact that the effective thickness of the plate depends on the point of incidence is sometimes a disadvantage. This difficulty is overcome in the Soleil compensator which consists of two thin wedges and a plane-parallel plate cut as shown. The bottom wedge can be moved as indicated. The combined effect of

the wedges is that of a plane-parallel plate of variable thickness and this, combined with the top plane-parallel plate, gives, in effect, a thin plate of variable
thickness but whose thickness is the same at all points across it.

22–16. Analysis of Elliptically Polarized Light using a Babinet Compensator

It is first necessary to calibrate the compensator. To do this, it is placed
between a polarizer and a crossed analyser so that the plane polarized light from
the polarizer has its plane of vibration at about 45° to the axes of the wedges
[see Fig. 22–28(a)]. At points where the effective thickness of the compensator
is $2p\pi$ (p integral) the emergent light is plane polarized in the same plane as the

Fig. 22–28. Analysis of elliptically polarized light.

incident light and is removed by the analyser. Now the compensator has constant thickness along lines parallel to the edges of the wedges so that, across the
aperture of the compensator, one has a series of dark fringes as in (b). As one
moves across the aperture from A to B, the effective thickness of the compensator varies and the polarization of the emergent light varies as shown in (b).
There is, in general, a component of **D** in the plane of the analyser so that some
light is transmitted. If the original plane of vibration is exactly at 45° to the
axes of the wedges, one has maxima midway between the minima since the plate
gives a retardation of $(2p+1)\pi$ and the emergent light is plane polarized
perpendicular to the incident light, i.e. in the transparent direction of the
analyser. If the original plane of vibration is not exactly at 45°, the emergent
light is not exactly parallel to the transparent direction of the analyser when the
retardation is $(2p+1)\pi$ and the contrast in the fringes is reduced. As the wedge
of the compensator is moved, the position of zero effective thickness moves
across the wedge, i.e. the fringes move across the field of view. The movement
of the screw (θ) necessary to produce a shift of one fringe spacing is that which
changes the phase difference by 2π. The compensator is then adjusted until a
minimum falls on the cross-wires. The phase difference at that point in the
field of view is then $2p\pi$. The micrometer screw is then turned through $\theta/4$.
This makes the phase difference at the cross-wires $(2p+\frac{1}{2})\pi$. That is, one has a
quarter-wave plate in that part of the field of view. The polarizer is then removed

and the elliptically polarized light to be measured is passed into the compensator and analyser. These are rotated independently until the bands are as clear as possible and a dark band is brought on to the cross-wires. This corresponds to plane polarized light leaving the quarter-wave plate so that the axes of the ellipse must be parallel to the optic axes of the compensator wedges (the privileged directions).

The $\pi/2$ phase difference between the components of the ellipse is removed by the compensator to give the plane polarized emergent light, and the plane of vibration of the latter is determined by the ratio of the axes of the ellipse (see Fig. 22-29). It is perpendicular to the transparent direction of the analyser so

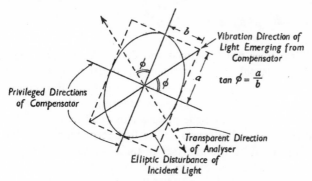

Fig. 22-29. Analysis of elliptically polarized light.

that the ratio of the axes of the ellipse is given by the tangent of the angle that the analyser makes with the principal directions of the compensator.

22-17. Passage of Collimated White Light through a Crystal Plate

In the previous section it has been assumed that the light is monochromatic. In general, a crystal plate introduces a phase difference which depends upon the wavelength. Frequently the path difference $(n_E - n_O)d$ remains approximately constant throughout the visible spectrum so that the phase difference, $(2\pi/\lambda)(n_E - n_O)d$, varies by a factor of about 2. Thus if plane polarized white light is passed through a crystal cut parallel to the optic axis, the polarization of the emergent light will vary with wavelength. If this light is passed through an analyser, the transmitted intensity will vary with wavelength and the emergent beam will be coloured. In particular, if the plate is replaced by a Babinet compensator the fringes will be coloured. (The central fringe, corresponding to zero effective thickness, will be achromatic, e.g. will be black when the polarizer and analyser are crossed.) Again, a quarter-wave plate will give the nominal $\pi/2$ phase change for one wavelength only—usually for sodium light. If plane polarized white light enters a half-wave plate, only the sodium light will emerge plane polarized and an analyser set to extinguish this will transmit some light of other wavelengths. The emergent light has the characteristic reddish-violet colour which is usually called the *tint of passage* (see also § 23–8).

Consider, now, the case of a crystal cut parallel to the axis and placed between a polarizer and an analyser. Suppose the transparent directions of the polarizer and the analyser make angles θ and ϕ with the optic axis of the crystal. The incident plane polarized light has amplitudes $a \cos \theta$ and $a \sin \theta$ parallel to and perpendicular to the optic axis. The former has component $a \cos \theta \cos \phi$ and the latter $a \sin \theta \sin \phi$ in the transparent direction of the analyser. There will be a phase difference, δ, between these two components which are coherent since they are derived from the same plane polarized beam. Consequently, the resultant intensity transmitted by the analyser is given [from (6–9)] by

$$I = a^2 \cos^2 \theta \cos^2 \phi + a^2 \sin^2 \theta \sin^2 \phi + 2a^2 \sin \theta \cos \theta \sin \phi \cos \phi \cos \delta$$

$$= a^2 \cos^2 \theta \cos^2 \phi + a^2 \sin^2 \theta \sin^2 \phi + 2a^2 \sin \theta \cos \theta \sin \phi \cos \phi \left(1 - 2 \sin^2 \frac{\delta}{2} \right)$$

$$= a^2 \cos^2 (\theta - \phi) - a^2 \sin 2\theta \sin 2\phi \sin^2 \frac{\delta}{2}. \qquad \ldots \ldots \ldots (22\text{--}3)$$

The first term does not contain δ and therefore does not depend upon the thickness of the crystal or the wavelength. It depends solely upon the angle between the polarizer and the analyser, being a maximum when they are parallel and zero when they are crossed. The second term, involving δ, varies with wavelength, but is zero when either the polarizer or analyser is parallel to one of the privileged directions of the crystal. The first term represents the light which would be transmitted by the analyser in the absence of the crystal and shows that the transmitted light would be white. When summed for all wavelengths, the second term represents coloured light added to or subtracted from the white light. Now the sign of this term changes when either the polarizer or the analyser is rotated 90°, keeping the rest of the system fixed. Hence such a rotation changes the colour of the emergent beam to the complementary colour. For example, the colour of the emergent beam with crossed Nicols is complementary to that obtained when the analyser is rotated to make them parallel. If the analyser is replaced by a simple calcite crystal one will obtain two emergent beams—polarized at right angles and of complementary colours.

As a further example of the passage of white light through a crystal, suppose a thick plate is placed between a polarizer and a crossed analyser with the optic axis of the plate inclined at 45° to the plane of vibration of the light incident upon it. The emergent light will be plane, elliptically, or circularly polarized, depending upon the phase shift introduced by the plate, i.e. depending upon the wavelength. The analyser will remove those wavelengths for which the plate gives a phase shift that is a multiple of 2π and, if the light from the analyser enters a spectroscope, the spectrum will show a series of dark fringes. If the crystal plate is replaced by a Soleil compensator, one can adjust the equivalent thickness and control the fringe spacing.

When a very thick crystal plate is placed between crossed Nicols with white light, the wavelengths removed are very numerous and, since they are distributed throughout the spectrum, the emergent light still appears white. With thin plates relatively few wavelengths are removed and, in general, the emergent light is coloured. Thin pieces of many anisotropic substances such as mica, when chosen at random, show considerable variations of thickness and, between crossed Nicols in white light, show many variations of colour. The general effect is, of course, not restricted to uniaxial crystals cut and orientated in the particular way discussed above, although the discussion is restricted to the passage of approximately parallel light through the crystal.

22–18. Passage of Convergent Plane Polarized Pencils through Crystal Plates

(a) Experimental Arrangement

The light transmitted by a crystal plate depends upon the angle of incidence of the light and the orientation of the crystal axis. For a crystal cut in a given manner one can investigate the effect of varying the angle of incidence by mounting the crystal as shown in Fig. 22–30. The screen AB is in the focal plane of the lens L. P is the crystal plate and an analyser (not shown in the figure) is placed between P and L or between L and AB. It will be seen that rays which come to a focus at a point on AB must have been parallel when they passed through the crystal. That is to say, each point on AB corresponds to a given *direction* through the crystal and not to a given local region of it. Consequently, the variation of intensity across AB indicates the way in which the state of polarization of the transmitted light varies with angle of incidence on the crystal. It is necessary for all rays incident on the crystal in a given direction to have the same path through the crystal, so that the plate must be accurately plane parallel. For visual observation, and

Fig. 22–30. Passage of an oblique pencil through a crystal plate.

to obtain the necessary angular aperture, it is convenient to use a polarizing microscope with the Amici-Bertrand lens in position (see § 22–19). The system is then known as a *conoscope*. It will be seen that, owing to the effect of the Amici-Bertrand lens, each direction in the field of view corresponds to a single direction through the crystal and not to a single point on its surface.

(b) Uniaxial Crystal Cut Perpendicular to the Optic Axis

For any collimated pencil of coherent plane polarized rays incident obliquely on the crystal plate, there will, in general, be two emergent pencils. These will be coherent and plane polarized at right angles. If the crystal is fairly thin and the pencil of rays fairly broad, the two pencils will not be separated on emergence and one can superpose the emergent disturbances in the usual way. The crystal will introduce a phase difference between the perpendicularly polarized disturbances. This phase difference will depend upon the optical path difference through the crystal and, for a given crystal thickness and given wavelength, it will depend only upon the angle between the incident ray and the optic axis. Consequently, a movement of the crystal along the axis of the system does not affect the transmitted light. That is to say, it makes no difference to the observed effects if the crystal is located beyond the focus of the principal rays of the collimated pencils. Many students find it easier to visualize this arrangement with divergent pencils. Thus in Fig. 22–31 suppose the principal rays of the pencils diverge from the point P on the axis of the system. Consider the pencils whose principal rays are incident at points on the circumference of the circle

ABCD, centred on the axis. These pencils are equally inclined to the axis of the system and come to a focus at points on the circumference of a circle in the image plane. They also make equal angles with the optic axis of the crystal, so that equal phase differences are introduced between their emergent components. In particular, if the analyser and polarizer are crossed and the phase difference introduced by the crystal is a multiple of 2π, the resultant emergent disturbances

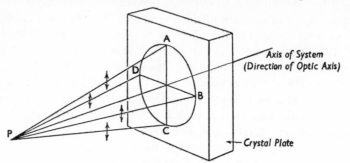

Fig. 22-31. Diverging cone incident on a crystal plate.

will be obstructed and there will be a dark ring in the field of view. For principal rays inclined to the axis at certain other angles, the phase differences between emergent components will be other multiples of 2π. That is, there will be a series of concentric dark rings in the image plane or field of view and, between these dark rings, there will be maxima. The radii of the bright and dark rings depend upon the wavelength and coloured rings will be observed when white light is used. However, since there is symmetry about the axis of the system, the colour is constant round any circle centred on the axis. Such a line is called an *iso-chromatic line*. Suppose, now, that the plane of vibration of the incident light

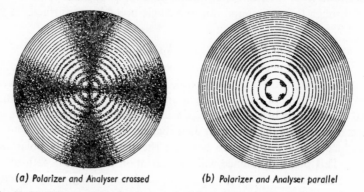

(a) Polarizer and Analyser crossed   (b) Polarizer and Analyser parallel

Fig. 22-32. Rings and brushes for a uniaxial crystal cut perpendicular to the axis.

is parallel to AC. Pencils whose principal rays are incident at points along AC have their plane of vibration in the plane of incidence, and those whose principal rays are incident along BD have their plane of vibration perpendicular to the plane of incidence. The former have no component of **D** in the direction corresponding to the O-ray, and the latter give no E-ray in the crystal; for these pencils the vibration is in a privileged direction. Consequently, the emergent rays will be polarized in the same plane as the incident rays and will be obstructed by the crossed analyser. In the field of view this gives two perpendicular diameters of zero intensity. Since these dark lines will be the same for all wavelengths, they are called the *achromatic* lines or *isogyres*. The isochromatic maxima are, of course, interrupted by the achromatic lines, and the intensities of the former build up slowly as one moves away from the latter. The isochromatic lines are usually called the *rings* and the achromatic lines are called the *brushes* since they are less sharp. When the analyser and polarizer are parallel, the complementary patterns are observed. Fig. 22–32 shows the rings and brushes for a uniaxial crystal cut perpendicular to the axis and placed between crossed and parallel Nicols.

(c) Isochromatic Surfaces

With a crystal plate in converging (or diverging) pencils it is necessary to know the way in which the phase difference between the O and E disturbances depends

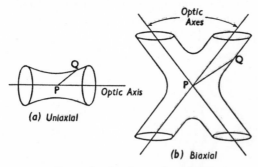

Fig. 22–33. Isochromatic surfaces.

upon the direction of the light. Suppose that one takes a point P in an anisotropic medium and that one has plane waves passing through P such that the O- and E-wave normals are along PQ [Fig. 22–33(a) or (b)]. If the disturbances are in phase at P the phase difference, δ, at Q will depend on the length and direction of PQ. Taking P as origin, let Q move in such a way that the length PQ always corresponds to a given phase difference. The locus of Q will be a surface of constant phase difference for waves from P, and by taking a number of different values of δ a family of surfaces is obtained. They are known as *isochromatic surfaces* (sometimes as Bertin's surfaces). Fig. 22–33 shows typical isochromatic surfaces for uniaxial and biaxial media.

As was pointed out above, a movement of the crystal along the axis of the system does not affect the pattern observed with a conoscope. It is now convenient to take the intersection point of the principal rays (the point P in Fig. 22–31) to be on the first surface of the crystal. Taking this as the origin for the isochromatic surfaces (P in Fig. 22–33), the wave normal directions in the crystal that correspond to a given phase difference on emergence are found by joining P to points on the curve of intersection of the appropriate isochromatic surface with the second surface of the crystal plate. For a uniaxial crystal cut perpendicular to the optic axis as described above, this intersection is a circle for each isochromatic surface. In this case the observed isochromatic lines have the same form as the intersections of the isochromatic surface with the crystal surface but, in general, this is not so because, for crystals cut with other orientations of the optic axis, wave normals in different azimuths are refracted differently on emergence. That is to say, those which are equally inclined to the axis of the system within the crystal are not equally inclined to the axis after emergence. However, the observed isochromatic lines do bear a superficial resemblance to the intersections of the isochromatic surfaces with the crystal face, and these intersections can be used to give a qualitative explanation of the form of the isochromatic lines. It should be noted that for a given incident wave normal there are, in general, two wave normals in the crystal. Hence the phase difference required is not that between waves whose normals are parallel. This effect also can be neglected in an elementary treatment of the subject.

(d) Uniaxial Crystal Cut Parallel to the Optic Axis

By considering the intersections of the isochromatic surfaces with the crystal surface as described above one can explain, in general terms, the hyperbolic form of the isochromatic lines obtained when a uniaxial crystal is cut parallel to the optic axis (see Fig. 22–34).

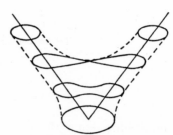

Fig. 22–34. Isochromatic lines for a uni-axial crystal cut parallel to the axis.

Fig. 22–35. Sections across an isochro-matic of a biaxial crystal.

(e) Biaxial Crystal Cut Perpendicular to the Direction Bisecting the Optic Axes

The shape of an isochromatic surface is shown in Fig. 22–33(*b*). If, at various distances from P, one takes sections normal to the direction bisecting the optic axes, one obtains the curves shown in Fig. 22–35. These, then, are the forms of

(a)   (b)   (c)

Fig. 22–36. Isochromatic lines for a biaxial crystal cut perpendicular to the bisector of the angle between the axes.

the intersections of the second crystal surface with various isochromatic surfaces if one takes the origin P to be on the first surface of the crystal plate. This gives a qualitative explanation of the isochromatic lines actually observed (see Fig. 22–36). The shape of the brushes, or achromatic lines, depends upon the orientation of the polarizer and analyser to the planes of the optic axes. In (a) the plane containing the axes is parallel to the principal section of the polarizer; in (b) the crystal has been rotated slightly from this position; and (c) shows the pattern for a crystal at an angle of 45°. In each case the polarizer and analyser are crossed and the crystal is cut perpendicular to the bisector of the angle between the axes.

22–19. The Polarizing Microscope

Fig. 22–37(a) shows, schematically, the arrangement for straightforward examination of specimens between a polarizer and analyser. In the past, Ahrens

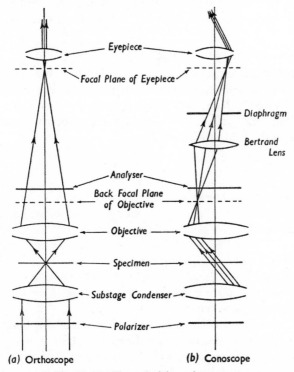

(a) Orthoscope   (b) Conoscope

Fig. 22–37. The polarizing microscope.

prisms were in common use, and since it was necessary for collimated light to traverse the analyser, the prism was placed between two extra lenses. Sheets of Polaroid are now used for the polarizer and analyser and the extra lenses are no longer required. It is usually convenient for the specimen to be carried on a revolving circular stage or on a stage which enables it to be tilted as well as rotated. When it is desired to examine a crystal plate in converging pencils of parallel rays, an additional *Amici-Bertrand lens* is interposed as in (b). This converts the system into a *conoscope*. It will be seen that each point in the field of view corresponds to a given *direction* through the crystal. In effect, the Bertrand lens and the eyepiece constitute a system used to examine the pattern in the back focal plane of the objective. This corresponds to the pattern in the plane AB of the lens L in Fig. 22–30 (§22–18). When the Bertrand lens is in use, a small aperture is positioned conjugate to the specimen as shown in the figure. In consequence, only a small area of the specimen is used and a plane-parallel element can be selected.

In order to analyse the light transmitted by the specimen, a quartz compensator or a quarter-wave plate can be interposed between the objective and the analyser. It is also possible in some instruments to locate a quartz wedge in the focal plane of the eyepiece. The advantage of this method is that the graduations on the wedge, which indicate its thickness, are in focus with either of the arrangements shown in Fig. 22–37. In addition, the eyepiece is often fitted with a rotating analyser; obviously this can be done less clumsily with Polaroid than with any calcite prism analyser. With the conoscopic system it is sometimes convenient to mount a quartz wedge in the back focal plane of the objective.

22–20. The Kerr Electro-optical Effect

When placed in an electric field, many substances behave like a uniaxial crystal (usually positive) whose optic axis is parallel to the lines of force. The effect was discovered by Kerr, in 1895, using glass. If n_1 and n_2 are the refractive indices for light whose planes of vibration are respectively parallel to and perpendicular to the field, it is found that

$$n_1 - n_2 = k\lambda E^2, \qquad \ldots \ldots \ldots \quad (22\text{--}4)$$

where E is the electric intensity and λ is the wavelength. k is known as Kerr's constant and has been determined for a wide range of solids, liquids, and gases. If E is in e.s.u. one has, for sodium light, $k = 2 \cdot 5 \times 10^{-11}$ for carbon dioxide at N.T.P., $4 \cdot 7 \times 10^{-7}$ for water, $2 \cdot 2 \times 10^{-5}$ for nitrobenzene, and $2 \cdot 9 \times 10^{-9} - 1 \cdot 5 \times 10^{-8}$ for various glasses, λ being measured in cm.

The effect can be investigated by employing the substance concerned as the dielectric in a parallel plate condenser, this so-called *Kerr Cell* being placed between a polarizer and an analyser.

The theory of the Kerr effect is beyond the scope of this book. It has been assumed that an applied electric field induces an electric moment in non-polar molecules and changes the moment of polar molecules. There is also a reorientation of the molecules which causes the medium as a whole to become anisotropic. This explains the delay that occurs between the application of the field and the appearance of the maximum effect. The delay can be several seconds in the case of some solids but is very small ($\sim 10^{-11}$ sec.) for non-polar liquids with small molecules.

The Kerr effect must not be confused with the *electric double refraction* observed in the region of absorption lines. It is found that in the presence of an electric field the absorption frequencies are dependent upon the polarization of the light. Thus for frequencies near an absorption line the velocity of light will depend on the state of polarization, i.e. the medium is birefringent.

22-21. The Voigt and Cotton-Mouton Effects

The *Cotton-Mouton effect* (discovered in 1905) is the magnetic analogue of the Kerr electro-optical effect. It is found that in the presence of a transverse magnetic field many liquids became doubly refracting. As with the Kerr effect, the difference between the refractive indices is proportional to the square of the field strength and, in a similar manner, it is attributed to a re-orientation of molecules in the presence of the field. In the analogue of equation (22–4) the constant has rather smaller values, e.g. $-1 \cdot 1 \times 10^{-14}$ for water. A very much smaller effect is the *magnetic double refraction* or *Voigt effect* (discovered 1902) which is analogous to the electric double refraction referred to in the previous section. In a similar manner it is attributed to the effect of the field on the absorption frequencies which become dependent on the polarization of the light. Electric and magnetic double refraction are related, in similar ways, to the Stark and Zeeman effects respectively.

22-22. The Photo-elastic Effect

It was found by Brewster in 1816 that a transparent isotropic medium becomes optically anisotropic when a mechanical stress is applied. If a body under stress is placed between a polarizer and a crossed analyser, the birefringence of the body will cause some light to be transmitted by the analyser. When investigating the effect, the observing system must be focused on the specimen itself, and the variations of intensity (and of colour if white light is used) will depend on the local variations of birefringence throughout the specimen. It is found that the privileged directions of **D** are along the directions of the principal stresses. If n_P and n_Q are the refractive indices for light whose vibration directions are parallel to the principal stresses P and Q respectively, then one has

$$n_P - n_Q \propto (Q - P).$$

In many engineering problems it is very useful to build a model of the structure concerned in some transparent material; when the structure is loaded the nature of the stresses can be observed. For example, *isochromatic lines* are the loci of points in the model at which $(P - Q)$ has the same value.

In the manufacture of many optical instruments, care must be taken to avoid the setting up of stresses in the glass. In the production of the glass itself the annealing process must be controlled with great care and, in the instrument, attention must be given to the way in which the components are held in position. At every stage the glass is viewed between a polarizer and crossed analyser in a *polariscope*.

CHAPTER XXIII

OPTICAL ACTIVITY

23–1. Optically Active Crystals

IF a beam of light enters a plane-parallel plate cut from an ordinary uniaxial crystal, there are, in general, two emergent beams, and these are plane polarized at right angles. If, however, one has light incident normally on a plate cut perpendicular to the optic axis, the O and E disturbances are propagated with equal velocities and the phase difference between them remains constant. That is to say, the state of polarization of the emergent light is identical with that of the incident light. With some crystals, of which quartz is a well known example, it is found that if plane polarized light is incident normally on a plate cut perpendicular to the axis, the emergent beam is also plane polarized but its plane of vibration is different from that of the incident beam. The effect was discovered in 1811 by Arago. It is found that the rotation of the plane of vibration is proportional to the thickness of the crystal plate, and does not depend upon the orientation of the plane of vibration of the incident light. Crystals that rotate the plane of vibration in this way are said to be *optically active*. Looking against the oncoming light, crystals that rotate the plane of vibration in a clockwise direction are said to be *right-handed* or *dextro-rotatory*; those that rotate it in an anticlockwise direction are *left-handed* or *laevo-rotatory*. Quartz exists in both forms. The rotation produced by a plate 1 mm. in thickness is called the *specific rotation*. For sodium light the specific rotation is 21·7° for quartz, 3·67° for sodium chlorate, and 325° for cinnabar. The effect is found also in biaxial crystals.

23–2. Rotatory Dispersion

The specific rotation depends on the wavelength of the light and was found by Biot to be approximately proportional to $(1/\lambda^2)$. More accurate investigations showed that rotatory dispersion follows a law similar to that governing ordinary dispersion of the refractive index. For example, throughout most of the visible spectrum the specific rotation of quartz is given by an equation of the Cauchy type:

$$\alpha = A + \frac{B}{\lambda^2}. \qquad \cdots \cdots \quad (23\text{–}1)$$

Near absorption lines one has anomalous rotatory dispersion comparable with anomalous dispersion of the refractive index.

Suppose a collimated beam of white light is incident normally on a quartz plate cut perpendicular to the axis and placed between crossed Nicols. Wavelengths for which the plate gives a rotation of a multiple of π will be removed by the analyser, and, if the transmitted light is passed into a spectroscope, the spectrum will show a number of dark bands. The intensity will reach a maximum for wavelengths that have been rotated an odd multiple of $\pi/2$, and for intermediate wavelengths the analyser will transmit the component that is parallel to the transparent vibration direction. If the quartz plate is very thin, the rotation is small and does not vary widely throughout the visible region. Consequently, the light transmitted by the analyser appears white or grey. If the quartz plate is very thick, the transmitted light is white because the many obstructed wavelengths are distributed throughout the spectrum. For a plate of moderate thickness, however, one or two spectral regions are obstructed and the transmitted light appears coloured. If the analyser is replaced by an ordinary calcite prism, there are two emergent beams. One contains wavelengths which a crossed analyser would pass, and the other those which the analyser would obstruct. Consequently, the two beams have complementary colours. If they are made to overlap, a white beam is produced—another convenient way of demonstrating the combination of complementary colours.

23–3. Fresnel's Theory

For a non-active crystal, only plane polarized disturbances can be propagated in directions other than the optic axis. For a point source in such a medium the

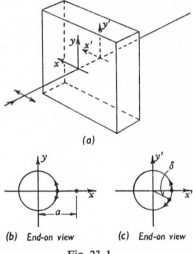

(a)

(b) End-on view　　　(c) End-on view

Fig. 23–1.
Fresnel's theory of optical activity.

wave surface is in two sheets, and these touch to give a common diameter parallel to the optic axis. This suggests that light in any state of polarization can be propagated along the optic axis. Fresnel assumed that in an optically active crystal only circularly polarized disturbances can be propagated in the direction of what would otherwise be the optic axis, and that the velocity of propagation is different for different directions of rotation. It is easy to show that a plane polarized disturbance can be resolved into two circularly polarized components with opposite directions of rotation. If these travel with different speeds, the phase difference between them is different at different distances through the crystal and this corresponds to a rotation of the plane of the resultant.

Suppose, for example, that plane polarized light is incident normally on an optically active crystal plate cut perpendicular to the axis. Let the first crystal face be in the xy-plane [see Fig. 23–1(a)], and let the plane polarized incident disturbance be represented by

$$x = a \cos \omega t. \quad \ldots \ldots (23–2)$$

This can be resolved into the two circular motions represented by

$$x = \frac{a}{2} \cos \omega t, \quad \left. \vphantom{\begin{array}{c}1\\1\\1\end{array}} \right\}$$
$$y = \frac{a}{2} \sin \omega t \quad \ldots \ldots (23–3)$$

and
$$x = \frac{a}{2} \cos \omega t,$$
$$y = -\frac{a}{2} \sin \omega t.$$
$$. . . . . . \quad (23\text{-}4)$$

The first pair of equations represents an anticlockwise, and the second a clockwise, circular motion. Both start from the point $x = a/2$ at time $t = 0$, and reference to the equations and to Fig. 23–1(b) shows that on superposition they give the linear motion represented by (23–2). It will be seen that two oppositely directed circular motions of equal frequency combine to give a linear motion along the diameter joining the points where the rotating radius vectors cross.

Now, according to Fresnel, the two circular components are propagated through the plate with different speeds. (The two circles are, of course, traversed at the same speed since they correspond to disturbances of the same frequency.) Consequently, when they emerge from the plate there is a phase difference δ between them. Suppose, for example, that the clockwise component advances in front of the other. Taking axes x' and y' (parallel to x and y) in the second crystal face, the result of this phase difference is that, if the anticlockwise rotation is at $x' = a/2$ at $t = 0$, the clockwise rotation has advanced through an angle δ beyond the x'-axis [Fig. 23–1(c)]. That is to say, the rotating radius vectors crossed at $-\delta/2$, and this gives the direction of the linear resultant disturbance which emerges—the plane of vibration has rotated clockwise through an angle $\delta/2$.

Analytically (since only relative phases matter) the emergent circular components can be represented by

$$x' = \frac{a}{2} \cos \omega t,$$
$$y' = \frac{a}{2} \sin \omega t$$
and
$$x' = \frac{a}{2} \cos (\omega t + \delta),$$
$$y' = -\frac{a}{2} \sin (\omega t + \delta).$$

Superposition gives

$$x' = \frac{a}{2} [\cos \omega t + \cos (\omega t + \delta)],$$

$$y' = \frac{a}{2} [\sin \omega t - \sin (\omega t + \delta)].$$

$$\therefore \quad x' = a \cos \left(\frac{\delta}{2}\right) \cos \left(\omega t + \frac{\delta}{2}\right),$$
$$y' = -a \sin \left(\frac{\delta}{2}\right) \cos \left(\omega t + \frac{\delta}{2}\right).$$
$$. . . \quad (23\text{-}5)$$

Since these two perpendicular linear components are in phase the resultant is along the line inclined to the x' axis at angle $-\delta/2$.

If n_C and n_A are the refractive indices of the crystal in the direction of the optic axis for clockwise and anticlockwise circularly polarized light, and d is the thickness of the crystal plate, the phase difference δ is given by

$$\delta = \frac{2\pi d}{\lambda}(n_A - n_C), \quad \ldots \ldots \quad (23\text{–}6)$$

i.e.   rotation of plane of vibration $= (\pi d/\lambda)(n_A - n_C)$.   .   (23–7)

It will be seen that in a right-handed (dextro-rotatory) crystal, the clockwise circularly polarized component travels more quickly than the other, whereas in a left-handed crystal it is the slower component. The existence of these circularly polarized components was demonstrated by Fresnel using a train of left- and right-handed quartz prisms as indicated by Fig. 23–2. For the clockwise component the refractive index of the second prism is higher than that of the first,

Fig. 23–2. Fresnel's prism system for separating circular components of plane polarized or unpolarized light.

but for the anticlockwise component it is lower. Consequently, there is double refraction at this surface and the circularly polarized components are separated slightly. At the interface between the second and third prisms the right-handed component is entering a less dense medium and the left-handed component is entering a denser medium. The obliquity of the surface causes the angular separation between the rays to be increased. This continues throughout the train of prisms until two approximately circularly polarized beams emerge. (As will be seen below, the disturbances propagated in a direction which is slightly inclined to the optic axis are, in fact, elliptically polarized.) If the incident light is unpolarized each linear component splits up in this way.

23–4. Wave Surface for Quartz

For a non-active uniaxial crystal the wave surface consists of a sphere and either an inscribed prolate spheroid or an escribed oblate spheroid. These two sheets of the wave surface touch at two points and the line joining the points of contact gives the direction of the optic axis. The radius vector from the centre to any point on one of the sheets of the wave surface is proportional to the ray velocity in that direction and corresponds to one of the two possible plane polarized disturbances. If the crystal is optically active there are two possible velocities in the direction corresponding to the optic axis, so that the two sheets of the wave surface do not touch. There is another important difference: in the direction of the axis the radius vector to each sheet of the wavefront represents a possible velocity of circularly, not linearly, polarized light. In directions perpendicular to the axis the possible velocities now correspond to *approximately* plane polarized rays. For quartz the two sheets of the wave surface resemble those of a positive uniaxial crystal except that they do not touch. What would normally be the spherical sheet is distorted outwards by a small amount in the region of the axis, and the other sheet is distorted inwards. The wave surface takes the form indicated in Fig. 23–3. It is important to realize that the separa-

tion of the two sheets along the axis is very much smaller than that in the perpendicular direction and that both are exaggerated in the figure. For example, for sodium light travelling perpendicular to the optic axis one has (at 18°C.) $n_E = 1·55336$, $n_O = 1·54425$, the latter being also the mean of n_C and n_A for light along the axis. It follows that the separation of the sheets of the wave surface in the direction perpendicular to the axis is about $0·006r$ where r is the radius of the approximately spherical sheet. For sodium light along the axis, the specific rotation is found to be 21·7° per mm. Using equation

Fig. 23–3. Wave surface for quartz.

(23–7) this gives, for right-handed quartz $(n_A - n_C) \fallingdotseq 0·00007$ so that the separation of the sheets of the wave surface is about $0·000045r$.

As stated above, the wave surface gives the velocities of circularly polarized light along the axis, and of approximately plane polarized light in the perpendicular directions. They are the only types of disturbance which can be propagated without change in those directions. It was shown by Airy that in intermediate directions the wave surface gives the velocities of elliptically polarized disturbances. Thus any disturbance in these directions is resolved into elliptically polarized components. The major axes of the ellipses are in the vibration directions of the plane polarized disturbances for an inactive crystal. As one moves away from the direction of the axis the eccentricities of the ellipses increase rapidly and in most directions one can look upon the wave surface as indicating the velocities of the two possible plane polarized disturbances appropriate to an inactive crystal. That is to say, it is only for directions close to the optic axis that the properties of an active crystal differ markedly from those of an inactive one. For example, at 10° away from the optic axis the ratio of the axes of the ellipse is 7·8.

(a)   (b)

Fig. 23–4. Resolution of plane polarized light into elliptically polarized components.

Fig. 23–4(a) illustrates the double refraction of a ray incident normally on a quartz plate cut almost perpendicular to the axis. Both the refracted rays are elliptically polarized; they lie very close together and the eccentricities of the ellipses are the same. The relative intensities of the two refracted rays are determined by the state of polarization of the incident light, and if the latter is unpolarized the refracted rays will have equal intensities. If the incident light is plane polarized with **D** in a principal section as illustrated, the major axis of one ellipse will be the same as the minor axis of the other. For example, in Fig. 23–4(*b*) the two elliptic motions illustrated are the components of the linear motion of amplitude OP. For other states of polarization of the incident light the relative intensities and phases of the elliptic components will be different.

$$\delta \qquad 0 \qquad \frac{\pi}{2} \qquad \pi \qquad \frac{3\pi}{2} \qquad 2\pi$$

Fig. 23–5. Recombination of elliptic components.

Again, for the example illustrated, the two refracted paths are not widely different and, for a moderately thin crystal plate and a beam of finite width, the emergent disturbances can be assumed to be superposed. There will be a certain phase difference between the elliptic components shown in (*b*) and, in general, the resultant will be elliptically polarized. Fig. 23–5 shows the state of polarization of the resultant for different values of the phase difference δ.

When a quartz plate cut perpendicular to the axis is placed between a polarizer and an analyser and illuminated by convergent pencils as in § 22–18, the patterns observed are very similar to those obtained with a non-active crystal. The chief difference is that for light which has passed parallel, or nearly parallel, to the optic axis the crystal gives a rotation of the plane of vibration. The result is that, in general, the centre of the pattern with a crossed analyser is bright instead of dark.

23–5. The Cornu Prism

If it is desired to use a uniaxial crystal in a prism spectrograph, the prism is cut with the optic axis along the path of the light in the prism [see Fig. 23–6(*a*)]. However, with an optically active crystal such as quartz, this arrangement still gives a doubling of each spectrum line since for each incident ray, one has two circularly polarized emergent rays corresponding to slightly different refractive indices. To overcome this difficulty

Fig. 23–6. Crystal prisms and lens.

Cornu used a composite prism employing both left- and right-handed quartz as indicated in (*b*). When used at minimum deviation, this prism gives a single emergent beam since the phase difference introduced in one half is removed in the other.

If a Littrow system is required, one of the components of the Cornu prism can be used alone, the surface AB being coated to give the plane mirror. The clockwise circularly polarized vibrations approaching the reflecting surface become the anticlockwise components after reflection, and the anticlockwise become the clockwise. It will be seen that the phase difference resulting from the passage through the prism in one direction is removed by the passage in the reverse direction.

One can also use quartz lenses with a construction similar to that of the Cornu prism [see Fig. 23–6(c)]. The composite lens consists of two plano-convex components, one of left- and the other of right-handed quartz.

Fused quartz components are sometimes used since these are not birefringent. It is, however, difficult to produce large components free from inhomogeneities.

23–6. Optical Activity in Liquids

It was found by Biot that many liquids and solutions are optically active, i.e. rotate the plane of vibration when plane polarized light is passed through them. The optical activity of most crystals is associated with the absence of a centre of symmetry in the fundamental crystal form; this causes the velocity of circularly polarized light to depend upon the direction of rotation. Now a liquid is iso-tropic in the sense that the molecules are randomly orientated throughout it and, consequently, the optical activity is attributed to the asymmetrical structure of the molecules themselves. One might say that there is a preferential direction of rotation associated with each molecule. If, at first sight, it seems that the random orientation of the molecules in a liquid would cause this to be ineffective in a finite volume, it is worth noting that, no matter how the screw is positioned, the rotation associated with the advance of a right-handed screw is always the same. Thus some optical activity is caused by the structural dissymmetry of crystals and some by molecular dissymmetry. The latter remains when the substance is in the fused state or is in solution but the former disappears when the crystal is dissolved or fused. When a substance shows both kinds of dissym-metry the activity associated with the crystal structure predominates.

It was shown above that the rotation produced by an active crystal is propor-tional to the thickness of crystal traversed. This means that it is proportional to the number of fundamental rotating elements traversed. In the same way it is found that the rotation produced by a solution of an active substance in an inactive solvent is proportional to the length of path in the solution and to the concentration. Measurement of the rotation is now a widely used method of determining the concentration of sugar solutions.

Usually the rotation produced by a liquid is considerably less than that produced by a crystal. For example, 10 cm. of turpentine rotates sodium light $-37°$ (i.e. anticlockwise), whereas an equal thickness of quartz would rotate it $\pm 2172°$. For this reason the standard path length for a liquid is taken as 10 cm. instead of 1 mm. For an active liquid, or for a solution of an active substance such as sugar in an inactive solvent, one defines the *specific rotation* or *rotatory power* (α) as the rotation produced by a 10 cm. column of liquid containing 1 gm. of active substance per c.c. of solution. Thus for a solution containing m grams per c.c. the rotation for a path length l is given by

$$\theta = \frac{\alpha m l}{10},$$

i.e.
$$\alpha = \frac{10\theta}{ml} \qquad . \quad . \quad . \quad . \quad . \quad . \quad (23–8)$$

and for a pure liquid m is simply the density.

The product of the specific rotation and the molecular weight of the active substance is known as the *molecular rotation*.

Careful investigation has shown that the rotation is not *exactly* proportional to the concentration, and in accurate work a suitable correction must be made. It is found also that the rotation depends upon the temperature and, to a slight extent, upon the solvent employed.

Liquids show rotatory dispersion similar to that of a crystal. In particular, the rotatory dispersions of sugars are very similar to the rotatory dispersion of quartz; the importance of this fact will be seen in § 23–9.

23–7. Polarimeters

Instruments that measure the rotation of the plane of vibration produced by a solution are known as *polarimeters*; those that are intended for measurements on sugar solutions in particular are called *saccharimeters*. If an optically active solution is placed between crossed Nicols (polarizer and analyser), some light is transmitted by the analyser. Obviously the rotation of the solution for a given wavelength can be measured by rotating the analyser or the polarizer until there is again no transmitted light (see § 22–6). Until recently, most saccharimeters have employed a fixed polarizer and analyser, the rotation of the solution being balanced out by a quartz compensator. As will be seen in § 23–9, this enabled white light to be used. This was an advantage because high intensity monochromatic sources were not available or were inconvenient for routine use such as that for which saccharimeters are required. Instruments designed as saccharimeters are usually provided with a scale which indicates sugar concentration directly.

The simplest form of polarimeter contains only a polarizer and an analyser. For example, Biot used a reflecting plate of glass as the polarizer and employed a calcite crystal as an analyser, and Nörrenberg used glass plates for both polarizer and analyser. The first polarimeter to employ Nicols was that due to Mitscherlich (1844). The rotation produced by the optically active medium was measured by rotating the analyser until the transmitted light was extinguished. This gave the vibration direction of the light entering the analyser but did not indicate whether the plane of vibration was rotated clockwise or anticlockwise in order to reach that orientation. In addition, one could not tell whether the plane of vibration had rotated through (say) θ or $p\pi+\theta$. These ambiguities can be removed by reducing the thickness of active medium traversed and observing the new position of the analyser for extinction. As pointed out in § 22–7, the field of view is not uniformly dark with crossed Nicols; with this polarimeter one rotates the analyser until the dark shadow lies across the centre of the field. The orientation of this dark band depends on the orientation of the analyser and, consequently, it is changed when the active material is interposed. Again, the dark band is not well defined and the setting of the analyser is rather uncertain.

Sénarmont's polarimeter employs a pair of thin quartz wedges cut perpendicular to the optic axis. One wedge is of laevo- and the other of dextro-quartz (see Fig. 23–7). Suppose plane polarized light passes through this composite plate. For ray (1) the path in dextro-quartz is longer than that in laevo-quartz and the net result is that the plane of vibration is rotated clockwise (looking against the oncoming light). Similarly, the plane of vibration of ray (3) is rotated anticlockwise and ray (2), which traverses equal thicknesses of each wedge, emerges with its plane of vibration unchanged. If a composite plate of this type is placed between crossed Nicols, the field of view will show dark bands where the plate gives a rotation of 0, $\pm\pi$, $\pm2\pi$, etc. At intermediate points the rotation introduced by the plate causes the emergent light to have a component of vibration parallel to the principal section of the analyser, so that some light is transmitted. In practice the wedge angles are very small and only the central dark band is observed. If an optically active substance is interposed between analyser and polarizer, the dark band moves across the field to the point which corresponds to an equal and opposite rotation in the composite plate. The

Fig. 23–7. Composite plate for Sénarmont's polarimeter.

analyser is then rotated to return the dark band to the centre of the field. In a modified form of this instrument one half of the aperture was occupied by a prism of the form described above, and the other half by a similar wedge in which the laevo- and dextro-components were interchanged. The end-point adjustment of the instrument is then the alignment of the fringes in the two halves of the field of view.

The most accurate single-field polarimeter is that due to Wild. The arrangement is shown in Fig. 23–8. The analyser A is fixed and the observer can rotate the polarizer P by means of a long shaft, and can read the rotation by means of a suitable viewing-system. The liquid under test is contained in the tube T. This is followed by the *Savart prism* S which consists of two thin plates of quartz cut at 45° to the optic axis and cemented together with their principal sections at right angles. S is fixed in the analyser mounting so that the bisector of the angle

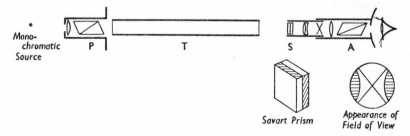

Mono-
chromatic   P   T   S   A
Source

Savart Prism   Appearance of Field of View

Fig. 23–8. Wild's polarimeter.

between the principal sections of its two halves is parallel to the principal section of the analyser, i.e. horizontal. If the Nicols are crossed the field of view contains a series of parallel horizontal fringes. As P is rotated the fringes become fainter, and, when the principal section of P is parallel to the principal section of either half of S, they disappear in the centre of the field as indicated in the figure. P is adjusted until the ends of the remaining fringes are symmetrically placed with respect to the cross-wires carried in the analyser mount (see Fig. 23–8). This is the zero position of P. When the active liquid is interposed the fringes return, and P is rotated until the field regains its original appearance. The accuracy of this instrument is comparable with that obtained with modern variable half-shadow instruments.

When a Savart plate is used with an analysing Nicol the appearance of the fringes provides a sensitive method of detecting partial polarization of the light entering the plate.

23–8. Half-shadow End-point Indicators

With a simple polarizer-analyser system the intensity of the field of view is very insensitive to small rotations of the analyser from the position of extinction. Consequently, the analyser cannot be set with great accuracy. Suppose that the polarizer gives plane polarized light but that one has slightly different planes of vibration in the two halves of the aperture. For example, suppose that, looking towards the oncoming beam of light, the planes of vibration are as indicated by Fig. 23–9. Suppose, now, that the analyser is rotated until its principal section is parallel to AB. Then the light in each half of the aperture has a small component of **D** in the transparent direction of the analyser, and the two halves of the aperture will appear equally and weakly illuminated. If the analyser is rotated through an angle $\theta/2$, the intensity of one side falls to zero while that

Fig. 23–9. The half-shadow principle: cross-section of beams showing vibration directions.

of the other increases. The position of the analyser that gives equal brightness in the two halves of the aperture can be found more precisely than the position that gives extinction in one half. In a polarimeter employing this method one simply adjusts the analyser for equality of illumination in the two halves of the field. The adjustment is repeated with the optically active medium between polarizer and analyser and the angle turned through by the analyser gives the rotation produced by the medium under test. It is interesting to note that the two halves of the field are also of equal brightness when the principal section of the analyser is perpendicular to AB. However, the brightnesses are then near their maxima and a small rotation of the analyser produces only a small change in the relative brightness.

The angle θ is known as the *shadow angle* so that the *half-shadow angle*, $\theta/2$, is the angle through which the analyser must be turned from the equality-of-brightness position in order to extinguish one half of the field. A number of half-shadow devices will now be described.

The Biquartz. The biquartz, devised by Soleil, was originally intended for use with white light in a saccharimeter but, as will be seen below, it can be used also with monochromatic light to give a half-shadow end-point device of the type described above. The biquartz is a quartz disc cut perpendicular to the axis, one half of the disc being of laevo- and the other of dextro-quartz. The thickness of the disc (3·75 mm.) is such that, for the mean yellow light in the region of maximum luminosity with a normal white source, the plane of vibration undergoes a rotation of $\pi/2$—clockwise in one half of the disc and anticlockwise in the other. Thus for yellow light the biquartz consists of two quarter-wave plates,

18*

where the term is used in a rather different sense from that employed in §22–13. The biquartz is placed immediately after an ordinary polarizer whose principal section PP' (Fig. 23–10) is parallel to the diameter separating the two halves of the disc. With white light the rotatory dispersion of the quartz causes the

Fig. 23–10. The biquartz.

Fig. 23–11. The biquartz as mono-chromatic half-shadow device.

vibration directions of red, yellow, and blue light to be as indicated in the figure. If the principal section of the analyser is parallel to that of the polarizer, the yellow light is extinguished, but in each half of the aperture some red and blue light is transmitted. The two halves of the field are equally illuminated with a reddish-violet *sensitive* or *transition tint*—the *tint of passage*. A small rotation of the analyser causes one half of the field to become distinctly red and the other to become blue. The setting of the analyser for a colour match can be done very accurately. The application of the biquartz in the Soleil saccharimeter with white light is discussed in §23–9. When sodium light alone is used the biquartz becomes an ordinary half-shadow device. Each half gives a rotation of 82° so that the vibration directions are as shown in Fig. 23–11. Obviously, the two halves of the field of view appear equally bright if the principal section of the analyser is normal to AB. It will be seen that the half-shadow angle is 8°. In the figure the dividing line of the biquartz is parallel to the principal section of the polarizer, but this is not essential. The two halves of the field will always be matched when the polarizer and analyser are parallel.

The Cornu-Jellett Prism. A half-shadow device was constructed from a Nicol by Jellett in 1860 and modified by Cornu in 1870. In the later form a thin wedge was removed from a Nicol as indicated by Fig. 23–12(*a*) and the remaining parts brought together as in (*b*). The vibration directions of the transmitted rays are then as indicated, and the mode of action is as described above. One can use

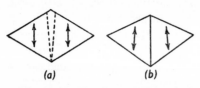

Fig. 23–12. The Cornu-Jellett prism.

such a prism as the polarizer or as the analyser in a polarimeter employing monochromatic light. The half-shadow angle is half the angle of the wedge which is removed; usually it is $2\frac{1}{2}°$.

Laurent Half-wave Plate. It was shown in §22–13 that if plane polarized light enters a half-wave plate (cut parallel to the optic axis) with the vibration direction inclined at angle θ to the axis, the vibration direction of the emergent light is inclined at angle $-\theta$—the plane of vibration is rotated through angle 2θ. The discussion in § 22-13 referred to a negative crystal but applies equally well to a positive crystal such as quartz. In the Laurent polarimeter, a half-wave plate of quartz is placed across one half of the aperture of the polarizer. The arrangement is shown in Fig. 23-13. The half-wave plate W is mounted, for convenience, on a glass plate that covers the whole aperture. The observing lens

Fig. 23-13. The Laurent polarimeter.

system L is focused on the plane of the half-wave plate which then covers half the sharply divided field of view. If the optic axis of the half-wave plate is inclined at angle θ to the vibration direction of the light from the polarizer P, the plate introduces a rotation 2θ. That is, the disturbances in the two halves of the field of view have vibration directions inclined at angle 2θ. The effect is similar to that obtained with the Cornu-Jellett prism, and θ is the half-shadow angle. In the present system, however, θ can be varied simply by rotating the polarizer. This was the first polarimeter to have a *variable half-shadow angle*. With regard to the choice of half-shadow angle, it will be seen that the smaller it is, the less bright will be the field of view when the two halves match. On the other hand, a smaller half-shadow angle gives a greater change in relative intensities for a given rotation of the analyser since a rotation through the half-shadow angle always reduces the ratio of the intensities from unity to zero. With transparent media and a bright source a half-shadow angle of $2\frac{1}{2}°$ has been widely used; for absorbing media it may be desirable to increase it to between $5°$ and $10°$ in order to secure a sufficiently bright field of view.

The Lippich Polarizer. The chief disadvantage of the Laurent system is that it can be used only with monochromatic light of the wavelength for which the plate is a half-wave plate. A more satisfactory system was devised by Lippich (1885) and this forms the basis of most modern polarimeters and saccharimeters. After the polarizer (now usually a prism of the Glazebrook-Thompson type) a

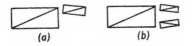

Fig. 23-14. Lippich polarizers.

smaller prism is placed across half the aperture [Fig. 23-14(a)]. The observer sights on the edge of the smaller prism and this prism must be tilted as in the figure until there is no overlapping of the halves of the field nor any separation between them. The principal section of the smaller prism is inclined at angle θ to that of the larger. Consequently, disturbances emerging from the smaller prism have their vibration direction inclined at angle θ to that of disturbances in the other half of the field. The intensity of the light emerging from the small prism is reduced by a factor $\cos^2 \theta$ since the prisms are partially crossed, and the intensity is further reduced by the extra absorption and partial reflections. In consequence, the principal section of the analyser is not exactly perpendicular to the bisector of the shadow angle θ when the halves of the field are matched. Obviously the shadow angle can be varied simply by rotating one of the prisms —usually the larger.

Lippich also produced a triple-field polarizer by employing two small prisms, each occupying one-third of the aperture of the large prism [see Fig. 23–14(b)]. The principal sections of the small prisms are parallel and are inclined at angle θ to that of the large prism, the centre of the aperture of the large prism being left clear. The analyser is rotated until all three parts of the field are matched. This can be done only if the source and eye are lined up symmetrically with respect to the two small prisms. With the double-field polarizer it is possible to change the relative intensities of the two halves of the field by an error of alignment, so that an incorrect setting of the analyser is made.

Since convenient high-intensity monochromatic sources have become readily available, ordinary polarimeters (frequently of the Lippich double- or triple-field type) have been calibrated for use as routine saccharimeters. With instruments of this type an accuracy of $0.005°$ has been obtained in the measurement of the rotation. For instruments intended for less accurate work polaroid components are now employed in place of polarizing prisms.

In recent years photo-electric polarimeters have been developed. In principle, the two halves of the field of a visual instrument are presented in succession to a photo-electric detector, and the end-point is a zero A.C. component in the output.

23–9. Compensating Saccharimeters

As mentioned in § 23–7, many saccharimeters have employed a compensator to balance out the rotation introduced by the solution. Fig. 23–15 shows two

Fig. 23–15. Quartz compensators.

forms of quartz wedge compensator. In (a) the two wedges of dextro-quartz and the plate of laevo-quartz are cut perpendicular to the optic axis. The wedge angles are usually about 3°. By moving the wedges as indicated the path in dextro-quartz can be varied and can be made smaller than, or greater than, the thickness of the fixed plate. That is, the combination can produce a net rotation in either direction. In (b) one wedge is of dextro- and the other of laevo-quartz. Again the net rotation can be in either direction. With both compensators the net rotation is the same for all parts of the aperture.

The compensator can be mounted immediately in front of the analyser. With no solution present the analyser or polarizer is adjusted until the parts of the field are matched (using one of the end-point indicators described in the previous section). The solution is then interposed and the rotation produced by the solution is balanced out by the compensator by adjusting the latter until the parts of the field again match. The movement of the compensator wedges is indicated on a linear scale which can be calibrated to indicate either rotation in degrees or sugar concentration.

Fortunately the rotatory dispersion of quartz in the visible region is almost identical with that of cane sugar. Consequently, if the compensator balances the rotation of the sugar solution for one wavelength, it does so for all, and one may therefore employ white light. For example, a biquartz can be used and the compensator adjusted to bring back the sensitive tint in both halves of the field. It is easy to see that the rotatory dispersion of the substance under test precludes the use of white light in an ordinary polarimeter. The rotatory dispersions of sugar and quartz are somewhat different at the blue end of the spectrum and some instruments employ a yellow filter to remove most of the blue light. Originally a 6% solution of potassium bichromate was used, the filter being

Fig. 23–16. Compensating saccharimeters.

1·5 cm. thick, but equivalent glass filters are now employed. Fig. 23–16 shows two types of compensating saccharimeter. That shown in (a) is a slight modification of the instrument devised by Soleil. P is the polarizer, B a biquartz, C the compensator, and A the analyser. The so-called *regulator* R is an additional Nicol followed by a thin quartz plate cut perpendicular to the optic axis. If the solution is coloured, or the source is a poor white, the various wavelengths in the emergent light are not present in those proportions which give the most sensitive tint. Now the rotatory dispersion of the quartz plate of the regulator will cause the planes of vibration of different wavelengths to be different, so that different wavelengths are transmitted unequally by P. By rotating the regulator Nicol the relative intensities of the various wavelengths can be varied until the sensitive tint is obtained.

Some saccharimeters have employed a Laurent plate in order to obtain a variable half-shadow angle but in most of the more recent instruments this is achieved by the use of a Lippich polarizer. The arrangement is shown in Fig. 23–16(b). Parallel light traverses the polarizer P, tube T, compensator C, and analyser A. The observing lens system L is focused on the edge of the small polarizing prism. F is a standard bichromate filter or its equivalent. With this arrangement white light can be used but the sensitive tint is not employed as end-point indicator.

It was pointed out above that compensating saccharimeters were devised mainly in order to allow white light to be used, but this point has now lost its importance since convenient high intensity (quasi-) monochromatic sources are available. However, it may be an advantage to avoid a rotating analyser involving a circular scale, and Gates (1958) has described a recording photo-electric compensating saccharimeter that uses the Faraday effect (see §23–11) to provide the compensating rotation. The essential elements of the system are shown in Fig. 23–17. The modulator consists of a solenoid wound round a glass core. A 50 cycle a.c. is passed through the solenoid so that the light passes through an alternating magnetic field and the Faraday effect causes the plane of vibration to

Fig. 23–17. Recording saccharimeter using Faraday rotation.

oscillate about the central position with an amplitude of about 3°. The central position is rotated by the solution under test and, at balance, is returned to its original position by the d.c. field of the Faraday compensator. The analyser and polarizer are crossed, so that the intensity emerging from the analyser would be zero if there were no modulator. With the modulator operating, the intensity reaches a maximum at each extremity of the oscillating plane of vibration, so that it varies with a frequency double that of the applied a.c. If the compensation is incorrect the plane of vibration does not oscillate symmetrically about the extinction position and the intensity maxima are unequal. The varying intensity then has a component of the same frequency as the applied a.c., the phase of this component depending on which maximum is the larger and therefore indicating whether the compensating rotation is too large or too small, and the amplitude indicating the extent of the imbalance. The output from the photo-multiplier is then passed through a filter to remove the double frequency component and then to a phase-sensitive rectifier keyed to the modulation signal. The output then indicates the direction and magnitude of the imbalance and is used to control the current in the compensating solenoid. The current in the compensator is proportional to the rotation in the sample and is recorded.

23–10. Circular Dichroism. The Cotton Effect

The phenomenon of dichroism (selective absorption of plane polarized light) was described in § 22–8, and it is to be expected that some substances will show unequal absorption of left- and right-handed circularly polarized light. The effect was first observed by Haidinger in 1847 in certain quartz crystals, and was observed in solutions by Cotton in 1895. Cotton suggested the term *circular dichroism* and this phenomenon, together with the anomalous rotatory dispersion in the region of absorption which accompanies it, is now referred to as the *Cotton effect.*

23–11. The Faraday Effect

In 1845 Faraday discovered that if glass is placed in a strong magnetic field it rotates the plane of polarization when plane polarized light is passed in a direction in which the field has a component. This was one of the earliest indications of a connection between light and electromagnetism. The effect has since been observed in many solids, liquids, and gases, and it is found that, if *H* is the magnetic intensity parallel to the direction of propagation of the light, the rotation of the plane of polarization for light of a given wavelength is given by

$$\theta = VHl,$$

where *l* is the length of the path in the field and *V* is a constant known as Verdet's constant. *V* is different for different substances, a positive value indicating that the rotation is in the clockwise direction *when looking along the direction of the field*. That is to say, *θ* is in the direction of rotation of a current which would give a field in the direction of *H*. It is important to notice that with magnetic rotation the direction of rotation does not depend on the direction of propagation of the light. Consequently, if light is reflected to and fro through the substance concerned, the rotation continues to increase. With *natural* rotation, on the other hand, the rotation changes direction when the direction of the light is reversed. (It was seen that a positive crystal always rotates the plane of vibration clockwise when looking *towards the oncoming light*.)

For sodium light the value of *V* in minutes of arc per oersted per cm. is 0·013 for water, 0·043 for carbon bisulphide, and about 0·08 for flint glass. For solutions one defines the *specific magnetic rotation* as the ratio of the rotation to the rotation produced by the same path length in water divided by the strength of the solution in grams of solute per c.c. of solution. The molecular rotation is the specific magnetic rotation multiplied by the ratio of the molecular weight of the solute to that of water.

Magnetic rotation can be explained by assuming that in the presence of a magnetic field the velocity of circularly polarized light depends on the direction of rotation. This variation of velocity is associated with the fact that the absorption frequencies, and therefore the dispersion of the medium, depend on the polarization of the light. (See also § 22–21.) Away from an absorption band Verdet's constant is approximately proportional to $(1/\lambda^2)$.

Very strong effects are observed with thin transparent films of ferro-magnetic materials. For example, for iron the effect is many thousand times larger than for water.

CHAPTER XXIV

THE VELOCITY OF LIGHT

24-1. Introduction

IN view of the enormous speed of light, it is not surprising that it was in the field of astronomy that it was first shown that the speed is, in fact, finite rather than infinite; it was only when astronomical distances were involved that the time of transit could be measured. The first calculation of the speed of light was made by Römer in 1676 from the observed times of the eclipses of a satellite of the planet Jupiter (see § 24–2). Bradley's observations in 1727 on the aberration of light led to a value of the speed of light which was in reasonable agreement with Römer's result (see § 24–3). It was not until 1849 that Fizeau succeeded in making the first determination of the time of transit of a beam of light over a terrestrial distance (§ 24–4). This was followed by Foucault's rotating mirror experiment in 1850 (§ 24–5). The rotating mirror method was used in a modified form by Michelson in 1879 and in later experiments by Michelson and by Newcomb.

Meanwhile, Maxwell's electromagnetic theory was published (1873) and Hertz's experiments (1887) demonstrated the existence of the waves predicted by the theory. The agreement between the predicted properties of electromagnetic waves and the observed properties of light quickly confirmed beyond all reasonable doubt that light waves were electromagnetic waves. Now the theory indicates that the velocity of electromagnetic waves in free space is independent of the frequency and is equal to the ratio of the e.m.u. to the e.s.u. of charge. Thus the speed of light can be determined by measuring the speed of radio waves or by measuring the ratio of the units. These methods are capable of about the same accuracy as the modern optical methods. Recent experiments have included direct measurement of the speed of the high frequency waves used in radar (§ 24–11), measurement of the resonant frequency of a cavity resonator (§ 24–11), measurements with a micro-wave interferometer (§ 24–11), and direct measurement of the speed of light using a shutter involving a Kerr cell or a piezo-electric crystal (§§ 24–8, 24–9, 24–12).

It is only in terms of the theory of relativity that one can give a full discussion of the velocity of light in moving media and of the velocity relative to an observer in motion. These subjects are referred to briefly in this chapter but the theory of relativity is beyond the scope of the present book.

24-2. Römer's Method

At a time when the earth was in that part of its orbit which is nearest to Jupiter, Römer observed the interval between successive eclipses of Jupiter's innermost satellite. He then calculated when the hundredth eclipse would occur but found that the observed time was about 15 minutes later. Römer pointed out that the earth had moved farther away from Jupiter and that the delay could be explained by assuming that the light took that much longer to travel from

Jupiter to the earth. The increase in distance between the earth and Jupiter could be deduced from astronomical observations so that the velocity of light could be calculated. Römer pointed out that if his explanation was correct the observed times of the eclipses would be delayed more and more as the distance between the earth and Jupiter increased, and that the delays would decrease as the planets approached one another. The delay would become zero when they returned to their original positions. That is to say, the observed interval between eclipses should show a periodic variation. This was confirmed experimentally and Römer obtained the value of $3 \cdot 10 \times 10^{10}$ cm. sec.$^{-1}$ for the speed of light. More recent observations have given about $2 \cdot 98 \times 10^{10}$ cm. sec.$^{-1}$.

24–3. The Aberration of Light

Owing to parallax, there is an apparent movement of nearer stars relative to more distant ones as the earth moves round its orbit. Bradley discovered that, in addition, every star appears to be displaced in the direction in which the earth is moving, and that this displacement is independent of the distance of the star from the earth. The necessary change in the direction of the observing telescope can be likened to the change in tilt which one must give to one's umbrella when, after standing still, one commences to walk in the rain. The effect is known as the *aberration of light*. Suppose AB (Fig. 24–1) is the axis of an observing telescope which is moving from left to right with speed v. Suppose light from a distant star is inclined at angle θ to the horizontal and enters the telescope at A. If the telescope points in the *apparent* direction of the star, the light must travel along the axis of the telescope. While it is doing so, the telescope axis moves to the position A'B'. That is, the light travels from the original position of A to the displaced position of B (i.e. to B'). Thus $AA' \propto v$ and $AB' \propto c$. In the figure the magnitude of the angle $\delta\theta$ has been very much exaggerated—since $v \ll c$, $\delta\theta$ is always small. Therefore $\angle ABB' \doteqdot \theta$ and $\triangle ABB'$ gives $\sin \delta\theta / \sin \theta = BB'/AB' = v/c$. Hence one can write

Fig. 24–1.
The aberration of light.

$$\delta\theta = \frac{v}{c}\sin \theta. \qquad \ldots \ldots (24\text{–}1)$$

By measuring the magnitude of the aberration Bradley obtained about $3 \cdot 08 \times 10^{10}$ cm. sec.$^{-1}$ for the velocity of light. More recent measurements have given 299,714 km. sec.$^{-1}$. The above is a simple non-relativistic account of the phenomenon of aberration; the theory of relativity is beyond the scope of the present discussions and a complete account of the aberration of light cannot be given here.

24–4. Fizeau's Method

Fizeau's experiment was the first successful attempt to find the time taken for a beam of light to traverse a terrestrial distance. Light from the source S passes through L_1 and is reflected by the unsilvered glass plate P to come to a focus in the focal plane of L_2. Hence a collimated beam emerges from L_2 and travels to L_3 which is at the centre of curvature of the concave mirror M. After reflection at M the light retraces its path through L_3 and L_2 and passes through P to the eyepiece so that the observer sees an image of the source. The problem is to find the time taken for the light to travel to M and back—a distance of $1\cdot7266 \times 10^6$ cm. Fizeau placed a toothed wheel in the focal plane of L_2 as indicated in the figure so that as the wheel is rotated flashes of light travel to M and back. If the speed of rotation is gradually increased from zero, a stage will be reached when a space

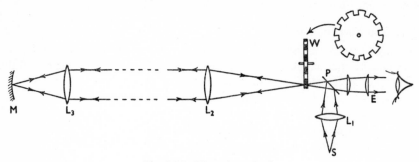

Fig. 24–2. Fizeau's method.

on the wheel is exactly replaced by a tooth during the time taken for the light to travel to M and back. The returning light will then be obstructed and the field of view will be dark. For a higher speed of rotation the light originally transmitted by one space will be able to return through the next space, and an image of the source will be seen. (It is actually seen by intermittent light but the frequency is so great that no flicker is noticed.) For a still higher speed the next tooth will obstruct the returning light, and the field of view will again be dark. Fizeau used a wheel with 720 teeth and found that the first eclipse occurred when the speed of the wheel was $12\cdot6$ revs per sec. This gives a transit time of $5\cdot5 \times 10^{-5}$ sec. so that $c = 3\cdot14 \times 10^{10}$ cm. sec.$^{-1}$. With a similar method Cornu (1874) increased the path length and was able to observe eclipses up to the thirtieth order.

The chief difficulty in Fizeau's method is deciding exactly when the eclipses are complete. This difficulty was overcome by Young and Forbes by placing another lens and mirror identical with L_3 and M at a greater distance, the two arrangements receiving light from L_2. The two images formed by the two returning beams were observed simultaneously and the speed of the wheel was found which gave images of equal intensity; it was then possible to calculate c. The result obtained was about $3\cdot01 \times 10^{10}$ cm. sec.$^{-1}$. The advantage of this method is that an observer can make an equality-of-brightness adjustment with considerable accuracy.

24–5. Foucault's Rotating Mirror Method

This method of measuring the velocity of light was originally suggested by Wheatstone but was first used successfully by Foucault. A plan of the arrangement is shown in Fig. 24–3. Light from the vertical slit source S passes through

the unsilvered plate P and the lens L and is reflected from the plane mirror R
which can be rotated about the vertical axis O. When R is suitably positioned
the light comes to a focus on the surface of the concave mirror M whose centre
is at O. If R is stationary, the light retraces its path through L, is reflected at P,
and forms an image of the slit at S'. Since M is centred at O the light retraces its
path for any position of R that causes the light to be incident somewhere on M.
Consequently, if R is rotated slowly there will be an intermittent image at S',
but while it is there it will be stationary. If R is rotated rapidly, the persistence
of the visual impression leads to an apparently continuous image. If,
however, the speed of rotation of
R is very great, the mirror will
move through a finite angle during
the time taken for the light to
travel from R to M and back. The
return beam will then traverse the
path indicated by the broken lines
and the slit image will be formed
at S''. By measuring the displacement S'S'' one can find the angle
turned through by R, and if the
speed of rotation of R is known, one
can find the time taken by the light
to travel from R to M and back. The
distance RM was only 4 metres
but in Foucault's final experiments
the light path was increased to 20
metres by using five fixed mirrors
instead of one. M was rotated slightly

Fig. 24–3. Foucault's rotating mirror method.

to reflect the light to a second mirror of the same radius. The light was
then reflected by a third and a fourth mirror and was incident normally on a
fifth, so that it retraced its path back to M. With the arrangement shown in
Fig. 24–3 the interval during which light is returned to R is proportional to the
angle subtended by M at R. That is, it is inversely proportional to the distance
RM. In consequence, the image observed at S'' gets fainter as the light path is
increased and the brightness can only be maintained by increasing the aperture
of M. Foucault overcame this difficulty by placing the lens L between R and M
and putting the source S close to R. When this is done the centre of M is almost
conjugate to O—actually it must be conjugate to S—and light is returned from
M to R as long as the central ray from R enters L. The interval during which
light returns to R is then proportional to the angle subtended at O by L and is
independent of the distance RM.

The length of the light path and the speed of rotation of R could be measured
accurately—the latter by means of a stroboscope—but the displacement S'S''
was only 0·7 mm., and could not be measured as accurately as the other two
quantities. Foucault's result for the speed of light was about $2·98 \times 10^{10}$ cm.
sec.$^{-1}$.

The rotating mirror method was also used by Cornu, by Michelson, and by

Newcomb. Michelson employed a much longer light path and was able to produce a displacement S'S" of 133 mm. The image could then be examined alongside the actual slit S and the Plate P could be dispensed with with a consequent saving of light. Newcomb used a square steel prism in place of the single mirror at R, so that light was directed towards M four times per revolution. This obviously increases the brightness of the image by a factor of four. Michelson and Pearson subsequently used 8-, 12-, and 16-sided mirrors in the Mount Wilson experiments. In the later measurements, attempts were made to ascertain the refractive index of the air and to calculate the velocity of light in a vacuum.

24–6. Michelson's Mount Wilson Determination

Fig. 24–4 shows the arrangement used at Mount Wilson in 1926. Light from the slit source S is reflected from one face of the octagonal mirror R and, after

Fig. 24–4. Michelson's Mount Wilson experiment.

reflection at M_1 and M_2, is collimated by the concave mirror M_3. (M_2 is slightly above, and M_6 slightly below, the plane of the diagram.) These components were at Mount Wilson. The light then travelled 22 miles to the concave mirror M_4 on Mount San Antonio. After reflection at the small plane (or, better, concave*) mirror M_5 placed at the focus of M_4, the light travelled back to M_3 and then via M_6, M_7, and the octagonal mirror, to form an image of S at E. M_3 and M_4 had focal lengths of 30 feet and apertures of 2 feet. If R rotates one-eighth of a revolution while the light travels to M_5 and back, the image of S observed at E occupies the same position as when R is stationary. Actually R rotated at about 528 revs per sec. and there was a small displacement of the image at E which was measured by means of a micrometer eyepiece. The speed of rotation of R was measured stroboscopically using an electrically maintained fork. The frequency of the fork and the distance between reference points at the two stations were measured by the U.S. Coast and Geodetic Survey. According to Dorsey, the light path was determined to an accuracy of about 1 in 200,000. This is better than the accuracy of the transit time, and of the estimated refractive index of the air. The result, as given by Michelson, was 299,796 km. sec.$^{-1}$ for the velocity in a vacuum. Birge (1941) has pointed out that the correction to a vacuum was made incorrectly (see § 24–10) and that the result should be 2 km. sec.$^{-1}$ higher.

Michelson attempted to increase the light path to 82 miles by employing reflectors at Mount San Jacinto but this was a failure owing to bad atmospheric conditions.

* Michelson does not state explicitly which was, in fact, used.

24–7. The One-mile Evacuated Pipe Experiment

The accuracy of measurement achieved in Michelson's Mount Wilson experiments was such that the uncertainty of the atmospheric conditions was one of the most important sources of error in finding the velocity in a vacuum. In order to overcome this difficulty Michelson planned an experiment in which the

Fig. 24–5. The one-mile evacuated pipe experiment.

light path was in a long evacuated pipe. The experiment was eventually completed by Pearson and Pease after Michelson's death in 1931. An iron pipe 3 feet in diameter and 1 mile long was constructed with carefully sealed joints and, by reflecting the light to and fro along the pipe, a light path of nearly 13 kilometres was achieved. In the various determinations the pressure in the pipe varied between 5·5 and 0·5 mm. of mercury. The arrangement of the optical system is shown in Fig. 24–5. The rotating mirror R had thirty-two faces and light from the slit S was reflected into the pipe from one face of R. After being reflected at M_1 it was collimated by M_2, passed over M_4, and reflected to and fro between the plane mirrors M_3 and M_4 as indicated. Finally, it returned via M_3, M_2, and R, to form an image of S at S′. M_2 had a focal length of 50 ft. and was 40 in. in diameter. As before, R was rotated at such a speed that one face just replaced the next during the time of transit of the light. A correction was made for the residual air in the pipe, and the final result for the velocity in a vacuum was 299,774 $\pm$11 km. sec.$^{-1}$.

24–8. The Use of a Kerr Cell Optical Shutter

By placing a Kerr cell (see § 22–20) between crossed Nicols or crossed polaroids, one can construct a very convenient optical shutter. The arrangement

Fig. 24–6. Kerr cell optical shutter.

is shown in Fig. 24–6. The light is plane polarized by the polarizer P and passes through the Kerr cell to the analyser A. (Nitrobenzene is a suitable liquid for use in the cell since its Kerr constant is relatively large.) When there is no p.d. across the cell no light emerges from the analyser. If a p.d. is applied, the liquid in the cell acts as a uniaxial crystal whose axis is parallel to the lines of force. It follows that if the lines of force are not parallel to or perpendicular to the plane of vibration of the incident light, the latter is resolved into O and E components. These components travel with different speeds, so that a phase difference is introduced between them. Hence, in general, elliptically polarized light emerges from the cell and some light is transmitted by the analyser. Usually the plane

Fig. 24–7.
Characteristic of a Kerr cell shutter.

of vibration of the light entering the Kerr cell is at 45° to the field. The phase difference δ between the O and E components emerging from the cell is proportional to the square of the applied p.d. (see § 22–20), and the intensity of the light transmitted by the analyser is given by $I=I_0 \sin^2 (\delta/2)$ [see equation (22–3)]. Actually it is usual to superpose a steady p.d. across the plates in order to work on the more linear part of the cell characteristic (see Fig. 24–7). The intensity of the light transmitted by the analyser then varies about a mean value with a frequency equal to that of the alternating components of the applied field.

A Kerr cell optical shutter was first used in a determination of the velocity of light by Karolus and Mittelstaedt in 1925. The method resembles that of Fizeau, the toothed wheel being replaced by the Kerr cell shutter. The advantage of using the Kerr cell is that the frequency with which the light beam can be modulated is increased enormously and much shorter light paths can be employed. The arrangement is shown in Fig. 24–8. The principal section of the Nicol N_2 is perpendicular to the principal sections of N_3 and N_1. K_1 and K_2 are Kerr cells, S is the source, and M is a plane mirror. Light from N_1 is transmitted by N_2 only if there is a field across K_1, and light from N_2 is transmitted by N_3 only if

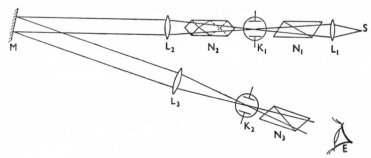

Fig. 24–8. Method of Karolus and Mittelstaedt.

there is a field across K_2 when the light reaches it. Suppose that a simple alternating p.d. is applied across the cells. If K_2 is synchronized with K_1 and the period of the applied p.d. is large compared with the time of transit of the light, light will be transmitted by N_3. Suppose the frequency of the applied p.d. is now increased until the time of transit is one quarter of a period. An intensity maximum will leave K_1 when the p.d. is at a maximum, but by the time it reaches K_2 the p.d. has fallen to zero and the intensity transmitted by N_3 will be

at a minimum. As the frequency is increased further, minima will occur when
the time of transit of the light is 3/4, 5/4, 7/4 of a period. Mittelstaedt observed
these minima up to the eighth with a light path of over three hundred metres.
The final result for the velocity of light in a vacuum was 299,778 ± 10 km. sec.$^{-1}$.
Further experiments employing Kerr cells were carried out by Hüttel (1940)
and by Anderson (1937 and 1940). Anderson's second determination is discussed in the next section. These experiments can be looked upon as marking
the end of an era and a careful analysis of the position was given in 1941 by
Birge (see § 24–10). Kerr cells have also been used in the more recent experiments
by Bergstrand.

24–9. Anderson's Method

The optical system used by Anderson is shown in Fig. 24–9. Light from the
source S (a 1000 watt water-cooled mercury arc) is modulated by the Kerr cell

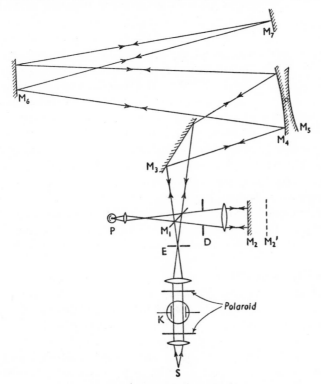

Fig. 24–9. Anderson's method.

arrangement at K and is amplitude divided at the semi-reflecting plate M_1. E is
an aperture containing cross-wires to facilitate alignment. One beam is reflected
back from M_2 and passes to the photo-multiplier tube at P; the other passes via
M_3 to the concave mirror M_4 and then to M_7 and back, finally entering P via
M_1. D is an iris diaphragm which can be used to adjust the intensity of the light
entering P after traversing the short path. The output from P is fed to an
amplifier tuned to the frequency of the alternating component of the p.d. applied

to the Kerr cell. If the two beams enter the photo-tube with their modulation variations in phase, the photo-electric current contains a large component whose frequency is that to which the amplifier is tuned. The output is then at a maximum. If, on the other hand, the modulation waves of the two beams are out of phase, the photo-electric current (though unchanged in magnitude) has only a small component that can be amplified. The output is then a minimum, and this minimum is most clearly defined if D is adjusted until the two beams have equal intensities. The procedure was as follows. By rotating the mounting, mirror M_4 was replaced by a mirror M_5 which returned the light to M_3. (M_4 had a diameter of 9 inches and a focal length of about 5 metres and M_5 had a diameter of 8 inches but a focal length of about 2·5 metres, the two being mounted back to back.) With M_5 in position, the position of M_2 was adjusted by means of a micrometer screw until the amplified current was a minimum. M_4 was then put in position and M_2 moved until the current was again a minimum. The time

Fig. 24–10. Detection of the light beams.

taken for the light to travel from M_4 to M_7 and back, plus the time for the distance $2M_2M_2'$, minus the time for the distance $2M_4M_5$, was then equal to an integral multiple of the modulation period. The light path was about 172 metres and was measured to an accuracy of 1 part in 200,000. The frequency of modulation was 19·2 megacycles per second and was measured to an accuracy of 1 part in 10^6. (The bias voltage on the Kerr cell was between 5000 and 10,000 and the R.F. voltage was about 1000.) The result for the velocity of light in a vacuum was 299,776 ±14 km. sec.$^{-1}$. One difficulty is that the two beams of light are effectively combined and detected when the photo-electrons reach the anode and not when the light beams reach the cathode. Now, if the two beams of light are not exactly coincident, the transit times of the electrons may be different (Fig. 24–10) and may cause an apparent phase difference between the light beams. Anderson considered this to be the main limitation in accuracy.

24–10. The Position in 1941

In 1941 Birge gave a critical review of the various determinations of the velocity of light and other physical constants. He pointed out that up to 1940 all workers had converted their results for the velocity in air to those for the velocity in a vacuum by using the wave refractive index instead of the group refractive index. The refractive index as determined by Snell's law of refraction gives the ratio of the wave velocities in the media concerned, but in all the experiments on the velocity of light the light beam is modulated so that the disturbances are propagated with the group velocity (see § 6–8). Thus one should convert the results from air to vacuum by means of the group index. Anderson did this in his second determination. The small correction needed in the evacuated tube experiment can be neglected, but the results given by other workers require revision.

One of the difficulties in deciding the "best value" for the velocity of light is that of estimating the relative accuracy of the various experiments. For example, the ranges of uncertainty quoted by various workers do not always have the same significance. Birge analysed the various methods and calculated or estimated the so-called probable error for each.

In addition to the ordinary optical methods described above, there are two indirect determinations of c which should be mentioned:

(1) In 1906 and 1907 Rosa and Dorsey carried out a very accurate determination of the ratio of the electromagnetic and electrostatic units. As has already been pointed out, this gives a value for the velocity of electromagnetic waves in a vacuum. The value of c given by the results of Rosa and Dorsey could not be decided until later, when the ratio of the international ohm to the absolute ohm had been found with sufficient accuracy.

(2) In 1923 Mercier measured the velocity of propagation of electromagnetic waves guided by parallel wires. It is necessary to make certain corrections to obtain a value for the propagation of waves in the free air and a further correction is required to find the velocity in a vacuum.

The results obtained by Mercier and by Rosa and Dorsey have been analysed by Birge and the final results and estimated accuracy are given in the table below. Birge considers that none of the results obtained before 1906 should be included when calculating the most probable value of c. The results obtained between 1906 and 1941 are as follows:

Workers	Date	Method	Result Originally Announced (km.sec.$^{-1}$)	Corrected Result (km.sec.$^{-1}$)	Probable Error
Rosa and Dorsey	1906	Ratio of Units	299,710	299,784	10
Mercier	1923	Waves on Wires	299,700	299,782	30
Michelson	1927	Rotating Mirror	299,796	299,798	15
Mittelstaedt	1928	Kerr cell	299,778	299,786	10
Michelson, Pease, and Pearson	1933	Rotating Mirror	299,774	299,774	4
Anderson	1937	Kerr cell	299,764	299,771	10
Hüttel	1937	Kerr cell	299,768	299,771	10
Anderson	1940	Kerr cell	299,776	299,776	6

The weighted mean given by Birge is 299,776 ± 4 km. sec.$^{-1}$.

A very extensive critical review of the existing results was given in 1944 by Dorsey. He pointed out that many of the earlier reports did not give sufficient details to enable a reader to estimate the reliability of the results. After a careful analysis of the various reports he suggested a new weighted mean of 299,773 ± 10 km. sec.$^{-1}$. Dorsey pointed out that the search for systematic errors does not usually seem to have been sufficiently thorough.

24-11. Use of Radar, Cavity Resonators, and Micro-wave Interferometry and Spectroscopy

When radar came into use during the war, it was necessary to assume a value for the velocity of electromagnetic waves in order to be able to calculate the distance of the target. The accuracy of the radar method was checked by using targets at known distances. The above value was assumed for the velocity of electromagnetic waves in a vacuum, and corrections were made for the refractive index of the air and for the effect of radiation reflected or scattered from the ground. It was then found that the distances given by the radar method were always too small by about 1 part in 20,000. This could be put right by assuming a correspondingly larger value for the velocity of the waves but an error of this magnitude came as a surprise in view of the results quoted in § 24–10. It is obvious that by employing known distances the radar apparatus can be used to determine the velocity of the radio waves, and the result obtained in 1949 by Aslakson for the velocity in a vacuum was 299,792 $\pm$2·4 km. sec.$^{-1}$. A subsequent determination in 1951 gave 299,794·2 $\pm$1·9 km. sec.$^{-1}$.

Meanwhile, Essen and Gordon-Smith (1947) had made a very accurate measurement of the resonant frequency of a cavity resonator. Since micro-waves travel along a metal tube or wave guide with little attenuation, a closed guide constitutes an electrical resonator. Essen and Gordon-Smith used a resonator which consisted of an accurately made cylindrical cavity in a block of copper. Copper was used because it is desirable for the walls of the cavity to have a high conductivity. The dimensions of the cavity were accurately measured interferometrically, the cavity was evacuated, and the high frequency fed to a probe. The frequency was then adjusted until resonance occurred, a second probe being connected to a detector. If the dimensions of the cavity and the resonant frequency are known, the velocity of the waves can obviously be found. Although the waves in a guide do not travel with the free-space velocity, the latter can be calculated; the value obtained was 299,792$\pm$3 km. sec.$^{-1}$. Further experiments with cavity resonators were conducted in 1950 by Essen in England, and by Hanson and Bol in America. Essen's result was 299,792·5$\pm$ 1 km. sec.$^{-1}$, the maximum possible error being given as $\pm$ 3. The result announced by Bol was 299,789·3 $\pm$ 0·3 km. sec.$^{-1}$, the systematic error being estimated at not more than +0·5. However, Dayhoff (1952) considered that if a proper correction is made for the skin effect Bol's result becomes 299,794·3 km. sec.$^{-1}$.

In 1951 Froome used a micro-wave analogue of the Michelson interferometer in order to make an accurate determination of a wavelength in the region of 1·25 cm. The fixed arm and the beam divider were enclosed in a wave guide, and the variable path was in free space. The intensity of the beam traversing the fixed path was varied to give good contrast between the maxima and minima. These were detected by a superheterodyne receiver as the path difference was changed. The frequency (24,000 Mc/s) was measured accurately by comparison with a high harmonic of a quartz oscillator, and the velocity was calculated from the product of the frequency and wavelength. The result was 299,792·6 $\pm$0·7 km. sec.$^{-1}$.

It should be noted that with this microwave analogue of the Michelson interferometer diffraction effects are much greater than with the optical interfero-meter. This is because the wavelength is very much longer. Since the source is only a few wavelengths in diameter one has almost true spherical waves instead of the plane waves one gets with the Twyman-Green modification. In a second series of experiments Froome (1954) used a new form of interferometer. This had two transmitting horns facing one another and two receiving horns placed back to back between them. The outputs from the receivers were superposed and the phase difference between them varied by moving the receiving horns together along the line joining the transmitters. The wavelength was measured by finding the positions for interference minima. The result obtained from the second determination was 299,792·7 ±0·3 km. sec.$^{-1}$. Important sources of error were the effect of diffraction and random scattering by fixed objects in the laboratory. In his final series of experiments Froome (1958) doubled the range over which the receiving horns could be moved to 2 metres; employed a higher frequency (72,000 Mc/s—wavelength about 4 mm.) and improved the location of the equipment to give a tenfold reduction of the diffraction and scattering errors; and used a cavity resonator to measure the refractive index of the air in the neighbourhood of the interferometer. As a result of these improvements Froome was able to make what is probably the most accurate determination of c so far achieved, the largest remaining uncertainty then arising from the use of the length standards in measuring the displacement of the receiving horns. Froome's final value was 299,792·50 ±0·10 km.sec.$^{-1}$.

The advantage of employing micro-waves in an interferometer is that it is possible to measure both the wavelength and the frequency; in optical interference experiments only the wavelength can be determined. However, it is possible to combine wavelength measurements made optically with frequency measurements made electrically in the following manner. Energy levels associated with the rotation-vibration bands in infra-red spectra are also responsible for the micro-wave spectra, and measurements in the infra-red region in terms of wavelength can therefore be combined with micro-wave measurements in terms of frequency to give a value for c.

The method, first suggested by Douglas, involves the calculation of the rotational constant B'' of the ground state of a linear molecule; I.R. spectroscopy yields a value in wave-number units and microwave spectroscopy yields a value in frequency units, the ratio giving c. In the first determination of c by this method Rank, Vander Sluis, and Ruth (1952) measured the wavelengths of the absorption lines of the 004–000 and 103–000 bands of HCN in the "photographic infra-red" (0·8μ). They crossed a Fabry-Perot etalon with a plane grating spectrograph and combined their results with the microwave measurements of Nethercot, Klein, and Townes, to get $c=299,776$ km. sec.$^{-1}$. The original estimate of the accuracy was ±6 but subsequently it was pointed out that defects in the grating could have contributed a systematic error as large as 14 km. sec.$^{-1}$. Rank, Shearer, and Wiggins (1954) used the HCN 002–000 band at 1·53μ. They employed an etalon in conjunction with a grating and used a grating value for the wavelength of an absorption line in order to calibrate the interferometer, this calibration being the least reliable part of the experiment. Combination with the microwave measurements of Nethercot and Klein gave $c=299,789.8$ ±3·0 km. sec.$^{-1}$. A better value was derived from these measurements by Rank, Bennett, and Bennett (1955) by obtaining a more accurate value of the wavelength of the line used to calibrate the interferometer. They were able to use the interferometer to calibrate this line against the Hg^{198} green line, thus avoiding the grating calibration. The new value for c was 299,791·9 ±2·2 km. sec.$^{-1}$. The measurements on the HCN 002–000 band wave repeated by Rank,

Guenther, Shearer, and Wiggins (1957) to get $c=299,793\cdot2\pm1\cdot8$ km. sec.$^{-1}$ Rank, Guenther, Saksena, Shearer, and Wiggins (1957) proceeded to measure interferometrically 33 lines of the 2–0 band of CO at $2\cdot3\mu$, and combined their results with the microwave measurements of Cowan and Gordy to get $c=299,793\cdot7 \pm0\cdot7$ km. sec.$^{-1}$. Plyler, Blaine, and Conner (1955) had made some rather less accurate measurements of the CO band using a grating and had taken the microwave results of Gilliam, Johnson, and Gordy, to get $c=299,792 \pm6$ km. sec.$^{-1}$ (the Cowan and Gordy results give $299,793\cdot4 \pm5\cdot8$ km. sec.$^{-1}$). The accuracy assumed by Rank *et al* (1957) was based on the assumption that the microwave measurements made a negligible contribution to the errors but some later measurements by Jones and Gordy (1964) throw some doubt on this; these later results decrease the 1957 value for c by $2\cdot8$ km. sec.$^{-1}$ and put it well below the values obtained in all other recent determinations; one feels inclined to suspect the 1964 microwave result.

A new infra-red technique was used by Rank, Eastman, Rao, and Wiggins (1962). They used a double-pass echelle spectrograph with a replica echelle of high quality to measure the 1–0, 2–0, 3–0, bands of HCl^{35} and the 1–0, 2–0, bands of DCl^{35} in the range 2–5μ. The microwave measurements of Gordy and Cowan give $c=299,793\cdot1 \pm0\cdot65$ km. sec.$^{-1}$ from the DCl^{35} bands and the 1964 microwave measurements by Gordy and Jones yield $299,792\cdot8 \pm0\cdot4$ km. sec.$^{-1}$ from the HCl^{35} bands.

Florman (1955) has made the lowest frequency (173 Mc/s) high precision determination of the velocity of light. He measured the wavelength by measuring the phase difference between disturbances received at two different distances from the R.F. transmitter, the distance between the receivers having been measured by the usual surveying methods. The frequency was measured and the speed calculated to be $299,795\cdot1 \pm3\cdot1$ km. sec.$^{-1}$.

24–12. Recent Optical Experiments and Summary

In view of the disagreement between the results given by the experiments on radio waves and those given by the pre-war optical methods, it is obvious that further optical experiments were called for. Four post-war optical determinations have been made: by Bergstrand, by Houstoun, by Schöldström, and by Edge.

Anderson's greatest difficulty was the alignment of the beams entering the photo-tube. In the method used by Bergstrand this difficulty is avoided. The principle is as follows. By using a Kerr cell the light from the source S [Fig. 24–11(a)] is modulated by the high frequency crystal-controlled oscillator O. The light is reflected from the mirror M to the photo-tube P which gets its operating voltage from O. Thus the sensitivity of the tube varies with the same frequency as the intensity of the light. Suppose, for example, that the maxima of the source intensity and photo-tube sensitivity occur simultaneously. It will be seen that an intensity maximum will arrive at P at a time of high or low sensitivity, depending on the distance $D=SMP$. That is, the photo-electric current will vary with D, the variation being of the form represented by curve (1) in Fig. 24–11(b). If one had a similar apparatus in which the maxima of the source intensity coincided with the minima of the photo-tube sensitivity, the current would follow curve (2). If these two currents are passed in opposite directions through a measuring instrument, the difference curve (3) is recorded. The advantage of an arrangement of this type is that one has sharply defined values of D where the current is zero, instead of rather ill-defined values where the current is either a maximum or a minimum. It is impracticable to arrange two identical sets of apparatus as suggested above, but it is possible to make one

Fig. 24–11. Principle of Bergstrand's method.

apparatus do the work of each in turn. This can be achieved by periodically reversing the phase of the light modulation relative to that of the detector, the period being long compared with that of the modulation, but short compared with the response time of the measuring instrument. The phase of the light modulation is reversed by reversing the direction of the bias voltage that is applied to the Kerr cell. Ideally, the bias voltage would have a square wave form; this was approximated to by cutting off the top of a sine wave.

Fig. 24–12. Bergstrand's method.

The experimental arrangement is illustrated by Fig. 24–12. S is the source (a 30-watt filament lamp); K C is the Kerr cell arrangement; O_1 is the high frequency modulation oscillator (2000 volts, 8 Mc/s); O_2 is the low frequency bias oscillator (5000 volts, 50 c/s); P is the photo-tube; M_2 and M_4 are concave spherical mirrors (apertures 46 cm., focal lengths 75 cm.); M_3 is plane, and M_1

and M_5 are plano-concave lenses silvered on their rear surfaces. The spherical aberration of M_2 and M_4 is balanced by the lens mirrors M_1 and M_5, and the chromatic aberration of the latter does not matter since only yellow light is used. If $2D$ is the total light path, the phase lag between source and receiver for the modulation waves is $\omega(2D/c)$ where $\omega/2\pi$ is the modulation frequency. The current in the meter G will be zero if this phase change is $\pi/2-p\pi$ (p integral). Actually there are some rather uncertain time delays including the interval between the application of a voltage to the Kerr cell and the emergence of the corresponding intensity from the analyser, the transit time of the electrons in the photo-tube, and the transference time of the voltage from the Kerr plates to the photo-anode. These, and certain other factors, can be taken account of by writing, for the condition for zero current,

$$\omega\left(t-\frac{2D}{c}\right)=\frac{\pi}{2}-p\pi,$$

t being the total time uncertainty.

Hence
$$D=K+\frac{2p-1}{8}\lambda,$$

where λ ($=2\pi c/\omega$) is the modulation wavelength and K is a constant. K can be eliminated by taking two values of D. If D_N is the difference one has

$$D_N=\frac{N}{4}\lambda,$$

where N is an integer. N can be found by using approximate values of λ and D_N since it must be integral, so that if D_N is known accurately λ can be found. If the frequency is known c can then be calculated. In effect, Bergstrand made adjustments for values of D of approximately 90 metres and 7000 metres. With M_3 fixed at 7000 metres the frequency was adjusted to give zero deflection. The light was then reflected from a movable mirror at 90 metres and the mirror adjusted for zero deflection. The mirror at 90 metres was convex so that the image formed at the receiver was the same as that for a plane mirror at 7 km. In 1955 Schöldström made another determination using Bergstrand's method and in 1956 Edge gave two results based on measurements by Mackenzie over two ordinance survey base lines. All these results agree very well with the values obtained from experiments involving measurements on microwaves (see table opposite).

In the other post-war optical determination of the velocity of light, Houstoun employed a new type of optical shutter. Stationary ultrasonic waves were set up in a piezo-electric quartz oscillator. When a high frequency p.d. is applied across a quartz crystal, standing ultrasonic waves are set up so that one has variations of density across the crystal, the magnitude of the spatial variations varying periodically with time. In consequence, the crystal behaves as an intermittent diffraction grating and the intensity of, say, the first order maximum varies periodically. In this way Houstoun was able to obtain a beam of light which was modulated with a very high frequency (about 100 Mc/s). The light in the first order maximum passed to a mirror and back, and returned towards the source if it arrived back when the grating was effective. Thus the crystal replaced the toothed wheel in an experiment which resembled that of Fizeau. The accuracy of Houstoun's initial results is less than that of Bergstrand's results, but Houstoun claims that the accuracy of his method can be improved considerably. The result obtained was 299,782 ± 9 km. sec.$^{-1}$ but was originally announced as 299,775.

Date	Workers	Method	Result (km. sec.$^{-1}$)
1947	Essen and Gordon-Smith	Cavity Resonator	299,792 ± 4
1949	Aslakson	Radar	299,792·4 ± 2·4
1949	Bergstrand	Kerr Shutter	299·793 ± 2
1950	Essen	Cavity Resonator	299,792·5 ± 1
1950	Bol	Cavity Resonator	299,794 ± 1
1950–1	Bergstrand	Kerr Shutter	299,793·1 ± 0·2
1951	Aslakson	Radar	299,794·2 ± 1·9
1951	Froome	Microwave Interferometer	299,792·6 ± 0·7
1954	Froome	Microwave Interferometer	299,792·7 ± 0·3
1955	Florman	R.F.	299,795·1 ± 3·1
1955	Rank et al	Band Spectra	299,791·9 ± 2·2
1955	Schöldström	Kerr Shutter	299,792·4 ± 0·4
1956	Edge	Kerr Shutter	299,792·4 ± 0·5
			299,792·2 ± 0·4
1957	Rank et al	Band Spectra	299,793·2 ± 1·8
1957	Rank et al	Band Spectra	299,793·7 ± 0·7
1958	Froome	Microwave Interferometer	299,792·50 ± 0·10
1962	Rank et al	Band Spectra	299,793·1 ± 0·65
1964	Rank et al	Band Spectra	299,792·8 ± 0·4

The table gives a summary of the best post-war determinations of c and excludes certain results that do not seem to constitute a useful advance. Some of the values given in the table differ from those announced originally owing to the subsequent discovery of sources of error. Some of the "possible errors" also differ from those announced originally; as far as possible those given in the table represent estimates (not always by the original workers) of combinations of random and possible systematic errors. When comparing these results with the earlier ones it must be remembered that the limits given by Birge are simply the estimated probable errors* and exclude systematic errors. In 1957 the XIIth General Assembly of International Scientific Radio Union recommended the adoption of the value 299,792·5 ± 0·4 km. sec.$^{-1}$ and this value was accepted by the International Union for Geodesy and Geophysics. Apparatus similar to that used by Bergstrand (known as a Geodimeter) is now employed to measure distances, assuming the above value for c.

24–13. The Velocity of Light in Material Media

The experiments described in the preceding sections were devised in order to measure the velocity of light in air or a vacuum. Foucault (1850) was the first

* For experimental results exhibiting only random errors the probable error defines the range for which the probability that the true result is included is $\frac{1}{2}$.

to compare the velocity of light in a medium denser than air with that in air. At the time this was regarded as an important experiment which would decide between the rival theories of light. Newton's corpuscular theory explained refraction by assuming that light travelled faster in the medium with the larger refractive index (defined from Snell's law in the form $n \sin I = n' \sin I'$), whereas the wave theory indicated that the velocity decreased as the refractive index increased.

Foucault's apparatus is shown in Fig. 24–13. R is a rotating mirror which reflects light from the source S to the equidistant concave mirrors M_1 and M_2 which are centred at R. The tube T contains water. If R is stationary in position (1) the light from S is focused on M_1 and returns via the plate P to form an image of S at S'. If R is in position (2) light passes to M_2 and back to form a second image coincident with the first at S'. Since S and M_2 are in conjugate planes of L_1 when T is absent, it is necessary to add a weak converging lens L_2 in order to obtain a sharp image at S' when T is in position. The image observed is that of a fine wire along the middle of the slit S. If R is rotated rapidly, the images at S' separate and are displaced to S_1'' and S_2''. Foucault found that the image formed by light which passed through the water was displaced more than the other. This shows that the transit time of that light is the greater so that the speed of light in water is less than that in air.

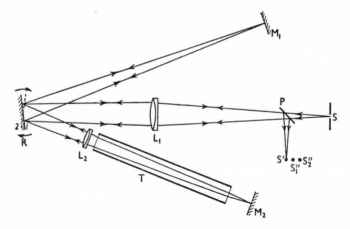

Fig. 24–13. Foucault's method for the speed of light in material media.

Foucault's result was only qualitative, but Michelson repeated the experiment in 1885 and obtained quantitative results. He obtained 1·33 for the ratio of the velocity of light in air to the velocity in water, and 1·758 for ratio of the velocity in air to the velocity in carbon disulphide. Now the refractive index calculated from Snell's law gives the wave velocity, and from this the group velocity can be calculated if the dispersion is known. The calculated ratio of the group velocities in air and water is not widely different from the calculated ratio of the wave velocities and, within the limits of experimental error, agrees with Michelson's result. On the other hand, the ratio of the group velocities for air and carbon disulphide is found to be about 1·745 for $\lambda 5800$ angstroms whereas the ratio of the wave velocities is 1·64. There is some doubt about the mean wavelength of the light used by Michelson but the results quoted above indicate that it is the group velocities which are measured in these experiments. It is rather surprising that until 1941 this fact was not taken into account in the results given by various observers for the velocity of light in a vacuum (see § 24–10). Michelson's experiments also indicate that the velocity of red light in CS_2 is slightly greater than the velocity of blue light, which agrees with the observed dispersion of the refractive index.

Michelson's result for the velocity of light in carbon disulphide was confirmed by Gouy in 1886 using the rotating mirror method. Further experiments by Gutton in 1912 gave results for carbon disulphide and for monobromnaphthalene which were also in agreement with the calculated group velocities.

In a more accurate series of experiments in 1944 using the piezo-electric light modulator already described, Houstoun measured the group velocity in water for the red, green, and blue light transmitted by a set of filters. The group indices obtained from these results were in good agreement with the calculated values. The results for red, green, and blue light were as follows (calculated values of the group and phase indices are shown in brackets): red, 1·3485 (1·3482, 1·333); green, 1·3570 (1·3572, 1·336); blue, 1·3668 (1·3655, 1·338).

Recently (1954) Bergstrand has measured the group velocity of light in glass and in calcite. The method employs the piezo-electric light modulator and the results confirm the theoretical expression for the group velocity. For calcite, measurements in various directions confirm the shapes of the wave surfaces.

24–14. The Velocity of Light in a Moving Medium

Fig. 24–14 shows the apparatus used by Fizeau in 1859 in order to find the effect of the motion of the medium on the velocity of light. In principle, the

Fig. 24–14. Fizeau's determination of the speed of light in a moving medium.

arrangement resembles the Rayleigh refractometer. Light from the slit source S is collimated by lens L_1 and passes through the water circulating system to M, and back. It will be seen that a double slit fringe system will be formed at S'. One beam passes along AB and returns along CD, while the other passes along DC and returns along BA. Consequently, if water circulates as shown, one beam always travels in the same direction as the water, and the other travels in the opposite direction. Thus if the velocity of the light in the moving water is different in the two directions, a phase difference will be introduced between the beams and there will be a displacement of the fringes at S'. The experiment was repeated by Michelson with a modified form of the apparatus. The results obtained by Fizeau and Michelson do not correspond to a Newtonian addition of the velocities of light and medium but are consistent with the relation

$$c'=c+v\left(1-\frac{1}{n^2}\right),$$

where v is the speed of the water. This result was first explained by assuming that light was propagated with a fixed velocity relative to an aether which was dragged along by the water, but the results can be explained in terms of relativity theory without any special assumptions.

24-15. The Michelson-Morley Experiment

At one time it was thought that light is propagated with a fixed speed relative to an all-pervading aether with respect to which the earth can be either stationary or in motion. If the earth is moving relative to the aether the speed of light with respect to the earth is then different in different directions. The Michelson-Morley experiment (1881-7) was devised in order to detect this motion of the earth through the aether. In principle the apparatus is simply a Michelson interferometer. Fig. 24-15(a) shows the light paths on the assumption that the

Fig. 24-15. The Michelson-Morley experiment.

earth and apparatus are at rest in the aether and (b) shows the paths on the assumption that the apparatus is moving from left to right through the aether with uniform speed. In (a) $PM_1=PM_2=l$ so that the beams traverse equal paths and localized fringes are observed in the plane of M_1. In (b) M_1 and M_2 are the positions of the mirrors in the aether when the light leaves P. M_1 moves to M_1' while the light travels from P to the mirror, and P moves to P' while the light travels to M_1' and back. M_2 is at M_2' when reflection occurs. Let the velocity of the light relative to the aether be c and let the velocity of the apparatus through the aether be v. Let t_1 be the time taken for the light to travel from P to M_2', and t_2 the time from M_2' to P'. Then $M_2M_2'=vt_1$, $PM_2'=l+vt_1$, and $M_2'P'=l-vt_2$. Also, since these distances are traversed at speed c, one has

$$ct_1=l+vt_1$$

and

$$ct_2=l-vt_2.$$

Hence

$$t_1=\frac{l}{c-v}$$

and

$$t_2=\frac{l}{c+v}.$$

Now in the total time (t_1+t_2) the path length through the aether traversed by the light is given by

$$c(t_1+t_2)=c\left(\frac{l}{c-v}+\frac{l}{c+v}\right)=\frac{2lc^2}{c^2-v^2}\fallingdotseq 2l\left(1+\frac{v^2}{c^2}\right),$$

where powers of v/c higher than the second have been neglected since it can be assumed that v/c is small. For the other beam the path length is $PM_1'P'=2PM_1'$,

where $$PM_1'=\sqrt{l^2+(M_1M_1')^2}.$$

Since M_1 travels a distance M_1M_1' while light travels a distance PM_1', one has

$$M_1M_1'=PM_1'\frac{v}{c},$$

$$\therefore \quad (PM_1')^2=l^2+(PM_1')^2\frac{v^2}{c^2}$$

or $$(PM_1')^2=\frac{l^2}{1-\dfrac{v^2}{c^2}},$$

$$\therefore \quad \text{Path length}=2PM_1'=\frac{2l}{\left(1-\dfrac{v^2}{c^2}\right)^{\frac{1}{2}}}\fallingdotseq 2l\left(1+\frac{v^2}{2c^2}\right).$$

Hence the beams traverse paths which differ by lv^2/c^2.

It will be seen that if the interferometer is rotated through 90° the path lengths of the beams are interchanged and there will be a displacement of the fringes if there is any relative motion of the apparatus through the aether. Michelson and Morley made the light paths very large by reflecting the light to and fro across the apparatus, but no displacement of the fringes was observed as the apparatus was rotated in the laboratory.

The null result of the Michelson-Morley experiment could be explained by assuming that at the time of the experiment the earth was stationary with respect to the aether. However, the null result was always obtained when the experiment was repeated, and it seems very unlikely that the earth is the one body in the universe which is permanently at rest in the aether. FitzGerald and Lorentz showed that one can explain the null result by assuming that when an arm of the interferometer lies in the direction of the aether-earth velocity, it contracts to a length $l\sqrt{1-v^2/c^2}$. In a sense this contraction is included in Einstein's theory of relativity but in that theory absolute rest and absolute velocity are meaningless and one cannot speak of an aether at absolute rest with respect to which the velocity of light must be measured and with respect to which anything may be said to have absolute motion.

APPENDIX

SOME SUGGESTIONS FOR FURTHER READING

I. BOOKS

An indication of the field covered is given when this is not obvious from the title.

BAKER, B. B., and COPSON, E. T., *The Mathematical Theory of Huygens' Principle* (O.U.P.).

BAUER, G., *Measurement of Optical Radiations* (Focal Press). Covers all spectral regions.

BENNETT, A. H., JUPNIK, H., OSTERBERG, H., and RICHARDS, O. W., *Phase Microscopy* (Wiley). Includes a general discussion of diffraction theory of the microscope.

BERAN, M. J., and PARRENT, G. B., *Theory of Partial Coherence* (Prentice-Hall).

BORN, M., and WOLF, E., *Principles of Optics* (Pergamon). Covers a field similar to that covered by the present book but at a more advanced level.

BOUTRY, G. A. (Trans. R. Auerbach), *Instrumental Optics* (Hilger). Covers paraxial and elementary aberration theory of image-forming and spectroscopic instruments, and includes vision and visual instruments.

BOUWERS, A., *Achievements in Optics* (Elsevier). Includes reflecting systems, aberrant images, and phase contrast.

BROUWER, W., *Matrix Methods in Optical Instrument Design* (W. A. Benjamin). Includes paraxial and primary aberration theory of telescopes, microscopes, cameras, and spectroscopes.

BROWN, E. B., *Modern Optics* (Reinhold). Geometrical and physical optics and applications to optical instruments and devices. Includes discussion of laser sources.

CAGNET, M., FRANÇON, M., and THRIERR, J. C., *Atlas of Optical Phenomena* (Springer-Verlag). Photographs of interference and diffraction patterns.

CANDLER, C., *Modern Interferometers* (Hilger). Gives basic theory of the use of interferometers in metrology and spectroscopy.

COX, A., *A system of Optical Design* (Focal Press). Mainly on aberration theory and lens design, but includes chapters on image formation.

DITCHBURN, R. W., *Light* (Blackie). Coverage similar to present book with extension into quantum optics. Emphasis on Fourier methods.

FRANÇON, M. (Trans. Barbara Jeffrey and ed. J. H. Sanders), *Diffraction—Coherence in Optics* (Pergamon). On coherence, diffraction, image formation.

FRANÇON, M., *Modern Applications of Physical Optics* (Interscience). A brief review, mainly on applications of interferometry and on image formation.

FRANÇON, M., *Progress in Microscopy* (Pergamon). Includes a general discussion of image formation in a microscope.

GARBUNY, M., *Optical Physics* (Academic Press). Deals with the interaction between light and matter—emission, absorption, and propagation in material media.

GRAHAM, C. H. (Ed.), *Vision and Visual Perception* (Wiley).

GUILD, J., *Diffraction Gratings as Measuring Scales* (O.U.P.). A practical guide to the metrological use of moire fringes.

GUILD, J., *The Interference Systems of Crossed Diffraction Gratings* (O.U.P.). A full discussion of the theory of moire fringes.

HAVELOCK, T., *The Propagation of Disturbances in Dispersing Media* (C.U.P.). Gives a full discussion of group velocity.

HEAVENS, O. S., *Optical Properties of Thin Solid Films* (Butterworth).

HERZBERGER, M., *Modern Geometrical Optics* (Interscience). An advanced book covering paraxial and primary and higher order aberration theory.

HOPKINS, H. H., *The Wave Theory of Aberrations* (O.U.P.).

JENKINS, F. A., and WHITE, H. E., *Fundamentals of Optics* (McGraw-Hill). Coverage similar to present book.

JUDD, D. B., and WYSZECKI, G., *Colour in Business, Science, and Industry* (Wiley).

KINGSLAKE, R. (Ed.), *Applied Optics and Optical Engineering* (Academic Press). 5 vols. proposed. Vol. I includes photometry, light sources, optical materials, survey of basic geometrical and physical optics. Vol. II includes vision, photography, and photo-electric and thermal detectors. Vol. III discusses optical components, including design, production, and testing, and proposed Vols. IV and V will deal with the main kinds of optical instruments.

KLINE, M. K., and KAY, I. W. *Electromagnetic Theory and Geometrical Optics* (Interscience). An advanced book developing geometrical optics and diffraction theory from Maxwell's equations, including propagation in anisotropic media.

KRUG, W., RIENITZ, J., and SCHULZ, G. (Trans. J. Home Dickson), *Contributions to Interference Microscopy* (Hilger).

LINFOOT, E. H., *Fourier Methods in Optical Image Evaluation* (Focal Press).

LINFOOT, E. H., *Recent Advances in Optics* (O.U.P.). Covers coherence and image formation, Foucault test, Schmidt and other aspheric systems.

LUNEBURG, R. K., *Mathematical Theory of Optics* (University of California Press). An advanced book developing both the geometrical and diffraction theories of optical instruments from Maxwell's equations, including geometrical and diffraction theories of aberrations.

MARION, J. B., *Classical Electromagnetic Radiation* (Academic Press). Includes basic electromagnetic theory, reflection, refraction, dispersion, interference and diffraction.

MARTIN, L. C., *Geometrical Optics* (Pitman). Includes basic geometrical optics, paraxial theory of instruments, introduction to aberrations, photometry.

MARTIN, L. C., *Technical Optics* (Pitman). Vol. I includes paraxial theory, aberrations, image formation, vision; Vol. II includes more detailed discussion of telescopes, microscopes, and cameras, photometry of instruments, testing of instruments, and aspherics.

MARTIN, L. C., *The Theory of the Microscope* (Blackie). On the theory of image formation with special reference to the microscope.

MERTZ, L., *Transformations in Optics* (Wiley). Includes Fourier Transform Spectroscopy, and Holography.

MEYER, C. F., *Diffraction of Light, X-rays, and Material Particles* (Chicago U.P.). Easy to read, mainly on light, including gratings.

O'NEILL, E. L., *Introduction to Statistical Optics* (Addison-Wesley). Deals with diffraction and image formation (including effect of aberrations), partial coherence, and partial polarization.

ROSSI, B., *Optics* (Addison-Wesley). Coverage similar to present book, with less on optical instruments but extension into quantum optics.

SANDERS, J. H., *Velocity of Light* (Pergamon). Includes reprints of the original papers by Michelson, Pease, and Pearson; by Essen and Gordon-Smith; and by Bergstrand.

SHURCLIFF, W. A., *Polarized Light* (Harvard U.P. and O.U.P.).

SHURCLIFF, W. A., and BALLARD, S. S., *Polarized Light* (van Nostrand).

SMITH, R. A., JONES, F. E., and CHASMAR, R. P., *The Detection and Measurement of Infra-Red Radiation* (Clarendon Press).

SOMMERFELD, A. (Trans. Laporte, O., and Moldauer, P. A.), "Optics" (*Lectures in Theoretical Physics, Vol. IV*) (Academic Press). Particularly useful for diffraction; also covers reflection and refraction, dispersion, crystal optics.

STOKES, A. R., *The Theory of the Optical Properties of Inhomogeneous Materials* (Spon).

STONE, J. M., *Radiation and Optics* (McGraw-Hill). Gives systematic treatment of electromagnetic theory, interference, diffraction, image formation, crystal optics. Emphasis on Fourier methods.

STROKE, G. W., *An Introduction to Coherent Optics and Holography* (Academic Press).
STRONG, J., *Concepts of Classical Optics* (Freeman). Ranges over whole field of geo-
metrical and physical optics.
TOLANSKY, S., *An Introduction to Interferometry* (Longmans).
TOLANSKY, S., *High Resolution Spectroscopy* (Methuen).
TOLANSKY, S., *Multiple Beam Interferometry of Surfaces and Films* (O.U.P.).
TOLANSKY, S., *Surface Microtopography* (Longmans).
VAN DE HULST, H. C., *Light Scattering by Small Particles* (Wiley).
VAŠÍČEK, A., *Optics of Thin Films.* (North-Holland).
WALSH, J. W. T., *Photometry* (Constable).
WELFORD, W. T., *Geometrical Optics* (North-Holland). Deals with paraxial and
elementary aberration theory of optical instruments.
WRIGHT, W. D., *The Measurement of Colour* (Hilger).
WRIGHT, W. D., *Photometry and the Eye* (Hatton Press).

II. REVIEW ARTICLES

The series *Progress in Optics* edited by E. Wolf and published by North-Holland contains review articles ranging over the whole field of theoretical and experimental
optics; the list of reviews given below includes those that have appeared in the first
five volumes of this series in the fields covered in the present book.

ABELÈS, F., "Methods for Determining Optical Parameters of Thin Films" (*Progress in Optics*, II, 1963).
BARAKAT, R., "The Intensity Distribution and Total Illumination of Aberration-Free Diffraction Images" (*Progress in Optics*, I, 1961).
BERGSTRAND, E., "Determination of the Velocity of Light" (*Handbuch der Physik*, Vol. XXIV) (Springer–Verlag 1956). Gives classified list of references.
BOUWKAMP, C. J., "Diffraction Theory" (*Reports on Progress in Physics*, 17, 1954).
BRADDICK, H. J. J., "Photoelectric Photometry" (*Reports on Progress in Physics*, 23, 1960).
BRYNGDAHL, O., "Applications of Shearing Interferometry" (*Progress in Optics*, IV, 1965).
BURCH, J. M., "The Metrological Applications of Diffraction Gratings" (*Progress in Optics*, II, 1963).
DORSEY, N. E., "The Velocity of Light" (*Trans. Phil. Soc. Am.*, 34 (Part I), 1944).
FIORENTINI, A., "Dynamic Characteristics of Visual Processes" (*Progress in Optics*, I, 1961).
FROOME, K. D., "Microwave Determinations of the Velocity of Light" (*J. Brit. I.R.E.*, 16, 1956).
GABOR, D., "Light and Information" (*Progress in Optics*, I, 1961).
HEAVENS, O. S., "Optical Properties of Thin Films" (*Reports on Progress in Physics*, 23, 1960).
HOPKINS, H. H., "Application of Frequency Response, Techniques in Optics" (*Proc. Phys. Soc.*, 79, 1962).
JACOBSSON, R., "Light Reflection from Films of Continuously Varying Refractive Index" (*Progress in Optics*, V, 1966).
JACQUINOT, P., "New Developments in Interference Spectroscopy" (*Reports on Progress in Physics*, 23, 1960).
JACQUINOT, P., and ROIZEN-DOSSIER, B., "Apodisation" (*Progress in Optics*, III, 1964).
KOTTLER, F., "Diffraction at a Black Screen" (*Progress in Optics*, IV, 1965).
KUHN, H., "New Techniques in Optical Interferometry" (*Reports on Progress in Physics* 14, 1951).
LIPSON, H., and TAYLOR, C. A., "X-ray Crystal-Structure Determination as a Branch of Physical Optics" (*Progress in Optics*, V, 1966).
MULLIGAN, J. F., and MCDONALD, D. F., "Some Recent Determinations of the Velocity of Light" (*Am.J.Phys.*, 25, 1957).

MURATA, K., "Instruments for the Measuring of Optical Transfer Functions" (*Progress in Optics*, V, 1966).

RAMACHANDRAN, G. N., and RAMASESHAN, S., "Crystal Optics" (*Handbuch der Physik*, Vol. XXV/1) (Springer–Verlag 1961).

RANK, D. H., "The Band Spectrum Method of Measuring the Velocity of Light" (*J. Molecular Spec.* (U.S.A.), **17**, 1965).

RATCLIFFE, J. A., "Some Aspects of Diffraction Theory and Their Applications to the Ionosphere" (*Reports on Progress in Physics*, **19**, 1956).

ROUARD, P., and BOUSQUET, P., "Optical Constants of Thin Films" (*Progress in Optics*, **IV**, 1965).

RUBINOWICZ, A., "The Miyamoto-Wolf Diffraction Wave" (*Progress in Optics*, **IV**, 1965).

STEEL, W. H., "Two-Beam Interferometry" (*Progress in Optics*, V, 1966).

STROKE, G. W., "Ruling, Testing and Use of Optical Gratings for High Resolution Spectroscopy" (*Progress in Optics*, **II**, 1963).

TSUJIUCHI, J., "Correction of Optical Images by Compensation of Aberrations and by Spatial Frequency Filtering" (*Progress in Optics*, **II**, 1963).

WELFORD, W. T., "Aberration Theory of Gratings and Grating Mountings" (*Progress in Optics*, **IV**. 1965).

WOLF, E., "The Diffraction Theory of Aberrations" (*Reports on Progress in Physics*, **14**, 1951).

WYNNE, C. G., "New Lens Systems" (*Reports on Progress in Physics*, **19**, 1956).

EXAMPLES

QUESTIONS* set at London, Oxford, and Cambridge examinations are marked as follows:

London: M.Sc., B.Sc. Special Parts I and II, and B.Sc. General Part II—LM, LS I, LS II, and LG II.

Oxford: Honour Moderations in Natural Science, and Finals—OM and OF.

Cambridge: Preliminary Examination in Natural Science, Parts I and II, and Tripos, Parts I and II—CP I, CP II, CT I, and CT II.

CHAPTERS I–V

1. Explain "Fermat's Principle of Stationary Time", illustrating your account by using the principle to solve some problems in geometrical optics.
   (CT I)

2. An object is placed 1 metre in front of a screen. Using a certain converging lens, it is found that there are two positions of the lens between the object and the screen which give sharp images on the screen. The images have lengths 4 cm. and 0·25 cm. Find the length of the object and the focal length of the lens.

3. A thin plano-convex lens of refractive index 1·64 has a power of 0·1 cm.$^{-1}$ in air. Find the focal lengths, and the positions of the principal and nodal points (a) when the lens has water (index 1·33) on the plane side and air on the curved side, (b) when the lens has water on the curved side and air on the plane side.

4. A converging meniscus lens has radii of curvature 10 cm. and 20 cm., and has an axial thickness of 5 cm.; it is made of glass of refractive index 1·64 and is in air. Find the focal length of the lens and the positions of the nodal points.

5. Find the cardinal points for a hemispherical glass lens of radius 10 cm. and refractive index 1·64 in air.

6. A converging meniscus lens has radii of curvature 20 cm. and 30 cm. and axial thickness 6 cm. It is made of glass of refractive index 1·52 and has water (index 1·33) on its concave side and air on its convex side. Find the positions of the cardinal points.

7. Verify the results given on page 388 for the positions of the cardinal points of the schematic eye specified on page 387.

8. State briefly what is meant by the principal planes, nodal planes, and principal foci of a lens system. Make the necessary calculations and show by a clear drawing the paths of (i) a ray incident parallel to the axis, (ii) a ray incident through the first principal point of a system of which the first component is a thin converging lens, focal length $7\frac{1}{2}''$, and the second, distant $6''$, a thin diverging lens, focal length $2''$. Derive any formulae employed.
   (LS I)

* *Acknowledgments.* We are indebted to the following for permission to reproduce questions from past examination papers: The University of Cambridge; the University of London; the University of Oxford.

9. Define the principal points of a lens system and derive an expression for the focal length of a combination of two thin lenses in air in terms of their focal lengths and distance apart. How would you determine the focal length of such a combination experimentally?

   A thin converging lens of focal length 20 cm. forms an image 4 mm. high of a distant object. Determine the nature and focal length of a second lens which, when placed 5 cm. behind the first lens, produces an image 1 cm. high of the same object on a screen in the focal plane of the combination. (LS I)

10. With the aid of a diagram, explain the method of formation of a real image 0·75 cm. long of an extremely distant object subtending an angle of 0·015 radians at the point of observation, by a coaxial lens system comprising one converging and one diverging lens, of focal lengths 10 and 5 cm. respectively.

   Deduce the positions of the principal and focal planes of the lens system and represent them on a diagram drawn very approximately to scale. (LS I)

11. Define the cardinal points of a lens system. Light from a distant object is incident on a system consisting of a thin converging lens of focal length 12 cm. placed 6 cm. in front of a thin diverging lens of focal length 24 cm. Explain, with the aid of a diagram, why the position of the image is unaffected if the lens system is slightly rotated about an axis perpendicular to its principal axis and 2 cm. in front of the converging lens.

   At what distance from the converging lens do conjugate object and image planes coincide? (LS I)

12. Define the terms *principal points*, *nodal points* and *principal foci* as applied to a coaxial lens system and illustrate the use of these points in the construction giving the position of the image of a point object on the axis of the system. An object is located 100 cm. in front of a thin converging lens of focal length 20 cm. behind which there is a diverging lens of the same focal length at a distance of 10 cm. Show that the lens system can be rotated through a small angle about a point midway between the two principal points without causing displacement of the image. (LS I)

13. Define the terms entrance pupil, exit pupil, and chief ray. A thin converging lens of focal length 5 cm. and diameter 6 cm. has a 2·5 cm. diameter stop situated 2 cm. in front of it. A line object 2·1 cm. high is located with its lower end on the lens axis 10 cm. in front of the lens. Find the position and size of the exit pupil and draw a diagram approximately to scale of the marginal rays and the chief ray from the upper end of the object. (LS I)

14. Explain the meaning of the "cardinal points" of a thick lens. A thick plano-convex lens, of refractive index μ, has a curved face of radius R and thickness h at the centre. Find the position of the cardinal points for paraxial rays, and comment upon how their position depends upon the value of μ and hence upon the wavelength of light used. Show that the position of the focal point on the plane side of the lens is independent of wavelength if $(\mu-1)^2 h = \mu^2 R$.

   In what sense, if this condition is satisfied, can the lens be considered to be achromatic? (OM)

15. Discuss the relative merits of Ramsden and Huygens eyepieces. The lenses in a Huygens eyepiece have focal lengths of 2 cm. and 4 cm. What is the distance between the lenses and where are the cardinal points of the eyepiece?

16. Find the positions of the cardinal points in an eyepiece consisting of two thin converging lenses each of focal length 4 cm. and separated by a distance of 3 cm.

   The eyepiece is used in an astronomical telescope in normal adjustment. The diameter of the objective is 5 cm. and its focal length is 60 cm. Find the position and diameter of the exit pupil. (LG II)

17. A thin lens of crown glass is to be combined with a thin lens of flint glass to form a thin doublet that has the same focal length for a given pair of wavelengths. Deduce expressions for the powers of the crown and flint components in terms of the power of the doublet and the dispersive powers of the glasses.

   Using the glasses specified below, find the focal lengths of the crown and flint components necessary to give a diverging doublet of focal length 10 cm., achromatized for the C and F lines.

   Crown $n_d=1 \cdot 51690$, $n_C=1 \cdot 51429$, $n_F=1 \cdot 52282$

   Flint $n_d=1 \cdot 62258$, $n_C=1 \cdot 61749$, $n_F=1 \cdot 63476$

18. A plane mirror is placed behind the convex surface of a converging meniscus lens. A small object is placed on the other side of the lens close to the axis. It is found that an image is formed alongside the object for the following distances of the object from the lens: 10 cm., 7·5 cm., 2·3 cm. If the plane mirror is removed, the first of these images disappears. Find the refractive index of the lens.

19. Describe how the refractive index of a liquid may be measured in the visible region as a function of wavelength, and estimate the accuracy you could achieve. Explain why liquid prisms are sometimes used in spectrometers. (OM)

20. Discuss the relative merits of critical-angle and non-critical-angle methods in the precision refractometry of liquids.

   Describe in detail a method of investigating the variation, with concentration, of the refractive index of a *dilute* solution. (LS I)

21. A Pulfrich refractometer is provided with standard prisms having refractive indices of 1·6200 and 1·7500. What ranges of refractive indices can be measured with these prisms using a refracting angle of (a) 90°, (b) 60°?

CHAPTERS VI–IX

1. Discuss the distinction between *phase* and *group* velocities and derive an equation relating them. What bearing has this distinction on the determination of the velocity of light?

   Calculate the group velocity of light of wavelength $\lambda=5 \times 10^{-5}$ cm. in carbon disulphide for which

$$\mu=1 \cdot 577+\frac{1 \cdot 78 \times 10^{-10}}{\lambda^2}$$

   ($c=3 \times 10^{10}$ cm. per sec.). (LS I)

2. Explain carefully what is meant by group velocity, giving examples from various types of wave motion. Derive an expression for the relation between group velocity and phase velocity.

   The refractive index of a certain glass is given by the formula $\mu = A + (B/\lambda_0^2)$ where λ_0 is the wavelength *in vacuo*. Show that the ratio of group velocity to phase velocity is

   $$(A\lambda_0^2 + B)/(A\lambda_0^2 + 3B).$$

   (CT I)

3. In Young's double slit experiment the separation of the slits is 1·9 mm. and the fringe spacing is 0·31 mm. at a distance of 1 metre from the slits. Find the wavelength of the light. What is the visibility of the fringes if (*a*) the slits give equal intensities, (*b*) the intensity from one slit is four times that from the other.

4. Explain the resultant intensity when two beams of light are superimposed (*a*) when they are coherent, and (*b*) when they are incoherent. Apply this to a discussion of the interference fringes obtained in the Lloyd's mirror arrangement.

   In a Lloyd's mirror experiment calculate the ratio of the intensities at the interference maxima and minima if the mirror reflects only 75% of the light incident upon it.   (OM)

5. Explain the principles involved in the production of interference fringes by the method of division of wave-front. What form would such fringes take when two images of a point source are produced on the axis by a split convex lens, the two halves being displaced along the axis relative to one another?

   In an experiment with Fresnel's biprism, fringes for light of wavelength 5×10^{-5} cm. are observed 0·2 mm. apart at a distance of 175 cm. from the prism. The prism is made of glass of refractive index 1·5 and is 25 cm. from the illuminated slit.

   Calculate the angle at the vertex of the biprism.   (OM)

6. Discuss the interference effects observed when a wave-front of monochromatic light is divided into two parts of equal width. Illustrate your answer by considering the character and location of the fringes for various kinds of interferometer, and in each case state what happens when white light is substituted for monochromatic light.

   A concave mirror is cut along a diameter and the two halves rejoined at an angle of 40′ with each other so as to increase the concavity. A point source of monochromatic light, wavelength 6×10^{-5} cm., is placed at the focal distance from the mirror and close to its axis. Draw a sketch diagram of the region in which fringes are to be expected. Describe the form of the fringes and calculate their width.   (CT I)

7. Fringes of equal thickness are observed in a thin glass wedge of refractive index 1·52. The fringe spacing is 1 mm. and the wavelength of the light is 5893 Å. Find the angle of the wedge in seconds of arc.

8. A thin equiconvex lens of focal length 4 metres and refractive index 1·52 rests on and in contact with an optical flat and, using light of wavelength 5460 angstroms, Newton's rings are viewed normally by reflection. What is

the diameter of the fifth bright ring? What would be observed if (a) white light were used, (b) the lens were lifted slowly off the flat?

9. Fringes of equal inclination are observed in a Michelson interferometer. As one of the mirrors is moved back 1 mm. 3663 fringes move out from the centre of the pattern. Calculate the wavelength of the light.

10. Describe the use of an interferometer as applied *either* to the accurate measurement of refractive index *or* to the examination of surfaces.

A Michelson interferometer is set up using parallel light from a point source and interference fringes are observed arising from imperfections in a plane glass plate which is inserted normal to one of the beams. The interferometer mirrors are then removed and the fringes formed by multiple reflection within the plate itself are observed. If the same number, m, of fringes occur between the points P_1, P_2 on the plate in each of these experiments, show that the thickness of the plate is the same at P_1 and P_2 but that the mean refractive index differs by $m\lambda/2D$, where D is the thickness of the plate and λ is the wavelength of the light. (OF)

11. Explain the formation of Newton's rings and of the rings seen in a Fabry-Perot interferometer. How would you obtain photographs of these two ring systems whose general appearance was very nearly the same? Would there remain any geometrical difference in your photographs?

The Newton's rings are formed between a plane glass plate and a spherical glass surface of radius 100 cm., and the photograph is taken with magnification 5. The photograph of the Fabry-Perot rings is taken on a photographic plate in the focal plane of a telescope of focal length 50 cm. When the two photographs are superimposed a few rings near the centre are found to coincide. What is the separation of the reflecting surfaces in the Fabry-Perot interferometer? (CT I)

12. Describe a refractometer suitable for the determination of the refractive index of a gas and explain how it could be used to investigate the variation of the refractive index of air with density.

A refractometer with tubes 1 metre long initially contains air at atmospheric pressure at 20°C. When the pressure in one tube is reduced by 20 cm. of Hg, a shift of 130 fringes of light of wavelength 5460 Å is observed. Calculate the refractive index of air at S.T.P. for this wavelength. (LS I)

13. Explain the formation of fringes in a Michelson interferometer illuminated by (a) monochromatic light, (b) white light. If one mirror is slowly moved back with velocity v calculate directly the number of monochromatic fringes passing a point in the field of view in one second. Show that the same result is obtained by a treatment which considers the beats formed between the incident light and the reflected light whose frequency has been modified by the Doppler effect at the moving mirror. (LS I)

14. Describe the formation of the fringes in the Jamin interferometer. Explain how the instrument is used for refractive index measurements. What would be the effect upon the fringe pattern if the reflectivity of the silvering on one plate were to fall to half that on the other? (LS I)

15. Describe how the fine and hyperfine structure of the light from a gas such as neon may be investigated by means of a Fabry-Perot etalon. Give any

relevant theory and compare the advantages and disadvantages of this instrument with those of an echelon grating.

If two lines differing in wavelength by 1 Å are to be resolved, what must be the distance between the plates of the Fabry-Perot etalon if the reflecting power (ratio of intensities) of the silvered surfaces for the light in question is 0·95?   (CT II)

16. Describe how interference fringes are formed in the Fabry-Perot interfero-meter. Show that if there is no loss at the reflecting surfaces the maximum intensity in the interference pattern viewed by transmission is the same as the intensity in the absence of the interferometer.

What are the possible values of the distance between the plates of a Fabry-Perot interferometer which gives fringes in which the maxima due to the sodium D_1 line coincide with the minima due to the sodium D_2 line? Outline the method of use of the interferometer to measure the relative intensities of the sodium D lines.

(Wavelength of D_1 line$=5896$ Å, of D_2 line$=5890$ Å.)   (OF)

17. Give the theory of the formation of interference fringes produced by multiple reflection in a plane parallel film and mention some uses to which these are put.

What plate separation is required for a Fabry-Perot interferometer to make available between the orders at 4000 Å a wavelength range of 0·04 Å?
                                                                        (LS I)

18. Derive the expression for the distribution of intensity in the transmitted Fabry-Perot fringe system. Discuss the effect of the magnitude of the reflection coefficient upon the character of the fringes.

If the angular radius of the first bright fringe is 44′ and the order of interference at the centre of the fringe system is $4128+\varepsilon$, calculate the value of the fraction ε.   (LS I)

19. Explain the formation of Brewster's fringes and describe briefly their use in interferometry.

Two different Fabry-Perot etalons are placed one behind the other. White light passes normally through both. When the shorter of the two etalons is turned through an angle of 0·01571 radian, Brewster's fringes are seen centrally in the field of view. If the length of the inclined etalon is 0·50027 cm. and that of the other nearly four times as great, calculate the length of the latter.   (LS I)

20. The upper half of the slit of a spectroscope is illuminated with a mercury lamp and the lower half of the slit is illuminated with white light through a thin Fabry-Perot etalon. If there are 20 fringes in the continuous spectrum between the blue and green mercury lines, what is the thickness of the etalon? (Wavelengths of mercury lines: 5461 Å and 4358 Å.)

CHAPTERS X–XIII

1. Parallel monochromatic light is incident normally on a slit, passes through a converging lens near the slit, and is brought to a focus on a screen. Obtain an expression for the intensity distribution on the screen. Point out (a) the inclinations to the axis of the system for which minima occur, (b) the conditions under which maxima occur.

If the incident light is *white*, and the slit has a width of 0·080 cm. and the lens has a focal length of 80 cm., find the wavelengths in the visible region which are missing on the screen at a distance of 0·30 cm. from the axis of the system.   (LG II)

2. Explain what is meant by the chromatic resolving power, $\lambda/\delta\lambda$, of an optical instrument.

Deduce an expression for the resolving power of a prism of material for which the refractive index n is given by $n=a+b/\lambda^2$, where a and b are constants. Calculate a value for the minimum length of side of an equilateral prism, of material for which $b=9·84\times10^{-11}$ cm², which will resolve the D lines of sodium (wavelengths 5890, 5896 Å).   (LS I)

3. Describe and give the theory of Michelson's stellar interferometer. For the star Betelgeuse the mirror separation for the first disappearance of the fringes was 3 metres. If the distance of the star from the earth is $1·7\times10^{15}$ km., calculate its diameter, assuming the effective wavelength of the emitted light to be 5750 Å.   (LS I)

4. What is meant by Fraunhofer diffraction? Under what conditions may it be observed?

A reflecting astronomical telescope focuses light from a field of stars on to a photographic plate, using a concave mirror with radius 60 cm. and focal length 700 cm. Describe and explain the photographs which may be obtained when the front of the telescope tube is covered with the following screens:

(*a*) An opaque cover with two circular apertures 20 cm. in diameter and 100 cm. apart.

(*b*) A transmission grating in which the amplitude of transmitted light varies sinusoidally across the grating with a periodicity of 0·1 cm.

(*c*) A square mesh wire net, with wires 0·1 cm. thick spaced apart by 2 cm.

(*d*) A mosaic screen complementary to the wire mesh in (*c*).   (CT I)

5. Explain Babinet's principle of complementary screens and describe how it can be used to determine the size of small particles. A lunar corona subtends an angle of 5° at the eye of an observer. Assuming this to be due to diffraction by water droplets in the atmosphere, calculate their diameter. Take the effective wavelength of the light to be 5000 Å.   (LS I)

6. Sodium light is incident normally on a plane transmission grating having 3000 lines per cm. Find the direction of the first order for the D lines and the width of the grating necessary to resolve them. (Wavelengths of D lines: 5890 Å and 5896 Å.)

7. Light is incident at 70° on a plane reflection grating which has 6000 lines per cm. ruled over a width of 3 cm. What is the maximum resolving power available at a wavelength of 5000 Å? Find the corresponding angle of diffraction and the smallest resolvable difference in wavelength.

8. Derive, with full explanation, an expression for the intensity of light diffracted in the nth order by a plane grating consisting of parallel opaque strips of width a separated by transparent spaces of width b, when light of intensity I and wavelength λ falls normally on the grating. (Assume a and b large compared with λ.)

The following angles of diffraction, and estimates of intensity, were obtained with such a grating used at normal incidence with a wavelength of 5000 Å.

0° 17′ very strong	1° 9′ weak	2° 18′ weak
0° 34′ strong	1° 26′ medium	2° 35′ weak
0° 51′ weak	1° 43′ weak	3° 9′ weak

Obtain from these such information as you can about the values of a and b.
(LS I)

9. Explain the use of amplitude phase diagrams in diffraction problems.

A diffraction grating consists of two types of slit, A and B, in a regular alternating sequence ABABAB. . . . The slits are equally spaced and of the same width, but the amplitude diffracted by B is twice that diffracted by A. Compare the diffraction pattern from this grating with that from an ordinary grating consisting only of A slits spaced at a distance equal to that between adjacent A and B slits in the first grating. (CP I)

10. Obtain an expression for the intensity of a beam diffracted from a plane grating when monochromatic light is incident normally upon it. If the widths of the grating bars and spaces are respectively $2 \cdot 5 \times 10^{-4}$ and $1 \cdot 5 \times 10^{-4}$ cm., compare the intensities of the 3rd and 4th orders of spectra for light of wavelength 5000 Å. (LS I)

11. Give the theory of the reflection echelon. How is it used in practice? What advantages has it over the transmission echelon? Calculate the resolving power, for light of wavelength 3000 Å, of a reflection echelon having ten steps each 2 cm. thick. (LS I)

12. A collimated beam of light of wavelength $5 \cdot 46 \times 10^{-5}$ cm. is incident normally on a thin opaque screen containing a circular aperture of diameter 5 mm. Find the positions of the axial points of maximum and minimum intensity.

13. Explain the action of a zone plate and show that the object and image distances obey the ordinary thin lens formula.

A zone plate is found to give a series of images of a point source on its axis. If the strongest and second strongest images are at distances of 30 cm. and 6 cm. respectively from the zone plate, both on the same side remote from the source, calculate the distance of the source from the zone plate, the principal focal length and the radius of the first zone.
(Wavelength of light 5×10^{-5} cm.) (CP I)

14. Describe the construction and action of a zone plate. Show that for points on its axis it is equivalent to a lens with chromatic aberration.

A zone plate is illuminated by parallel white light. A lens of crown glass is to be placed in contact with it so that the resulting image is free from chromatic aberration. Design a suitable lens and find the position of the image, if the zone plate has a 'principal' focal length of 100 cm. for red light of wavelength 8×10^{-5} cm.
(Refractive index of crown glass=$1 \cdot 500$ for wavelength 8×10^{-5} and $1 \cdot 535$ for wavelength 4×10^{-5} cm.) (CT I)

15. Light of wavelength 5893 Å emerges from a narrow slit and is diffracted by a thin wire parallel to the slit. Approximately evenly spaced fringes are

observed within the geometrical shadow of the wire. Find the diameter of the wire if the bright fringes are 0·1 mm. apart at a distance of 20 cm. from the wire.

CHAPTERS XIV–XVI

1. Discuss the usefulness of the Rayleigh criterion for the resolving power of optical instruments.

   Derive an approximate expression for the resolving power of a telescope, and compare it with the resolving power when the same telescope is used with a cover which only exposes two small areas, one at either side of the aperture.

   Show without exact theory how a comparison may be made between the resolving powers of a Fabry-Pérot interferometer and a diffraction grating.
   (CT I)

2. Discuss the formation of an image by a microscope whose lenses are free from aberration, explaining the degree to which the image resembles the object. Distinguish between the case when the object is self-luminous and that in which the object is viewed by transmitted light. What limits the resolution in the two cases?

   Describe and explain one substantial improvement that has been made in microscopy in recent years.
   (CT II)

3. The largest useful magnifying power (M.P.) of a microscope is about 600 times the numerical aperture (N.A.). Justify this statement and calculate the M.P. of an eyepiece to be used with an objective of focal length 3 mm. and N.A. 0·80, in order to give the recommended overall M.P. of 480. (Take λ=5000 Å, the optical tube length as 16 cm., the least distance of distinct vision as 25 cm., and the angular resolution of the eye as 2′.)   (LS I)

4. A compound microscope is focused so that the final image is at infinity. The instrument uses an objective of focal length 4 mm. and N.A. 0·72, working at a tube length of 160 mm., and employing light of wavelength 0·59 μ. The observer can resolve 0·1 mm. at the near point (D_v=25 cm.), and is employing the minimum necessary magnifying power. Find the focal length of the eyepiece and the diameter of the exit pupil.

5. Outline the use of Fourier methods in the diffraction theory of image formation. To what extent does the diffraction pattern of a diffraction pattern reproduce the original diffracting object?

   Discuss the meaning of resolving power in the case of (a) a microscope objective, and (b) a spectrometer.   (CT II)

6. Discuss the Rayleigh limit of resolution as applied to the resolving power, the longitudinal range of focusing without impairing image sharpness, and the tolerable aberrations of optical systems.

   An astronomical telescope has a well-corrected objective of diameter 30 cm. and focal length 450 cm. Calculate (a) the minimum magnifying power of the eyepiece and its focal length if the optimum resolution is to be achieved, (b) the precision with which this eyepiece must be focused in order to achieve the optimum resolution, and (c) the resolving power of the instrument under these conditions. Assume the resolving power of the eye is 1·5 minutes of arc.   (CT II)

7. Deduce from first principles the nature of the monochromatic aberrations that an axially symmetrical system may exhibit.

   A wide aperture lens is to form a geometrically perfect image of a small object lying near to and perpendicular to the optical axis. Show that the sine condition should be satisfied for all zones of the aperture, and state which aberrations are thereby corrected. Give an example of an optical instrument in which you would expect this form of correction to be employed. Why are the other aberrations less important in this case? (LM)

8. What determines the resolving power of optical instruments?

   A telescope has an objective with a diameter of 5 cm. and a focal length of 1·5 m. If the eye can just distinguish points with an angular separation of 1′, estimate the maximum value of the focal length of the eyepiece which may be employed in order that the resolution should be limited by the telescope rather than by the eye. The wavelength of light may be taken to be 5×10^{-5} cm.

   An opaque screen having a pair of narrow parallel slits of separation d is placed over the objective of a telescope, the diameter of the objective being greater than d. The telescope is used to view a distant slit which is of width W and parallel to the other slits. Explain what is seen as W is increased from a very small value. What practical use has been made of the effect? (OF)

9. Discuss the defects that may occur in photographic objectives and the methods by which they are corrected.

   The radius of the entrance pupil of a camera objective is 1 cm. With an object at 4 metres the magnification is 1/100. If the permissible radius of confusion on the plate is 0·05 mm., what is the depth of the field? (LS I)

10. With each of two lenses it is found that with the reference sphere centred at the paraxial focus the primary marginal spherical wavefront aberration is one wavelength. The image-forming cones of rays have semi-angles of (a) 2° and (b) 10°. Find the longitudinal spherical ray aberration for each lens. ($\lambda = 5000$ Å.)

11. A point object is imaged by a small concave mirror of radius of curvature 10 cm. The object is 30 cm. from the mirror and is 10° off axis. Find the separation of the focal lines.

12. A thin converging crown glass lens ($n_d = 1·51690$, $V = 60·6$) has a focal length of 10 cm. If the aperture stop is at the lens and the object plane is at infinity, find the radius of curvature of the Petzval surface and the separation of the focal lines for an object 5° off axis.

   The above lens is replaced by a thin converging achromatic doublet of the same focal length, employing the same crown glass in conjunction with a dense flint ($n_d = 1·62258$, $V = 36·0$). Find the new Petzval radius and the new astigmatic difference of focus.

CHAPTERS XVII and XVIII

1. A colour C is matched by a mixture of certain monochromatic red, green and blue matching stimuli with luminous fluxes in the proportions $1 : 10 : 0·1$. The luminous fluxes of the matching stimuli necessary to

match the standard white are in the proportions $1 : 4\cdot6 : 0\cdot06$. Find the unit trichromatic equation for the colour C.

2. A plane screen receives light from an infinite, uniformly diffuse, plane surface of luminance L lying parallel to it. Find the illumination on the screen.

3. Show how the brightness of a perfectly diffusing surface is related to its intensity of illumination.

   A short, opaque cylinder, with a perfectly diffusing surface is illuminated with parallel light from a direction perpendicular to the axis of the cylinder. It is viewed from a considerable distance in a direction perpendicular to the axis of the cylinder and making an angle ϕ with the incident light. Find an expression for the apparent brightness of different parts of the illuminated surface. Calculate the total luminous flux per unit solid angle diffused in the direction such that $\phi = \pi/2$ if the incident flux of F lumens cm.$^{-2}$ and the radius of the cylinder is equal to its length l. (OM)

4. The aperture settings on a photographic lens are labelled $f/2\cdot8$, $f/4$, $f/5\cdot6$, $f/8$, $f/11$, $f/16$. Why is this a convenient choice?

5. Discuss the brightness of the image of an extended source when viewed through a telescope.

   With the object of increasing the intensity of spectrum lines by improving the light gathering power of a standard spectrometer, an instrument is built in which the collimator lens has a focal length one quarter that of the telescope lens, the diameters of the two lenses being the same. Discuss the efficiency of such an optical system. (LS I)

6. A uniform point source is placed at the centre of a sphere of radius 100 cm., the inside surface of the sphere being uniformly diffusing with a reflection factor $0\cdot8$. An identical source is placed at the centre of a similar sphere of radius 150 cm. and reflection factor $0\cdot9$. Compare the illuminations on the surfaces of the spheres.

CHAPTERS XIX–XXI

1. Assuming Maxwell's equations of the electromagnetic field, establish relations between (a) the directions, (b) the amplitudes of the electric and magnetic fields in a progressive plane wave in a homogeneous isotropic dielectric.

   The root-mean-square value of the displacement current density in a uniform plane-polarized sinusoidal electromagnetic wave in free space is 10^{-9} amp cm.$^{-2}$. If the frequency is 10^8 sec^{-1}, obtain values for the amplitudes of the electric and magnetic fields in the wave. (LS I)

2. Prove by means of Maxwell's equations that in a plane electromagnetic wave in an isotropic dielectric medium the vectors $\mathbf{E}$ and $\mathbf{H}$ of the electric and magnetic field strength are normal to each other and normal to the direction of the wave propagation. Derive expressions for the wave velocity and the electromagnetic energy flow.

   Calculate the r.m.s. electric field strength in the sun's radiation at the surface of the earth from the known value of the radiation intensity ($1\cdot9$ cal. minute^{-1} cm.$^{-2}$). (LS I)

3. Discuss the concept of Displacement Current. Deduce the conductivity of a medium of dielectric constant 5 when the magnitude of the conduction and displacement currents are equal at a frequency of 10^6 sec^{-1}.

   What is the attenuation per cm. of the amplitude of a plane wave of the above frequency when propagated in such a medium? (Assume $\mu = 1$.)
                                                                              (LS I)

4. Obtain an expression for the ratio of the amplitudes of the electric and magnetic vectors in a plane polarized light wave in a dielectric.

   Find the reflected intensity when the light is incident normally at a plane surface of separation between air and diamond of refractive index 2·42.
                                                                              (LS I)

5. Unpolarized light is incident at 45° on a glass of refractive index 1·52. The reflected light is passed through a Nicol. Find the ratio of the maximum and minimum intensities transmitted by the Nicol as it is rotated.

6. Circularly polarized light is to be produced by means of two successive internal reflections in a Fresnel rhomb. If the refractive index is 1·52, find the appropriate angles of incidence.

7. Circularly polarized monochromatic light is incident on the surface of a metal. For an angle of incidence of 72° 30′ it is found that the reflected light is extinguished by a Nicol whose principal section is inclined to the plane of incidence at an angle of 43° 30′. Calculate the refractive index, extinction coefficient, and reflection coefficient at normal incidence.

                              CHAPTERS XXII and XXIII

1. A plane-parallel quartz plate 0·5 mm. thick is cut with its faces parallel to the optic axis and placed between crossed Nicols with its axis at 45° to the principal sections of the Nicols. If the difference between the principal refractive indices for quartz is 0·009 and is independent of wavelength, find the wavelengths in the visible region that will not be transmitted through the system.

2. A plate of uniaxial crystal cut with its faces parallel to the axis is viewed between crossed Nicols in a parallel beam of monochromatic light. Explain the effects observed when the crystal is rotated.

   A thin quartz wedge, of angle 1/50th radian, cut with the optic axis at right angles to the edge, is placed between crossed Nicol prisms such that the optic axis bisects the angle between the vibration directions of polarizer and analyser. Calculate the separation between the fringes seen on the wedge for a wavelength of 6000 Å given that the ordinary and extraordinary refractive indices of quartz for this wavelength differ by 0·009.   (LS I)

3. What is meant by elliptically polarized light? Show that plane and circularly polarized light are special cases of elliptically polarized light.

   Describe the propagation of light in a uniaxial doubly refracting crystal. How may a plate cut from such a crystal be used to convert plane polarized light into circularly polarized light? Calculate the thickness of such a plate made from calcite, for which the principal refractive indices are $n_o = 1\cdot658$ and $n_e = 1\cdot486$ at the wavelength of the light used, 5890 Å.   (OF)

4. Elliptically polarized light is passed through a quarter-wave plate and then

through a Nicol. Extinction occurs when the optic axis of the plate and the principal section of the Nicol are inclined to the horizontal at angles of 30° and 60° respectively, the angles being measured in the same direction. Find the orientation of the ellipse and the ratio of its axes.

5. Explain how some form of polarizing prism works.

   A quartz quarter-wave plate which is designed for light of wavelength 5893 Å is used in conjunction with a Nicol prism to produce circularly polarized light. Show that if there is also present some light of wavelength 5460 Å, this latter will be elliptically polarized with axes at 45° to the axes of the plate. Find the ratio of the major and minor axes of the ellipse.

   At 5893 Å the ordinary and extraordinary indices of refraction of quartz are 1·544 and 1·553 respectively, and at 5460 Å they are 1·546 and 1·555. (OF)

6. What is a *quarter-wave plate* and how is it used? In a Laurent polarimeter, where a half-wave plate is used to divide the field, the plane of vibration of the incident plane polarized light makes an angle of 5° with the optic axis of the half-wave plate and the analysing Nicol is set in turn in the two positions giving equal brightness in the two parts of the field of view. What is the ratio of the intensities observed in these two positions? (LG II)

7. Discuss the phenomenon of the rotation of the plane of polarization of light by optically active materials.

   The specific rotation of quartz at 5086 Å is 29·73 deg./mm. Calculate the difference in the refractive indices. (LS I)

8. A plane parallel quartz plate of thickness 2 cm. is cut with its faces perpendicular to the optic axis and placed between crossed Nicols. Find the wavelengths in the visible region that will not be transmitted through the system. (The specific rotation of quartz in degrees per mm. is given by a formula of the Cauchy type where $A = -2$ and $B = 8·2 \times 10^8$, λ being in angstroms.)

9. Plane polarized monochromatic light is passed through a 20 cm. tube containing an aqueous solution of sucrose and then along the axis of a glass rod of length 25 cm. around which is wound a uniform solenoid containing 5000 turns of wire. It is found that with a current of 0·96 amp. round the solenoid the Faraday rotation in the glass exactly balances the rotation in the solution. Find the concentration of the sucrose solution. (Verdet constant for the glass = 0·08 minutes oersted^{-1} cm.$^{-1}$, specific rotation of sucrose solution (1 gm. per cc.) = 66 deg. per decimetre.)

ANSWERS

1. See § 1–9.

2. 1 cm., 16 cm.

3. (a) $f, f' = 10$ cm., $13 \cdot 3$ cm.; P and P′ at lens; N and N′ $3 \cdot 3$ cm. beyond plane surface. (b) f, f', $27 \cdot 5$ cm., $20 \cdot 6$ cm.; P and P′ at lens; N and N′ $6 \cdot 8$ cm. beyond convex surface.

4. $f, f' = \pm 26 \cdot 15$ cm.; P.Ps $2 \cdot 55$ and $0 \cdot 10$ cm. in front of convex surface.

5. P.Ps and N.Ps at, and $3 \cdot 9$ cm. from, pole of curved surface; F and F′ $15 \cdot 6$ cm. from curved surface and $9 \cdot 53$ cm. from plane surface.

6. Distances from pole of convex surface: P.Ps $1 \cdot 23$ cm. and $0 \cdot 72$ cm.; N.Ps $15 \cdot 02$ cm. and $15 \cdot 53$ cm.; P.Fs $50 \cdot 44$ cm. and $64 \cdot 74$ cm.

8. P.Ps 90″ and 18″ in front of converging lens; $f' = 30''$.

9. Diverging lens of focal length 25 cm.

10. Equation 2–19 gives f' of system; then find $d = 6$ cm. P.Ps 60 cm. and 24 cm. in front of converging lens; P.Fs 110 cm. from converging and 20 cm. from diverging lens.

11. Rotation is about nodal point—see Fig. 4–11. Real object $8 \cdot 74$ cm. in front or virtual object $2 \cdot 74$ cm. behind.

12. Rotation is about point midway between object and image and midway between principal points.

13. 10/3 cm. in front of lens; diameter 25/6 cm.

14. Put $dl_2'/d\mu = 0$ where l_2 is distance of focus from surface; achromatism of l_2' similar to achromatism of f' with doublet. (Fig. 16–15.)

15. See §§ 3–11 and 3–12. $d = 3$ cm. P.Ps and N.Ps 2 cm. and 1 cm. from eye lens; P.Fs 2/3 cm. and 5/3 cm. from eye lens—similar to Fig. 3–12(a).

16. P.Ps and N.Ps between and $2 \cdot 4$ cm. from lenses; F.Ps $0 \cdot 8$ cm. outside lenses. EP′ $0 \cdot 97$ cm. beyond eye lens, diameter $0 \cdot 267$ cm.

17. Crown: $4 \cdot 05$ cm. (diverging). Flint: $6 \cdot 81$ cm. (converging).

18. $1 \cdot 50$.

19. See §§ 5–8, 5–9, 5–12, 5–13, 5–14, 5–15.

20. See § 5–14. See §§ 5–8, 5–12, 5–14, 8–13, 11–14.

21. (a) $1 \cdot 2746$ to $1 \cdot 6200$ and $1 \cdot 4362$ to $1 \cdot 7500$ ($\sqrt{n^2 - 1}$ to n).
    (b) 1 to $1 \cdot 6200$ and 1 to $1 \cdot 7500$ (1 to n).

1. See §§ 6–8, 24–10, 24–13. $1 \cdot 675 \times 10^{10}$ cm. sec.$^{-1}$. (Taking λ to be the vacuum wavelength.)

2. See § 6–8.

3. $5 \cdot 89 \times 10^{-5}$ cm. (*a*) unity, (*b*) $0 \cdot 80$.

4. See §§ 6–1 to 6–4. 194.

5. See §§ 7–1 and 7–7. 177° 42′.

6. See Chapter 7. Linear $\cos^2$ fringes parallel to axis of rotation of one mirror relative to other (inclined plane waves). Fringe width (spacing) $= 2 \cdot 58 \times 10^{-3}$ cm.

7. 40″.

8. $6 \cdot 39$ mm. (*a*) Few coloured rings at centre only. (*b*) Fringes move towards centre.

9. $5 \cdot 46 \times 10^{-5}$ cm.

10. See §§ 8–13, 11–14, or § 9–14. o.p.d. with mirrors $= 2[(n_2 - 1)d_2 - (n_1 - 1)d_1]$. o.p.d. without mirrors $= 2(n_2 d_2 - n_1 d_1)$.

11. In outer parts of pattern Fabry-Perot fringes have diameters slightly larger than Newton's rings. (Consider approximations made on pages 138 and 141.) 1 cm.

12. See §§ 8–13 and 11–14. $1 \cdot 000289$.

13. See §§ 8–7 and 8–8. $(2v/\lambda)$ fringes per sec. (Effective source moves with speed $2v$.)

14. See § 8–13. Fringe visibility falls to $0 \cdot 943$.

15. See §§ 9–3, 9–4 and 12–15. $8 \cdot 6 \times 10^5 \; \lambda^2$ cm.

16. See § 9–1. $0 \cdot 0145$ cm. or odd multiple.

17. See Chapter IX. 2 cm.

18. See § 9–1. $0 \cdot 338$.

19. See §§ 9–7 and 9–9. $2 \cdot 00083$.

20. See § 9–12. $2 \cdot 16 \times 10^{-3}$ cm.

CHAPTERS X–XIII

1. See §§ 11–1 to 11–3. 4286 Å, 5000 Å, 6000 Å, 7500 Å.

2. See § 11–5. $2bt/\lambda^3$ for isosceles prism at minimum deviation, t being length of base. $1 \cdot 02$ cm.

3. See §§ 11–12, 11–13. $3 \cdot 98 \times 10^8$ km.

4. (*a*) Airy discs $85 \cdot 4 \; \lambda$ diameter, fringes $7 \; \lambda$ apart across axial ones.
   (*b*) Double images $1 \cdot 4 \times 10^4 \; \lambda$ apart.
   (*c*) Each star—bright central image with square array of weak secondary maxima $350 \; \lambda$ apart parallel to wires; radial spectra.
   (*d*) Arrays with same periodicity but much weaker central maxima.

5. See §§ 10–12, 11–9. $1 \cdot 88 \times 10^{-3}$ cm.

6. 10° 11′, $0 \cdot 327$ cm.

7. $1 \cdot 08 \times 10^5$, 59° 21′, $0 \cdot 046$ Å.

8. See § 12–8. 0° 17′ is first order, 7th and 10th orders unobserved $(a+b) = 0 \cdot 100$ mm. 7th and 10th very weak if b slightly less than $2 \cdot 5 \; a$.

9. See §§ 6–2, 11–2, 12–1, 13–5. If simple grating gives principal max. of unit intensity, mixed grating gives principal max. of intensity $2\frac{1}{4}$ in same positions, plus max. of intensity $\frac{1}{4}$ midway between them.

10. See §§ 12–7 and 12–8. 0·26.

11. See §§ 12–9 and 12–15. $1·33 \times 10^6$.

12. MIN at $11·4/2p$ metres, MAX at $11·4/(2p+1)$ metres.

13. See § 13–3. If source distance$=l$, radius of central zone$=R$, then for point l' beyond plate path via zone edge exceeds $(l+l')$ by $R^2/2l+R^2/2l'$. Get MAX if this$=(p+\frac{1}{2})\lambda$ ∴ $1/l'+1/l=(2p+1)\lambda/R^2=1/f'$ if $l'=f'$ when $l=\infty$. Strongest max. if $p=0$. $l=30$ cm., $f'=15$ cm., $R=0·274$ mm.

14. See § 13–3. Focal length of zone plate $\propto \lambda^{-1}$ (see previous question). ∴ Plate corresponds to converging lens with negative chromatic aberration. ∴ need converging lens for achromatism. Sum of powers of plate and lens same for red and violet if lens has total curvature $1/7$. E.g. equiconvex with radii 14 cm. Focal length of combination for red and violet$=12·3$ cm.

15. 1·18 mm.

CHAPTERS XIV–XVI

1. See §§ 11–5, 11–6, 14–5; 14–6, 11–13; page 167.

2. See §§ 14–7, 14–10, 14–11, 14–12; 14–13.

3. See § 14–8. $\times 9$.

4. 5 cm., 0·18 cm.

5. See §§ 14–11, 14–15. Extent to which intermediate pattern is transmitted determines spatial frequencies (Fourier components) reproduced in image. See §§ 14–5, 11–5.

6. See §§ 14–5, 14–9, 15–14. (*a*) $\times 11·9$, 2·1 cm.
    (*b*) $\pm 0·0225$ cm. (*c*) 0·42 sec. (Taking $\lambda=5000$ Å and $D_v=25$ cm.)

7. See §§ 15–5, 14–3, 15–11. Microscope objective because it has a wide aperture but a small field.

8. See §§ 9–3, 11–5, 12–6, 14–5, 14–6, 14–7, 14–12. 6·29 cm.

9. See Chapters XV and XVI. Depth of focus$=\pm 0·02$ cm. Depth of Field: 2·7 metres to 8 metres (too large to use equation 2–11).

10. 1·64 mm., 0·066 mm.

11. 0·22 cm.

12. 15·2 cm., 0·0760 cm.; 13·8 cm., 0·0760 cm.

CHAPTERS XVII and XVIII

1. 1·0 C$=0·207$ R$+0·449$ G$+0·344$ B.

2. πL lumen cm.$^{-2}$.

3. See § 18–3. Luminance at any point$=(F \cos \theta)/\pi$ where θ is angle between incident rays and normal to cylinder surface, but with sudden cut-off at

$\theta=90°-\phi$ on side of rays remote from ϕ since this is edge of cylinder as seen by observer. $Fl^2/2\pi$.

4. Squares of denominators increased by factor of 2 at each step. Hence area of entrance pupil and illumination of image reduced by factor of approximately 2.

5. See § 18–6. (*a*) If slit wide no gain because more light spread over proportionally greater image area. (*b*) If slit narrow enough for image width to be determined by diffraction—gain inversely proportional to focal length of collimator.

6. $E_1/E_2=1\cdot125$.

CHAPTERS XIX–XXI

1. See § 19–4. E (e.s.u.)$=H$ (e.m.u.)$=8\cdot485\times10^{-8}$.

2. See §§ 19–4, 19–5. $0\cdot0235$ e.s.u.

3. See § 19–2. $2\cdot5\times10^6$ e.s.u. $0\cdot02\%$ reduction in amplitude.

4. See § 19–4. $0\cdot172$ for unit incident intensity.

5. $10\cdot3$.

6. 55° 27′ or 47° 33′.

7. $n=0\cdot158$, $K=19\cdot1$, $R=0\cdot94$.

CHAPTERS XXII and XXIII

1. 4091 Å, 4500 Å, 5000 Å, 5625 Å, 6429 Å, 7500 Å.

2. See § 22–12. $\frac{1}{3}$ cm.

3. See § 6–16. Cut plate parallel to axis. Thickness $8\cdot56\times10^{-5}$ cm. or an odd multiple of this.

4. Minor axis inclined to horizontal at 30°; ratio of axes$=1\cdot732$ (tan 60°).

5. See §§ 22–5 and 22–7. $1\cdot13$.

6. See §§ 22–13 and 22–14. 131.

7. See Chapter XXIII. $8\cdot4\times10^{-5}$.

8. 4180 Å, 4650 Å, 5320 Å, 6400 Å.

9. $0\cdot061$ gm. per cc.

INDEX

4837